D0919770
YORK JUNIOR COLLEGE LIBRARY
YORK, PENNA.

YORK [illegible] LIBRARY

Vector and Tensor Analysis

YORK JUNIOR COLLEGE LIBRARY
YORK, PENNA.

11111

NATHANIEL COBURN
Associate Professor of Mathematics
University of Michigan

THE MACMILLAN COMPANY · NEW YORK

COPYRIGHT, 1955, BY THE MACMILLAN COMPANY

PUBLISHED SIMULTANEOUSLY IN CANADA

All rights reserved—no part of this book may be reproduced in any form without permission in writing from the publisher, except by a reviewer who wishes to quote brief passages in connection with a review written for inclusion in magazine or newspaper.

PRINTED IN THE UNITED STATES OF AMERICA

First Printing

QA
261
C58

To my wife

6/13/60 C+H 6.75

PREFACE

This text is the outgrowth of notes used by the author in courses on vector analysis at the senior-graduate level, and on compressible fluids and turbulence at the graduate level, at the University of Michigan. In the latter courses, the author has used some of the topics covered in the tensor analysis section of the present text as review material.

The vector analysis sections include the algebra of vectors, vector differentiation, and integration, and are illustrated by specific examples. Further, numerous hints have been included to facilitate the solution of the problems. Since cylindrical and spherical coordinates are two of the most frequently used coordinate systems by the engineer and physicist, considerable emphasis has been placed on the discussion of these systems. In a two-hour, one-semester course, the author has been able to cover Chapters I through III and a portion of the material introducing tensor analysis in Chapter V.

Tensors have been introduced in the vector analysis sections as a generalization of the directed line segments which represent vectors. This use of the direct quantities is limited to the generalizations of theorems in vector analysis. Further, as a generalization of the scalar product, the vector product, and the direct product of two vectors, a distributive star product has been used. In Chapter V, the transition from these direct quantities to their components is initiated. By studying tensors in various preferential groups of Cartesian coordinate transformations in Euclidean three-space, an attempt has been made to bridge the gap between vectors and tensors. Chapters VII and IX contain a detailed study of tensors in general curvilinear coordinate systems. Here, topics such as parallelism, the intrinsic and imbedding theory of surfaces, the orthogonal decomposition of tensors, and integrability conditions for systems of linear partial differential equations have been studied. The theory of these sections is mainly concerned with Euclidean three-space.

This has been done in order to make the material easier to understand and because most of the applications are in such spaces. However, whenever possible, the corresponding problem for n-space has been mentioned. In particular, this is true for the theorems of Stokes and Gauss, which are verified for n-dimensional Euclidean space in Chapter VIII. Finally, it should be noted that several topics have been included which some students may find too theoretical. These topics (Appendix I on linear dependence, Appendix II on matrices and their relation to tensors, Sections 50 and 51 on m-directions and the theorems of Stokes and Gauss) may be omitted in a first reading without disrupting the continuity of the text. However, the theorem of Gauss (the divergence theorem) for Euclidean four-space is needed for the introduction to compressible fluids. Hence, at this stage, the student may find it desirable to read Sections 50 and 51.

In the applications of vector and tensor analysis, an attempt has been made to highlight some of the general theory of (1) rigid bodies and perfect fluids by vector analysis; (2) differential geometry, elasticity (finite deformations), viscous fluids, three-dimensional compressible fluids, and turbulence by tensor analysis. Further, some of the problems of the vector analysis section (Chapter III) are taken from potential theory.

Very little attempt has been made to assign credit to original contributions. Instead, references to the general literature have been given when feasible. The author is indebted to the following of his colleagues for valuable suggestions: Professors R. C. F. Bartels, A. H. Copeland, C. L. Dolph, W. Kaplan, E. D. Rainville, E. H. Rothe, and Dr. T. R. Jenkins. Further, he is indebted to his students for valuable comments, and, in particular, to Mr. Robert Wasserman who read the entire manuscript and corrected the proof sheets. Finally, he wishes to thank his many colleagues who checked various portions of the proofs; Mrs. Marybeth Barth and Mrs. Edith Fisher for their help with the typing; his son, Lewis Alan, for his aid in the proof reading; the staff of The Macmillan Company for editorial advice.

N. C.

CONTENTS

Part I

VECTOR ANALYSIS

Part I

VECTOR ANALYSIS

Chapter I

THE FUNDAMENTAL OPERATIONS

1. Scalars and Vectors. In order to introduce the ideas of scalars and vectors, we consider a simple example. Let A, B denote two points of ordinary Euclidean three-space and consider a *displacement from* point A *to* point B. With this displacement (or directed line segment), we associate three quantities: (1) a direction, AB or BA; (2) a sense, A to B; (3) a magnitude, the distance between A and B. The magnitude associated with the displacement is a scalar quantity. Thus, we see that two ideas are expressed in the term *scalar:* (1) a *numerical quantity;* (2) *independence of the coordinate system or reference system.* Note that the direction of the above displacement is *not* a scalar. Although a particular number may be assigned to any direction (say, North 30° West), this number depends upon the reference system. The above example is concerned with a scalar function of two points, A, B. One can easily give an example of a scalar field, that is, a scalar associated with each point of space. The distance between any point of space and the origin of a reference frame in space is a very simple scalar field.

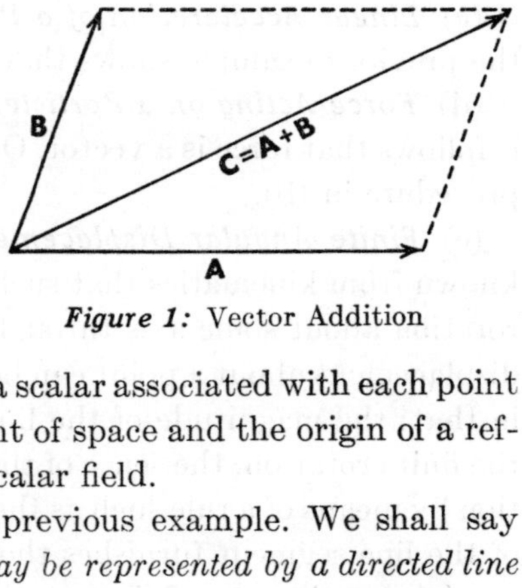

Figure 1: Vector Addition

To define vectors, we return to the previous example. We shall say that[1]: (1) *if a quantity of a given type may be represented by a directed line segment,* (2) *if two quantities of the given type add as do directed line segments, then the quantities are vectors.* Hence, vectors may be geometrically represented by arrows (the arrowhead determines the sense of the line segment; the length of the arrow determines the magnitude of the line segment; the direction of the arrow determines the direction of the line segment). We shall use boldface type, such as **A,** to denote vectors. It may be well to

[1] All vectors except base vectors (such as **i, j, k** of Section 5) are independent of the coordinate system.

recall that directed line segments add by the parallelogram law. Thus, if **A, B** are directed line segments with common origin O and if **C** is their sum, then **C** is the diagonal of the parallelogram formed with **A, B** as sides.

Let us consider some physical quantities and determine whether they are vectors, scalars, or belong to other categories.

(a) ***Linear Displacements of a Particle.*** These quantities are evidently vectors. In fact, they are the prototype of vectors.

(b) ***Linear Velocity of a Particle.*** Evidently, any linear velocity of a particle may be represented by a directed line segment, in that: the magnitude of the line segment determines the magnitude of the velocity, the sense of the line segment determines the sense of the velocity, and the direction of the line segment determines the direction of the velocity. Hence, the crucial question is whether velocities are compounded according to the parallelogram law. That is, if a particle is simultaneously given two different velocities, then is the resultant velocity the one which is obtained from the parallelogram law? Consistency of classical physical theory and experiment requires that the answer to this question be yes. Hence, the linear velocity of a particle is a vector. In the theory of relativity, the velocities of a particle do *not add by* the parallelogram law.

(c) ***Linear Acceleration of a Particle.*** Consideration similar to that of the previous example shows that this quantity is a vector.

(d) ***Force Acting on a Particle.*** From (c) and Newton's law of motion, it follows that force is a vector. Or an alternative approach is to adopt the procedure in (b).

(e) ***Finite Angular Displacement about a Point of a Rigid Body.*** It is known from kinematics that such a displacement is equivalent to a finite rotation about some axis through the point. Hence, a particular angular displacement about a point can be represented by a directed line segment, in that: the magnitude of the line segment determines the magnitude of the finite rotation, the sense of the line segment fixes the sense of the rotation by means of a rule such as the right-hand screw rule, and the direction of the line segment furnishes the axis of rotation. Again we come to the crucial question. Are finite rotations compounded according to the parallelogram law? Here the answer is no. This can be shown as follows. It is a simple consequence of the parallelogram law that addition is commutative: that is, $\mathbf{A} + \mathbf{B} = \mathbf{B} + \mathbf{A}$. Consider the rigid body formed by three wires at right angles to each other. Rotate through 90° about one wire and then rotate through 90° about any other wire. Interchange the order of the rotations. Are the final configurations identical? Actually, finite rotations can be represented in some sense by more general quantities than vectors. These quantities are called *dyads* or *tensors*. The important point is that not all physical quantities need be vectors or scalars.

2. Types of Vectors. In this section, we wish to call attention to the fact that different physical quantities, which may be represented by vectors, need not be represented by the same type of vector.

(a) ***Free Vectors.*** These vectors are of very common occurrence. In fact, we shall deal mainly with this type of vector in the first few sections of our work. The characteristic property of these vectors is that they are invariant (not altered) under parallel translation. Such vectors may be added by merely translating all of these vectors parallel to themselves to a common origin and then using the parallelogram law. The translational displacement vector of a rigid body is a simple example of such a vector. See also (a), (b), (c), (d), of the previous section.

(b) ***Sliding Vectors.*** These vectors are of considerable use in statics. They are characterized by the fact that they are unaltered under a more restrictive set of motions than general parallel translations. These vectors may be translated parallel to themselves only along their lines of action. The vectors along a given line of action may be immediately combined by addition of line segments. However, a systematic approach to the general theory of addition, etc., of such vectors necessitates the introduction of moments of a vector. This theory leads to the theory of "motors," "rotors," etc. One can easily understand this new development by use of an example. Consider a system of forces acting on a rigid body. These forces may be considered as acting at any point along their lines of action. If one translates any one force parallel to itself and not along its line of action, then the resultant force "plus" a couple are equivalent to the original force. We shall not treat the theory of sliding vectors in our future work.

(c) ***Bound Vectors (or Vector Fields).*** The later sections of our work will deal exclusively with scalar, vector, and tensor fields. By a *vector field* we mean that with each point of Euclidean three-space (or some more general space) is associated a vector. The question arises as to how vectors at two distinct points P, Q may be compared (added, subtracted, etc.). *One solution is to displace the vector at P by parallelism to the point Q (or conversely) and then apply the parallelogram law.* However, one must always remember that the resultant vector is a function of the two points P, Q. This would lead to considerable complication in the theory. The actual solution is to compare the vectors as indicated at Q and then pass to the limit as Q moves into coincidence with P. This leads to vector differentiation and integration. Thus, the theory of free vectors and vector fields in Euclidean space depends upon use of parallel displacement. Now let us consider, briefly, the problem of non-Euclidean spaces (a plane is a Euclidean two-space, the surface of a sphere is non-Euclidean two-space). For such spaces, parallel displacement has no meaning, as yet. A method for defining parallel displacements in such spaces was developed[2] independently by T. Levi-Civita and J. A. Schouten about 1917. In the latter part of the section on tensor analysis we shall treat this development.

3. The Laws of Vector Addition; Multiplication of Vectors by Scalars. We assume the parallelogram law of addition of vectors and examine some properties of vector addition, multiplication of vectors by scalars, and some questions of notation.

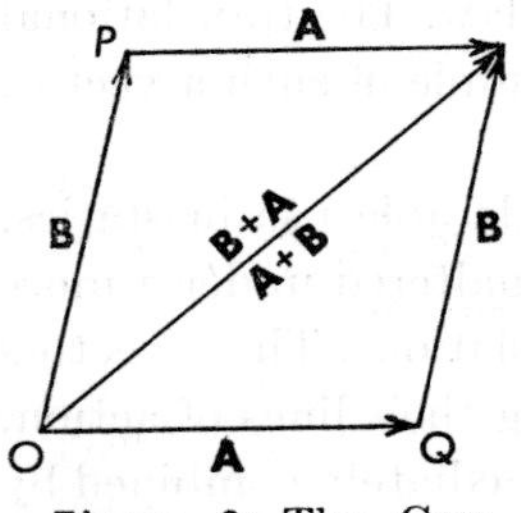

Figure 2: The Commutative Law of Vector Addition

(a) ***Commutative Law of Addition,*** $\mathbf{A} + \mathbf{B} = \mathbf{B} + \mathbf{A}$. Consider two vectors **A, B.** By the assumption of invariance of the vectors under parallel displacement, we may translate these vectors to a common origin and construct a unique parallelogram with **A, B** as sides and $\mathbf{A} + \mathbf{B}$ or $\mathbf{B} + \mathbf{A}$ as a unique diagonal (see Figure 2).

(b) ***Associative Law of Addition,*** $(\mathbf{A} + \mathbf{B}) + \mathbf{C} = \mathbf{A} + (\mathbf{B} + \mathbf{C})$. Using the above mentioned construction, we find from the figure below that $(\mathbf{A} + \mathbf{B}) + \mathbf{C} = \mathbf{A} + (\mathbf{B} + \mathbf{C})$.

(c) ***Multiplication of a Vector by a Scalar,*** $c\mathbf{A}$. If $c > 0$ is a scalar, then we define $c\mathbf{A}$ to mean a vector with the same sense and direction as **A** but

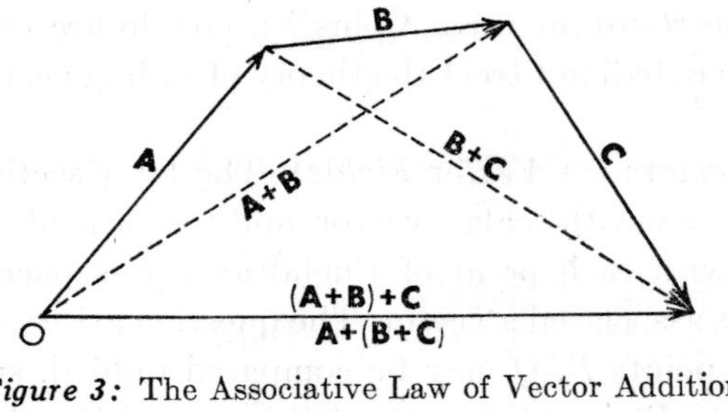

Figure 3: The Associative Law of Vector Addition

whose magnitude is c times as large. If $c < 0$, then $c\mathbf{A}$ has the opposite sense to **A** but the same direction and its magnitude is c times that of **A.**

[2] T. Levi-Civita, *Nozioni di parallelisimo in una varieta qualunque e conseguente specificazione geometrica della curvatura Riemanniana,* Rend. Cir. Mat. Palermo, Bd. 42, S 173–205; J. A. Schouten, *Die direkte Analysis zur Neueren Relativitätstheorie,* Verhandelinger Kon. Akad. v. Wetenschappen Ameterdam, Bd. 12, Nr. 6, 95 S.

The following laws can be verified for the products of vectors by scalars:

$$(a + b)\mathbf{A} = a\mathbf{A} + b\mathbf{A}$$
$$a(\mathbf{A} + \mathbf{B}) = a\mathbf{A} + a\mathbf{B}$$
$$a(b\mathbf{A}) = (ab)\mathbf{A}.$$

(d) ***Vector Subtraction,* A − B.** We define **A − B** to mean **A + (−B)**. Let us write, **A − B = X.** By adding **B** to both sides of this relation, we

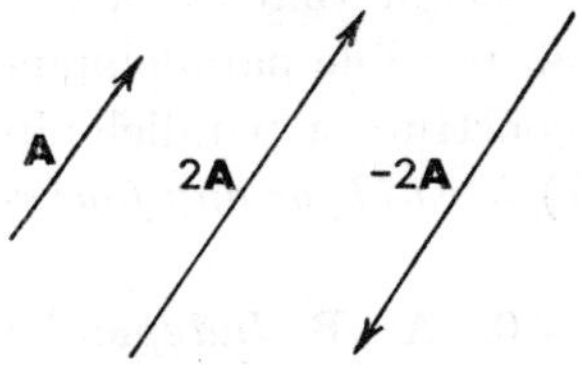

Figure 4: The Multiplication of a Vector by a Scalar

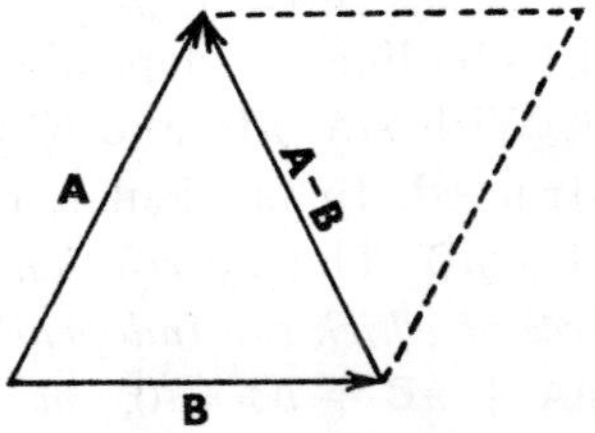

Figure 5: The Representation of Vector Subtraction by a Parallelogram Diagonal

find by use of the associative law (b) that **A = X + B.** Thus **X = A − B** is a vector such that when added to **B** furnishes **A.** From Figure 5, we see that **A − B** must be the indicated diagonal.

(e) ***Vector Equations.*** In virtue of the associative law of vector addition, vector equations involving addition or subtraction may be treated as ordinary algebraic equations. To solve the equation, **X + A = A,** one must introduce the zero vector, **0.** Henceforth, we shall denote this vector by the same symbol as the zero scalar.

(f) ***Notation.*** It is quite common to use two notations for vectors:

(1) to denote a vector whose origin is O and whose terminal point is P, one may write $\overrightarrow{\mathrm{OP}}$ or simply **A**;

(2) to denote a vector whose origin is O and whose terminal point is P, one may write **P.**

The second notation is usually used when several of the vectors under consideration have a given origin (or initial point). Further, we denote the magnitude of this vector by either $|\overrightarrow{\mathrm{OP}}|$ or $|\mathbf{A}|$ or $|\mathbf{P}|$.

4. The Meaning of Linear Vector Equations (Linear Dependence).

(a) $m\mathbf{A} + n\mathbf{B} = 0,\ m,\ n \neq 0$. The vectors **A, B** are said to be linearly dependent. Evidently, equation (a) implies that $\mathbf{A} = -(n/m)\mathbf{B}$. That is, **A** is parallel to **B.** Conversely, if **A** is parallel to **B** then equation (a) is valid.

(b) $m\mathbf{A} + n\mathbf{B} + l\mathbf{C} = 0$, $m, n, l \neq 0$. The vectors **A, B, C** are said to be linearly dependent. Let us assume **A, B** are independent. That is, scalars m and n do not exist so that $m\mathbf{A} + n\mathbf{B} = 0$. Then, one may write equation (b) in the form $l\mathbf{C} = -m\mathbf{A} - n\mathbf{B}$. That is, **C** lies in the plane of **A** and **B.** Conversely, if **C** lies in a plane determined by **A, B,** then scalar multipliers exist such that (b) is valid. This follows directly from the parallelogram law.

(c) $m\mathbf{A} + n\mathbf{B} + l\mathbf{C} + p\mathbf{D} = 0$, $m, n, l, p \neq 0$. The vectors **A, B, C, D** are said to be linearly dependent. Let us assume that **A, B, C** are independent. With $m\mathbf{A}$, $n\mathbf{B}$, and $l\mathbf{C}$ as sides, all possible parallelopipeds may be constructed. In particular, one may construct a parallelopiped with diagonal $-p\mathbf{D}$. Thus, *a relation of type* (*c*) *is valid for any four vectors in space three of which are independent.*

(d) $m\mathbf{A} + n\mathbf{B} + l\mathbf{C} = 0$, $m + l + n = 0$, **A, B** ***Independent.*** The above relation determines a useful geometric configuration. Consider the problem of dividing a line in a given ratio $(a:b)$. Let A, B be the end points of the line and let C be the desired point so that, $AC:CB = a:b$. Let O be an arbitrary point and let $\mathbf{A} = \overrightarrow{\text{OA}}$, $\mathbf{B} = \overrightarrow{\text{OB}}$, $\mathbf{C} = \overrightarrow{\text{OC}}$; then $b\overrightarrow{\text{AC}} = a\overrightarrow{\text{CB}}$. From Figure 6 we find $\overrightarrow{\text{AC}} = \mathbf{C} - \mathbf{A}$, $\overrightarrow{\text{CB}} = \mathbf{B} - \mathbf{C}$. These last two relations lead to the formula,

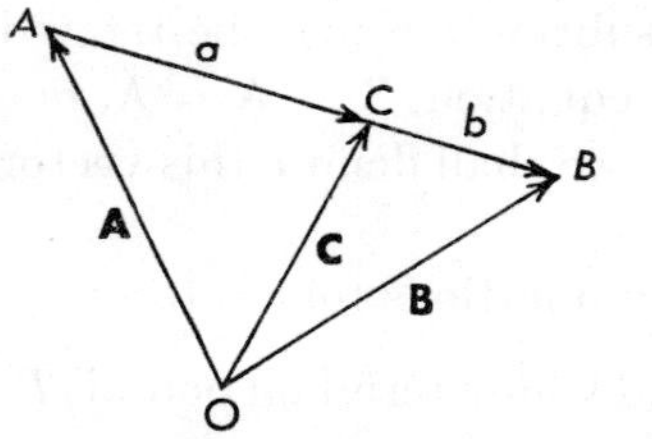

Figure 6: The Vector Which Divides a Line Segment in a Given Ratio

$$\mathbf{C} = \frac{b\mathbf{A} + a\mathbf{B}}{a + b}. \tag{4.1}$$

If this equation is written in the form $m\mathbf{A} + n\mathbf{B} + l\mathbf{C} = 0$, then $l + m + n = 0$. Thus, if **C** is a vector to some point on the line determined by **A, B,** then equation (d) of this section is satisfied. Conversely, if (d) is satisfied, then the terminal point of **C** lies on a line determined by the terminal points of **A** and **B.** This last result follows by reversing the order of the steps in the above argument.

The equation (4.1) is exactly the formula from analytic geometry for dividing a line in a given ratio. Note, as a/b goes from 0 to 1, the point C moves from A to the midpoint of AB; as a/b goes from 1 to ∞ to -1, the point C moves to B and to the right of B; as a/b goes from 0 to -1, the point C moves from A indefinitely to the left of A. In particular, we note that $a/b = 1$ determines the midpoint of AB. Dividing the numerator and denominator of the right-hand side of (4.1) by b, we obtain the well-known midpoint formula,

$$\mathbf{C} = \frac{\mathbf{A} + \mathbf{B}}{2}. \tag{4.2}$$

(e) $m\mathbf{A} + n\mathbf{B} + l\mathbf{C} + p\mathbf{D} = 0$, $m + n + l + p = 0$, **A, B, C** ***Independent.*** By use of an argument similar to that of the preceding section, one may show that **D** is a vector to some point of the plane determined by the terminal points of **A, B, C.**

Illustrative Example: The following example indicates how the results of (d) and (e) may be used in proving some theorems in plane geometry. The figure with vertices A, B, C, D is a parallelogram; show that the diagonals bisect each other.

Solution: Let O be an arbitrary point (not A, B, C, D, or E) of the plane. Then $\mathbf{A} = \overrightarrow{\mathrm{OA}}$, etc. From the well-known fact that the opposite sides of a parallelogram are parallel and equal, we obtain

$$\mathbf{B} - \mathbf{A} = \mathbf{C} - \mathbf{D}, \qquad \mathbf{C} - \mathbf{B} = \mathbf{D} - \mathbf{A}.$$

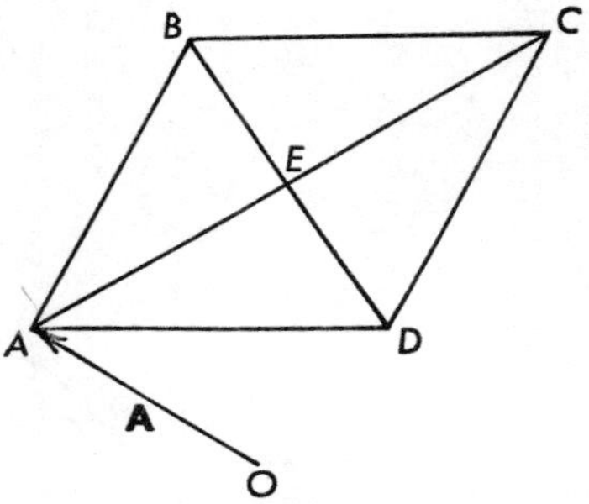

Figure 7: The Diagonals of a Parallelogram Bisect Each Other

To obtain the vectors from O to the points of the diagonals, we seek combinations of **B, D** and **A, C.** From the above formulas, we find that

$$\mathbf{B} + \mathbf{D} = \mathbf{C} + \mathbf{A}.$$

This last formula is easily interpreted. The midpoint of the diagonal BD is determined by the vector $\mathbf{X} = (\mathbf{B} + \mathbf{D})/2$. Hence, **X** terminates also on the midpoint of the diagonal AC, and the midpoints of the two diagonals are the same point, $\mathbf{X} = \mathbf{E}$ (see Figure 7).

Problem 4.1: AB is a line segment and O (not A or B) is an arbitrary point. Find the vector to that point of AB which is: (1) one-third of the distance from A to B; (2) one-third of the distance from B to A.

Problem 4.2: ABC is a triangle. Lines are drawn from A and C to the midpoints of the opposite sides. Show that these lines trisect each other. *Hint:* Let E, D be the midpoints; then $2\mathbf{D} = \mathbf{A} + \mathbf{B}$, $2\mathbf{E} = \mathbf{C} + \mathbf{B}$. Eliminating **B,** we find $2\mathbf{D} + \mathbf{C} = 2\mathbf{E} + \mathbf{A}$; interpret this relation.

Problem 4.3: Prove that the lines joining the midpoints of the sides of any quadrilateral, taken in order, enclose a parallelogram.

Problem 4.4: A line is drawn connecting the midpoints of the two nonparallel sides of a trapezoid. Show that this line is parallel to the other two parallel sides and equal to half the sum of these sides.

Problem 4.5: $ABCD$ is a parallelogram. Lines are drawn from A to the midpoints of BC and CD. Show that they trisect the diagonal BD.

5. Rectangular Components of a Vector. We introduce a Cartesian rectangular coordinate system in space and study vectors with respect to such a coordinate system. A right-handed system will be used. This means that if one rotates from Ox into Oy, then Oz lies in the direction in which

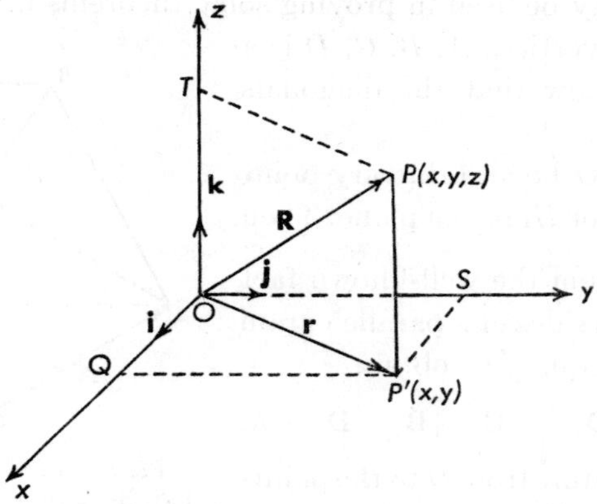

Figure 8: The Radial Vectors, **R** and **r**

a right-hand screw would advance. The lines Ox, Oy, Oz, indicate the positive directions of the coordinate axis.

Let **i, j, k** denote unit vectors along Ox, Oy, Oz, respectively. Note that the directions of the vectors **i, j, k** depend upon the orientation of the coordinate system. Consider a point P of space whose coordinates are (x, y, z). Let P' denote the projection of P on the (x, y) plane. We denote the vector $\overrightarrow{OP}$ by **R** and the vector $\overrightarrow{OP'}$ by **r**.

By construction, $P'Q$ is perpendicular to OQ, $P'S$ is perpendicular to OS, and PT is perpendicular to OT. Evidently, $OQ = x$, $OS = y$, $OT = z$. Through use of the parallelogram law of addition, we find

$$\mathbf{r} = \mathbf{i}x + \mathbf{j}y \tag{5.1}$$
$$\mathbf{R} = \mathbf{i}x + \mathbf{j}y + \mathbf{k}z.$$

Since the plane of $P'P$, $P'Q$ is perpendicular to OQ, we see that $OQ = x$, $OS = y$, $OT = z$, are the projections of **R** on the x, y, z axis, respectively.

If **A** is an arbitrary vector, by a similar procedure, we find

$$\mathbf{A} = A_x\mathbf{i} + A_y\mathbf{j} + A_z\mathbf{k} \tag{5.2}$$

where A_x, A_y, A_z are the projections of **A** on the x, y, z axis, respectively. The quantities A_x, A_y, A_z are called the x, y, z components of **A,** respectively; these quantities are not scalars.

By use of the associative law of addition 3(b), we find that if $\mathbf{B} = B_x\mathbf{i} + B_y\mathbf{j} + B_z\mathbf{k}$, then

$$\mathbf{A} + \mathbf{B} = (A_x + B_x)\mathbf{i} + (A_y + B_y)\mathbf{j} + (A_z + B_z)\mathbf{k}. \tag{5.3}$$

6. The Scalar or Dot Product (A · B). We *define* this product to be the *following scalar quantity:*

$$\mathbf{A} \cdot \mathbf{B} = |\mathbf{A}|\,|\mathbf{B}| \cos\theta, \qquad 0 \le \theta \le \pi \tag{6.1}$$

where θ is the angle between the vectors (see Figure 9). Since $|\mathbf{B}| \cos\theta$ represents the magnitude of the projection of **B** on **A** (which we denote by $\text{Proj}_{\mathbf{A}}\,\mathbf{B}$), we may write our previous relation in the form

$$\mathbf{A} \cdot \mathbf{B} = |\mathbf{A}|\,\text{Proj}_{\mathbf{A}}\,\mathbf{B} = |\mathbf{B}|\,\text{Proj}_{\mathbf{B}}\,\mathbf{A}. \tag{6.2}$$

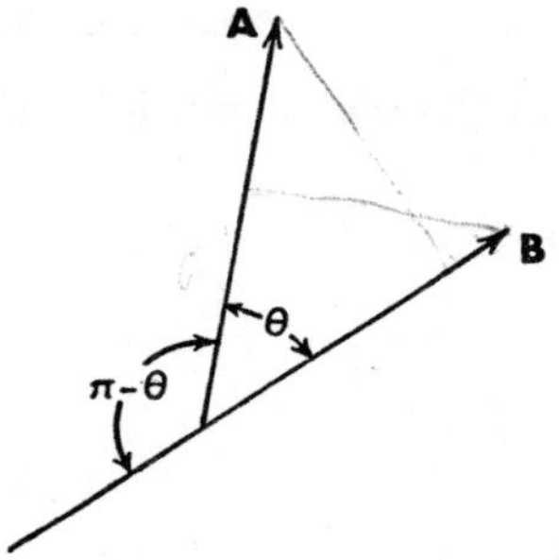

Figure 9: The Angle θ of the Scalar Product

In particular, we note *that if* $|\mathbf{A}|, |\mathbf{B}| \neq 0$, *then the necessary and sufficient condition for* $\mathbf{A} \cdot \mathbf{B} = 0$ *is that* **A** *be orthogonal to* **B**.

We shall derive some fundamental properties of this product.

(a) ***Commutative,*** $\mathbf{A} \cdot \mathbf{B} = \mathbf{B} \cdot \mathbf{A}$. This result follows from the definition.

(b) ***Associative, No Meaning.*** Since $\mathbf{A} \cdot (\mathbf{B} \cdot \mathbf{C})$ has no meaning, one cannot discuss the associative law.

(c) ***Distributive,*** $\mathbf{A} \cdot (\mathbf{B} + \mathbf{C}) = \mathbf{A} \cdot \mathbf{B} + \mathbf{A} \cdot \mathbf{C}$. If a product is neither commutative nor associative, it may still have some uses. But if a product is not distributive, then its use is very limited. Thus, it becomes important to verify relation (c).

We shall use result (6.2) to prove this property. From Figure 10, we see that

$$\text{Proj}_{\mathbf{A}}\,\mathbf{B} + \text{Proj}_{\mathbf{A}}\,\mathbf{C} = \text{Proj}_{\mathbf{A}}\,(\mathbf{B} + \mathbf{C}).$$

By multiplying this last relation by $|\mathbf{A}|$ the desired result is obtained.

(d) ***Scalar Multiplication Table for the Unit Vectors* i, j, k.** Evidently, $\mathbf{i} \cdot \mathbf{i} = 1$, $\mathbf{j} \cdot \mathbf{j} = 1$, $\mathbf{k} \cdot \mathbf{k} = 1$, $\mathbf{i} \cdot \mathbf{j} = 0$, etc. These results can be expressed

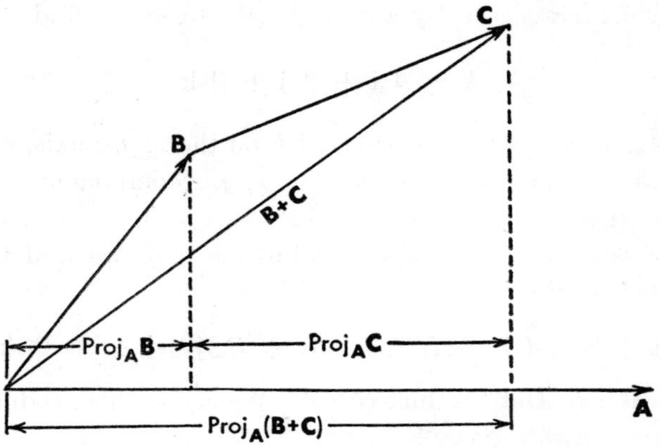

Figure 10: The Distributive Law for the Scalar Product

in the scalar multiplication table,

$\cdot$	**i**	**j**	**k**
i	1	0	0
j	0	1	0
k	0	0	1

(6.3)

(e) ***Scalar Multiplication of Vectors via Components.*** From the validity of the distributive law (c) and the multiplication rules (d), it follows that

$$\mathbf{A} \cdot \mathbf{B} = A_x B_x + A_y B_y + A_z B_z. \tag{6.4}$$

This last relation can be used to deduce the well-known formula for $\cos \theta$ when θ is the angle between **A, B.** We find

$$\cos \theta = \frac{\mathbf{A} \cdot \mathbf{B}}{|\mathbf{A}|\,|\mathbf{B}|} = \frac{A_x B_x + A_y B_y + A_z B_z}{|\mathbf{A}|\,|\mathbf{B}|}.$$

Further, by use of (6.4) it follows that $|\mathbf{A}|^2 = A_x^2 + A_y^2 + A_z^2$. Thus, the formula for $\cos \theta$ may be expressed entirely in terms of the components of vectors **A, B.**

(f) ***Physical Interpretation of the Scalar Product.*** Imagine a constant force **F** acting on a particle moving along a vector **R**, then

$$\mathbf{F} \cdot \mathbf{R} = |\mathbf{F}|\,|\mathbf{R}| \cos \theta$$

where θ is the angle between **F, R.** But, by definition the right-hand side of this last relation is the work done by **F.**

Illustrative Example: Find the angle between the vectors $\mathbf{A} = \mathbf{i} - \mathbf{j}$, $\mathbf{B} = 2\mathbf{j} + \mathbf{k}$.

Solution: By use of the components of **A, B,** we find $\mathbf{A} \cdot \mathbf{B} = (1)(0) + (-1)(2) + (0)(1) = -2$. Hence, from the definition of the scalar product, $|\mathbf{A}|\,|\mathbf{B}| \cos \theta = -2$. Use of the formulas of (e) furnishes the relations $|\mathbf{A}| = \sqrt{1+1} = \sqrt{2}$, $|\mathbf{B}| = \sqrt{4+1} = \sqrt{5}$. From these relations, we find $\cos \theta = \dfrac{-2}{\sqrt{10}} = -\dfrac{\sqrt{10}}{5}$.

Problem 6.1: If $\mathbf{A} = \mathbf{i} - 2\mathbf{j} + 4\mathbf{k}$, determine the unit vector along **A**.

Problem 6.2: Find the projection of $\mathbf{A} = 3\mathbf{i} + 2\mathbf{j} - \mathbf{k}$ on $\mathbf{B} = \mathbf{i} - 3\mathbf{j} + \mathbf{k}$.

Problem 6.3: Show that the vectors $\mathbf{A} = \mathbf{i} - \mathbf{j} - \mathbf{k}$, $\mathbf{B} = 2\mathbf{i} + 3\mathbf{j} - \mathbf{k}$ are perpendicular. Find the magnitude of these vectors.

Problem 6.4: Show that the vectors $\mathbf{A} = 3\mathbf{i} + 4\mathbf{j}$, $\mathbf{B} = 2\mathbf{k}$, $\mathbf{C} = 3\mathbf{i} + 4\mathbf{j} + 2\mathbf{k}$ form a right triangle.

Problem 6.5: If R denotes the magnitude of the radius vector **R** and $\mathbf{R}_1$ denotes a unit vector in the direction of **R,** then $\mathbf{R} = \mathbf{R}_1 R$. Determine the expression for $\mathbf{R}_1$ in terms of components. *Hint:* Let $\mathbf{R}_1 = a\mathbf{i} + b\mathbf{j} + c\mathbf{k}$. Forming the scalar product of both sides of the equation with **i,** we obtain $\mathbf{i} \cdot \mathbf{R}_1 = a$. But $\mathbf{i} \cdot \mathbf{R}_1 = \cos \alpha$, where α is the angle between **R** and Ox.

Problem 6.6: Let **A, B, C** denote the sides of a triangle. Hence, $\mathbf{A} = \mathbf{C} - \mathbf{B}$ and $\mathbf{A} \cdot \mathbf{A} = (\mathbf{C} - \mathbf{B}) \cdot (\mathbf{C} - \mathbf{B})$. By expanding both sides of this last equation, verify the law of cosines.

Problem 6.7: If **R** is the radius vector and **A** is a constant vector, show that $(\mathbf{R} - \mathbf{A}) \cdot \mathbf{A} = 0$ is the equation of a plane by: (1) expressing **R, A** in terms of components and evaluating the above equation; (2) geometric interpretation of the equation.

Problem 6.8: By use of the two methods of the above problem, show that $(\mathbf{R} - \mathbf{A}) \cdot \mathbf{R} = 0$ is the equation of a sphere.

7. The Vector or Cross Product ($\mathbf{A} \times \mathbf{B}$). Let **n** denote a unit vector perpendicular to the plane of **A, B** and oriented so that **A, B, n** taken in that order form a right-hand system. Then $\mathbf{A} \times \mathbf{B}$ is defined by the following vector

$$\mathbf{A} \times \mathbf{B} = |\mathbf{A}|\,|\mathbf{B}| \sin \theta\, \mathbf{n}, \qquad 0 \leq \theta \leq \pi \tag{7.1}$$

where θ is the angle included between **A, B.** From the definition, it follows $\mathbf{A} \times \mathbf{B}$ may be obtained by the following geometric construction (see Figure 11). Let M be a plane perpendicular to **A** and passing through the initial point of the vector. Perform the following three operations: (1)

project **B** on M determining **B**′; (2) rotate this projection through 90° determining **B**″, so that it lies along **n**; (3) multiply the resulting vector, **B**″, by |**A**|. We shall use this construction in showing the validity of the distributive law for the cross product.

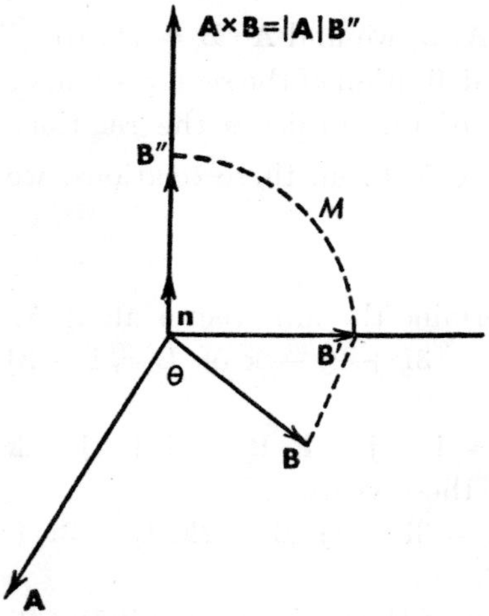

Figure 11: The Construction of **A** × **B**

From the definition (7.1), one important result follows immediately: if |**A**|, |**B**| ≠ 0, *then the necessary and sufficient* condition for **A** × **B** = 0, is that **A** be parallel to **B**.

As in the case of the scalar product we shall derive some fundamental properties of this product.

(a) ***Anticommutative,*** **A** × **B** = −**B** × **A**. From the definition, it follows that cross product is not commutative but is anticommutative.

(b) ***Not Associative.*** The question of whether this product is associative depends upon whether **A** × (**B** × **C**) = (**A** × **B**) × **C**, for all vectors, **A**, **B**, **C**. If we let **A** = **B**, and **C** be arbitrary, we obtain a contradiction.

(c) ***Distributive,*** **A** × (**B** + **C**) = **A** × **B** + **A** × **C**. To verify relation (c), we use the geometric construction given in Figure 11. Consider the triangle whose sides are the vectors **B**, **C**, **B** + **C**. First, we note that (**B** + **C**)′ = **B**′ + **C**′. That is, when the triangle with sides **B**, **C**, **B** + **C** is projected into the plane M, the resulting figure is a triangle with sides **B**′, **C**′, (**B** + **C**)′. Rotating about **A** as an axis through 90°, changes the triangle into a new triangle. Hence, (**B** + **C**)″ = **B**″ + **C**″. Through multiplication of this last equation by |**A**| and use of the previous interpretation of the cross product, we find that the cross product is distributive.

(d) ***Vector Multiplication Table for the Unit Vectors*** **i**, **j**, **k**. By use of the definition of the vector product, (7.1), we can easily verify the following table:

×	**i**	**j**	**k**
i	0	**k**	−**j**
j	−**k**	0	**i**
k	**j**	−**i**	0

(7.2)

(e) ***Vector Multiplication of Vectors via Components.*** Use of the distributive law (c) and the table (7.2) shows that

$$\mathbf{A} \times \mathbf{B} = (A_yB_z - A_zB_y)\mathbf{i} + (A_zB_x - A_xB_z)\mathbf{j} + (A_xB_y - A_yB_x)\mathbf{k}$$

By formal use of the expansion laws for determinants, we find that the above equation may be expressed by the "formal" determinant

$$\mathbf{A} \times \mathbf{B} = \begin{vmatrix} \mathbf{i} & \mathbf{j} & \mathbf{k} \\ A_x & A_y & A_z \\ B_x & B_y & B_z \end{vmatrix}.$$

(f) ***Geometric Interpretation; Area of a Parallelogram.*** By use of the definition of $\mathbf{A} \times \mathbf{B}$ (7.1), we see that

$$|\mathbf{A} \times \mathbf{B}| = |\mathbf{A}|\,|\mathbf{B}| \sin \theta.$$

But the right-hand side of this equation represents the area of the parallelogram whose sides are **A, B.** Hence, the *magnitude* of $\mathbf{A} \times \mathbf{B}$ represents the area of a parallelogram whose sides are **A** and **B.**

(g) ***Rotation of a Rigid Body about an Axis; the Angular Velocity Vector, ω.*** It is evidently possible to represent the angular velocity by a directed line segment along the instantaneous axis of rotation. The magnitude of the segment represents the magnitude of the angular velocity; the sense of the segment is related to the angular rotation by the right-hand screw rule. It remains to be shown that if $\boldsymbol{\omega}_1$ represents one angular velocity and $\boldsymbol{\omega}_2$ represents another angular velocity, then the sum $\boldsymbol{\omega}_1 + \boldsymbol{\omega}_2$ as obtained from the parallelogram law represents the resultant angular velocity. We assume that the axes of the rotations corresponding to the two angular velocities have a point O in common. For the present, we treat $\boldsymbol{\omega}$ as *a vector whose physical representative may or may not satisfy the proper addition law.*

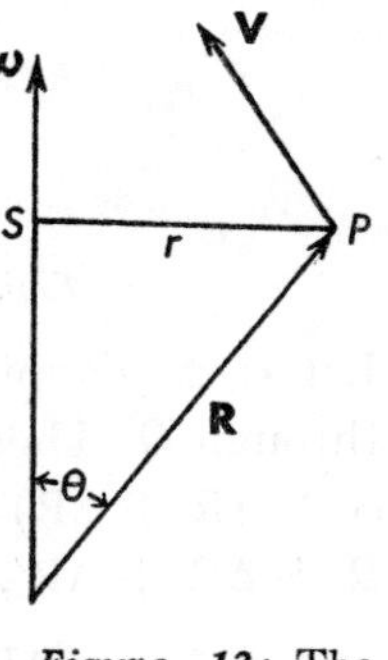

Figure 12: The Velocity, **V,** and the Angular Velocity, **ω**

First, we consider the linear velocity, **V,** of any point P of the rigid body. Evidently, **V** lies in a plane perpendicular to **ω.** If SP is perpendicular to **ω**, then **V** is also orthogonal to SP (see Figure 12). Further, the magnitude of **V** is $|\boldsymbol{\omega}|r = |\boldsymbol{\omega}|\,|\mathbf{R}| \sin \theta$. From this, it is easily verified that

$$\mathbf{V} = \boldsymbol{\omega} \times \mathbf{R}. \tag{7.3}$$

In Section 10, we shall discuss vector differentiation. At present, we shall anticipate this discussion and assume $\Delta\mathrm{R} = \mathbf{V}\,\Delta t$, approximately, where

$\Delta\mathbf{R}$ is the increase in $\mathbf{R}$ due to the "small" rotation $\boldsymbol{\omega}\,\Delta t$ (Δt is the increase in time). Thus, instead of the above equation for $\mathbf{V}$, we consider the equation for the displacement $\Delta\mathbf{R}$,

$$\Delta\mathbf{R} = \boldsymbol{\omega} \times \mathbf{R}\,\Delta t$$

which is correct to first-order terms.

With the aid of this last relation, we shall show that[3] *if* $\boldsymbol{\omega}$ *adds according to the parallelogram law then consistent physical results are obtained.* That is, $\boldsymbol{\omega}_1 + \boldsymbol{\omega}_2$ can be used to represent a physical angular velocity compounded of $\boldsymbol{\omega}_1$ and $\boldsymbol{\omega}_2$. The displacement, $\Delta\mathbf{R}$, due to $\boldsymbol{\omega}_1$ is $\Delta\mathbf{R} = \boldsymbol{\omega}_1 \times \mathbf{R}\,\Delta t$. The position vector of P after the small rotation, $\boldsymbol{\omega}_1\,\Delta t$, is $\mathbf{R} + \Delta\mathbf{R}$.

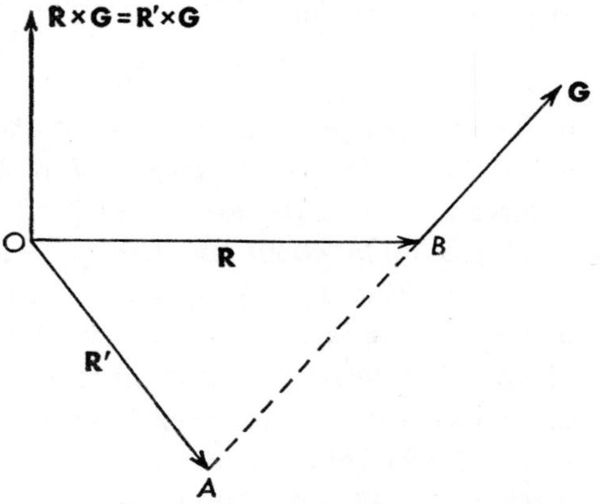

Figure 13: The Moment of a Vector, **G**, about a Point

Let $\boldsymbol{\omega}_2\,\Delta t$ denote a second small rotation about another axis passing through O. Then, the increment in the position vector becomes, $\Delta\mathbf{R}' = \boldsymbol{\omega}_2 \times (\mathbf{R} + \Delta\mathbf{R})\,\Delta t$. The final position vector of P after both rotations is $\mathbf{R} + \Delta\mathbf{R} + \Delta\mathbf{R}'$. From the last two relations, we find that

$$\Delta\mathbf{R} + \Delta\mathbf{R}' = [\boldsymbol{\omega}_1 \times \mathbf{R} + \boldsymbol{\omega}_2 \times (\mathbf{R} + \Delta\mathbf{R})]\,\Delta t.$$

Since our equations are correct only as far as first-order terms are concerned, we omit the $\Delta\mathbf{R}$ in the right-hand side of the above equation and find that

$$\Delta\mathbf{R} + \Delta\mathbf{R}' = (\boldsymbol{\omega}_1 + \boldsymbol{\omega}_2) \times \mathbf{R}\,\Delta t.$$

Thus, "small" rotations or angular velocities may be represented by vectors.

(h) ***Moment of a Vector about a Point,*** $\mathbf{M} = \mathbf{R} \times \mathbf{G}$. We define the moment of a vector $\mathbf{G}$ about a point O to be $\mathbf{R} \times \mathbf{G}$; where $\mathbf{R}$ is the vector

[3] J. L. Synge and B. A. Griffith, *Principles of Mechanics*, McGraw-Hill, New York, 1949, p. 281.

from O to any point of **G**. For this definition to have sense, we must show (see Figure 13) that

$$\mathbf{M} = \mathbf{R} \times \mathbf{G} = \mathbf{R}' \times \mathbf{G}.$$

Since $\overrightarrow{AB} = \lambda\mathbf{G}$, where λ is some scalar, we may write

$$\mathbf{R} = \mathbf{R}' + \lambda\mathbf{G}.$$

Forming the cross product of both sides of this last equation with **G**, we obtain the desired conclusion.

The moment of a vector or system of vectors occurs frequently in mechanics. Thus, if $\mathbf{L} = m\mathbf{V}$, where **L** is the linear momentum, m is the mass, and **V** is the velocity of a particle, then $\mathbf{R} \times \mathbf{L}$ is called the angular momentum of the particle about O. If **F** is a force, then $\mathbf{R} \times \mathbf{F}$ is called the moment of **F** about O. It is easy to verify that the projection of $\mathbf{R} \times \mathbf{F}$ on any line through O is the well known "*moment of the force about the line.*" For vector purposes, *moment about a point* is a much more useful notion. Now, to the physicist and engineer moment has some physical significance. They feel that moment should indicate the tendency of a rigid body to rotate. Therefore, the question arises whether the mathematical vector, $\mathbf{R} \times \mathbf{F}$, measures this physical moment. The question is, "Do physical moments about a point add according to the parallelogram law?" This question is answered in the affirmative by the following fundamental theorem of statics: The necessary and sufficient condition for equilibrium of a rigid body is that $\Sigma\mathbf{F}_i = 0$, $\Sigma\mathbf{M}_i = 0$, where $\mathbf{F}_i$ and $\mathbf{M}_i$ represent the external forces and their moments about any point, respectively, and Σ denotes the sum of all such vectors. That is, the physicist and engineer would like to add moments in such a manner that for equilibrium the sum of the moments is zero. The above theorem shows that *vector addition* is the proper type of addition for moments about a point.

Problem 7.1: Determine the area of the parallelogram formed by the vectors $\mathbf{A} = \mathbf{i} + 3\mathbf{j} - \mathbf{k}$, $\mathbf{B} = 2\mathbf{i} - \mathbf{j} + 2\mathbf{k}$.

Problem 7.2: Find the unit vector **n** orthogonal to both $\mathbf{A} = \mathbf{i} - \mathbf{j} + 2\mathbf{k}$ and $\mathbf{B} = 2\mathbf{i} + 2\mathbf{j} - \mathbf{k}$.

Problem 7.3: A plane is determined by the points $A(1, 2, 4)$, $B(2, -1, 1)$, and $C(2, -2, -1)$. Determine the unit vector, **n**, orthogonal to this plane.

Problem 7.4: By projecting OA of the above problem onto **n**, determine the distance from the origin to the plane.

Problem 7.5: Find the vector in the plane ABC (of Problem 7.3) which is perpendicular to CB. *Hint:* What vector is obtained if **n** is crossed with some vector in the plane?

Problem 7.6: Find the shortest distance between the skew lines determined by the points: $A(1, 2, -1)$ and $B(0, 2, 3)$; $C(2, -1, 1)$ and $D(1, 3, -1)$. *Hint:* From solid geometry, it is known that the shortest distance between two lines lies along their common perpendicular.

Problem 7.7: If A, B, C, D are the points of Problem 7.6, find the perpendicular distance from D to the plane of A, B, C.

Problem 7.8: A circular plate of radius b initially rotates about an axis passing through the center of the plate and inclined at an angle of 45° to the line perpendicular to the plate. Let the coordinate axis be chosen so that the initial angular velocity vector lies in the xOz plane and that the xOy plane coincides with the plane of the plate. If ω is the magnitude of the angular velocity, determine the following initial quantities:

(1) the angular velocity vector, $\boldsymbol{\omega}$, in terms of its components;
(2) the linear velocity of any point in the plate;
(3) the linear momentum vector of the element of mass at (x, y);
(4) the angular momentum vector of the element of mass at (x, y).

8. The Triple Scalar or Box Product, A · (B × C). This triple mixed

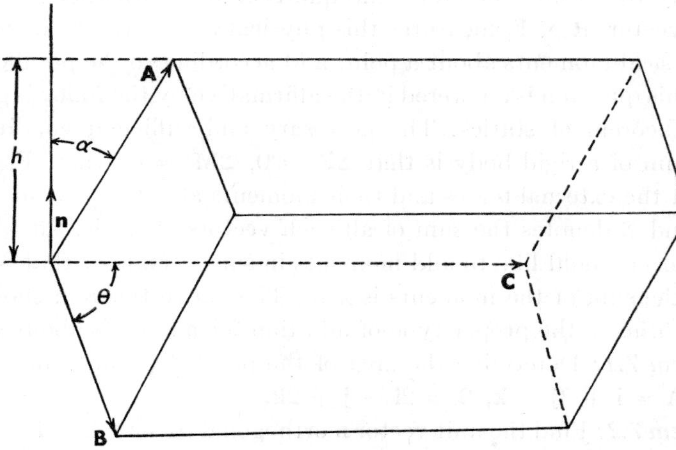

Figure 14: The Triple Scalar Product

product is a scalar. Since $(\mathbf{A} \cdot \mathbf{B}) \times \mathbf{C}$ has no significance, there is no possibility of confusion if the parentheses in $\mathbf{A} \cdot (\mathbf{B} \times \mathbf{C})$ are omitted. Thus, one often writes this product as: $\mathbf{A} \cdot \mathbf{B} \times \mathbf{C}$ or $[\mathbf{ABC}]$ or $(\mathbf{A}, \mathbf{B}, \mathbf{C})$.

(a) ***Geometric Significance of*** $\mathbf{A} \cdot \mathbf{B} \times \mathbf{C}$. By definition of the cross and scalar products, we find

$$\mathbf{A} \cdot \mathbf{B} \times \mathbf{C} = S(\mathbf{A} \cdot \mathbf{n}) = Sh$$

where S is the area of the parallelogram whose sides are **B**, **C**, and h is the altitude of the parallelopiped, whose sides are **A**, **B**, **C**. Thus, the triple scalar product is equal to the volume of this parallelopiped. Evidently, this volume can be determined equally well by $\mathbf{B} \cdot \mathbf{C} \times \mathbf{A}$ or $\mathbf{C} \cdot \mathbf{A} \times \mathbf{B}$.

(b) ***Principle of Interchange of Dot and Cross in the Triple Scalar Product.*** From the above discussion, it follows that

$$\mathbf{A} \cdot \mathbf{B} \times \mathbf{C} = \mathbf{A} \times \mathbf{B} \cdot \mathbf{C} = \mathbf{C} \cdot \mathbf{A} \times \mathbf{B} = \mathbf{C} \times \mathbf{A} \cdot \mathbf{B}. \tag{8.1}$$

Equations (8.1) show that the *dot and cross may be interchanged in the triple scalar product without altering the value of this product.* This principle is of great value in verifying vector identities.

(c) ***The Triple Scalar Product as a Determinant.*** If we express **A**, **B**, **C** in terms of components, then by direct expansion we find that

$$\mathbf{C} \cdot \mathbf{A} \times \mathbf{B} = C_x(A_yB_z - A_zB_y) + C_y(A_zB_x - A_xB_z) + C_z(A_xB_y - A_yB_x).$$

If we expand the following determinant and use the above relation, we obtain the important formula

$$\begin{vmatrix} C_x & C_y & C_z \\ A_x & A_y & A_z \\ B_x & B_y & B_z \end{vmatrix} = \mathbf{C} \cdot \mathbf{A} \times \mathbf{B}. \tag{8.2}$$

9. The Triple Vector Product, A × (B × C). In this product, the position of the parenthesis is important. It is easily verified that, $\mathbf{A} \times (\mathbf{B} \times \mathbf{C}) \neq (\mathbf{A} \times \mathbf{B}) \times \mathbf{C}$.

The following expansion formula, involving the triple vector product, is of great importance in our future work,

$$\mathbf{A} \times (\mathbf{B} \times \mathbf{C}) = (\mathbf{A} \cdot \mathbf{C})\mathbf{B} - (\mathbf{A} \cdot \mathbf{B})\mathbf{C}. \tag{9.1}$$

Equation (9.1) may be checked by expanding both sides in terms of components. In the tensor analysis section we shall furnish a direct derivation of this result.

Illustrative Example: Show that $(\mathbf{C} \times \mathbf{A}) \cdot (\mathbf{A} \times \mathbf{B}) \times (\mathbf{B} \times \mathbf{C}) = [\mathbf{ABC}]^2$.

Solution: Let $\mathbf{A} \times \mathbf{B} = \mathbf{D}$; then $(\mathbf{A} \times \mathbf{B}) \times (\mathbf{B} \times \mathbf{C}) = \mathbf{D} \times (\mathbf{B} \times \mathbf{C}) = (\mathbf{D} \cdot \mathbf{C})\mathbf{B} - (\mathbf{D} \cdot \mathbf{B})\mathbf{C}$. Replacing **D** by $\mathbf{A} \times \mathbf{B}$, this last expansion becomes

$$(\mathbf{A} \times \mathbf{B}) \times (\mathbf{B} \times \mathbf{C}) = (\mathbf{A} \times \mathbf{B} \cdot \mathbf{C})\mathbf{B} - (\mathbf{A} \times \mathbf{B} \cdot \mathbf{B})\mathbf{C}.$$

By interchange of dot and cross, the last term in the above equation vanishes. Forming the scalar product of $\mathbf{C} \times \mathbf{A}$ with the resulting equation, we obtain

$$(\mathbf{C} \times \mathbf{A}) \cdot (\mathbf{A} \times \mathbf{B}) \times (\mathbf{B} \times \mathbf{C}) = [\mathbf{ABC}](\mathbf{C} \times \mathbf{A} \cdot \mathbf{B}).$$

By interchange of the dot and cross, we find that $(\mathbf{C} \times \mathbf{A} \cdot \mathbf{B}) = [\mathbf{ABC}]$. This verifies the above identity.

Problem 9.1: Show that $\mathbf{A} \times (\mathbf{B} \times \mathbf{C}) + \mathbf{C} \times (\mathbf{A} \times \mathbf{B}) - \mathbf{B} \times (\mathbf{A} \times \mathbf{C}) = 0$.

Problem 9.2: Expand $(\mathbf{A} \times \mathbf{B}) \times (\mathbf{B} \times \mathbf{C})$ in two forms. *Hint:* Let $(\mathbf{A} \times \mathbf{B}) = \mathbf{D}$ and expand; then let $(\mathbf{B} \times \mathbf{C}) = \mathbf{E}$ and expand.

Problem 9.3: Find an expansion for $(\mathbf{A} \times \mathbf{B}) \cdot (\mathbf{C} \times \mathbf{D})$.

Problem 9.4: Show that $(\mathbf{A} \times \mathbf{B}) \cdot (\mathbf{C} \times \mathbf{D}) + (\mathbf{B} \times \mathbf{C}) \cdot (\mathbf{A} \times \mathbf{D}) + (\mathbf{C} \times \mathbf{A}) \cdot (\mathbf{B} \times \mathbf{D}) = 0$.

Problem 9.5: By expanding $(\mathbf{A} \times \mathbf{B}) \times (\mathbf{C} \times \mathbf{D})$ in two forms and equating these two forms, one obtains an equation for $\mathbf{D}$ in terms of $\mathbf{A}, \mathbf{B}, \mathbf{C}$. Find this relation. Note, this relation is an analytic scheme for determining the scalars m, n, l, p in 4(c).

Problem 9.6: By use of the triple scalar product, find the volume of the parallelopiped whose sides are $\mathbf{A} = 2\mathbf{i} + \mathbf{j}$, $\mathbf{B} = 2\mathbf{j} - 3\mathbf{k}$, $\mathbf{C} = \mathbf{i} + \mathbf{j} - \mathbf{k}$.

Problem 9.7: Show that the vectors $\mathbf{A} = \mathbf{i} - \mathbf{j} + 3\mathbf{k}$, $\mathbf{B} = 2\mathbf{i} + 4\mathbf{j} - \mathbf{k}$, $\mathbf{C} = 5\mathbf{i} + 7\mathbf{j} + \mathbf{k}$ are all parallel to a plane.

Problem 9.8: Consider the vectors $\mathbf{A} = 3\mathbf{i} - \mathbf{j}$, $\mathbf{B} = \mathbf{i} + \mathbf{j} - 2\mathbf{k}$. By use of the triple cross product, find a vector lying in the plane of $\mathbf{A}, \mathbf{B}$ and perpendicular to $\mathbf{A}$.

Problem 9.9: Give a geometric interpretation of the relation $(\mathbf{A} \times \mathbf{B}) \cdot (\mathbf{C} \times \mathbf{D}) = 0$.

Problem 9.10: Expand $[(\mathbf{A} \times \mathbf{B}) \times (\mathbf{B} \times \mathbf{C})] \times (\mathbf{C} \times \mathbf{A})$ in the following two forms: (1) in terms of linear combinations of $\mathbf{A}, \mathbf{C}$; (2) in terms of linear combinations of $\mathbf{A} \times \mathbf{B}, \mathbf{C} \times \mathbf{B}$.

Problem 9.11: Show that if the ordered triad $\mathbf{A}, \mathbf{B}, \mathbf{C}$ forms a right-hand system, then the triple scalar product $(\mathbf{A}, \mathbf{B}, \mathbf{C})$ is positive. *Hint:* Since the ordered triad $\mathbf{A}, \mathbf{B}, \mathbf{A} \times \mathbf{B}$ forms a right-hand system, $(\mathbf{A}, \mathbf{B}, \mathbf{A} \times \mathbf{B}) > 0$. Let $\mathbf{C} = a\mathbf{A} + b\mathbf{B} + c\mathbf{A} \times \mathbf{B}$ and show that the sign of c determines the orientation of the triad $\mathbf{A}, \mathbf{B}, \mathbf{C}$.

ADDITIONAL PROBLEMS

1. A, B, C, D, E are the vertices of a regular pentagon whose center is F. Show that $\overrightarrow{FA} + \overrightarrow{FB} + \overrightarrow{FC} + \overrightarrow{FD} + \overrightarrow{FE} = 0$ by vector methods.
2. Prove the following theorem of Desargues: Two triangles are situated in space so that the three points of intersection of corresponding sides

fall along a line; show that the lines passing through the corresponding vertices intersect in a common point.

3. Prove that the sum of the squares of the sides of any quadrilateral is equal to the sum of the squares of the two diagonals plus four times the square of the line which joins the midpoints of these diagonals.
4. $\mathbf{R}_0$, $\mathbf{R}_1$, $\mathbf{R}_2$ are vectors from the origin to three arbitrary points in space. Determine the vector equation of a plane which passes through the terminal point of $\mathbf{R}_0$ and contains the vector, $\mathbf{R}_1 - \mathbf{R}_2$. (By the vector equation of a plane, we mean the condition which **R**, the radius vector to points of the plane, must satisfy.)
5. $\mathbf{R}_0$, $\mathbf{R}_1$, $\mathbf{R}_2$, $\mathbf{R}_3$ are vectors from the origin to four arbitrary points of space. Determine an expression for the distance between the terminal point of $\mathbf{R}_0$ and the plane determined by the terminal points of $\mathbf{R}_1$, $\mathbf{R}_2$, $\mathbf{R}_3$.
6. For the vectors of Problem 5, find the shortest distance between the lines determined by the terminal points of $\mathbf{R}_0$, $\mathbf{R}_3$ and those of $\mathbf{R}_1$, $\mathbf{R}_2$.
7. Discuss the locus determined by the condition

$$(\mathbf{R} - \mathbf{A}) \cdot (\mathbf{R} + \mathbf{A}) = 0.$$

8. Prove that

$$[(\mathbf{A} \times \mathbf{P}), (\mathbf{B} \times \mathbf{Q}), (\mathbf{C} \times \mathbf{R})] + [(\mathbf{A} \times \mathbf{Q}), (\mathbf{B} \times \mathbf{R}), (\mathbf{C} \times \mathbf{P})] + [(\mathbf{A} \times \mathbf{R}), (\mathbf{B} \times \mathbf{P}), (\mathbf{C} \times \mathbf{Q})] = 0.$$

Chapter II

DIFFERENTIATION THEORY

10. Scalar, Vector, and Tensor Fields. The term *field* signifies: (1) a region of three-space, (2) a surface or family of surfaces, (3) a curve or family of curves, to each point of which there is attached a unique scalar, ϕ, vector, $\mathbf{F}$, or more general quantity (tensor). According to the nature of the attached quantity and the domain under consideration, we talk of a one-dimensional vector field, etc. For the present, we shall not define the term *tensor* in a concise fashion. The reason for this is that a general tensor cannot be represented in a simple geometric manner. In the general theory, we consider both scalars and vectors as simple types of tensors. The usual terminology is that scalars are tensors of order zero and vectors are tensors of order one. We shall ask the reader to allow for the possible existence of more general quantities—tensors of order two, three, etc. For the present, one may think of a scalar or vector field when we use the script letters $\mathcal{A}$, $\mathcal{B}$, etc.

We shall assume that the reader is familiar with the concepts of continuity and differentiability of functions of several variables. Hence, the limit idea furnishes nothing new when applied to tensor fields of order zero (scalar fields). However, for tensor fields of order one (vector fields), two possible approaches exist. First, one may consider the limit idea in terms of Cartesian rectangular components of the vector. Secondly, one may discuss the limit idea in terms of the direct quantity—the vector. Corresponding to these two methods of attack, one may define the derivative, $d\mathbf{F}/dt$, of $\mathbf{F}(t)$, by

$$\frac{d\mathbf{F}}{dt} = \mathbf{i}\,\frac{dF_x}{dt} + \mathbf{j}\,\frac{dF_y}{dt} + \mathbf{k}\,\frac{dF_z}{dt} \tag{10.1}$$

or by

$$\frac{d\mathbf{F}}{dt} = \lim_{\Delta t \to 0} \frac{\Delta \mathbf{F}}{\Delta t} \tag{10.2}$$

It is easily shown that these two definitions are essentially equivalent. However, the second definition does have a geometric significance which is not evident in the first.

11. Differentiation Rules for Sums and Products. We shall use one-dimensional vector fields in deriving these rules. However, the rules are applicable to two- and three-dimensional tensor fields when ordinary derivatives are replaced by partial derivatives.

(a) ***Differentiation of a Sum,*** $\frac{d}{dt}(\mathbf{F} + \mathbf{G}) = \frac{d\mathbf{F}}{dt} + \frac{d\mathbf{G}}{dt}$. This rule may be verified either by expanding each side in terms of Cartesian rectangular components (10.1) or by use of the second definition (10.2).

(b) ***Differentiation of a Product,*** $\frac{d}{dt}(\mathbf{F}*\mathbf{G}) = \frac{d\mathbf{F}}{dt}*\mathbf{G} + \mathbf{F}*\frac{d\mathbf{G}}{dt}$. In order to avoid needless repetition, we shall not consider the scalar and vector products separately. Instead, we indicate a general multiplication operation by a star (*). Thus, the scalar product occurs when the dot is substituted for the star; the vector product arises when the cross is substituted for the star. In fact, one can treat products of the type $\phi\mathbf{F}$ by allowing the star to represent ordinary multiplication. Again, by writing **FG** and allowing the star to indicate such multiplication (i.e., $\mathbf{F}*\mathbf{G} = \mathbf{FG}$), we obtain a dyad, or tensor of the second order. In our future work, we shall call multiplications of the type $\phi\mathbf{F}$, **FG**, *ordinary multiplication.*

For formula 11(b) to be valid, regardless of the particular nature of the star multiplication and of the quantities being multiplied, one condition *must* be satisfied. This condition is that the *star multiplication must be distributive.* Henceforth, we shall assume that all star multiplications have this property. In fact, we have verified this property for the scalar and vector products in 6(c) and 7(c). Two other results are needed to facilitate the derivation of 11(b): The limit of a star product is the star product of the limits, when all the limits exist; the limit of a sum of tensors must be the sum of the limits. When the star products have been properly defined in terms of components, these results are easily verified.

To derive 11(b), we go through the following limit process and find

$$\begin{aligned}\frac{d}{dt}\mathbf{F}*\mathbf{G} &= \lim_{\Delta t\to 0}\frac{\mathbf{F}(t+\Delta t)*\mathbf{G}(t+\Delta t) - \mathbf{F}(t)*\mathbf{G}(t)}{\Delta t}\\ &= \lim_{\Delta t\to 0}\left[\frac{\mathbf{F}(t+\Delta t)-\mathbf{F}(t)}{\Delta t}*\mathbf{G}(t+\Delta t) + \mathbf{F}(t)*\frac{\mathbf{G}(t+\Delta t)-\mathbf{G}(t)}{\Delta t}\right]\\ &= \frac{d\mathbf{F}}{dt}*\mathbf{G} + \mathbf{F}*\frac{d\mathbf{G}}{dt}.\end{aligned}$$

Problem 11.1: What is meant by the terms "tensor of order one," "tensor of order zero"?

Problem 11.2: List the various possible meaningful interpretations of the stars in $\mathbf{F}*(\mathbf{G}*\mathbf{H})$. (For instance, $\mathbf{F}\cdot\mathbf{G}\times\mathbf{H}$, etc.).

Problem 11.3: By use of 11(b), derive the formula for $\frac{d}{dt}[\mathbf{F}*(\mathbf{G}*\mathbf{H})]$.

Hint: Let $\mathcal{A} = \mathbf{G}*\mathbf{H}$ and use the rule $\frac{d}{dt}(\mathbf{F}*\mathcal{A}) = \frac{d\mathbf{F}}{dt}*\mathcal{A} + \mathbf{F}*\frac{d\mathcal{A}}{dt}$.

Problem 11.4: Find the value of $\frac{d}{dt}\left[\mathbf{F}\cdot\frac{d\mathbf{F}}{dt}\times\frac{d^2\mathbf{F}}{dt^2}\right]$.

Problem 11.5: Find the value of $\frac{d}{dt}\left[\mathbf{F}\times\left(\frac{d\mathbf{F}}{dt}\times\frac{d^2\mathbf{F}}{dt^2}\right)\right]$.

Problem 11.6: If $\mathbf{G}$ is a vector of constant magnitude show that $\frac{d\mathbf{G}}{dt}\cdot\mathbf{G} = 0$.

12. One-Dimensional Fields; Elementary Curve Theory. A useful one-dimensional field associated with a curve C is the radius vector field $\mathbf{R}$,

$$\mathbf{R} = \mathbf{i}x(t) + \mathbf{j}y(t) + \mathbf{k}z(t) \tag{12.1}$$

where t is a permissible parameter for the curve. We assume that the functions $x(t)$, $y(t)$, $z(t)$ possess third derivatives.

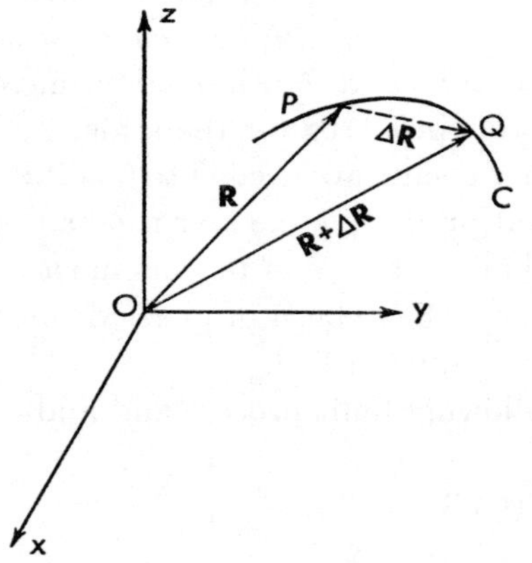

Figure 15: The Radius Vector Field, $\mathbf{R}$

From calculus it is known that the limit of the ratio of the chord PQ to the arc PQ is 1. That is, if s is the arc length parameter, then

$$\lim_{\Delta s\to 0}\left|\frac{\Delta\mathbf{R}}{\Delta s}\right| = \left|\frac{d\mathbf{R}}{ds}\right| = 1.$$

Further, from the geometry, it appears that the unit vector $\frac{d\mathbf{R}}{ds}$ lies along the tangent to C. In the future we denote this vector by $\mathbf{t}$, and write

$$\mathbf{t} = \frac{d\mathbf{R}}{ds} = \mathbf{i}\frac{dx}{ds} + \mathbf{j}\frac{dy}{ds} + \mathbf{k}\frac{dz}{ds}. \tag{12.2}$$

It will be recalled that curvature of a plane curve is defined as the limit of the difference, $\Delta\theta$, in angle between two tangents to the curve at P, P' divided by the arc length $PP' = \Delta s$. Consider the space curve C and the unit tangent vector field, $\mathbf{t}$. By parallel displacement of $\mathbf{t}(P')$ to point P, we see that $\Delta\theta = |\Delta\mathbf{t}|$ approximately, since $|\mathbf{t}| = 1$. Thus, a reasonable definition of the curvature, κ for space curves is

$$\kappa = \left| \frac{d\mathbf{t}}{ds} \right| = \lim_{\Delta s \to 0} \frac{\Delta\theta}{\Delta s} \tag{12.3}$$

Let us ask "what is the direction of $\frac{d\mathbf{t}}{ds}$?" By applying the rule for product

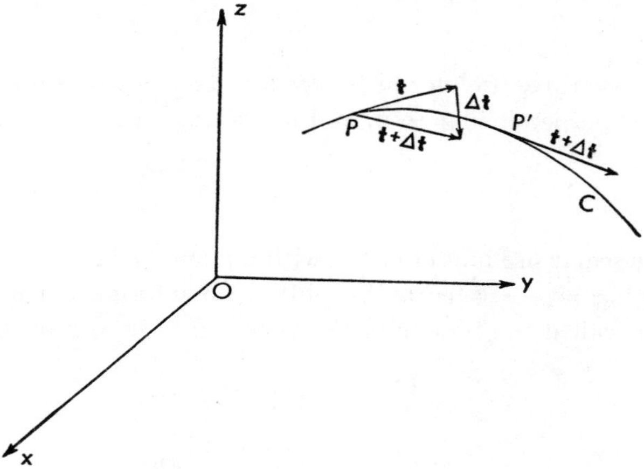

Figure 16: The Vector Field, **t**, and the Vector Increment, **Δt**

differentiation to the relation, $\mathbf{t} \cdot \mathbf{t} = 1$, we find that

$$\mathbf{t} \cdot \frac{d\mathbf{t}}{ds} = 0.$$

That is, $\frac{d\mathbf{t}}{ds}$ is orthogonal to **t**. Since, at each point P of C, there exists a whole plane of directions orthogonal to **t**, it is evident that this condition does not completely fix $\frac{d\mathbf{t}}{ds}$. Hence, we introduce the particular direction normal to **t** along which $\frac{d\mathbf{t}}{ds}$ lies. We call this direction the "principal normal" to the curve C and let **n** denote a unit vector in this direction. Through use of (12.3) we may write

$$\frac{d\mathbf{t}}{ds} = \kappa\mathbf{n}. \tag{12.4}$$

As for plane curves, one may show that the limiting circle defined by "three adjacent points," lies in the plane of **n**, **t**, and has its center at a distance κ^{-1} from P along **n**.

In order to study $\frac{d\mathbf{n}}{ds}$, we introduce the unit binormal vector, $\mathbf{b} = (\mathbf{t} \times \mathbf{n})$. The sign of **b** is chosen so that the ordered vectors **t, n, b** form a right-hand system similar to **i, j, k**. Further, since **t, n, b** are three independent vectors, we may express the derivative of **n** as a linear combination of the vectors **t, n, b** as in

$$\frac{d\mathbf{n}}{ds} = \alpha\mathbf{t} + \beta\mathbf{n} + \tau\mathbf{b}, \tag{12.5}$$

where α, β, τ are three undetermined scalars. To evaluate these scalars, we note that **t** is perpendicular to **n**, and **n** is a unit vector. Thus

$$\mathbf{t} \cdot \frac{d\mathbf{n}}{ds} = -\mathbf{n} \cdot \frac{d\mathbf{t}}{ds} = -\kappa, \qquad \mathbf{n} \cdot \frac{d\mathbf{n}}{ds} = 0.$$

Forming the scalar product of (12.5) with **t, n** and using the above results, we find that $\alpha = -\kappa$, $\beta = 0$. We obtain no information as to τ. The quantity τ is called the torsion of the curve and (12.5) reduces to

$$\frac{d\mathbf{n}}{ds} = -\kappa\mathbf{t} + \tau\mathbf{b}. \tag{12.6}$$

To determine the significance of τ, we study $\frac{d\mathbf{b}}{ds}$. Again, we write

$$\frac{d\mathbf{b}}{ds} = \bar{\alpha}\mathbf{t} + \bar{\beta}\mathbf{n} + \bar{\gamma}\mathbf{b}. \tag{12.7}$$

Since **t, b, n** are mutually orthogonal unit vectors, we find that

$$\mathbf{t} \cdot \frac{d\mathbf{b}}{ds} = -\mathbf{b} \cdot \frac{d\mathbf{t}}{ds} = 0, \qquad \mathbf{n} \cdot \frac{d\mathbf{b}}{ds} = -\mathbf{b} \cdot \frac{d\mathbf{n}}{ds} = -\tau, \qquad \mathbf{b} \cdot \frac{d\mathbf{b}}{ds} = 0.$$

Forming the scalar products of (12.7) with **t, n, b** and using these last results we obtain

$$\frac{d\mathbf{b}}{ds} = -\tau\mathbf{n}. \tag{12.8}$$

The three formulas, (12.4), (12.6), and (12.8), are known as the Frenet formulas in differential geometry. These formulas are of great importance in the study of the intrinsic nature of curves. Thus, for a plane curve, **t, n** lie in the plane of the curve (say, the x,y-plane). Hence, $\mathbf{b} = \mathbf{k}$ and $\frac{d\mathbf{b}}{ds} = 0$. That is, $\tau = 0$ for plane curves. Conversely, if $\tau = 0$, it can be shown that the curve is plane. The name "torsion" for τ is due to this result. The sign of τ for a space curve may be positive or negative. For a plane curve, it is customary to assume that the pair **t, n** are oriented in the sense of the pair **i, j**. Thus, the curvature of a plane curve may be positive or negative. For space curves, no such orientation exists. In this case, it is customary to consider the curvature, κ, as positive. The importance of curvature and torsion is due to the following theorem: If the curvature and torsion are known differentiable functions of arc length, then the Frenet formulas determine a unique curve, except for a rigid body motion, in space.

13. Velocity and Acceleration. By definition, the velocity vector, **V**, and the acceleration vector, **A**, of a particle moving along a curve C, are defined by

$$\mathbf{V} = \frac{d\mathbf{R}}{dt}, \qquad \mathbf{A} = \frac{d\mathbf{V}}{dt}.$$

The parameter, t, is the time. By use of the chain rule for differentiation we obtain

$$\mathbf{V} = \frac{d\mathbf{R}}{ds}\frac{ds}{dt} = \mathbf{t}v$$

where v or ds/dt is the magnitude of the velocity vector. Differentiation of the formula for **V** and use of the first Frenet formula furnishes the relation

$$\mathbf{A} = \frac{dv}{dt}\mathbf{t} + \kappa v^2\mathbf{n}.$$

Thus, the acceleration vector *lies in the plane of* **t, n** *and has the tangential component* $\frac{dv}{dt}$, *and normal component* κv^2.

Illustrative Example: Given the curve defined by $\mathbf{R} = \mathbf{i}t + \mathbf{j}t^2 + \mathbf{k}2t$, where t is a parameter.

(1) Find the element of arc ds along this curve ($(ds)^2 = d\mathbf{R} \cdot d\mathbf{R}$).
(2) Find the unit tangent vector **t**.
(3) Find the curvature κ.

Solution: The parametric equations of the curve are $x = t$, $y = t^2$, $z = 2t$; $ds^2 = (5 + 4t^2)\,dt^2$; since $\frac{dx}{ds} = \frac{dx}{dt}\frac{dt}{ds}$, we find $\frac{dx}{ds} = (5 + 4t^2)^{-1/2}$, $\frac{dy}{ds} = 2t(5 + 4t^2)^{-1/2}$, $\frac{dz}{ds} = 2(5 + 4t^2)^{-1/2}$; by (12.2), $\mathbf{t} = (5 + 4t^2)^{-1/2}(\mathbf{i} + 2t\mathbf{j} + 2\mathbf{k})$; $\frac{d\mathbf{t}}{ds} = \frac{d\mathbf{t}}{dt}\frac{dt}{ds} = (5 + 4t^2)^{-2}(-4t\mathbf{i} + 10\mathbf{j} - 8t\mathbf{k})$; by (12.4), $\kappa = \left(\frac{d\mathbf{t}}{ds} \cdot \frac{d\mathbf{t}}{ds}\right)^{1/2} = (5 + 4t^2)^{-2}(80t^2 + 100)^{1/2}$.

Problem 13.1: For the curve, $\mathbf{R} = \mathbf{i}t + \mathbf{j} \sin t + \mathbf{k} \cos t$, find (1) ds; (2) $\mathbf{t}$; (3) κ; (4) $\mathbf{n}$; (5) τ.

Problem 13.2: For the curve $\mathbf{R} = \mathbf{i} \cos 2t + \mathbf{j} \sin 2t$, find (1) ds; (2) $\mathbf{t}$; (3) κ; (4) $\mathbf{n}$; (5) $\mathbf{b}$; (6) τ.

Problem 13.3: Consider a particle whose radius vector is $\mathbf{R} = \mathbf{i} \cos 2t + \mathbf{j} \sin 2t$, where t is the time. Find: (1) the equations of the path; (2) the velocity vector and the acceleration vector.

Problem 13.4: If the radius vector of a particle is $\mathbf{R} = \mathbf{i}t + \mathbf{j} \sin t + \mathbf{k} \cos t$, where t is the time, find: (1) the equations of the path; (2) the velocity vector and the acceleration vector.

14. Orthogonal Coordinate Systems. In this section we shall briefly discuss the structure of coordinate systems in Euclidean three space. From our viewpoint a coordinate system may be considered to consist of: (1) three families of independent surfaces, the coordinate surfaces; (2) three families of curves which are the intersections of the coordinate surfaces, the coordinate curves or lines; (3) the intersections of the coordinate lines, the points of three space. We shall limit our future discussion in vector analysis to the consideration of *orthogonal* coordinate systems. This means that the three families of coordinate surfaces are mutually orthogonal at each point of space. In the next three paragraphs we shall consider coordinate systems from each of the three above-mentioned viewpoints.

(a) ***Coordinate Surfaces.*** Here we are interested in the geometric description of the coordinate surfaces. That is, are these surfaces spheres, planes, cones, etc.? Or, alternatively, what are the equations of the coordinate surfaces in terms of Cartesian orthogonal coordinates? We shall consider this description for the examples of (d), (e), and (f) below.

(b) ***Coordinate Curves (Base Vectors).*** One method of describing the coordinate curves uses *unit vector fields* which are tangent to these curves. These vector fields are called *base* (*or measure*) *vectors*. At each point P, one must define three unit vectors. We shall illustrate this point further in the examples. However, we must note that the introduction of ordered base vectors defines an orientation on each coordinate surface.

(c) ***Coordinate Points (Coordinate Transformations).*** The simplest method for determining the coordinates of a point P in some coordinate system is to relate the Cartesian orthogonal coordinates, x, y, z, of P to the new coordinates. The resulting equations are called the *coordinate transformation formulas*.

We consider three particular coordinate systems in the following sections in order to illustrate the above discussion.

(d) ***Cartesian Orthogonal Coordinates.*** The three families of coordinate surfaces are the parallel planes, x = constant, y = constant, z = constant. Further, the base vectors are **i, j, k.** These vectors are drawn in the sense of increasing values of the x, y, z coordinates. This implies that the coordinate surfaces have been oriented so that a rotation from **i** into **j** determines **k,** a rotation from **j** into **k** determines **i,** etc., according to the right-hand screw law.

(e) ***Cylindrical Coordinates.*** Here, the three families of coordinate surfaces are coaxial cylinders, planes passing through this axis and planes perpendicular to this axis. If the axis is chosen to be Oz, then the equations of these surfaces are:

$r = \sqrt{x^2 + y^2}$ = constant, which are circular right cylinders, about Oz as axis;

$\theta = \arctan y/x$ = constant, which are half planes, through the Oz axis; (14.1)

z = constant, which are planes perpendicular to Oz.

It is easily verified by geometry that the coordinate surfaces are mutually orthogonal. The coordinate lines are:

r = constant, z = constant, which are circles lying in planes orthogonal to Oz;

r = constant, θ = constant, which are lines parallel to Oz;

z = constant, θ = constant, which are lines passing through Oz and orthogonal to Oz.

The base vectors of the first of the above families of coordinate lines are denoted by $\boldsymbol{\theta}_1$; the base vectors of the second family are denoted by **k**; the base vectors of the third family are denoted by $\mathbf{r}_1$. These vectors are sensed in the direction of the increasing coordinate variable along the coordinate line and such that the ordered triad $\mathbf{r}_1$, $\boldsymbol{\theta}_1$, **k** forms a right-handed system. The following figure indicates the coordinate surfaces, the coordinate lines, and the base vectors passing through a point P. A pictorial representation of the coordinate surface variables (often called coordinate variables) is given by $QP = r$, $SP = z$, $\measuredangle TQP = \theta$.

Solving the equations (14.1) for x, y, z, we obtain the inverse formulas

$$x = r\cos\theta, \qquad y = r\sin\theta, \qquad z = z. \tag{14.2}$$

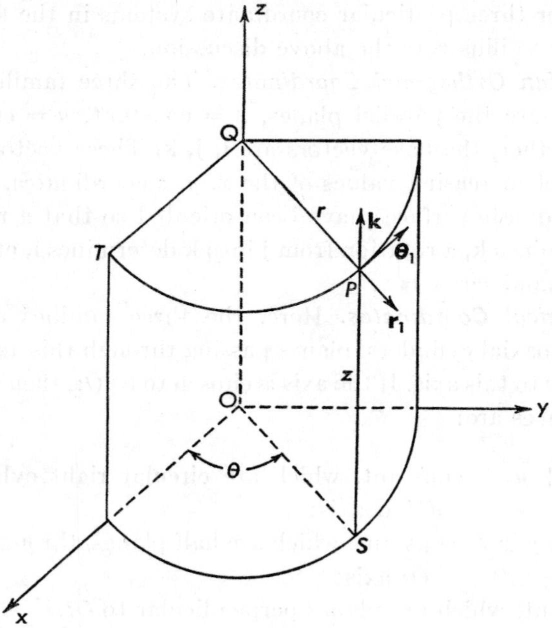

Figure 17: Cylindrical Coordinates in Euclidean Space

In particular, if $z = 0$ in the above discussion, then cylindrical coordinates reduce to the well-known polar coordinates. The formulas (14.2) may be considered as defining a mapping from the (x, y, z) space to the (r, θ, z) space. In this case, all the points of Euclidean three-space map into the region of cylindrical (r, θ, z) space defined by $0 \leq \theta < 2\pi$, $0 \leq r < \infty$, $-\infty < z < \infty$ (see Figure 18). That is, unless some such restriction is placed on the variables θ, r, z, the *mapping* or *transformation* formulas (14.2) will not possess unique inverses. Instead of the range $0 \leq \theta < 2\pi$, it is frequently found desirable to use a range such as $\alpha \leq \theta < 2\pi + \alpha$, $-\pi \leq \alpha \leq \pi$. The line $r = 0$ is a singular line of the mapping.

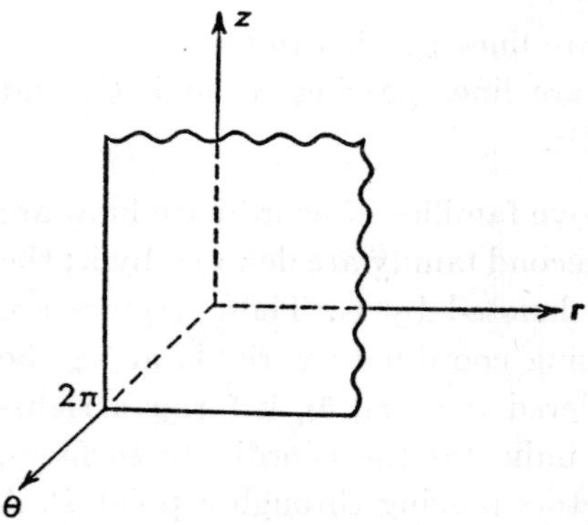

Figure 18: Cylindrical Mapping of Space

We now determine the fundamental formulas relating the base vectors $\mathbf{r}_1$, $\boldsymbol{\theta}_1$, $\mathbf{k}$ and $\mathbf{i}$, $\mathbf{j}$, $\mathbf{k}$. Since $\mathbf{i}$, $\mathbf{j}$ are unit vectors parallel to Ox, Oy, respectively, at P, we find by the use of Figure 19 and vector addition that

$$\mathbf{r}_1 = \mathbf{i} \cos \theta + \mathbf{j} \sin \theta, \qquad \boldsymbol{\theta}_1 = -\mathbf{i} \sin \theta + \mathbf{j} \cos \theta. \tag{14.3}$$

Since **i**, **j**, **k** are constant vectors (constant magnitude and direction), we

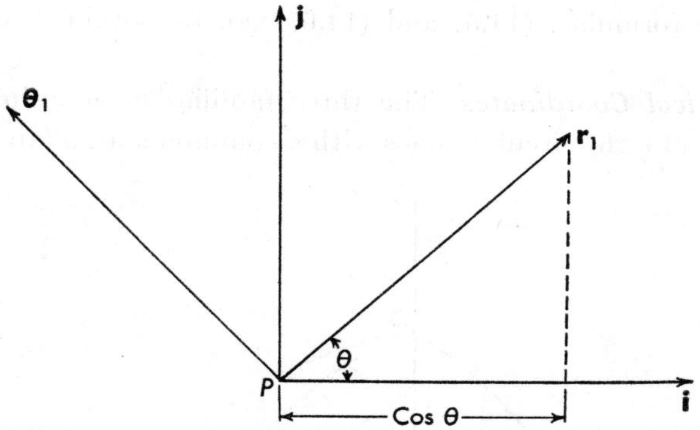

Figure 19: The Relation between $\mathbf{r}_1$, $\boldsymbol{\theta}_1$, and **i**, **j**

can apply the differentiation laws of Section 11 and show that

$$\frac{\partial \mathbf{r}_1}{\partial r} = 0, \qquad \frac{\partial \mathbf{r}_1}{\partial \theta} = -\mathbf{i} \sin \theta + \mathbf{j} \cos \theta = \boldsymbol{\theta}_1, \qquad \frac{\partial \mathbf{r}_1}{\partial z} = 0, \text{ etc.}$$

These formulas may be summarized in the table:

$\frac{\partial}{\partial}$	$\mathbf{r}_1$	$\boldsymbol{\theta}_1$	$\mathbf{k}$
r	0	0	0
θ	$\boldsymbol{\theta}_1$	$-\mathbf{r}_1$	0
z	0	0	0

(14.4)

There exist two additional relations that are of importance in cylindrical coordinates. First, in Cartesian orthogonal coordinates, the element of arc is

$$ds^2 = (dx)^2 + (dy)^2 + (dz)^2.$$

By use of the transformation formulas relating the Cartesian coordinates x, y, z and the cylindrical coordinates r, θ, z, (14.2), we find that

$$ds^2 = r^2(d\theta)^2 + (dr)^2 + (dz)^2. \tag{14.5}$$

Secondly, by solving (14.3) for **i, j, k** in terms of $\mathbf{r}_1$, $\boldsymbol{\theta}_1$, **k** and substituting this result into the formula for the radius vector field **R**, (12.1), we obtain the relation

$$\mathbf{R} = r\mathbf{r}_1 + z\mathbf{k}. \tag{14.6}$$

Both of the formulas, (14.5) and (14.6), can be obtained directly from Figure 17.

(f) ***Spherical Coordinates.*** The three families of coordinate surfaces are a family of right circular cones with a common axis, a family of planes

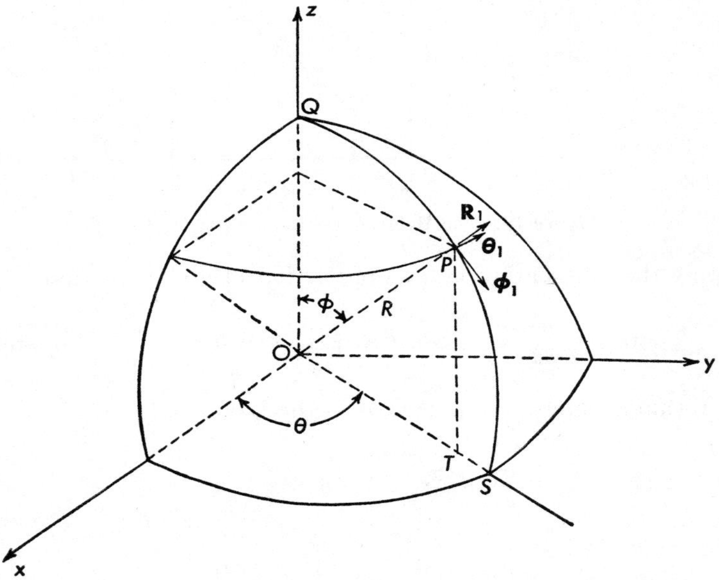

Figure 20: Spherical Coordinates in Euclidean Space

passing through this axis, a family of spherical surfaces with origin as center. If the axis is chosen to be Oz, then the equations of these surfaces are:

$R = \sqrt{x^2 + y^2 + z^2}$ = constant, which are spheres with center at the origin;

$\theta = \arctan y/x$ = constant, which are half planes through Oz; (14.7)

$\phi = \arctan \dfrac{\sqrt{x^2 + y^2}}{z}$ = constant, which are cones (of one nappe).

From geometrical considerations, it follows that these coordinate surfaces are mutually orthogonal. The coordinate lines are:

R = constant, ϕ = constant, which are small circles lying in planes orthogonal to Oz;

R = constant, θ = constant, which are great circles lying in planes passing through Oz;

ϕ = constant, θ = constant, which are radial lines passing through the origin.

The base vectors of the first of the above families of coordinate lines are denoted by $\boldsymbol{\theta}_1$; the base vectors of the second family are denoted by $\boldsymbol{\phi}_1$; the base vectors of the third family are denoted by $\mathbf{R}_1$. It is assumed that the ordered triad $\boldsymbol{\phi}_1, \boldsymbol{\theta}_1, \mathbf{R}_1$ forms a right-handed system. The first family of coordinate lines in cylindrical and spherical coordinates are identical. Thus, the base vectors $\boldsymbol{\theta}_1$ are equal. We illustrate the coordinate surfaces, the coordinate lines, and the base vectors passing through a point P in the following figure. The coordinate variables may be represented by $OP = R$, $\measuredangle QOP = \phi$, $\measuredangle xOS = \theta$. Note that OT, the projection of OP on plane xOy, is equal to the variable r of cylindrical coordinates and PT is equal to z in cylindrical coordinates.

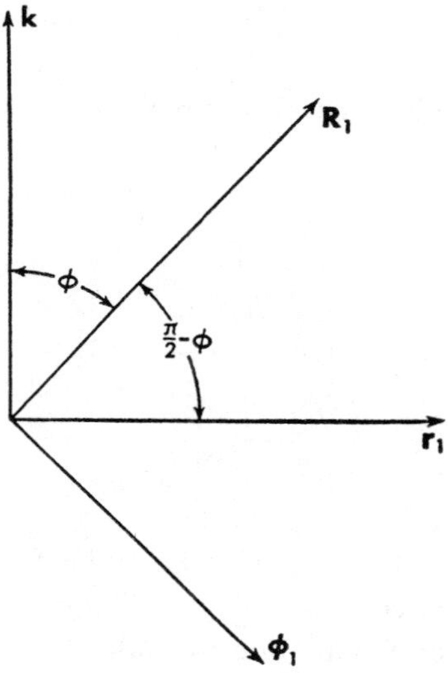

Figure 21: The Relation between $\mathbf{k}$, $\mathbf{r}_1$, and $\mathbf{R}_1$, $\boldsymbol{\phi}_1$

The coordinate transformations relating the coordinate variables (R, ϕ, θ) of point P to the (x, y, z) of point P are determined by relations (14.7). Solving these equations for x, y, z, we obtain the inverse transformation formulas

$$x = R \sin \phi \cos \theta, \qquad y = R \sin \phi \sin \theta, \qquad z = R \cos \phi. \tag{14.8}$$

By comparing the transformation formulas relating Cartesian coordinates to cylindrical and spherical coordinates, or by use of Figure 20, we find that the variables r, z are related to R, ϕ by means of $r = R \sin \phi$, $z = R \cos \phi$. Again, we note that the mapping from the (x, y, z) space to the (R, ϕ, θ) space is multivalued unless we restrict the range of the spherical coordinates so that $0 \le R < \infty$, $0 \le \phi \le \pi$, $0 \le \theta < 2\pi$, or in some equivalent manner. The point, $R = 0$, is the singular point of the map.

By use of Figure 21 and vector addition we find that

$$\mathbf{R}_1 = \mathbf{r}_1 \sin \phi + \mathbf{k} \cos \phi, \qquad \boldsymbol{\phi}_1 = \mathbf{r}_1 \cos \phi - \mathbf{k} \sin \phi.$$

Replacing $\mathbf{r}_1$ by its expression in terms of $\mathbf{i}$, $\mathbf{j}$, $\mathbf{k}$ [see (14.3)], we obtain

$$\begin{aligned} \mathbf{R}_1 &= \mathbf{i}\cos\theta\sin\phi + \mathbf{j}\sin\theta\sin\phi + \mathbf{k}\cos\phi, \\ \boldsymbol{\phi}_1 &= \mathbf{i}\cos\theta\cos\phi + \mathbf{j}\sin\theta\cos\phi - \mathbf{k}\sin\phi, \\ \boldsymbol{\theta}_1 &= -\mathbf{i}\sin\theta + \mathbf{j}\cos\theta. \end{aligned} \tag{14.9}$$

Through use of the above relations we may compute the differentiation formulas for the unit vectors $\mathbf{R}_1$, $\boldsymbol{\phi}_1$, $\boldsymbol{\theta}_1$. Thus, by differentiation of (14.9), we obtain

$$\frac{\partial \mathbf{R}_1}{\partial \phi} = \mathbf{i}\cos\theta\cos\phi + \mathbf{j}\sin\theta\cos\phi - \mathbf{k}\sin\phi = \boldsymbol{\phi}_1.$$

The partial differentiation table which corresponds to (14.4) is

$\frac{\partial}{\partial}$	$\mathbf{R}_1$	$\boldsymbol{\phi}_1$	$\boldsymbol{\theta}_1$
R	0	0	0
ϕ	$\boldsymbol{\phi}_1$	$-\mathbf{R}_1$	0
θ	$\boldsymbol{\theta}_1\sin\phi$	$\boldsymbol{\theta}_1\cos\phi$	$-\mathbf{R}_1\sin\phi - \boldsymbol{\phi}_1\cos\phi$

(14.10)

The following formulas for $\mathbf{R}$ and ds^2 in spherical coordinates are often of considerable use. They are obtained in exactly the same manner as the corresponding formulas in cylindrical coordinates:

$$ds^2 = R^2(d\phi)^2 + (dR)^2 + R^2\sin^2\phi(d\theta)^2 \tag{14.11}$$

$$\mathbf{R} = R\mathbf{R}_1. \tag{14.12}$$

The tables in (14.4) and (14.10) will be of importance in the remainder of this chapter. As an example of the application of these formulas, we consider the following problem.

Illustrative Example: If C is a curve, $R = R(t)$, $\phi = \phi(t)$, $\theta = \theta(t)$, determine $\frac{d\mathbf{R}_1}{dt}$.

Solution: With the aid of the chain rule, we find that

$$\frac{d\mathbf{R}_1}{dt} = \frac{\partial \mathbf{R}_1}{\partial R}\frac{dR}{dt} + \frac{\partial \mathbf{R}_1}{\partial \phi}\frac{d\phi}{dt} + \frac{\partial \mathbf{R}_1}{\partial \theta}\frac{d\theta}{dt}.$$

By use of (14.10), the above formula becomes

$$\frac{d\mathbf{R}_1}{dt} = \boldsymbol{\phi}_1\frac{d\phi}{dt} + \boldsymbol{\theta}_1\sin\phi\frac{d\theta}{dt}.$$

Problem 14.1: Verify the formula $ds^2 = r^2(d\theta)^2 + (dr)^2 + (dz)^2$ by direct calculation.

Problem 14.2: Derive the formulas, $\mathbf{R} = r\mathbf{r}_1 + z\mathbf{k}$, $\mathbf{R} = R\mathbf{R}_1$.

Problem 14.3: Derive the formulas for $\frac{\partial \mathbf{r}_1}{\partial \theta}, \frac{\partial \boldsymbol{\theta}_1}{\partial \theta}$, by geometrical methods.

Problem 14.4: Derive the formulas for $\frac{\partial \mathbf{R}_1}{\partial \theta}, \frac{\partial \boldsymbol{\phi}_1}{\partial \theta}$, by analytical methods.

15. The Velocity and Acceleration Vectors in Cartesian Orthogonal, Cylindrical, and Spherical Coordinates. The basic formulas for the theory of this section are

$$\mathbf{R} = \mathbf{i}x + \mathbf{j}y + \mathbf{k}z = r\mathbf{r}_1 + z\mathbf{k} = R\mathbf{R}_1$$

and the definitions of the velocity and acceleration vectors. With the aid of these and the tables, (14.4) and (14.10), all of the desired results may be easily obtained.

(a) ***Cartesian Orthogonal Coordinates.*** Through use of the above formula for $\mathbf{R}$, we find that the components of the velocity and acceleration vectors, $\mathbf{V}$ and $\mathbf{A}$ respectively, are (when t is the time parameter),

$$\mathbf{V} = \frac{d\mathbf{R}}{dt} = \mathbf{i}\frac{dx}{dt} + \mathbf{j}\frac{dy}{dt} + \mathbf{k}\frac{dz}{dt} \tag{15.1}$$

$$\mathbf{A} = \frac{d\mathbf{V}}{dt} = \mathbf{i}\frac{d^2x}{dt^2} + \mathbf{j}\frac{d^2y}{dt^2} + \mathbf{k}\frac{d^2z}{dt^2}. \tag{15.2}$$

(b) ***Cylindrical Coordinates.*** By differentiation of $\mathbf{R}$ with respect to the time parameter, we obtain: $\mathbf{V} = r(d\mathbf{r}_1/dt) + \mathbf{r}_1(dr/dt) + \mathbf{k}(dz/dt)$. Use of the chain rule for differentiation and (14.4) furnishes the relation

$$\frac{d\mathbf{r}_1}{dt} = \frac{\partial \mathbf{r}_1}{\partial r}\frac{dr}{dt} + \frac{\partial \mathbf{r}_1}{\partial \theta}\frac{d\theta}{dt} + \frac{\partial \mathbf{r}_1}{\partial z}\frac{dz}{dt} = \boldsymbol{\theta}_1\frac{d\theta}{dt}$$

and similarly, $d\boldsymbol{\theta}_1/dt = -\mathbf{r}_1\, d\theta/dt$. Thus, the equation for $\mathbf{V}$ becomes

$$\mathbf{V} = r\frac{d\theta}{dt}\boldsymbol{\theta}_1 + \frac{dr}{dt}\mathbf{r}_1 + \frac{dz}{dt}\mathbf{k}. \tag{15.3}$$

By differentiation of (15.3) with respect to t, and use of the formulas for $d\mathbf{r}_1/dt$, $d\boldsymbol{\theta}_1/dt$, we obtain the expression for the acceleration vector,

$$\mathbf{A} = \mathbf{r}_1\left[\frac{d^2r}{dt^2} - r\left(\frac{d\theta}{dt}\right)^2\right] + \boldsymbol{\theta}_1\left[r\frac{d^2\theta}{dt^2} + 2\frac{d\theta}{dt}\frac{dr}{dt}\right] + \mathbf{k}\frac{d^2z}{dt^2}. \tag{15.4}$$

(c) ***Spherical Coordinates.*** Differentiating $\mathbf{R}$ with respect to the time parameter we obtain $\mathbf{V} = R(d\mathbf{R}_1/dt) + \mathbf{R}_1(dR/dt)$. By chain rule differentiation and use of (14.10) we find

$$\frac{d\mathbf{R}_1}{dt} = \boldsymbol{\phi}_1 \frac{d\phi}{dt} + \boldsymbol{\theta}_1 \sin\phi \frac{d\theta}{dt}, \qquad \frac{d\boldsymbol{\theta}_1}{dt} = -(\mathbf{R}_1 \sin\phi + \boldsymbol{\phi}_1 \cos\phi)\frac{d\theta}{dt}.$$
$$\frac{d\boldsymbol{\phi}_1}{dt} = -\mathbf{R}_1 \frac{d\phi}{dt} + \boldsymbol{\theta}_1 \cos\phi \frac{d\theta}{dt},$$

Substituting the first of these relations into the formula for **V**, we obtain the formula for the velocity vector in spherical coordinates

$$\mathbf{V} = \mathbf{R}_1 \frac{dR}{dt} + \boldsymbol{\phi}_1 R \frac{d\phi}{dt} + \boldsymbol{\theta}_1 R \sin\phi \frac{d\theta}{dt}. \tag{15.5}$$

By differentiation of (15.5) and use of the formulas for $d\mathbf{R}_1/dt$, etc., we obtain

$$\begin{aligned}\mathbf{A} = \mathbf{R}_1 &\left[\frac{d^2R}{dt^2} - R\left(\frac{d\phi}{dt}\right)^2 - R\left(\sin\phi\frac{d\theta}{dt}\right)^2\right] \\ &+ \boldsymbol{\phi}_1\left[\frac{d}{dt}\left(R\frac{d\phi}{dt}\right) + \frac{dR}{dt}\frac{d\phi}{dt} - R\sin\phi\cos\phi\left(\frac{d\theta}{dt}\right)^2\right] \\ &+ \boldsymbol{\theta}_1\left[\sin\phi\frac{d\theta}{dt}\frac{dR}{dt} + R\cos\phi\frac{d\theta}{dt}\frac{d\phi}{dt} + \frac{d}{dt}\left(R\sin\phi\frac{d\theta}{dt}\right)\right].\end{aligned} \tag{15.6}$$

Problem 15.1: Consider the case of plane motion, $z = 0$, and show by use of the transformation formulas that the formula $\mathbf{V} = \mathbf{i}\frac{dx}{dt} + \mathbf{j}\frac{dy}{dt}$ becomes $\mathbf{V} = r\frac{d\theta}{dt}\boldsymbol{\theta}_1 + \frac{dr}{dt}\mathbf{r}_1$.

Problem 15.2: If $\mathbf{r}_1$ is the radial base vector in cylindrical coordinates, derive the formula for $\frac{d^2\mathbf{r}_1}{dt^2}$ in terms of $\mathbf{r}_1$, $\boldsymbol{\theta}_1$, $\mathbf{k}$.

Problem 15.3: If $\mathbf{R}_1$ is the radial base vector in spherical coordinates, derive the formula for $\frac{d^2\mathbf{R}_1}{dt^2}$ in terms of $\mathbf{R}_1$, $\boldsymbol{\theta}_1$, $\boldsymbol{\phi}_1$.

Problem 15.4: A particle moves along the circle, $x^2 + y^2 = b^2$, in the plane $z = 0$, with constant angular velocity. Determine its linear velocity and acceleration vectors, **V** and **A**.

Problem 15.5: A particle moves along the curve $\phi = \theta^2$ on the sphere $x^2 + y^2 + z^2 = a^2$ so that $\frac{d\theta}{dt} = 1$. Find its velocity and acceleration vectors, **V** and **A**, when $\theta = \pi/4$.

16. Moving Reference Frames. In this section we consider two Cartesian orthogonal coordinate systems: $O'x'y'z'$, $Oxyz$, with origins at O'

and O, respectively. Further, we assume that $O'x'y'z'$ is a fixed coordinate system and $Oxyz$ is rigidly attached to some rigid body moving in space. This second coordinate system is often called a moving reference frame.

(a) ***The Radius Vectors,*** $\mathbf{R}'$, $\mathbf{R}_0'$, $\mathbf{R}$. Let $\mathbf{R}$ denote the position vector of a point P with respect to $Oxyz$; $\mathbf{R}'$, the position vector of P with respect to

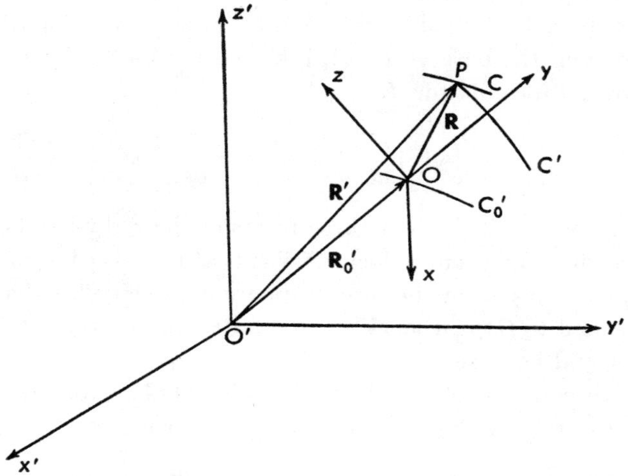

Figure 22: Moving Reference Frames

$O'x'y'z'$; $\mathbf{R}_0'$, the position vector of O with respect to $O'x'y'z'$. Further, let (x, y, z) be the coordinates of P with respect to $Oxyz$; (x', y', z') be the coordinates of P with respect to $O'x'y'z'$; (x_0', y_0', z_0') be the coordinates of O with respect to $O'x'y'z'$. Finally, we introduce the base vectors $\mathbf{i}, \mathbf{j}, \mathbf{k}$ of $Oxyz$ and $\mathbf{i}', \mathbf{j}', \mathbf{k}'$ of $O'x'y'z'$. Evidently, we may express $\mathbf{R}, \mathbf{R}', \mathbf{R}_0'$ by the formulas

$$\mathbf{R} = \mathbf{i}x + \mathbf{j}y + \mathbf{k}z, \qquad \mathbf{R}' = \mathbf{i}'x' + \mathbf{j}'y' + \mathbf{k}'z',$$
$$\mathbf{R}_0' = \mathbf{i}'x_0' + \mathbf{j}'y_0' + \mathbf{k}'z_0'. \tag{16.1}$$

Further, from Figure 22 it is evident that: $\mathbf{R}' = \mathbf{R}_0' + \mathbf{R}$.

(b) ***The Velocity Vectors,*** $\mathbf{V}'$, $\mathbf{V}_0'$, $\mathbf{V}$. Consider a motion of the above configuration in which: O describes a curve denoted by $\mathbf{C}_0'$ when referred to $O'x'y'z'$; P describes a curve denoted by C' when referred to $O'x'y'z'$ or C when referred to $Oxyz$. From the relation between $\mathbf{R}, \mathbf{R}', \mathbf{R}_0'$, we find that: $d\mathbf{R}'/dt = d\mathbf{R}_0'/dt + d\mathbf{R}/dt$, or

$$\mathbf{V}' = \mathbf{V}_0' + \mathbf{V}. \tag{16.2}$$

These velocities will be denoted by the following terms:

$\mathbf{V}' = d\mathbf{R}'/dt$ = absolute velocity of P;
$\mathbf{V}_0' = d\mathbf{R}_0'/dt$ = velocity of the moving origin O;
$\mathbf{V} = d\mathbf{R}/dt$ = relative velocity of P.

Since $\mathbf{i}', \mathbf{j}', \mathbf{k}'$ are constant vector fields, the formulas for $\mathbf{V}', \mathbf{V}_0'$ in terms of components are obtained by differentiation of x', y', z' or x_0', y_0', z_0' in (16.1). However, the base vectors $\mathbf{i}, \mathbf{j}, \mathbf{k}$ are functions of time. This leads to the following formula for $\mathbf{V}$,

$$\mathbf{V} = \frac{d\mathbf{R}}{dt} = \mathbf{i}\frac{dx}{dt} + \mathbf{j}\frac{dy}{dt} + \mathbf{k}\frac{dz}{dt} + x\frac{d\mathbf{i}}{dt} + y\frac{d\mathbf{j}}{dt} + z\frac{d\mathbf{k}}{dt}. \tag{16.3}$$

It is customary to call the first three terms of the right-hand side of this last relation the "apparent velocity," $\mathbf{V}_A$; that is, $\mathbf{V}_A = \mathbf{i}\,dx/dt + \mathbf{j}\,dy/dt + \mathbf{k}\,dz/dt$. One reason for the term "apparent velocity" is that if P were rigidly attached to $Oxyz$, then $\mathbf{V}_A = 0$, and to an observer at O, the particle at P would have zero velocity.

The last three terms of the right-hand side of the expression for $\mathbf{V}$ are due to the rotation of $Oxyz$. We denote these terms by

$$\mathbf{V}_\omega = x\frac{d\mathbf{i}}{dt} + y\frac{d\mathbf{j}}{dt} + z\frac{d\mathbf{k}}{dt}.$$

Let us evaluate the derivatives $\frac{d\mathbf{i}}{dt}, \frac{d\mathbf{j}}{dt}, \frac{d\mathbf{k}}{dt}$. Since $\mathbf{i}, \mathbf{j}$ are unit vectors, the vectors $\frac{d\mathbf{i}}{dt}, \frac{d\mathbf{j}}{dt}$ are orthogonal to $\mathbf{i}, \mathbf{j}$ respectively. Hence, we may write

$$\frac{d\mathbf{i}}{dt} = \gamma\mathbf{j} - \beta\mathbf{k}, \qquad \frac{d\mathbf{j}}{dt} = \alpha\mathbf{k} - \mu\mathbf{i}$$

where $\alpha, \beta, \gamma, \mu$ are the components of $\frac{d\mathbf{i}}{dt}, \frac{d\mathbf{j}}{dt}$. By differentiation of $\mathbf{i} \cdot \mathbf{j} = 0$, we obtain

$$\frac{d\mathbf{i}}{dt} \cdot \mathbf{j} + \mathbf{i} \cdot \frac{d\mathbf{j}}{dt} = 0. \tag{16.4}$$

Forming the scalar product of $\frac{d\mathbf{i}}{dt}$ with $\mathbf{j}$, and of $\frac{d\mathbf{j}}{dt}$ with $\mathbf{i}$ and substituting into (16.4), we see that $\gamma = \mu$. By use of a similar procedure, we can prove that

$$\frac{d\mathbf{k}}{dt} = \beta\mathbf{i} - \alpha\mathbf{j}.$$

If we let $\alpha = \omega_x$, $\beta = \omega_y$, $\gamma = \omega_z$ then the formulas for the derivatives of **i**, **j**, **k** may be written as

$$\frac{d\mathbf{i}}{dt} = \omega_z\mathbf{j} - \omega_y\mathbf{k}, \qquad \frac{d\mathbf{j}}{dt} = \omega_x\mathbf{k} - \omega_z\mathbf{i}, \qquad \frac{d\mathbf{k}}{dt} = \omega_y\mathbf{i} - \omega_x\mathbf{j}. \quad (16.5)$$

Let us introduce the vector, $\boldsymbol{\omega} = \omega_x\mathbf{i} + \omega_y\mathbf{j} + \omega_z\mathbf{k}$. Then the last set of formulas may be simplified to read

$$\frac{d\mathbf{i}}{dt} = \boldsymbol{\omega} \times \mathbf{i}, \qquad \frac{d\mathbf{j}}{dt} = \boldsymbol{\omega} \times \mathbf{j}, \qquad \frac{d\mathbf{k}}{dt} = \boldsymbol{\omega} \times \mathbf{k}.$$

Substituting these into the equation for $\mathbf{V}_\omega$ we obtain the expression

$$\mathbf{V}_\omega = x\frac{d\mathbf{i}}{dt} + y\frac{d\mathbf{j}}{dt} + z\frac{d\mathbf{k}}{dt} = \boldsymbol{\omega} \times \mathbf{R}.$$

With the aid of the previous results, we see that the equation for $\frac{d\mathbf{R}}{dt}$, (16.3), reduces to

$$\frac{d\mathbf{R}}{dt} = \mathbf{V} = \mathbf{V}_A + \boldsymbol{\omega} \times \mathbf{R}. \quad (16.6)$$

The above formula for $\mathbf{V}_\omega$ appears to imply that $\boldsymbol{\omega}$ is the angular velocity vector of the reference frame $Oxyz$ [see (7.3)]. To verify this statement, we assume that O is a fixed point and P is fixed in $Oxyz$. From the previous definition of $\mathbf{V}_A$, $\mathbf{V}_0'$, it follows that $\mathbf{V}_A = \mathbf{V}_0' = 0$. Hence, by use of the relations for the absolute velocity (16.2) and the relative velocity (16.6), we find that

$$\mathbf{V}' = \mathbf{V} = \boldsymbol{\omega} \times \mathbf{R}.$$

Obviously, $\boldsymbol{\omega}$ is the angular velocity vector of the rigid body or reference frame.

Thus, we have reduced the absolute velocity, $\mathbf{V}'$, of (16.2) to the form

$$\mathbf{V}' = \mathbf{V}_0' + \mathbf{V}_A + \boldsymbol{\omega} \times \mathbf{R} \quad (16.7)$$

where $\mathbf{V}_0'$ is the velocity of O, $\mathbf{V}_A$ is the apparent velocity, $\boldsymbol{\omega} \times \mathbf{R}$ is due to the angular velocity $\boldsymbol{\omega}$ of the rotating frame.

We can apply the results of the previous discussion to any vector **H** measured in the moving frame. That is, if $\mathbf{H} = \mathbf{i}H_x + \mathbf{j}H_y + \mathbf{k}H_z$, then by differentiation, we find

$$\frac{d\mathbf{H}}{dt} = \mathbf{i}\frac{dH_x}{dt} + \mathbf{j}\frac{dH_y}{dt} + \mathbf{k}\frac{dH_z}{dt} + H_x\frac{d\mathbf{i}}{dt} + H_y\frac{d\mathbf{j}}{dt} + H_z\frac{d\mathbf{k}}{dt}.$$

If we introduce the "apparent derivative":

$$\frac{\delta \mathbf{H}}{\delta t} = \mathbf{i}\,\frac{dH_x}{dt} + \mathbf{j}\,\frac{dH_y}{dt} + \mathbf{k}\,\frac{dH_z}{dt},$$

and use the formulas for $\frac{d\mathbf{i}}{dt}$, etc., we see that the equation for $\frac{d\mathbf{H}}{dt}$ may be expressed in the following form

$$\frac{d\mathbf{H}}{dt} = \frac{\delta \mathbf{H}}{\delta t} + \boldsymbol{\omega} \times \mathbf{H}. \tag{16.8}$$

Problem 16.1: If $\mathbf{H} = 2t\mathbf{i} + t^2\mathbf{j} + (t^2 - 1)\mathbf{k}$, when measured in a frame moving with angular velocity, $\boldsymbol{\omega} = 2t^3\mathbf{i} + 3t\mathbf{j}$, find $\frac{d\mathbf{H}}{dt}$.

Problem 16.2: Show that $\frac{d\mathbf{i}}{dt} = \omega_z\mathbf{j} - \omega_y\mathbf{k}$ may be written as $\frac{d\mathbf{i}}{dt} = \boldsymbol{\omega} \times \mathbf{i}$.

Problem 16.3: Show that the moving frame which lies along $\mathbf{r}_1$, $\boldsymbol{\theta}_1$, $\mathbf{k}$ at each point, has angular velocity vector $\boldsymbol{\omega} = \mathbf{k}\,\frac{d\theta}{dt}$. By use of a moving reference frame whose origin O coincides with the origin of the fixed frame O' and whose axes are parallel to the previously mentioned moving frame, determine the velocity vector of cylindrical coordinates. *Hint:* To find $\boldsymbol{\omega}$, write $\boldsymbol{\omega} = a\mathbf{r}_1 + b\boldsymbol{\theta}_1 + c\mathbf{k}$, evaluate $(d\mathbf{r}_1/dt)$ etc., by use of (14.4), then evaluate $\boldsymbol{\omega}$ by use of the relation $(d\mathbf{r}_1/dt) = \boldsymbol{\omega} \times \mathbf{r}_1$, etc.

Problem 16.4: Show that the angular velocity vector for a moving frame whose axes lie along $\mathbf{R}_1$, $\boldsymbol{\phi}_1$, $\boldsymbol{\theta}_1$ at each point is: $\boldsymbol{\omega} = \frac{d\theta}{dt}\cos\phi\,\mathbf{i} - \frac{d\theta}{dt}\sin\phi\,\mathbf{j} + \frac{d\phi}{dt}\mathbf{k}$. By use of a moving frame, derive the velocity vector of spherical coordinates.

Problem 16.5: If $\frac{ds}{dt} = 1$ and $\boldsymbol{\omega} = \tau\mathbf{t} + \kappa\mathbf{b}$, show that the Frenet formulas of Section 12 may be written as $\frac{d\mathbf{t}}{dt} = \boldsymbol{\omega} \times \mathbf{t}$, $\frac{d\mathbf{n}}{dt} = \boldsymbol{\omega} \times \mathbf{n}$, $\frac{d\mathbf{b}}{dt} = \boldsymbol{\omega} \times \mathbf{b}$.

Comparing these last formulas with those for $d\mathbf{i}/dt$, etc., we see that $\boldsymbol{\omega} = \tau\mathbf{t} + \kappa\mathbf{b}$ is the angular velocity of the moving frame $\mathbf{t}$, $\mathbf{n}$, $\mathbf{b}$. The vector $\boldsymbol{\omega}$ for this frame is called the Darboux vector. Gaston Darboux (1842–1917) was a French geometer who used the idea of rotating frames in his investigations of differential geometry.

(c) ***The Acceleration Vectors.*** By differentiation of the absolute velocity $\mathbf{V}'$ of (16.7), we obtain the relation

$$\frac{d\mathbf{V}'}{dt} = \frac{d\mathbf{V}_0'}{dt} + \frac{d\mathbf{V}_A}{dt} + \frac{d\boldsymbol{\omega}}{dt} \times \mathbf{R} + \boldsymbol{\omega} \times \frac{d\mathbf{R}}{dt} \tag{16.9}$$

If we replace $\mathbf{H}$ by $\mathbf{V}_A$ and $\boldsymbol{\omega}$ in (16.8), we obtain the formulas

$$\frac{d\mathbf{V}_A}{dt} = \frac{\delta\mathbf{V}_A}{\delta t} + \boldsymbol{\omega} \times \mathbf{V}_A, \qquad \frac{d\boldsymbol{\omega}}{dt} = \frac{\delta\boldsymbol{\omega}}{\delta t} + \boldsymbol{\omega} \times \boldsymbol{\omega} = \frac{\delta\boldsymbol{\omega}}{\delta t}$$

Usually, the acceleration vectors in the above equations are denoted as follows:

$$\mathbf{A}_0' = \frac{d\mathbf{V}_0'}{dt} = \text{acceleration of the moving origin } O,$$

$$\mathbf{A}_A = \frac{\delta\mathbf{V}_A}{\delta t} = \text{apparent acceleration,}$$

$$\boldsymbol{\alpha} = \frac{d\boldsymbol{\omega}}{dt} = \frac{\delta\boldsymbol{\omega}}{\delta t} = \text{angular acceleration,}$$

$$\mathbf{A}' = \frac{d\mathbf{V}'}{dt} = \text{absolute acceleration.}$$

Through use of the new terminology, we find that the derivative of $\mathbf{V}'$ in (16.9) may be written as

$$\mathbf{A}' = \mathbf{A}_0' + \mathbf{A}_A + 2\boldsymbol{\omega} \times \mathbf{V}_A + \boldsymbol{\alpha} \times \mathbf{R} + \boldsymbol{\omega} \times (\boldsymbol{\omega} \times \mathbf{R}). \tag{16.10}$$

In the literature, the following terms of this last equation are given special names:

$2\boldsymbol{\omega} \times \mathbf{V}_A$ = Coriolis acceleration;

$\boldsymbol{\omega} \times (\boldsymbol{\omega} \times \mathbf{R})$ = centripetal acceleration.

Problem 16.6: From the definition of $\mathbf{V}_A$ and the meaning of the operator $\delta/\delta t$ write out the components of $\mathbf{A}_A$ in terms of $\mathbf{i}$, $\mathbf{j}$, $\mathbf{k}$. Indicate a reason for the name "apparent acceleration."

Problem 16.7: If $\boldsymbol{\omega}$ is orthogonal to $\mathbf{R}$, show that the centripetal acceleration is, $-\omega^2\mathbf{R}$.

Problem 16.8: A particle of mass m is attached to a string of length l and then revolved in the $O'x'y'$ plane about the point O' with constant angular velocity, ω. By use of a rotating frame attached to the particle, determine

(1) $\mathbf{V}_0'$, $\mathbf{V}_A$, $\boldsymbol{\omega} \times \mathbf{R}$, $\mathbf{V}'$;

(2) $\mathbf{A}_0'$, $\mathbf{A}_A$, $\boldsymbol{\alpha}$, $\boldsymbol{\omega} \times \mathbf{V}_A$, $\boldsymbol{\omega} \times (\boldsymbol{\omega} \times \mathbf{R})$, $\mathbf{A}'$.

Problem 16.9: By use of the same rotating frame as was used in Problem 16.3, find the acceleration vector in cylindrical coordinates.

Problem 16.10: By use of the same rotating frame as was used in Problem 16.4, find the acceleration vector in spherical coordinates.

(d) ***Application to Newton's Law of Motion.*** We shall now consider some consequences of Newton's law of motion. Newton's law is valid only for inertial frames (such as $O'x'y'z'$), or frames moving with constant translational velocity with respect to such frames. These frames are "defined" by the first law of motion. For such frames, Newton's second law becomes $\mathbf{F} = m\mathbf{A}'$, where m is the mass of the particle and $\mathbf{F}$ is the resultant force vector acting on the particle. By use of the acceleration vector (16.10) this law may be expressed as

$$\mathbf{F} = m\mathbf{A}_0' + m\mathbf{A}_A + 2m\boldsymbol{\omega} \times \mathbf{V}_A + m\boldsymbol{\alpha} \times \mathbf{R} + m\boldsymbol{\omega} \times (\boldsymbol{\omega} \times \mathbf{R}).$$

Now imagine an observer at O (the origin of the moving frame). He measures the acceleration $\mathbf{A}_A$ but is unaware of the existence of the other acceleration terms. Hence, in order to satisfy Newton's second law, the observer must consider the physical force $\mathbf{F}$ and in addition the "fictitious" forces $m\mathbf{A}_0'$, etc. That is, this observer writes Newton's law as follows:

$$\mathbf{F} - m\mathbf{A}_0' - 2m\boldsymbol{\omega} \times \mathbf{V}_A - m\boldsymbol{\alpha} \times \mathbf{R} - m\boldsymbol{\omega} \times (\boldsymbol{\omega} \times \mathbf{R}) = m\mathbf{A}_A. \quad (16.11)$$

Special names are given to some of these terms: $-2m\boldsymbol{\omega} \times \mathbf{V}_A$ is called the *Coriolis* force; $-m\boldsymbol{\omega} \times (\boldsymbol{\omega} \times \mathbf{R})$ is called the *centrifugal* force. From the philosophical viewpoint, equation (16.11) leads to a very unsatisfactory result in Newtonian mechanics. It must be remembered that there exist no completely satisfactory theoretical criteria for determining inertial frames. Hence, if an observer finds that no physical force is acting ($\mathbf{F} = 0$) on a door in a room but that the door is suddenly opened, he has two possible explanations: (1) magic; or (2) those pesky "fictitious" forces. One explanation is almost as bad as the other. The general theory of relativity furnishes a more reasonable explanation of this difficulty.

Problem 16.11: Consider the earth to be a sphere with surface $x^2 + y^2 + z^2 = a^2$, which rotates with constant angular velocity, $\boldsymbol{\omega} = \omega\mathbf{k}$. A particle has the instantaneous position vector, $\mathbf{R}$, and absolute velocity $\mathbf{V}'$, where

$$\mathbf{R} = 3\mathbf{i} + 4\mathbf{j} + (a^2 - 25)^{1/2}\mathbf{k}, \qquad \mathbf{V}' = \mathbf{i} - \mathbf{j} + \mathbf{k}.$$

Find the Coriolis force on the particle.

17. The Gradient of a Scalar Field, $\nabla\Omega$. In order to furnish a geometric interpretation of this vector field, we introduce the equipotential surfaces.

(a) ***The Equipotential Surfaces, $\Omega(x, y, z) =$ constant.*** Let $\Omega(x, y, z)$ be a scalar field. We assume that Ω is continuous and has continuous partial derivatives. In particular, we can consider this scalar field as composed of *equipotential* surfaces, $\Omega =$ constant. In the future, we shall assume that a unique surface passes through each point, P.

Illustrative Example: If $\Omega = x^2 + y^2 + z^2$, describe the equipotential surfaces.

Solution: The desired surfaces are spheres whose centers are at the origin.

Problem 17.1: If ϕ is the angle in spherical coordinates between Oz and $\mathbf{R}$, and $\Omega = \phi$, describe the equipotential surfaces.

Problem 17.2: If θ is the other angle in spherical coordinates, and $\Omega = \theta^2$, describe the equipotential surfaces.

Problem 17.3: If $\Omega = x^2 - y^2$, describe the equipotential surfaces.

Problem 17.4: If $\Omega = 1/R$, where R is the radial distance in spherical coordinates, describe the equipotential surfaces.

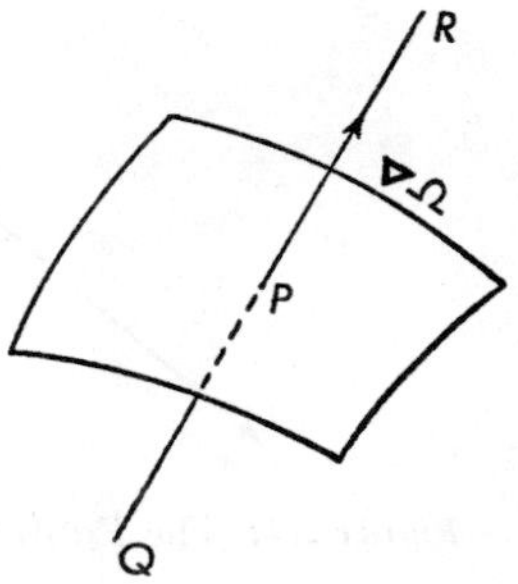

Figure 23: The Sense of $\nabla\Omega$

We introduce the vector field, gradient of $\Omega(\text{grad}\,\Omega)$, in *Cartesian orthogonal coordinates* by the definition

$$\text{grad } \Omega = \mathbf{i}\frac{\partial\Omega}{\partial x} + \mathbf{j}\frac{\partial\Omega}{\partial y} + \mathbf{k}\frac{\partial\Omega}{\partial z}. \tag{17.1}$$

If we define a *vector operator del*, ∇, in *Cartesian orthogonal coordinates* by

$$\nabla = \mathbf{i}\frac{\partial}{\partial x} + \mathbf{j}\frac{\partial}{\partial y} + \mathbf{k}\frac{\partial}{\partial z} \tag{17.2}$$

then one may replace the term "grad Ω" by $\nabla\Omega$.

We shall prove that $\nabla\Omega$ is related to the equipotential surfaces, $\Omega =$ constant, in the following manner:

If $\nabla\Omega \neq 0$ at any point P, then $\nabla\Omega$ is perpendicular to the equipotential surface, $\Omega = c$, passing through P. (17.3)

If dn is the element of arc of any curve C_n passing through P and orthogonal to $\Omega = c$ at P, then $|\nabla\Omega| = \left|\dfrac{d\Omega}{dn}\right|$. (17.4)

Consider a line normal to the equipotential surface, $\Omega = c$, passing through P. If $\nabla\Omega \neq 0$ at P and if Q, P, R are sufficiently close, Ω is either continually increasing or continually decreasing as one moves from Q to P to R. The vector $\nabla\Omega$ is sensed in direction of increasing Ω. (17.5)

Note that these results completely specify $\nabla\Omega$. Further, this description of $\nabla\Omega$ is completely independent of the coordinate system. The basic formula in the proof of these results is the chain rule relation

$$\frac{d\Omega}{ds} = \frac{\partial\Omega}{\partial x}\frac{dx}{ds} + \frac{\partial\Omega}{\partial y}\frac{dy}{ds} + \frac{\partial\Omega}{\partial z}\frac{dz}{ds}.$$

If s represents the arc length parameter along a curve C passing through

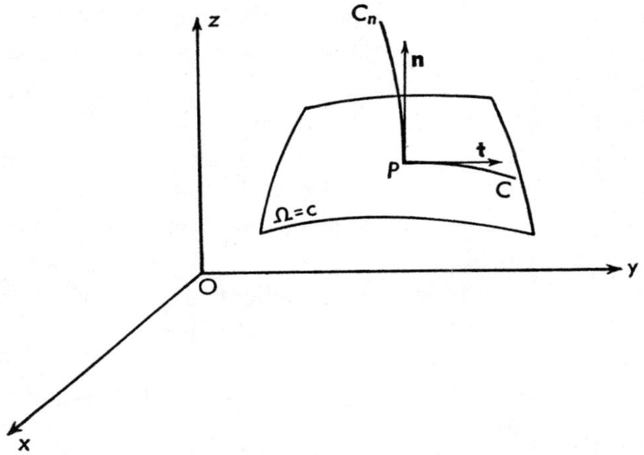

Figure 24: The Equipotential Surface, $\Omega = c$, through P and the Curves C, C_n

P and **t** the unit tangent vector of a curve C, then by forming the scalar product of $\mathbf{t} = \mathbf{i}\frac{dx}{ds} + \mathbf{j}\frac{dy}{ds} + \mathbf{k}\frac{dz}{ds}$ with $\nabla\Omega$, we may express the right-hand side of the above equation in the form

$$\frac{d\Omega}{ds} = \mathbf{t}\cdot\nabla\Omega. \tag{17.6}$$

(b) ***The Direction of*** $\nabla\Omega$ **[*Proof of* (*17.3*)].** Assume that the curve C is tangent to the equipotential surface, $\Omega = c$, passing through P. Hence, $\frac{d\Omega}{ds} = 0$. The equation (17.6) reduces to $\mathbf{t}\cdot\nabla\Omega = 0$. Since **t**, the tangent to C, is an arbitrary vector lying in the tangent plane to $\Omega = c$ at P, it follows that $\nabla\Omega$ must be normal to $\Omega = c$.

(c) ***The Magnitude of*** $\nabla\Omega$ **[*Proof of* (*17.4*)].** Consider the formula (17.6) for the case that C is a curve C_n normal to $\Omega = c$ at P. Let **n** denote the unit tangent vector along C_n and let dn denote the element of arc along C_n. Expanding the right-hand side of (17.6), we obtain

$$\frac{d\Omega}{dn} = |\mathbf{n}|\,|\nabla\Omega|\cos\theta \tag{17.7}$$

where θ is the angle between $\mathbf{n}$ and $\nabla\Omega$. From the result (b), we see that θ is 0 or π. Hence, our last equation furnishes the desired result $\left|\frac{d\Omega}{dn}\right| = |\nabla\Omega|$.

(d) ***The Sense of*** $\nabla\Omega$ [***Proof of*** **(*17.5*)**]. We note that $\mathbf{n}$ is such that it points in the direction of increasing arc length ($dn > 0$) of C_n. Let us assume that Ω decreases as we move along the positive direction of $\mathbf{n}$; then $\frac{d\Omega}{dn} < 0$. From (17.7) it follows that $\cos\theta = -1$ or $\theta = \pi$. That is, $\nabla\Omega$ is sensed opposite to $\mathbf{n}$. Thus, $\nabla\Omega$ must point in the direction of increasing Ω. This argument breaks down if $\nabla\Omega = 0$ or $\frac{d\Omega}{dn} = 0$ along the equipotential surface, $\Omega = c$. But this latter case is not important in our work.

(e) ***The Component of*** $\nabla\Omega$ ***in Any Direction.*** The formula (17.6) leads to another very important interpretation: The component of $\nabla\Omega$ in any direction is the rate of change of Ω with respect to the arc length of a curve in that direction. Further, this same formula leads to: The maximum rate of change of Ω with respect to arc length is in the direction which is perpendicular to $\Omega = c$ at P.

Illustrative Example: If $\Omega = \theta^2$, where θ is the polar angle of cylindrical or spherical coordinates, find $\nabla\Omega$.

Solution: To solve this problem, we consider a point P and the equipotential surface, $\Omega = c$, passing through P. This surface is the plane $\theta = \sqrt{c}$. Since $\nabla\Omega$ is orthogonal to this surface, $\nabla\Omega$ lies along $\boldsymbol{\theta}_1$. From the formula for the element of arc in polar coordinates of Section 14, we see that the element of arc, dn, of a curve tangent to the coordinate line in the $\boldsymbol{\theta}_1$ direction is $r\,d\theta$. Hence, the magnitude of $\nabla\Omega$ is $\frac{d\Omega}{dn} = \frac{2\theta\,d\theta}{r\,d\theta}$. Since $\Omega = \theta^2$ increases when θ increases, $\nabla\Omega$ lies along $\boldsymbol{\theta}_1$. Combining these results, we find that

$$\nabla\Omega = \frac{2\theta}{r}\,\boldsymbol{\theta}_1.$$

Problem 17.5: Verify that $\nabla\Omega$ is sensed along Ω increasing by assuming that Ω increases as one moves along the positive direction of $\mathbf{n}$.

Problem 17.6: (1) Find $\nabla\Omega$, when $\Omega = \theta^2 + r^2$, by use of the definition (17.2). Verify that your result may be expressed in the form $\nabla\Omega = \frac{2\theta}{r}\boldsymbol{\theta}_1 + 2r\mathbf{r}_1$; (2) Find $\nabla\Omega$ when $\Omega = \theta^2 r^2$.

Problem 17.7: Find $\nabla\Omega$, if $\Omega = \phi$, by use of: (1) the geometric properties of $\nabla\Omega$; (2) direct calculation.

Problem 17.8: Find $\nabla\Omega$, if $\Omega = R^n$, by use of: (1) the geometric properties of $\nabla\Omega$; (2) direct calculation. There are two separate cases: $n > 0$, $n < 0$. If $n - 1 < 0$, at which point does $\nabla\Omega$ fail to exist?

Problem 17.9: Let A and A' be two points in the xy-plane. Let r and r' denote the distances of a point P of the xy-plane from A and A', respectively. If $\Omega = r + r'$, give a geometric description of $\nabla\Omega$.

Illustrative Example: Show that $d\Omega = (d\mathbf{R} \cdot \nabla)\Omega$.

Solution: To derive this result, we expand the scalar operator $(d\mathbf{R} \cdot \nabla)$. Since $d\mathbf{R} = \mathbf{i}\,dx + \mathbf{j}\,dy + \mathbf{k}\,dz$, and ∇ is defined as $\mathbf{i}\frac{\partial}{\partial x} + \mathbf{j}\frac{\partial}{\partial y} + \mathbf{k}\frac{\partial}{\partial z}$, we obtain $(d\mathbf{R} \cdot \nabla) = dx\frac{\partial}{\partial x} + dy\frac{\partial}{\partial y} + dz\frac{\partial}{\partial z}$. Thus $(d\mathbf{R} \cdot \nabla)\Omega = dx\frac{\partial\Omega}{\partial x} + dy\frac{\partial\Omega}{\partial y} + dz\frac{\partial\Omega}{\partial z} = d\Omega$.

Problem 17.10: If x, y, z are functions of u, v, show that

$$\frac{\partial\Omega}{\partial u} = \left(\frac{\partial\mathbf{R}}{\partial u} \cdot \nabla\right)\Omega$$

where Ω depends on u, v.

Problem 17.11: Show that $\frac{d\mathbf{F}}{ds} = (\mathbf{t} \cdot \nabla)\mathbf{F}$ where $\mathbf{t} = \frac{d\mathbf{R}}{ds}$. What is the corresponding formula when s is not the arc length parameter?

Problem 17.12: Show that $(\mathbf{t} \cdot \nabla)\Omega = \mathbf{t} \cdot (\nabla\Omega)$.

Illustrative Example: Compute $\nabla\mathbf{F}$. The quantity $\mathcal{A} = \nabla\mathbf{F}$ is a dyad, or tensor of the second order.

Solution: We shall give a detailed treatment of these quantities in the section on tensors. Here, we shall formally expand $\nabla\mathbf{F}$ under the assumption that the product involved is distributive. From the definition of the del operator (17.2), we find

$$\begin{aligned}
\nabla\mathbf{F} &= \left(\mathbf{i}\frac{\partial}{\partial x} + \mathbf{j}\frac{\partial}{\partial y} + \mathbf{k}\frac{\partial}{\partial z}\right)(F_x\mathbf{i} + F_y\mathbf{j} + F_z\mathbf{k}) \\
&= \left(\mathbf{i}\frac{\partial}{\partial x} + \mathbf{j}\frac{\partial}{\partial y} + \mathbf{k}\frac{\partial}{\partial z}\right)F_x\mathbf{i} + \left(\mathbf{i}\frac{\partial}{\partial x} + \mathbf{j}\frac{\partial}{\partial y} + \mathbf{k}\frac{\partial}{\partial z}\right)F_y\mathbf{j} + \cdots \\
&= \mathbf{ii}\frac{\partial F_x}{\partial x} + \mathbf{ji}\frac{\partial F_x}{\partial y} + \mathbf{ki}\frac{\partial F_x}{\partial z} \\
&\quad + \mathbf{ij}\frac{\partial F_y}{\partial x} + \mathbf{jj}\frac{\partial F_y}{\partial y} + \mathbf{kj}\frac{\partial F_y}{\partial z} \\
&\quad + \mathbf{ik}\frac{\partial F_z}{\partial x} + \mathbf{jk}\frac{\partial F_z}{\partial y} + \mathbf{kk}\frac{\partial F_z}{\partial z}.
\end{aligned}$$

Note that the order of the factors **i**, **j**, **k** in a product has been unaltered. This is due to the fact that the dyad products such as **ij** are not commutative. That is, **ij** is not equivalent to **ji**.

Problem 17.13: Show by use of the above expansion that $(\mathbf{t} \cdot \nabla)\mathbf{F} = \mathbf{t} \cdot (\nabla\mathbf{F})$. By use of this result and that of Problem 17.11 we see that the component of $\nabla\mathbf{F}$ in any direction is the rate of change of **F** with respect to the arc length of a curve in that direction. This result generalizes (e) from scalar fields to vector fields.

Problem 17.14: Show that $(\mathbf{V} \cdot \nabla)\mathbf{R} = \mathbf{V} \cdot (\nabla\mathbf{R}) = \mathbf{V}$, where **R** is the radius vector field and **V** is an arbitrary vector field.

18. The Linear Vector Operator, ∇, in Cartesian and Curvilinear Orthogonal Coordinates. It is evident that by use of the definition (17.2) of ∇, one may form quantities such as $\nabla\Omega$, $\nabla \cdot \mathbf{F}$, $\nabla \times \mathbf{F}$, $\nabla\mathbf{F}$, etc. In order to treat these diverse products by one general theory, we introduce the star product $(*)$ of Section 11(b). Further, in order to simultaneously develop a theory for both $\nabla\Omega$ and $\nabla\mathbf{F}$, we reintroduce the general tensor $\mathcal{A}$. In our future work, we shall define the tensor $\nabla*\mathcal{A}$ in Cartesian orthogonal and curvilinear orthogonal coordinates and study some properties of this tensor.

(a) ***Cartesian Orthogonal Coordinates.*** From the definition of ∇ in (17.2) and the distributive nature of the star product, we may define $\nabla*\mathcal{A}$ in Cartesian orthogonal coordinates by: $\nabla*\mathcal{A} = \mathbf{i}\frac{\partial}{\partial x}*\mathcal{A} + \mathbf{j}\frac{\partial}{\partial y}*\mathcal{A} + \mathbf{k}\frac{\partial}{\partial z}*\mathcal{A}$. If we assume that differentiation and the star product are interchangeable (a result which is easily verified when $\mathcal{A}$ is a scalar or vector field), we may write the equation for $\nabla*\mathcal{A}$ in the form

$$\nabla*\mathcal{A} = \mathbf{i}*\frac{\partial\mathcal{A}}{\partial x} + \mathbf{j}*\frac{\partial\mathcal{A}}{\partial y} + \mathbf{k}*\frac{\partial\mathcal{A}}{\partial z}. \tag{18.1}$$

If $\mathcal{A}$ and $\mathcal{B}$ are tensors of the same order, so that their sum has significance, then from (18.1) one can easily show that $\nabla*(\mathcal{A} + \mathcal{B}) = \nabla*\mathcal{A} + \nabla*\mathcal{B}$. This equation indicates the reason why the vector operator ∇ is called linear.

To conclude this section, we consider some simple examples of the relation (18.1). The *scalar*, $\nabla \cdot \mathbf{F}$, is called the "divergence of **F**." If we expand **F** in terms of its components and use the definition (18.1), we obtain the relation

$$\nabla \cdot \mathbf{F} = \frac{\partial F_x}{\partial x} + \frac{\partial F_y}{\partial y} + \frac{\partial F_z}{\partial z}.$$

Again, the *vector*, $\nabla \times \mathbf{F}$, is called the "curl of **F**." Replacing the star of (18.1) by a cross and $\mathfrak{A}$ by **F**, we find by expanding in terms of components of **F**:

$$\nabla \times \mathbf{F} = \mathbf{i}\left(\frac{\partial F_z}{\partial y} - \frac{\partial F_y}{\partial z}\right) + \mathbf{j}\left(\frac{\partial F_x}{\partial z} - \frac{\partial F_z}{\partial x}\right) + \mathbf{k}\left(\frac{\partial F_y}{\partial x} - \frac{\partial F_x}{\partial y}\right).$$

Problem 18.1: Verify the expansion, $\nabla \cdot \mathbf{F} = \dfrac{\partial F_x}{\partial x} + \dfrac{\partial F_y}{\partial y} + \dfrac{\partial F_z}{\partial z}$.

Problem 18.2: Verify the expansion for $\nabla \times \mathbf{F}$.

Problem 18.3: Show that the right-hand side of $\nabla \times \mathbf{F}$ may be represented by the "determinant"

$$\begin{vmatrix} \mathbf{i} & \mathbf{j} & \mathbf{k} \\ \dfrac{\partial}{\partial x} & \dfrac{\partial}{\partial y} & \dfrac{\partial}{\partial z} \\ F_x & F_y & F_z \end{vmatrix}.$$

Problem 18.4: Prove that $\nabla \times \mathbf{R} = 0$, $\nabla \cdot \mathbf{R} = 3$.

(b) ***Curvilinear Orthogonal Coordinates.*** We have defined $\nabla * \mathfrak{A}$ in Cartesian orthogonal coordinates by means of the formula (18.1). Our problem is to define $\nabla * \mathfrak{A}$ for arbitrary curvilinear orthogonal coordinates, such as spherical or cylindrical coordinates, so that $\nabla * \mathfrak{A}$ does not depend upon the coordinate system. It will be recalled that in Section 17 we showed that $\nabla \Omega$ can be characterized in a manner independent of the coordinate system. Quantities which are independent of the coordinate system are called *invariants;* scalar fields or vector fields (except for the base vectors) are examples of invariants. A systematic approach to these quantities will be considered in the tensor analysis section of the text. In the present section, we shall approach the topic of invariants in a formal manner by defining the vector operator, ∇, in a general curvilinear orthogonal coordinate system.

Let us denote the element of arc by

$$ds^2 = (A_1\, d\alpha_1)^2 + (A_2\, d\alpha_2)^2 + (A_3\, d\alpha_3)^2 \tag{18.2}$$

where α_1, α_2, α_3 are the coordinate variables of the coordinate system (see Section 14 for the discussion of cylindrical and spherical coordinates). If we define ∇ by

$$\nabla = \frac{\mathbf{e}_1}{A_1}\frac{\partial}{\partial \alpha_1} + \frac{\mathbf{e}_2}{A_2}\frac{\partial}{\partial \alpha_2} + \frac{\mathbf{e}_3}{A_3}\frac{\partial}{\partial \alpha_3} \tag{18.3}$$

where $\mathbf{e}_1$, $\mathbf{e}_2$, $\mathbf{e}_3$ are the orthogonal unit base vectors of the coordinate system, then the fundamental property of Section 17(e) is preserved.

That is, since the element of arc, ds_i, along any coordinate line is $A_i\,d\alpha_i$, then $\mathbf{e}_i \cdot \nabla = d/ds_i$.

With the aid of (18.3), we may express $\nabla * \mathcal{A}$ by

$$\nabla * \mathcal{A} = \frac{\mathbf{e}_1}{A_1} * \frac{\partial \mathcal{A}}{\partial \alpha_1} + \frac{\mathbf{e}_2}{A_2} * \frac{\partial \mathcal{A}}{\partial \alpha_2} + \frac{\mathbf{e}_3}{A_3} * \frac{\partial \mathcal{A}}{\partial \alpha_3}. \tag{18.4}$$

It should be noted that this formula reduces to (18.1) for the case when the coordinate system is Cartesian orthogonal. In Section 46, the validity of (18.4) will be verified by use of tensor theory. General formulas for $\nabla \times \mathbf{F}$, $\nabla \cdot \mathbf{F}$ are given in Problems 19.9 and 19.10.

Illustrative Example: Find $\nabla \cdot \mathbf{F}$ in cylindrical coordinates.

Solution: Let $\mathbf{F} = F_r\mathbf{r}_1 + F_\theta\boldsymbol{\theta}_1 + F_z\mathbf{k}$. Further, $(ds)^2 = (dr)^2 + r^2(d\theta)^2 + (dz)^2$. Hence, if $\alpha_1 = r$, $\alpha_2 = \theta$, $\alpha_3 = z$, then $A_1 = 1$, $A_2 = r$, $A_3 = 1$, $\mathbf{e}_1 = \mathbf{r}_1$, $\mathbf{e}_2 = \boldsymbol{\theta}_1$, $\mathbf{e}_3 = \mathbf{k}$ and (18.4) becomes

$$\nabla \cdot \mathbf{F} = \mathbf{r}_1 \cdot \frac{\partial \mathbf{F}}{\partial r} + \frac{\boldsymbol{\theta}_1}{r} \cdot \frac{\partial \mathbf{F}}{\partial \theta} + \mathbf{k} \cdot \frac{\partial \mathbf{F}}{\partial z}.$$

Evaluating the partial derivatives of $\mathbf{r}_1$, $\boldsymbol{\theta}_1$, $\mathbf{k}$ in $\dfrac{\partial \mathbf{F}}{\partial r}$, etc., by use of the table of Section 14, we obtain

$$\nabla \cdot \mathbf{F} = \frac{\partial F_r}{\partial r} + \frac{F_r}{r} + \frac{1}{r}\frac{\partial F_\theta}{\partial \theta} + \frac{\partial F_z}{\partial z}.$$

Problem 18.5: If $\mathbf{F} = 2x\mathbf{i} + 3y\mathbf{j}$, find $\mathbf{F}$ in cylindrical coordinates and then compute $\nabla \cdot \mathbf{F}$. Check your result by calculating $\nabla \cdot \mathbf{F}$ in Cartesian orthogonal coordinates.

Problem 18.6: Find $\nabla \times \mathbf{F}$ in cylindrical coordinates.

Problem 18.7: Find $\nabla\Omega$ in spherical coordinates.

Problem 18.8: Find $\nabla \cdot \mathbf{F}$ in spherical coordinates.

Problem 18.9: Find $(\nabla \cdot \nabla)\Omega$ or $\nabla^2\Omega$ in cylindrical coordinates.

Problem 18.10: If $\mathbf{F} = F_r\mathbf{r}_1 + F_\theta\boldsymbol{\theta}_1 + F_z\mathbf{k}$ and $\mathbf{G} = G_r\mathbf{r}_1 + G_\theta\boldsymbol{\theta}_1 + G_z\mathbf{k}$, evaluate $\mathbf{F} \times (\nabla \times \mathbf{G})$ in cylindrical coordinates.

Problem 18.11: Prove that $\mathbf{e}_i = A_i\,\nabla\alpha_i$, where $\mathbf{e}_i$ is the base vector along the α_i = variable coordinate line.

The above theory may be extended to arbitrary (not necessarily orthogonal) curvilinear coordinates. Here, one must introduce the concept of reciprocal systems of base vectors. Due to the fact that the orthogonal coordinate systems are of great importance in physics while general curvilinear coordinate systems are of relatively little use, we shall not discuss the more general theory at this time.

19. Vector Expansions Involving ∇. Two methods are of general use in determining vector expansions involving ∇. We shall illustrate these methods by use of problems. Let us attempt to find the vector expansions for

$$\nabla \times (\Omega \mathbf{V}) \qquad \text{and} \qquad \nabla \times (\mathbf{V} \times \mathbf{W}).$$

(a) ***The Method Involving the Use of the Definition of $\nabla * \mathcal{Q}$.*** By the definition of $\nabla * \mathcal{Q}$, (18.1), we find

$$\nabla \times (\Omega \mathbf{V}) = \mathbf{i} \times \frac{\partial}{\partial x}(\Omega \mathbf{V}) + \mathbf{j} \times \frac{\partial}{\partial y}(\Omega \mathbf{V}) + \mathbf{k} \times \frac{\partial}{\partial z}(\Omega \mathbf{V}). \tag{19.1}$$

In view of the symmetry of the three terms in the right-hand side of this equation, we need only expand the first term. We obtain

$$\begin{aligned} \nabla \times (\Omega \mathbf{V}) &= \mathbf{i} \times \left(\frac{\partial \Omega}{\partial x}\mathbf{V} + \Omega \frac{\partial \mathbf{V}}{\partial x}\right) + \cdots, \\ &= \mathbf{i}\frac{\partial \Omega}{\partial x} \times \mathbf{V} + \Omega \mathbf{i} \times \frac{\partial \mathbf{V}}{\partial x} + \cdots, \end{aligned}$$

where the dots represent similar terms in **j**, and the partials with respect to y, and **k**, and the partials with respect to z. By definition of $\nabla * \mathcal{Q}$, we see that

$$\nabla \Omega = \mathbf{i}\frac{\partial \Omega}{\partial x} + \cdots, \qquad \nabla \times \mathbf{V} = \mathbf{i} \times \frac{\partial \mathbf{V}}{\partial x} + \cdots.$$

Hence, $\nabla \times (\Omega \mathbf{V})$ reduces to

$$\nabla \times (\Omega \mathbf{V}) = (\nabla \Omega) \times \mathbf{V} + \Omega \nabla \times \mathbf{V}.$$

It is seen from the above example that this method works well if one can recognize the component parts of an expansion as belonging to $\nabla \Omega$, $\nabla \times \mathbf{V}$, etc.

Secondly, we consider the expansion of $\nabla \times (\mathbf{V} \times \mathbf{W})$. From the definition of $\nabla * \mathcal{Q}$ of (18.1) and the triple vector expansion of Section 9, we obtain

$$\begin{aligned} \nabla \times (\mathbf{V} \times \mathbf{W}) &= \mathbf{i} \times \frac{\partial}{\partial x}(\mathbf{V} \times \mathbf{W}) + \cdots \\ &= \mathbf{i} \times \left(\frac{\partial \mathbf{V}}{\partial x} \times \mathbf{W}\right) + \mathbf{i} \times \left(\mathbf{V} \times \frac{\partial \mathbf{W}}{\partial x}\right) + \cdots \qquad (19.2) \\ &= (\mathbf{i} \cdot \mathbf{W})\frac{\partial \mathbf{V}}{\partial x} - \left(\mathbf{i} \cdot \frac{\partial \mathbf{V}}{\partial x}\right)\mathbf{W} + \left(\mathbf{i} \cdot \frac{\partial \mathbf{W}}{\partial x}\right)\mathbf{V} \\ &\qquad - (\mathbf{i} \cdot \mathbf{V})\frac{\partial \mathbf{W}}{\partial x} + \cdots. \end{aligned}$$

The second and third types of terms are easily recognized as the expansions of $\mathbf{W}(\nabla \cdot \mathbf{V})$ and $\mathbf{V}(\nabla \cdot \mathbf{W})$. To evaluate the first and fourth types of terms, we note that the first term is of the type

$$(\mathbf{W} \cdot \nabla)\mathbf{V} = \left(\mathbf{W} \cdot \mathbf{i}\frac{\partial}{\partial x}\right)\mathbf{V} + \cdots = (\mathbf{i} \cdot \mathbf{W})\frac{\partial \mathbf{V}}{\partial x} + \cdots.$$

Thus, the desired expansion is

$$\nabla \times (\mathbf{V} \times \mathbf{W}) = (\mathbf{W} \cdot \nabla)\mathbf{V} - (\nabla \cdot \mathbf{V})\mathbf{W} + (\nabla \cdot \mathbf{W})\mathbf{V} - (\mathbf{V} \cdot \nabla)\mathbf{W}. \quad (19.3)$$

(b) ***The Method Involving the Use of the Vector and Operator Properties of*** ∇. This method is more rapid than the method of the last section. However, this method calls for the exercise of great care in inserting dots or crosses in proper position. In fact, the method calls for a translation from the theory of tensor components to the theory of direct quantities of our present work. We shall illustrate the method of attack by considering the same examples.

To begin with, it must be remembered that ∇ has two types of properties: (1) vector properties; (2) differentiation properties. In (19.1), the cross must always be between the ∇ and the vector $\mathbf{V}$, in that order. We can interchange this order, but then a minus sign must be introduced. Thus, we find

$$\nabla \times (\Omega\mathbf{V}) = (\nabla_{\mathbf{V}} \times \mathbf{V})\Omega + (\nabla_{\Omega}\Omega) \times \mathbf{V}$$

where $\nabla_{\mathbf{V}}$ indicates that ∇ operates only on $\mathbf{V}$ and ∇_{Ω} indicates that ∇ operates only on Ω. If we use the parenthesis to indicate the termination of the range of applicability of ∇, then we may write the above equation as $\nabla \times (\Omega\mathbf{V}) = (\nabla \times \mathbf{V})\Omega + (\nabla\Omega) \times \mathbf{V}$. In fact, the expansion is more clearly expressed in the form

$$\nabla \times (\Omega\mathbf{V}) = \Omega\nabla \times \mathbf{V} - \mathbf{V} \times \nabla\Omega.$$

Consider the second example. Our problem is to expand $\nabla \times (\mathbf{V} \times \mathbf{W})$. We begin by treating ∇ as a vector and using the triple vector expansion of Section 9. However, it must be remembered that ∇ is to differentiate both $\mathbf{V}$ and $\mathbf{W}$. Hence, we write the triple vector expansion as follows:

$$\nabla \times (\mathbf{V} \times \mathbf{W}) = (\nabla_{\mathbf{V},\mathbf{W}} \cdot \mathbf{W})\mathbf{V} - (\nabla_{\mathbf{V},\mathbf{W}} \cdot \mathbf{V})\mathbf{W}. \quad (19.4)$$

The subscripts on ∇ in the above equation are to remind us that ∇ differentiates both $\mathbf{V}$ and $\mathbf{W}$. These subscripts may be removed by individually expanding the terms. Thus

$$(\nabla_{\mathbf{V},\mathbf{W}} \cdot \mathbf{W})\mathbf{V} = \mathbf{V}(\nabla \cdot \mathbf{W}) + (\mathbf{W} \cdot \nabla)\mathbf{V}.$$

Note, the dot is always between the ∇ and the $\mathbf{W}$. Similarly, we may expand the second term of (19.4). The result of this work leads to the formula (19.3).

Problem 19.1: Show that $\nabla \cdot (\Omega\mathbf{V}) = \Omega(\nabla \cdot \mathbf{V}) + \mathbf{V} \cdot \nabla\Omega$ by use of the above two methods.

Problem 19.2: Expand $\nabla \cdot (\mathbf{U} \times \mathbf{V})$ by either of the above methods.

Problem 19.3: Show that $\nabla \times (\nabla\Omega) = 0$ by use of either method. *Hint:* The first method, (a), calls for a complete expansion in this problem.

Problem 19.4: Show that $\nabla \cdot (\nabla \times \mathbf{V}) = 0$.

Problem 19.5: By use of the results $\nabla \cdot \mathbf{R} = 3$, $(\mathbf{V} \cdot \nabla)\mathbf{R} = \mathbf{V}$ of Problems 18.4 and 17.14, simplify the vector expansion for $\nabla \times (\mathbf{V} \times \mathbf{R})$.

Problem 19.6: Expand $\mathbf{V} \times (\nabla \times \mathbf{W})$.

Problem 19.7: Expand $\mathbf{R} \times (\nabla \times \mathbf{V})$.

Problem 19.8: Show that $\nabla \times (\nabla \times \mathbf{F}) = \nabla(\nabla \cdot \mathbf{F}) - \nabla^2\mathbf{F}$ where ∇^2 is the operator $\nabla \cdot \nabla$.

Hint: The first method of expansion entails much computation. The second method of expansion works best here. It should be recalled that in $\nabla \times (\nabla \times \mathbf{F})$, the ∇ operates only on $\mathbf{F}$. That is, $\frac{\partial}{\partial x}(uv) = u\frac{\partial v}{\partial x} + v\frac{\partial u}{\partial x}$ but $\frac{\partial}{\partial x}\left(\frac{\partial}{\partial x}v\right) = \frac{\partial^2 v}{\partial x^2}$.

Problem 19.9: By use of the relation, $\mathbf{e}_i = A_i \nabla\alpha_i$ of Problem 18.11, the relation $\mathbf{F} = F_1\mathbf{e}_1 + F_2\mathbf{e}_2 + F_3\mathbf{e}_3$ for an arbitrary vector $\mathbf{F}$ in terms of the base vectors $\mathbf{e}_i$ and the expansion

$$\nabla * \mathbf{F} = \sum_{i=1}^{3} (\nabla F_i * \mathbf{e}_i + F_i \nabla * \mathbf{e}_i)$$

show that

$$\nabla \times \mathbf{F} = \sum_{i,j=1}^{3} \left(\frac{1}{A_j}\frac{\partial F_i}{\partial \alpha_j} + \frac{F_i}{A_i A_j}\frac{\partial A_i}{\partial \alpha_j}\right) \mathbf{e}_j \times \mathbf{e}_i.$$

Problem 19.10: By use of the expansion for $\nabla \cdot (\mathbf{V} \times \mathbf{W})$ with $\mathbf{V} = \mathbf{e}_1$, $\mathbf{W} = \mathbf{e}_2$, show that: $\nabla \cdot \mathbf{e}_3 = A_3^{-1}\partial \ln(A_1A_2)/\partial\alpha_3$. Further, by use of this result show that

$$\nabla \cdot \mathbf{F} = \frac{1}{A_1A_2A_3}\left[\frac{\partial}{\partial \alpha_1}(A_2A_3F_1) + \frac{\partial}{\partial \alpha_2}(A_1A_3F_2) + \frac{\partial}{\partial \alpha_3}(A_1A_2F_3)\right].$$

ADDITIONAL PROBLEMS

1. If $\mathbf{r}_1$, $\mathbf{r}_2$ are the vectors from the points P_1 to P and P_2 to P, respectively, then an ellipse is determined by the condition, $|\mathbf{r}_1| + |\mathbf{r}_2| =$ constant. Show that for the ellipse:

(1) $$\mathbf{t} = \frac{d\mathbf{r}_1}{ds} = \frac{d|\mathbf{r}_1|}{ds}\mathbf{u} + |\mathbf{r}_1|\frac{d\mathbf{u}}{ds}$$

where $\mathbf{u}$ is a unit vector along $\mathbf{r}_1$, and hence,

$$\mathbf{t}\cdot\mathbf{u} = \frac{d|\mathbf{r}_1|}{ds}$$

(2) the tangent vector makes equal angles with $\mathbf{r}_1$, $\mathbf{r}_2$.

2. Show that the curvature and torsion of a space curve are determined by

$$\kappa = \frac{|\dot{\mathbf{R}} \times \ddot{\mathbf{R}}|}{|\dot{\mathbf{R}}|^3}, \qquad \tau = \frac{(\dot{\mathbf{R}} \cdot \ddot{\mathbf{R}} \times \dddot{\mathbf{R}}}{|\dot{\mathbf{R}} \times \ddot{\mathbf{R}}|^2},$$

where $\dot{\mathbf{R}} = d\mathbf{R}/dt$, etc.

3. By use of the Frenet formulas, show that if the radius vector $\mathbf{R}$ determines a curve lying on the sphere $(\mathbf{R} - \mathbf{C}) \cdot (\mathbf{R} - \mathbf{C}) = a^2$, then $\mathbf{R} = \mathbf{C} - \rho\mathbf{n} - (1/\tau)(d\rho/ds)\mathbf{b}$, where $\rho = \kappa^{-1}$ is the radius of curvature.

4. If a particle is acted upon by a central force varying inversely as the square of the distance, then by Newton's second law,

$$\frac{d\mathbf{V}}{dt} = -k\frac{\mathbf{r}_1}{r^2}$$

is the equation of motion in the plane. Show by vector methods that

(1) $\mathbf{r} \times \mathbf{V} = \mathbf{h}$, a constant vector; this result is called Kepler's law of areas;

(2) $\mathbf{h} = r^2\mathbf{r}_1 \times d\mathbf{r}_1/dt$.

5. A particle moves along a curve C; find the time derivative of the acceleration vector in terms of the vectors $\mathbf{t}$, $\mathbf{n}$, $\mathbf{b}$.

6. Consider the earth as a perfect sphere which rotates about a line from the center to the poles with angular velocity, $\omega\mathbf{k}'$. Assume that an inertial reference frame may be attached to the center of the earth and a rotating frame, $Oxyz$, is such that $\mathbf{k}$ passes through the center of the earth and a point P of colatitude, ϕ, of the earth. If $-mg\mathbf{k}$ is the resultant force due to gravity and the centrifugal force, derive the equations of motion for a particle falling toward the center of the earth. Show that if the $\mathbf{i}$ and $\mathbf{j}$ components of velocity vanish, then

these equations reduce to

$$\frac{d^2x}{dt^2} = 0, \qquad \frac{d^2z}{dt^2} = -g, \qquad \frac{d^2y}{dt^2} = -2\omega \sin \phi \frac{dz}{dt}.$$

7. Given the surfaces: $x^2 + y^2 + z^2 = 25$, $x^2 + y^2 - z^2 = 9$, find the component of $\nabla\Omega$, where $\Omega = x^2 + y^2 - 2z^2$, at $(1, -4, 2\sqrt{2})$ in the direction of the curve of intersection of the above surfaces.
8. If Ω is a twice differentiable scalar field, find $\nabla^2\Omega$ in spherical coordinates.
9. If $f(R)$ is a twice differentiable function of R, the distance variable in spherical coordinates, and $\boldsymbol{\phi}_1$ is a unit base vector of spherical coordinates, evaluate

$$\nabla \times [\nabla \times f(R)\boldsymbol{\phi}_1].$$

10. If the vector field **V** may be represented by

$$\mathbf{V} = \mathbf{A}g(\mathbf{a} \cdot \mathbf{R})$$

where **A, a** are constant vectors, **R** is the radius vector field, and g is an arbitrary differentiable function of the scalar product, $\mathbf{a} \cdot \mathbf{R}$, show that $\nabla \times \mathbf{V}$ is perpendicular to both **A** and **a**.

Chapter III

INTEGRATION THEORY

20. Introduction to Line, Surface, and Space Integrals. In this section we consider the integrals of scalar and vector fields over curves, surfaces, or space regions. Before proceeding to the discussion of the particular properties of these types of integrals, it appears desirable to discuss the definition of them.

The meaning of integration for scalar fields will be assumed to be known and only vector fields will be discussed. For simplicity, let us consider a vector field $\mathbf{F}(t)$ defined over a curve C, for which t is an appropriate parameter. There exist two methods for defining the definite integral: $\int_{t_0}^{t} \mathbf{F}(t)\, dt$. The first method is by use of the Cartesian rectangular components of $\mathbf{F}$. That is, we define the integral to mean

$$\int_{t_0}^{t} \mathbf{F}(t)\, dt = \mathbf{i} \int_{t_0}^{t} F_x(t)\, dt + \mathbf{j} \int_{t_0}^{t} F_y(t)\, dt + \mathbf{k} \int_{t_0}^{t} F_z(t)\, dt.$$

A second method is to define the integral as the limit of a sum of vectors, namely

$$\int_{t_0}^{t} \mathbf{F}(t)\, dt = \lim_{\substack{n \to \infty \\ \Delta t_i \to 0}} \sum_{i=1}^{n} \mathbf{F}(t_i)\, \Delta t_i.$$

From the geometric viewpoint, the last definition is preferable.

One must be aware of two points in order to properly use this second definition. First, the idea of a limit necessitates the use of the *magnitude* of the quantity under consideration. Since we have associated a magnitude with a vector $\mathbf{F}$, this point does not cause the difficulty. The real difficulty lies in the fact that we must be able to add vectors *located at various points of a domain*. This can only be done when the concept of parallelism for a vector field is independent of the field points under consideration. Euclidean three-space (also Euclidean n-space) has this property. However, even here, one must exercise care. The base vector fields $\mathbf{i}$, $\mathbf{j}$, $\mathbf{k}$ of a Cartesian coordinate system possess the desired property; the base vector fields $\mathbf{r}_1$, $\boldsymbol{\theta}_1$, of cylindrical coordinates do not possess this property. It is for this reason that in our first definition we used the base vectors **i, j, k.** Essentially, the first and second definitions of integrals are equivalent.

Finally, we note that *a sufficient condition for the existence of the above integral is that* **F** *be continuous.*

The above definitions can be readily extended to integrals over surfaces and space regions. Now we turn to the discussion of the particular types of integrals which are important in our work.

(a) ***Line Integrals.*** The term "line integral" denotes the integral of some scalar or vector field, $\mathcal{A}$, along a specified curve. In general, the specified curve C must be known. Then, the line integral to be considered is $\int_A^B \mathcal{A} * \mathbf{t}\, dt$. The limits, A, B, denote two points of the curve; **t** is the unit tangent vector field of the curve; t is a parameter which is a monotonic increasing function of the arc length parameter. In particular, if t is the arc length parameter s, and **R** is the radius vector field, then $d\mathbf{R} = \mathbf{t}\, ds$. If the integral depends only upon the points A, B and the integrand, then we say that "the line integral is independent of the path." Another important term is "the line integral around a closed path." The meaning of this term is quite evident. We denote such integrals by $\oint \mathcal{A} * \mathbf{t}\, dt$.

Illustrative Example: If $\phi = 6xy$, find $\int_{(0,0)}^{(1,2)} \phi\, d\mathbf{R}$ along $y^2 = 4x$.

Solution: Since $d\mathbf{R} = \mathbf{i}\, dx + \mathbf{j}\, dy$, and $dx = \dfrac{y\, dy}{2}$, and $\phi = \dfrac{6y^3}{4}$ along $y^2 = 4x$, the desired integral becomes

$$\mathbf{i} \int_0^2 \frac{3}{4} y^4\, dy + \mathbf{j} \int_0^2 \frac{3}{2} y^3\, dy = \frac{24}{5}\mathbf{i} + 6\mathbf{j}.$$

Problem 20.1: If $\mathbf{F} = x^2\mathbf{i} + y\mathbf{j}$, find $\int_{(0,0)}^{(1,2)} \mathbf{F} \times d\mathbf{R}$ along $y^2 = 4x$.

Problem 20.2: If $\mathbf{F} = x\mathbf{i} + y^2\mathbf{j} + 2z\mathbf{k}$, find $\int_{(0,0,0)}^{(1,3,2)} \mathbf{F} \times d\mathbf{R}$ along the path consisting of a portion of the x-axis, a line segment parallel to the y-axis, and a line segment parallel to the z-axis, taken in that order.

Problem 20.3: If $\mathbf{F} = \mathbf{i}x + \mathbf{j}y + \mathbf{k}z^2$, find $\int_{(0,0,0)}^{(1,3,2)} \mathbf{F} \cdot d\mathbf{R}$ along the path of Problem 20.2.

Problem 20.4: If $\mathbf{F} = \mathbf{R} = \mathbf{i}x + \mathbf{j}y + \mathbf{k}z$, find $\int_{(0,1)}^{(1,0)} \mathbf{F} \cdot d\mathbf{R}$ along: (1) the smaller arc of $z = 0$, $x^2 + y^2 = 1$; (2) $x + y = 1$, $z = 0$.

Problem 20.5: For the vector field of Problem 20.4, prove $\oint \mathbf{F} \cdot d\mathbf{R} = 0$ around every closed path. *Hint:* $\mathbf{F} \cdot d\mathbf{R} = \frac{1}{2} d(x^2 + y^2 + z^2)$.

Problem 20.6: If $\mathbf{F} = \dfrac{y\mathbf{i} - x\mathbf{j}}{x^2 + y^2}$, find $\displaystyle\int_{(1,0)}^{(0,1)} \mathbf{F} \cdot d\mathbf{R}$ along: (1) the first quadrant arc of $x^2 + y^2 = 1$; (2) $x + y = 1$.

Problem 20.7: (1) For the vector field of Problem 20.6, prove $\oint \mathbf{F} \cdot d\mathbf{R} = -2\pi$ along $x^2 + y^2 = 1$; (2) for the same vector field, prove $\oint \mathbf{F} \cdot d\mathbf{R} = 0$ along any closed path not containing the origin in the interior or on the boundary of the region determined by the path.

(b) ***Surface Integrals.*** The theory of surface integrals follows along the same lines as that of the previous line integrals. We consider orientable surfaces. That is, one-sided surfaces, such as the Möbius strip, will not be discussed. Usually, the unit normal vector to the surface, $\mathbf{n}$, plays the same role as $\mathbf{t}$ does in line integrals. Further, corresponding to the arc length element ds, we introduce the element of surface area, $d\sigma$. Note that s is a parameter but σ has no meaning. Another manner of stating this same idea is to say that ds is an exact differential when the curve C is given, but $d\sigma$ is not an exact differential when the surface S is given. For the present, we define $d\sigma$ as follows. Let

$$x = x(u, v), \qquad y = y(u, v), \qquad z = z(u, v) \tag{20.1}$$

define the surface S in terms of the parameters u, v. These equations define a *mapping of the* (u, v) *plane onto the surface.* Certain assumptions as to differentiability of this mapping must be made. For our present work, it is sufficient to assume that the first and second partial derivatives of the mapping functions (20.1) exist and are continuous. Further, a condition must be imposed on the mapping to assure the existence of two independent parameters. That is, the equations $x = (u + v)$, $y = (u + v)^2$ and $z = (u + v)^3$ define a curve C and not a surface S. The desired condition involves the Jacobians of (20.1). This theory would lead us far afield from our present subject matter. Hence, we shall assume that the mapping (20.1) defines a real surface and return to the definition of $d\sigma$. Let u, v be chosen to be x, y. Then (20.1) defines a projection from the surface to the x,y-plane. It appears geometrically reasonable to assume that the projection of the area element of the surface is the area element of the plane. Thus, we write

$$d\sigma|\cos \gamma| = dx\, dy \tag{20.2}$$

where $\cos \gamma = \mathbf{n} \cdot \mathbf{k}$. In a similar manner, one may define $d\sigma$ in terms of $dx\, dz$ or $dy\, dz$. We assume that these definitions are equivalent. A fuller treatment of this point will be furnished in Sections 26 and 49.

In our future work we shall generally deal with integrals of the types $\int_S \mathfrak{A} * \mathbf{n}\, d\sigma$ and $\oint_S \mathfrak{A} * \mathbf{n}\, d\sigma$. The first integral is taken over an open surface S; the second integral is taken over a closed surface.

Illustrative Example: Evaluate $\int_S \mathbf{F} \cdot \mathbf{n}\, d\sigma$ when $\mathbf{F} = \mathbf{i}x + 2y\mathbf{j}$ and S consists of that part of the surface $x + y = 1$ which lies in the first octant and is bounded by $z = 0$, $z = 2$, $x = 0$, $y = 0$. Let $\mathbf{n}$ be the outward drawn normal when $x + y = 1$ is considered as a face of the triangular prism formed by the above planes.

Solution: The important vector, $\mathbf{n}$, must be obtained. This can be easily accomplished by noting that ∇f is normal to $f(x, y, z) = c$. Hence, in our case, the unit vector $\mathbf{n} = (\mathbf{i} + \mathbf{j})/\sqrt{2}$. In the present work it will be desirable to use the relation, $d\sigma = |\sec \beta|\, dx\, dz$, where $\cos \beta = \mathbf{n} \cdot \mathbf{j} = 1/\sqrt{2}$, instead of (20.2). Hence, $\int_S \mathbf{F} \cdot \mathbf{n}\, d\sigma = \int_{S'} (x + 2y)\, dx\, dz = \int_{S'} [x + 2(1 - x)]\, dx\, dz = \int_0^1 dx \int_0^2 dz(2 - x) = 2 \int_0^1 (2 - x)\, dx = 3.$ Note, S' is the projection of S in the x,z-plane.

Illustrative Example: Evaluate $\oint_S \mathbf{F} \times \mathbf{n}\, d\sigma$ where $\mathbf{F} = \mathbf{i}y - \mathbf{j}x$ and S is the closed surface of the unit sphere, $x^2 + y^2 + z^2 = 1$.

Solution: We must determine the unit outward drawn normal, $\mathbf{n}$, of the sphere. By differentiation of $f(x, y, z) = x^2 + y^2 + z^2 - 1$, we see that the direction numbers of the normal are $(2x, 2y, 2z)$. The desired unit normal vector of S is $\mathbf{n} = x\mathbf{i} + y\mathbf{j} + z\mathbf{k}$. Thus $\mathbf{F} \times \mathbf{n}$ reduces to $-xz\mathbf{i} - yz\mathbf{j} + (x^2 + y^2)\mathbf{k}$. To evaluate $d\sigma$ we work with (20.2) and obtain $d\sigma = |\sec \gamma|\, dx\, dy$. Since $\cos \gamma = z = \pm \sqrt{1 - x^2 - y^2}$ on the unit sphere, $d\sigma$ has the value $dx\, dy/\sqrt{1 - x^2 - y^2}$. The desired integral reduces to

$$\iint_{S'} [-xz\mathbf{i} - yz\mathbf{j} + (x^2 + y^2)\mathbf{k}] \frac{dx\, dy}{\sqrt{1 - x^2 - y^2}}.$$

To evaluate the above integral we replace z by $\sqrt{1 - x^2 - y^2}$ on the upper half of the sphere, and by $-\sqrt{1 - x^2 - y^2}$ on the lower half of the sphere. In both cases the integral is taken over S' the interior of the unit circle, $x^2 + y^2 = 1$, which is the projection of both the upper half of the sphere and the lower half onto the x,y-plane. Thus, the terms in $\mathbf{i}$ and $\mathbf{j}$ reduce to zero in the above integral and the integral itself reduces to (in terms of polar coordinates)[1]

$$2\mathbf{k} \iint_{S'} \frac{x^2 + y^2}{\sqrt{1 - x^2 - y^2}}\, dx\, dy = 2\mathbf{k} \int_0^{2\pi} d\theta \int_0^1 \frac{r^3\, dr}{\sqrt{1 - r^2}} = \frac{8\pi}{3}\mathbf{k}.$$

[1] The integral in (r) is improper, but is easily evaluated.

Problem 20.8: If $\mathbf{F} = x\mathbf{i} - y\mathbf{j} + z^2\mathbf{k}$, find $\int_S \mathbf{F} \cdot \mathbf{n}\, d\sigma$ over that part of the surface of $x + y + z = 1$ which lies in the first octant. What are the two possible vectors, $\mathbf{n}$?

Problem 20.9: For the vector field $\mathbf{F} = y^2\mathbf{i} + x\mathbf{j}$ and open surface $x^2 + y^2 = 1$, $-2 < z < 2$, find $\int_S \mathbf{F} \cdot \mathbf{n}\, d\sigma$ over: (1) the half cylinder $y > 0$; (2) the whole surface.

Problem 20.10: If $\mathbf{F} = x\mathbf{i} - y\mathbf{j} + z\mathbf{k}$, find $\int_S \mathbf{F} \cdot \mathbf{n}\, d\sigma$ over the open hemispherical surface $x^2 + y^2 + z^2 = 1$, $z > 0$.

Problem 20.11: For the vector field, $\mathbf{F} = x\mathbf{i} - y\mathbf{j} + z\mathbf{k}$, find $\oint_S \mathbf{F} \cdot \mathbf{n}\, d\sigma$ over the closed spherical surface $x^2 + y^2 + z^2 = 1$. Let $\mathbf{n}$ be the outward drawn normal.

Problem 20.12: For the vector field $\mathbf{F} = y\mathbf{i} - x\mathbf{j} + z\mathbf{k}$, find $\oint_S \mathbf{F} \times \mathbf{n}\, d\sigma$ over the closed spherical surface $x^2 + y^2 + z^2 = 1$. Let $\mathbf{n}$ be the outward drawn normal.

Problem 20.13: For the vector field $\mathbf{F} = x\mathbf{i} - y\mathbf{j}$ and the closed cylindrical surface $x^2 + y^2 = 1$, $z = 0$, $z = 2$, find $\oint_S \mathbf{F}\, d\sigma$.

(c) ***Space Integrals.*** The integration theory for this type of integral is well known from calculus. These integrals may be expressed as triple integrals and evaluated by repeated integration. The only problem that may arise in connection with these integrals is that of determining the element of volume in various coordinate systems. That is, the integrals to be considered are of the form $\int_T \mathbf{F}\, d\tau$, where $d\tau$ is the element of volume in some coordinate system and T is the space region over which the integral is to be evaluated. We shall discuss the problem of defining volume in Section 49. For the present we consider only orthogonal curvilinear coordinate systems. Then, if [see the discussion following (18.3)] $ds^2 = (A_1\, d\alpha_1)^2 + (A_2\, d\alpha_2)^2 + (A_3\, d\alpha_3)^2$ is the arc length element of the coordinate system, it appears reasonable to assume that the volume of an elementary curvilinear parallelopiped formed by the coordinate lines is

$$d\tau = A_1A_2A_3\, d\alpha_1\, d\alpha_2\, d\alpha_3.$$

From the arc length formulas in *cylindrical* and *spherical coordinates* as introduced in Section 14, it follows that the volume elements in these coordinate systems are

$$d\tau = r\, dr\, d\theta\, dz, \qquad d\tau = R^2 \sin \phi\, d\phi\, d\theta\, dR \tag{20.3}$$

respectively.

Illustrative Example: Evaluate $\int_T \mathbf{F}\, d\tau$, where $\mathbf{F} = y\mathbf{i} - 3\mathbf{j}$, and T is the space region bounded by the unit sphere, $x^2 + y^2 + z^2 = 1$.

Solution: We shall use cylindrical coordinates, then the integral reduces to

$$\int\int\int_T (r \sin\theta\, \mathbf{i} - 3\mathbf{j}) r\, dr\, d\theta\, dz.$$

This multiple integral may be evaluated by the following repeated integral (or by inspection)

$$\int_0^{2\pi} d\theta \int_0^1 r\, dr \int_{-\sqrt{1-r^2}}^{\sqrt{1-r^2}} (r \sin\theta\, \mathbf{i} - 3\mathbf{j})\, dz = -4\pi\mathbf{j}.$$

Problem 20.14: Evaluate $\int_T \mathbf{F}\, d\tau$, where $\mathbf{F} = x^2\mathbf{i} - y\mathbf{j}$ and T is the space region bounded by $x^2 + y^2 = 1$, $z = 2$, $z = -2$.

Problem 20.15: Evaluate $\int_T \mathbf{F}\, d\tau$, where $\mathbf{F} = z^2\mathbf{k}$ and T is the space region bounded by $x^2 + y^2 + z^2 = 1$.

Problem 20.16: Evaluate $\int_T \nabla \cdot \mathbf{F}\, d\tau$, where $\mathbf{F} = \mathbf{R} = \mathbf{i}x + \mathbf{j}y + \mathbf{k}z$, and T is any space region.

Problem 20.17: Evaluate $\int_T \nabla \times \mathbf{F}\, d\tau$, where $\mathbf{F} = \mathbf{i}y - \mathbf{j}x$ and T is any space region.

21. Line Integrals Which Are Independent of the Path and the Potential Ω. We consider a continuous vector field $\mathbf{F}$ defined over a space region T. Let C be any smooth curve (or path) lying wholly within T and joining two points A, an initial point, and B, a terminal point. We ask, "when is the value of the line integral

$$\int_A^B \mathbf{F} \cdot \mathbf{t}\, ds = \int_A^B \mathbf{F} \cdot d\mathbf{R} \tag{21.1}$$

independent of the path?" In order to properly answer this question we shall prove three results which depend upon the existence of the relation $\mathbf{F} = \nabla\Omega$ between $\mathbf{F}$ and a scalar potential, Ω.

(a) ***Case where*** $\mathbf{F} = \nabla\Omega$. First, we prove: *If* $\mathbf{F} = \nabla\Omega$ *everywhere in the space region* T, *and* Ω *is single-valued in* T, *then the above integral is independent of the path.*

It should be noted that two conditions must be fulfilled for the above result to be valid. First, $\mathbf{F}$ must be the gradient of a scalar Ω, *everywhere in the space region T under consideration*, and secondly, Ω *must be single-valued in* T.

Now, we turn to the proof of the theorem. By use of our assumptions and the properties of the gradient, we find: $\mathbf{F} \cdot d\mathbf{R} = \nabla\Omega \cdot d\mathbf{R} = d\Omega$. Since this relation is valid everywhere in T, we find

$$\int_A^B \mathbf{F} \cdot d\mathbf{R} = \int_A^B d\Omega = \Omega(B) - \Omega(A).$$

The condition that Ω is single-valued implies that the right-hand side of the above integral has a definite value independent of the path.

We consider a few simple examples in order to illustrate this result.

Illustrative Example: Let $\mathbf{F} = \mathbf{i}\,2x + \mathbf{j}\,2y + \mathbf{k}\,2z$.

Solution: In this case $\mathbf{F} = \nabla\Omega$ in any *finite region* T, and $\Omega = x^2 + y^2 + z^2$. Since Ω is single-valued in T, our above result can be applied. We conclude that the line integral (21.1) for the above $\mathbf{F}$ is independent of the path for all paths in T.

Illustrative Example: Let $\mathbf{F} = \dfrac{\mathbf{R}}{R^3}$, where $\mathbf{R}$ is the radius vector field.

Solution: By use of the properties of the gradient (Section 17), we see that a *single-valued* potential, $\Omega = -1/R$, exists *except at* $R = 0$ such that $\mathbf{F} = \nabla\Omega$. Hence we *exclude the origin* from the region T and conclude that the line integral (21.1) of $\mathbf{F}$ is independent of the path for all paths in T.

Illustrative Example: Let $\mathbf{F} = \dfrac{\boldsymbol{\phi}_1}{R}$, where $\boldsymbol{\phi}_1$ is the base vector of spherical coordinates and R is the coordinate variable of that coordinate system.

Solution: From the properties of the gradient, we find $\Omega = \phi$ except at the origin. Further, from the discussion of Section 14, we see that, $0 \leq \phi < \pi$ (or ϕ may satisfy some equivalent restriction) in order that Ω be single-valued. Hence we can use the xOz plane as a cut or barrier. This barrier is such that, $0 < \theta < \pi$ and hence the restriction, $0 \leq \theta < 2\pi$ is satisfied. The desired space region T in which Ω is single-valued is $y > 0$. For any path in this region, the line integral (21.1) of the above vector, $\mathbf{F}$, is independent of the path. Note that $y = 0$ is the boundary of T.

Problem 21.1: Let $\mathbf{F} = \dfrac{x\mathbf{i} + y\mathbf{j}}{x^2 + y^2}$ and show that if the region T is the x,y-plane *with the origin* excluded, then $\mathbf{F}$ is the gradient of the single-valued potential $\Omega = \ln\,(x^2 + y^2)^{1/2}$. Thus, the line integral (21.1) for the above vector field $\mathbf{F}$ is independent of the path, providing the path does not pass through the origin. *Hint:* $\Omega = \ln r$.

Problem 21.2: Consider the vector field, $\mathbf{F} = \dfrac{(x-1)\mathbf{i} + y\mathbf{j}}{(x-1)^2 + y^2}$. Find the potential Ω and the plane region T so that $\mathbf{F} = \nabla\Omega$.

Problem 21.3: Consider the vector field, $\mathbf{F} = \dfrac{-y\mathbf{i} + x\mathbf{j}}{x^2 + y^2}$. Determine a region T and the function Ω so that $\mathbf{F} = \nabla\Omega$ in T. *Hint:* $\mathbf{F} = \boldsymbol{\theta}_1/r$ (see Section 14). Show that $\Omega = \theta$, by use of the principles of Section 17.

Problem 21.4: Consider the vector field, $\mathbf{F} = \dfrac{-(y-1)\mathbf{i} + x\mathbf{j}}{x^2 + (y-1)^2}$. Determine a region T and the function Ω so that $\mathbf{F} = \nabla\Omega$ in T.

Problem 21.5: Discuss the value of the line integral of equation (21.1) if $\mathbf{F} = \dfrac{-y\mathbf{i} + x\mathbf{j}}{x^2 + y^2}$ and the region T is bounded by: (1) two radial lines from the origin and two arcs of circles with centers at the origin; (2) two circles with centers at the origin.

Problem 21.6: Discuss the value of the line integral of equation (21.1) if $\mathbf{F} = \dfrac{x\mathbf{i} + y\mathbf{j}}{x^2 + y^2}$ and T is either of the two regions described in Problem 21.5.

Problem 21.7: Consider the vector field, $\mathbf{F} = \dfrac{-(y-1)\mathbf{i} + x\mathbf{j}}{x^2 + (y-1)^2} + \dfrac{-(y-2)\mathbf{i} + x\mathbf{j}}{x^2 + (y-2)^2}$. Determine a region T and the function Ω so that $\mathbf{F} = \nabla\Omega$ in T.

Problem 21.8: Consider the vector field, $\mathbf{F} = \dfrac{\boldsymbol{\phi}_1}{R} - \dfrac{\boldsymbol{\theta}_1}{R\sin\phi}$. Determine a region T and the function Ω so that $\mathbf{F} = \nabla\Omega$. *Hint:* Note that $\mathbf{F} = \mathbf{F}_1 - \mathbf{F}_2$.

(b) ***Line Integrals Independent of the Path.*** Next we shall prove a type of converse result to that of (a). *If the line integral* (21.1) *is independent of the path in some region T, then a scalar Ω, single-valued in T, exists so that* $\mathbf{F} = \nabla\Omega$.

Since the line integral is independent of the path, we may write

$$\Omega(x, y, z) = \int_{x_0,y_0,z_0}^{x,y,z} \mathbf{F}\cdot d\mathbf{R} = \int_{x_0,y_0,z_0}^{x,y,z} F_x\,dx + F_y\,dy + F_z\,dz.$$

Hence

$$\Omega(x + \Delta x, y, z) = \int_{x_0,y_0,z_0}^{x+\Delta x,y,z} F_x\,dx + F_y\,dy + F_z\,dz.$$

Subtracting the last two equations, we find

$$\Omega(x + \Delta x, y, z) - \Omega(x, y, z) = \int_{x,y,z}^{x+\Delta x,y,z} F_x\,dx + F_y\,dy + F_z\,dz.$$

If we evaluate the right-hand side of the above by integrating along the line $y =$ constant, $z =$ constant (why is this permissible?), then $dy =$

$dz = 0$ and our relation reduces to

$$\Omega(x + \Delta x, y, z) - \Omega(x, y, z) = \int_x^{x+\Delta x} F_x\, dx, \qquad y = c, \qquad z = c.$$

By use of the first theorem of the mean for integrals, we may write this last integral as

$$\Omega(x + \Delta x, y, z) - \Omega(x, y, z) = F_x(x + \theta\, \Delta x, y, z)\, \Delta x$$

where $0 \leq \theta \leq 1$. Dividing both sides by Δx and passing to the limit, we find: $\partial\Omega/\partial x = F_x$. In the same manner, one may show that: $\partial\Omega/\partial y = F_y$, $\partial\Omega/\partial z = F_z$. Hence it follows that $\mathbf{F} = \nabla\Omega$.

(c) ***The Relation between Line Integrals Which Are Independent of the Path and Line Integrals around Closed Paths.*** We shall prove: *If the line integral of* (21.1) *is independent of the path for all non-intersecting*

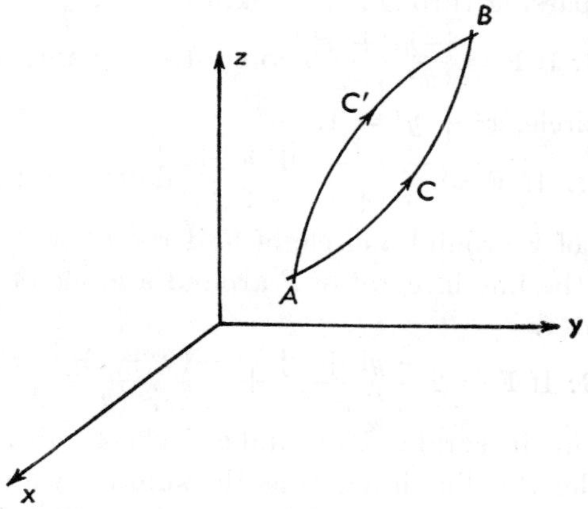

Figure 25: Paths C and C' Joining A and B

paths in a region T then the line integral of (21.1) *around every closed path in T is zero and conversely.*

Consider two paths in T joining points A and B (see Figure 25). If C and C' denote these paths, then by the conditions above,

$$\int_{A\ (\text{along } C)}^{B} \mathbf{F} \cdot d\mathbf{R} = \int_{A\ (\text{along } C')}^{B} \mathbf{F} \cdot d\mathbf{R}.$$

By interchanging the limits in the right-hand side of the above, we obtain

$$\int_{A\ (\text{along } C)}^{B} \mathbf{F} \cdot d\mathbf{R} = -\int_{B\ (\text{along } C')}^{A} \mathbf{F} \cdot d\mathbf{R}.$$

Combining both integrals, we see that $\oint \mathbf{F} \cdot d\mathbf{R} = 0$. The closed path consists of C from A to B, and C' from B to A.

The validity of the converse follows by merely reversing the order of the above steps, provided the paths do not intersect. In case the paths do intersect a finite number of times, the converse may be established by a simple extension of the argument for the case of non-intersecting paths.

The previous theorem may also be stated in the following form [see theorem (a)]: If $\mathbf{F} = \boldsymbol{\nabla}\Omega$, everywhere in a region T, and Ω is single-valued in T, then the line integral (21.1) around every closed path in T vanishes and conversely.

Problem 21.9: If $\mathbf{F} = \mathbf{R}_1/R^2$ show that the line integral around every closed path not passing through the origin is zero. *Hint:* Prove $\mathbf{F} = \boldsymbol{\nabla}\Omega$ and Ω is single-valued everywhere except at the origin.

Problem 21.10: If $\mathbf{F} = \dfrac{x\mathbf{i} + y\mathbf{j}}{x^2 + y^2}$, show that the line integral around every closed path not passing through the origin is zero.

Problem 21.11: If $\mathbf{F} = \dfrac{-y\mathbf{i} + x\mathbf{j}}{x^2 + y^2}$, compute the value of $\oint \mathbf{F} \cdot d\mathbf{R}$ along the closed unit circle, $x^2 + y^2 = 1$.

Problem 21.12: If $\mathbf{F} = \dfrac{-(y - 2)\mathbf{i} + x\mathbf{j}}{x^2 + (y - 2)^2}$, determine: (1) the value of the line integral of $\mathbf{F}$ around a circle of unit radius with $(0, 2)$ as center; (2) the value of the line integral of $\mathbf{F}$ around a circle of unit radius with the origin as center.

Problem 21.13: If $\mathbf{F} = 2\dfrac{-y\mathbf{i} + x\mathbf{j}}{x^2 + y^2} + \dfrac{-(y + 2)\mathbf{i} + x\mathbf{j}}{x^2 + (y + 2)^2}$, determine: (1) the value of the line integral of $\mathbf{F}$ around a circle of unit radius with origin as center (consider this line integral as the sum of two line integrals and evaluate each such integral separately); (2) the value of the line integral of $\mathbf{F}$ around a circle with center at $(0, -1)$ and radius 3.

The vector fields $\mathbf{F}$ in Problems 21.11 and 21.13 can be interpreted as the magnetic force field due to electric current flowing in wires which are orthogonal to the x,y-plane and situated at: $(0, 0)$ for the first problem and at $(0, 0)$, $(0, -2)$ for the second problem.

(d) *Applications to Mathematical Physics.* In mathematical physics, the line integral occurs frequently. Thus, in determining the work done by a force field in moving along a curve, we write

$$W = \int_{x_0, y_0, z_0}^{x,y,z} \mathbf{F} \cdot d\mathbf{R}, \text{ along } C.$$

Further, if it is agreed that x_0, y_0, z_0 is fixed, then $W = W(x, y, z, C)$, which indicates that W depends upon the curve C and x, y, z. For the so-called "conservative fields," W is independent of C. Further, in this case the physicist defines the potential function Ω by means of the relation: $W = -\Omega$, $\mathbf{F} = -\nabla\Omega$.

Another example of the line integral occurs in fluid dynamics. Here, the velocity vector field, **V**, plays the role of the force field in electrostatics or gravitation. If the line integral $\int_A^B \mathbf{V} \cdot d\mathbf{R}$ is independent of the path, then we may say that a velocity potential exists; and the fluid motion is said to be irrotational. The line integral around a closed path is called the *circulation*.

22. Green's Theorem in the Plane. Consider a region in the x,y-plane bounded by an oval, C. By definition, an oval is a closed curve with a continuous tangent and such that any line in the plane cuts the curve in at most two points. The term closed region, R, will denote the region of the x,y-plane interior to C *and* the boundary curve C. Let $u(x, y)$, $v(x, y)$ be functions which are single-valued, continuous, and which possess continuous partial derivatives in the closed region, R.

(a) ***Green's Theorem in the Plane.*** Under the above conditions, Green's theorem is contained in the following equation:

$$\oint u\,dx + v\,dy = \iint_R \left(\frac{\partial v}{\partial x} - \frac{\partial u}{\partial y}\right) dx\,dy. \tag{22.1}$$

The line integral around the closed curve C has a definite sense, as indicated by the arrow. In order to explicitly determine this sense, we need only define a rule for choosing the arc length parameter, s, to be positive. Let **n** denote the unit interior normal to C in the x,y-plane. We shall let the sense of increasing s (or of the positive direction of the unit tangent vector **t**) be determined by the requirement that the ordered triad consisting of the unit normal, **k**, to the plane at P, and the unit tangent and interior normal vectors at P shall form a right-hand system. This rule is equivalent to stating that the positive sense of s is chosen so that if an observer moves around the curve C in this sense, the inside of the curve will always be to the observer's left.

To verify Green's formula, we shall prove that

$$\oint u\,dx = -\iint_R \frac{\partial u}{\partial y}\,dx\,dy. \tag{22.2}$$

The multiple integral on the right can be replaced by the repeated integral

$$\iint_R \frac{\partial u}{\partial y}\,dx\,dy = \int_{x_0}^{x_1} dx \int_{y_1(x)}^{y_2(x)} \frac{\partial u}{\partial y}\,dy.$$

The points A, B of the oval are determined by the requirement that at A, B the tangent lines to the oval are vertical. Further, C_1 is the lower part of C, and C_2 is the upper part of C. By integration of this last relation we obtain

$$\iint_R \frac{\partial u}{\partial y}\, dx\, dy = \int_{x_0}^{x_1} [u(x, y_2) - u(x, y_1)]\, dx.$$

Inverting the order of integration of the first expression in the right-hand

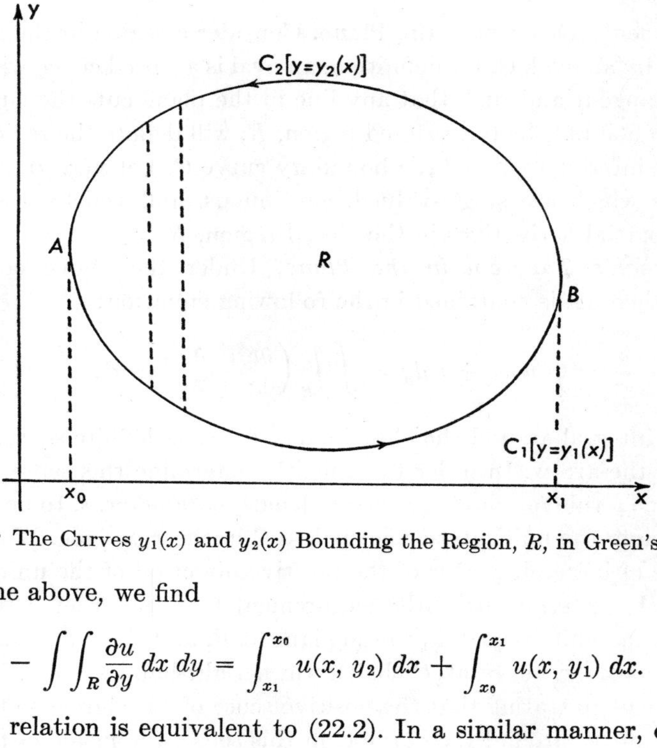

Figure 26: The Curves $y_1(x)$ and $y_2(x)$ Bounding the Region, R, in Green's Theorem

side of the above, we find

$$-\iint_R \frac{\partial u}{\partial y}\, dx\, dy = \int_{x_1}^{x_0} u(x, y_2)\, dx + \int_{x_0}^{x_1} u(x, y_1)\, dx.$$

This last relation is equivalent to (22.2). In a similar manner, one may prove that

$$\oint v\, dy = \iint_R \frac{\partial v}{\partial x}\, dx\, dy.$$

By adding (22.2) and the last equation, one obtains Green's theorem (22.1).

(b) ***Stokes's Theorem for the Plane.*** There are several interesting vector forms of Green's theorem. Let us define a vector field **F** by the equation: $\mathbf{F} = u\mathbf{i} + v\mathbf{j}$. Since $\mathbf{r} = x\mathbf{i} + y\mathbf{j}$, it follows that $d\mathbf{r} = \mathbf{i}\, dx +$

$\mathbf{j}\,dy$. Thus the left-hand side of (22.1) reduces to

$$\oint d\mathbf{r} \cdot \mathbf{F}.$$

From the expression for $\mathbf{F}$ and the definition of $\nabla \times \mathbf{F}$, we can easily show that

$$\nabla \times \mathbf{F} = \left(\frac{\partial v}{\partial x} - \frac{\partial u}{\partial y}\right)\mathbf{k}.$$

Now, the surface S defined by R has the unit normal vector $\mathbf{n} = \mathbf{k}$. Further, $dx\,dy$ is the element of area for this surface. Hence, the right-hand side of (22.1) may be written as

$$\int_S \mathbf{n} \cdot \nabla \times \mathbf{F}\, d\sigma.$$

and (22.1) may be written as

$$\oint d\mathbf{r} \cdot \mathbf{F} = \int_S \mathbf{n} \cdot \nabla \times \mathbf{F}\, d\sigma. \tag{22.3}$$

The formula (22.3) is *known as Stokes's theorem.* In Section 27 we shall generalize Stokes's formula to surfaces in Euclidean three-space and show that in (22.3), S may be replaced by an arbitrary surface.

(c) ***Gauss's Theorem in the Plane.*** Another interesting form of Green's theorem is obtained by introducing the unit *exterior normal,* $\mathbf{n}$, *to the curve* C. This vector, $\mathbf{n}$, lies in the plane of the curve and is determined by $\mathbf{n} = \mathbf{i}\dfrac{dy}{ds} - \mathbf{j}\dfrac{dx}{ds} = \mathbf{t} \times \mathbf{k}$. If we introduce the vector field, $\mathbf{G} = v\mathbf{i} - u\mathbf{j}$, then the left-hand side of (22.1) reduces to

$$\oint \mathbf{n} \cdot \mathbf{G}\, ds.$$

Further, the integrand of the right-hand side of (22.1) becomes $\nabla \cdot \mathbf{G}$, and Green's theorem may be written in the *Gauss form:*

$$\oint \mathbf{n} \cdot \mathbf{G}\, ds = \int\!\!\int_R \nabla \cdot \mathbf{G}\, d\sigma. \tag{22.4}$$

In Section 24 we shall show that Gauss's formula is valid when R is replaced by a *space* region T, and the boundary curve C by the *closed surface* S bounding T, or

$$\oint_S \mathbf{n} \cdot \mathbf{G}\, d\sigma = \int_T \nabla \cdot \mathbf{G}\, d\tau. \tag{22.5}$$

From the previous discussions it is evident that in the plane the formulas of Gauss and Stokes are two formulations of the same theorem

(Green's theorem). This conclusion remains valid in n-dimensional space, where the general result is usually referred to as Stokes's theorem. However, in three-space, there are differences in structure between the Gauss and Stokes formulation of this result. In the Stokes formulation one uses the unit tangent vector **t** *which lies on the boundary* of the surface S [see (22.3)]; in the Gauss formulation one uses the unit normal vector **n** *which lies outside the boundary* of the region T [see (22.5)]. These differences stem from the fact that the tangent vector is uniquely associated with the curve bounding S and that the normal vector is uniquely determined by the surface bounding a space region T.

(d) ***Line Integrals Which Are Independent of the Path.*** To conclude this section, we *consider again a plane region R bounded by an oval, C.* As before, we assume that u, v, $\frac{\partial u}{\partial y}$, $\frac{\partial v}{\partial x}$ are continuous in the closed region R. We shall prove the following result: *The necessary and sufficient condition that the line integral $\oint u\,dx + v\,dy$ shall vanish for every oval closed path in R is that $\frac{\partial u}{\partial y} - \frac{\partial v}{\partial x} = 0$ throughout R.*

To show the sufficiency of this condition, we assume that $\frac{\partial u}{\partial y} - \frac{\partial v}{\partial x} = 0$ throughout R. Applying Green's theorem to any subregion, R', of R, we see that $\oint u\,dx + v\,dy$ around the oval boundary C' of R' must vanish.

Next we wish to show that if $\oint u\,dx + v\,dy = 0$ for every oval curve C' in the region R, then $\frac{\partial u}{\partial y} - \frac{\partial v}{\partial x} = 0$ throughout R. Let us *assume the contrary, namely, $\frac{\partial u}{\partial y} - \frac{\partial v}{\partial x} > 0$ at some point P.* Since the derivatives are continuous, there must exist a small region R' surrounding P such that $\frac{\partial u}{\partial y} - \frac{\partial v}{\partial x} > 0$ throughout R'. We assume that R' is sufficiently smooth so that an oval curve C'' can be drawn inside R'. Now, we apply Green's theorem to the curve C'' and its interior R''. Since $\frac{\partial u}{\partial y} - \frac{\partial v}{\partial x} > 0$ throughout R'', the right-hand side of Green's formula [see (22.1)] must be positive. Hence, the integral $\oint u\,dx + v\,dy$ around C'' cannot vanish. But, this contradicts our original assumption. Hence, $\frac{\partial u}{\partial y} - \frac{\partial v}{\partial x} = 0$ at every point P of R.

The previous theory has been developed under the assumption that R is an oval-shaped region. Actually, the above results are applicable to any sufficiently regular so-called "simply connected plane region." We shall discuss this topic in the next section.

Problem 22.1: Evaluate $\oint (x^2 + y)\,dx + y^2\,dy$ around the unit circle by use of Green's theorem. Check your result by direct calculation.

Problem 22.2: Evaluate $\oint 2y^2\,dx - 5x\,dy$ around the triangle whose vertices are (0, 0), (1, 0), (0, 1), by use of Green's theorem.

Problem 22.3: Can you evaluate $\oint \frac{-y\,dx + x\,dy}{x^2 + y^2}$ around the unit circle with center at the origin by use of Green's theorem? Give reasons for your answer.

Problem 22.4: Derive the equation $\iint_R \frac{\partial v}{\partial x}\,dx\,dy = \oint v\,dy.$

Problem 22.5: Replace the vector $\mathbf{F} = u\mathbf{i} + v\mathbf{j}$ of (b) by $\mathbf{H} = -v\mathbf{i} + u\mathbf{j}$ and show that Green's formula may be written as $\oint d\mathbf{r} \times \mathbf{H} = \int_S (\mathbf{n} \times \nabla) \times \mathbf{H}\,d\sigma$.

Problem 22.6: Show that $\oint d\mathbf{r}\phi = \int_S \mathbf{n} \times \nabla\phi\,d\sigma$ by use of Green's formula. *Hint:* Take $\mathbf{n} = \mathbf{k}$.

Problem 22.7: Verify Gauss's theorem (22.5) for a cylinder of unit height whose generators are parallel to the z-axis and whose base is bounded by an oval in the x,y-plane. Assume that $\mathbf{G} = v(x, y, z)\mathbf{i} - u(x, y, z)\mathbf{j}$ and $u(x, y, z) = u(x, y, 0)$, $v(x, y, z) = v(x, y, 0)$. *Hint:* Show that

$$\int_0^1 dz \oint u\,dx = -\int_S \mathbf{n} \cdot \mathbf{j}u\,d\sigma$$

where S is the lateral surface of the cylinder, etc.

Problem 22.8: Show that, $\oint \mathcal{C}\,dx + \mathcal{B}\,dy = -\iint_R \left(\frac{\partial \mathcal{C}}{\partial y} - \frac{\partial \mathcal{B}}{\partial x}\right) dx\,dy,$ where $\mathcal{C}$, $\mathcal{B}$ are scalars or vectors (or even when they are tensors of the same type).

23. Green's Theorem for Multiply Connected Regions. In the previous section we have discussed Green's theorem for an oval-shaped region R. The oval region is a very simple example of a region of simple or zero connectivity. The general concept of connectivity is of a topological nature.

Here we offer a simplified geometric definition of this term. We say that a finite region of the x,y-plane has: (1) zero connectivity if every closed curve lying in the region can be shrunk to a point without crossing the boundaries of the region; (2) connectivity one if only one class of closed curves exists which can be deformed into each other but cannot be shrunk to a point without crossing a boundary of the region. Regions whose connectivity is greater than or equal to one are called multiply connected. Figure 27 illustrates a region of zero connectivity; Figure 28 illustrates a region of connectivity two. We shall not furnish a proof but merely state

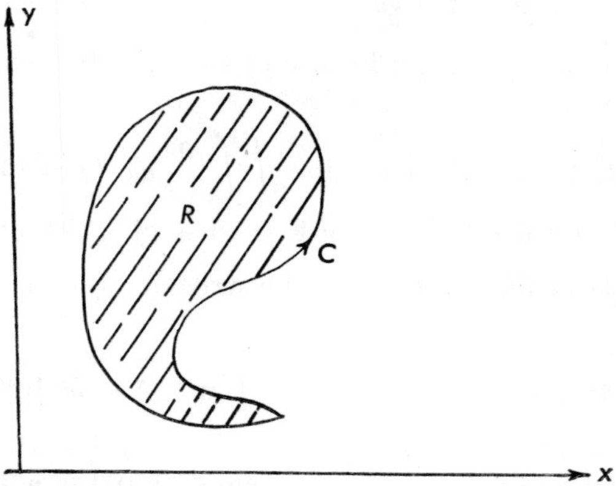

Figure 27: A Simply Connected Region, R (Zero Connectivity)

that Green's theorem is valid for a large class of regions of zero connectivity (for instance, regions for which the bounding curve C has a finite number of cusps).

In order to study Green's theorem for multiply connected regions, one must define the sense in which the interior boundaries are to be transcribed. Essentially, the same convention is adopted as in the previous case. For short, we say that "an observer traveling around the boundary C_i in the positive sense will always have the inside of R to his left" (see Figure 28). By introducing two cuts, a region of connectivity two can be reduced to a region of zero connectivity (see Figure 29). The boundary of the region R consists of (starting from A) A to A along C_3, A to B, B to C along C_0, C to D, D to D along C_1, D to C, C to B along C_2, B to A. To see that this region is simply connected, one imagines actual cuts existing along AB and CD and the region R, slightly distorted, by pulling aside the edges of R at A, B, C, D. Similar results are valid for regions of other connectivity.

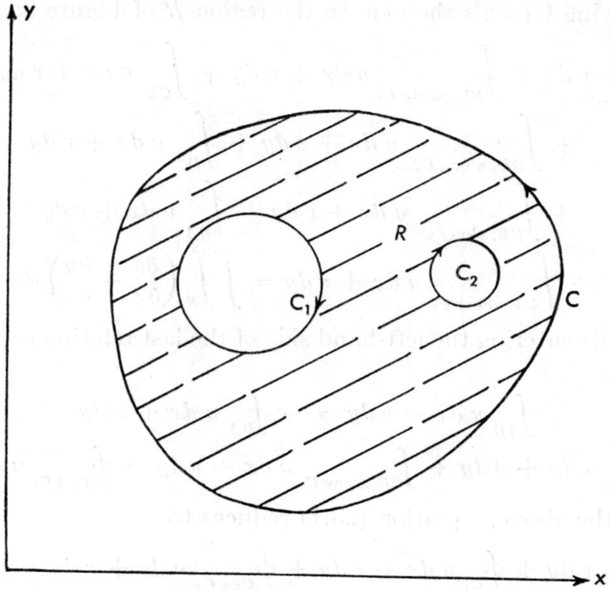

Figure 28: A Multiply Connected Region, R (Connectivity Two)

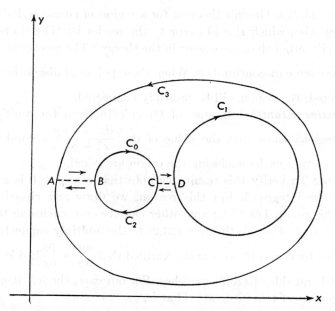

Figure 29: Cuts AB, CD in a Region of Connectivity Two Reduce the Region to One of Connectivity Zero

By applying Green's theorem to the region R of Figure 29, we obtain

$$\int_{AB} u\,dx + v\,dy + \int_{BC,\text{ along } C_0} u\,dx + v\,dy + \int_{CD} u\,dx + v\,dy$$
$$+ \int_{DD,\text{ along } C_1} u\,dx + v\,dy + \int_{DC} u\,dx + v\,dy$$
$$+ \int_{CB,\text{ along } C_2} u\,dx + v\,dy + \int_{BA} u\,dx + v\,dy$$
$$+ \int_{AA,\text{ along } C_3} u\,dx + v\,dy = \iint_R \left(\frac{\partial v}{\partial x} - \frac{\partial u}{\partial y}\right) dx\,dy. \quad (23.1)$$

The integrals entering the left-hand side of the last relation can be simplified. Thus,

$$\int_{AB} u\,dx + v\,dy = -\int_{BA} u\,dx + x\,dy,$$
$$\int_{BC,\text{ along } C_0} u\,dx + v\,dy + \int_{CB,\text{ along } C_2} u\,dx + v\,dy = \oint_{C_2+C_0} u\,dx + v\,dy.$$

By use of the above, equation (23.1) reduces to

$$\oint_{C_3} u\,dx + v\,dy + \oint_{C_1} u\,dx + v\,dy + \oint_{C_0+C_2} u\,dx + v\,dy =$$
$$\iint_R \left(\frac{\partial v}{\partial x} - \frac{\partial v}{\partial y}\right) dx\,dy \quad (23.2)$$

Equation (23.2) is Green's theorem for a region of connectivity two.

One question which should occur to the reader is: Why do regions of connectivity other than zero occur in the theory? The answer is that u, v, $\frac{\partial u}{\partial y}$, $\frac{\partial v}{\partial x}$ may have discontinuities. When these points of discontinuity have been deleted, the region will be multiply connected.

Illustrative Example: By use of Green's theorem for multiply connected regions show that the value of $\oint \frac{y\,dx - x\,dy}{x^2 + y^2}$ around any two non-intersecting paths enclosing the origin are equal.

Solution: To verify this result, we note that $x = y = 0$ is a singular point of the integrand. For this reason, we draw any closed curve C around this point. Let C' be any other closed curve enclosing the origin and let us apply Green's theorem (23.2) to the multiply connected region R bounded by C and C'. It is easily verified that $\frac{\partial u}{\partial y} = \frac{\partial v}{\partial x}$ inside R. Thus, the right-hand side of (23.2) vanishes. For our case, the left-hand side of (23.2) consists of two integrals. That is,

$$\oint_C u\,dx + v\,dy + \oint_{C'} u\,dx + v\,dy = 0.$$

By removing one of these integrals to the other side of the equation and changing the order of integration to compensate for the minus sign, we obtain the desired result. Note that Green's theorem does not furnish the value of either integral. This value can only be found by direct integration.

Problem 23.1: Discuss the values of $\oint \frac{(y-2)\,dx - x\,dy}{(y-2)^2 + x^2}$ for the following paths: (1) a circle of radius 1 with the origin as the center; (2) two circles with (0, 2) as center and of radius 1 and 2.

Problem 23.2: Compare the values of

$$\oint \frac{(y-2)\,dx - x\,dy}{x^2 + (y-2)^2} + \frac{(y-3)\,dx - x\,dy}{x^2 + (y-3)^2}$$

for the following paths: the circle $x^2 + y^2 = 25$ and the ellipse $\frac{x^2}{1} + \frac{y^2}{25} = 1$.

Problem 23.3: Compute the value of $\oint \frac{(y-1)\,dx - x\,dy}{x^2 + (y-1)^2}$ along the circle $x^2 + y^2 = 9$. *Hint:* Apply Green's theorem to the region bounded by $x^2 + y^2 = 9$ and $x^2 + (y-1)^2 = 1$.

Problem 23.4: Compute the value of

$$\oint \frac{(y-2)\,dx - x\,dy}{(y-2)^2 + x^2} + \frac{(y-3)\,dx - x\,dy}{(y-3)^2 + x^2}$$

along the circle $x^2 + y^2 = 16$ by applying Green's theorem and evaluating two line integrals.

Problem 23.5: If $\mathbf{F} = \mathbf{r}/r^2$, $\Omega = \theta^2$, and $\mathbf{n}$ is the unit exterior normal of a curve C, show by use of the Gauss form of Green's theorem (22.4) that $\oint \Omega\mathbf{F} \cdot \mathbf{n}\,ds$ has the same value for all paths enclosing the origin.

Problem 23.6: For the vector field $\mathbf{F} = \nabla\theta$, and the scalar field, $\Omega = r^2$, evaluate by use of Stokes's form of Green's theorem (22.3), $\oint_S \mathbf{n} \cdot \nabla \times \Omega\mathbf{F}\,d\sigma$, over the multiply connected region bounded by $x^2 + y^2 = 1$, $x^2 + y^2 = 4$.

Problem 23.7: Show that in the plane the angle subtended by any curve C at the origin is, $\theta = \int_C \mathbf{n} \cdot \nabla \ln r\,ds$, where $\mathbf{n}$ is normal to C and r is the radial distance.

24. Gauss's Theorem (The Divergence Theorem). We have demonstrated Gauss's theorem for the plane [equation (22.4)]. Our next task is to generalize this result to a space region T bounded by a closed orientable surface S.

(a) ***Gauss's Theorem for a Simply Connected Space Region.*** To simplify the discussion, we consider the case where the closed surface S is an oval-shaped surface (a surface cut by any line at only two points).

Let us map the surface S onto any one of the coordinate planes (say, the x,y-plane) by a projection. Then, any point $\bar{P}$ of the projection $\bar{S}$

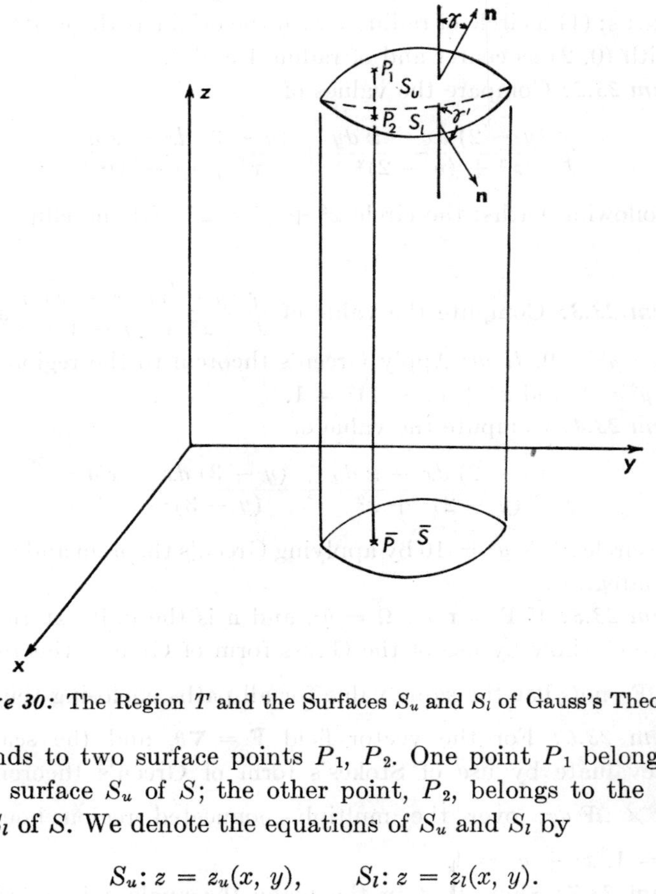

Figure 30: The Region T and the Surfaces S_u and S_l of Gauss's Theorem

corresponds to two surface points P_1, P_2. One point P_1 belongs to the "upper" surface S_u of S; the other point, P_2, belongs to the "lower" surface S_l of S. We denote the equations of S_u and S_l by

$$S_u: z = z_u(x, y), \qquad S_l: z = z_l(x, y).$$

Finally, we introduce the outward-drawn unit normal vector field, **n,** **at** each point P of S.

A general formulation of Gauss's theorem is the following: *If $\mathfrak{A}$ is a continuous field (scalar, vector, etc.) and if $\mathfrak{A}$ possesses continuous partial derivatives in the closed region T, then*

$$\int_T \nabla * \mathfrak{A}\, d\tau = \oint_S \mathbf{n} * \mathfrak{A}\, d\sigma. \tag{24.1}$$

Here, $d\tau$ is the element of volume and $d\sigma$ is the element of surface area. In terms of integral operators, Gauss's formula is contained in the following equation

$$\int_T \nabla * \, d\tau = \oint_S \mathbf{n} * \, d\sigma.$$

To verify this result, we recall the definition of $\nabla * \mathfrak{A}$ in rectangular Cartesian coordinates [see (18.1)]. Consider the triple integral

$$\int_T \mathbf{k} * \frac{\partial \mathfrak{A}}{\partial z} \, d\tau = \int_T \mathbf{k} * \frac{\partial \mathfrak{A}}{\partial z} \, dx \, dy \, dz.$$

Since the integrand is a continuous field, we may evaluate this integral by use of an iterated integral. Thus, the integral over T reduces to

$$\begin{aligned} \int_T \mathbf{k} * \frac{\partial \mathfrak{A}}{\partial z} \, dx \, dy \, dz &= \int_T \frac{\partial}{\partial z} (\mathbf{k} * \mathfrak{A}) \, dz \, dx \, dy \\ &= \int_{\bar{S}} [\mathbf{k} * \mathfrak{A}(x, y, z_u) - \mathbf{k} * \mathfrak{A}(x, y, z_l)] \, dx \, dy. \end{aligned} \tag{24.2}$$

On the upper part, S_u, of S, we see that (Figure 30)

$$dx \, dy = \cos \gamma \, d\sigma = (\mathbf{n} \cdot \mathbf{k}) \, d\sigma.$$

Whereas, for the lower part S_l of S, we see that

$$dx \, dy = -\cos \gamma \, d\sigma = -(\mathbf{n} \cdot \mathbf{k}) \, d\sigma.$$

By use of these relations we may express (24.2) in the form

$$\begin{aligned} \int_T \mathbf{k} * \frac{\partial \mathfrak{A}}{\partial z} \, d\tau &= \int_{S_u} (\mathbf{n} \cdot \mathbf{k}) \mathbf{k} * \mathfrak{A} \, d\sigma + \int_{S_l} (\mathbf{n} \cdot \mathbf{k}) \mathbf{k} * \mathfrak{A} \, d\sigma \\ &= \oint_S (\mathbf{n} \cdot \mathbf{k}) \mathbf{k} * \mathfrak{A} \, d\sigma. \end{aligned} \tag{24.3}$$

By projecting S onto the x,z-plane and the y,z-plane, we obtain, through similar reasoning, the following equations

$$\begin{aligned} \int_T \mathbf{j} * \frac{\partial \mathfrak{A}}{\partial y} \, d\tau &= \oint_S (\mathbf{n} \cdot \mathbf{j}) \mathbf{j} * \mathfrak{A} \, d\sigma, \\ \int_T \mathbf{i} * \frac{\partial \mathfrak{A}}{\partial x} \, d\tau &= \oint_S (\mathbf{n} \cdot \mathbf{i}) \mathbf{i} * \mathfrak{A} \, d\sigma. \end{aligned} \tag{24.4}$$

It is easily verified that $\mathbf{n} = (\mathbf{n} \cdot \mathbf{i})\mathbf{i} + (\mathbf{n} \cdot \mathbf{j})\mathbf{j} + (\mathbf{n} \cdot \mathbf{k})\mathbf{k}$. Upon adding the left-hand sides and right-hand sides of (24.3) and (24.4), and by using the relation for $\mathbf{n}$, we obtain Gauss's formula, (24.1).

Illustrative Example: If $\mathbf{F} = x\mathbf{i}$ find the value of $\oint_S \mathbf{F} \cdot \mathbf{n} \, d\sigma$, where S

is the closed surface $x^2 + y^2 + z^2 = 1$, by use of (1) direct integration; (2) Gauss's theorem.

***Solution of** (1):* $\mathbf{n} = x\mathbf{i} + y\mathbf{j} + z\mathbf{k}$ (the direction numbers of $\mathbf{n}$ are $\frac{\partial f}{\partial x}:\frac{\partial f}{\partial y}:\frac{\partial f}{\partial z}$ or $2x:2y:2z$ and $x^2 + y^2 + z^2 = 1$ on the surface). Hence $\mathbf{F} \cdot \mathbf{n} = x^2$. Further, $\sec \gamma = \frac{1}{z} = \frac{1}{\sqrt{1 - x^2 - y^2}}$ on the upper surface S_u, and $\sec \gamma' = -\frac{1}{\sqrt{1 - x^2 - y^2}}$ on the lower surface S_l. Thus,

$$\oint_S \mathbf{F} \cdot \mathbf{n}\, d\sigma = \int_{\bar{S}} x^2 \sec \gamma\, dx\, dy + \int_{\bar{S}} x^2 |\sec \gamma'|\, dx\, dy$$
$$= 2 \int_{\bar{S}} \frac{x^2}{\sqrt{1 - x^2 - y^2}}\, dx\, dy.$$

where $\bar{S}$ is the region bounded by the unit circle $x^2 + y^2 = 1$. Introducing polar coordinates, we find that

$$\oint_S \mathbf{F} \cdot \mathbf{n}\, d\sigma = 2 \int_0^1 \frac{r^3\, dr}{\sqrt{1 - r^2}} \int_0^{2\pi} \cos^2 \theta\, d\theta = \frac{4\pi}{3}.$$

***Solution of** (2):* Since $\nabla \cdot \mathbf{F} = 1$,

$$\oint_S \mathbf{F} \cdot \mathbf{n}\, d\sigma = \int_T \nabla \cdot \mathbf{F}\, d\tau = \int_T d\tau = \frac{4\pi}{3}.$$

Problem 24.1: Verify the equation $\mathbf{n} = (\mathbf{n} \cdot \mathbf{i})\mathbf{i} + (\mathbf{n} \cdot \mathbf{j})\mathbf{j} + (\mathbf{n} \cdot \mathbf{k})\mathbf{k}$.

Problem 24.2: Derive the formula $\int_T \nabla \cdot \mathbf{F}\, d\tau = \oint_S \mathbf{n} \cdot \mathbf{F}\, d\sigma$ by replacing $\mathfrak{A}$ by $\mathbf{F}$ and $*$ by $\cdot$ and reworking the various steps of the above proof. This form of Gauss's theorem shows one reason for the name, "divergence theorem," which is often associated with it.

Problem 24.3: If $\mathbf{F} = (x^2 - y^2)\mathbf{i}$ find $\oint_S \mathbf{F} \cdot \mathbf{n}\, d\sigma$ over the closed surface determined by $z = 0$, $z = 1$, $x = 0$, $x = 1$, $y = 0$, $y = 1$. Evaluate this integral by: (1) direct integration; (2) Gauss's theorem.

Problem 24.4: If $\mathbf{F} = 3\mathbf{k}$, find $\int \mathbf{F} \cdot \mathbf{n}\, d\sigma$ over the open hemisphere $x^2 + y^2 + z^2 = 1$, $z \geq 0$, by use of Gauss's theorem and an additional integration in the x,y-plane.

Problem 24.5: If $\mathbf{F}$ is normal to a closed surface S bounding a region T, show that $\int_T \nabla \times \mathbf{F}\, d\tau = 0$.

Problem 24.6: If $\mathbf{R} = x\mathbf{i} = y\mathbf{j} + z\mathbf{k}$ is the radius vector field, express $\int_T \mathbf{R}\, d\tau$ as a surface integral. *Hint:* Write $\mathbf{R} = \nabla \Omega$, and determine Ω.

Problem 24.7: Evaluate $\oint_S \mathbf{R} \times \mathbf{n}\, d\sigma$ over any closed surface.

Problem 24.8: Evaluate $\oint_S \mathbf{R} \cdot \mathbf{n}\, d\sigma$ over any closed surface.

Problem 24.9: If f is harmonic in a region T and hence satisfies the Laplace equation

$$\nabla^2 f = \nabla \cdot \nabla f = \frac{\partial^2 f}{\partial x^2} + \frac{\partial^2 f}{\partial y^2} + \frac{\partial^2 f}{\partial z^2} = 0$$

show that:

$$\oint_S \mathbf{n} \cdot \nabla f\, d\sigma = 0, \text{ where } S \text{ is a closed surface in } T.$$

Gauss's formula may be easily extended to regions bounded by other smooth surfaces. In fact, the surface bounding T may have a finite number

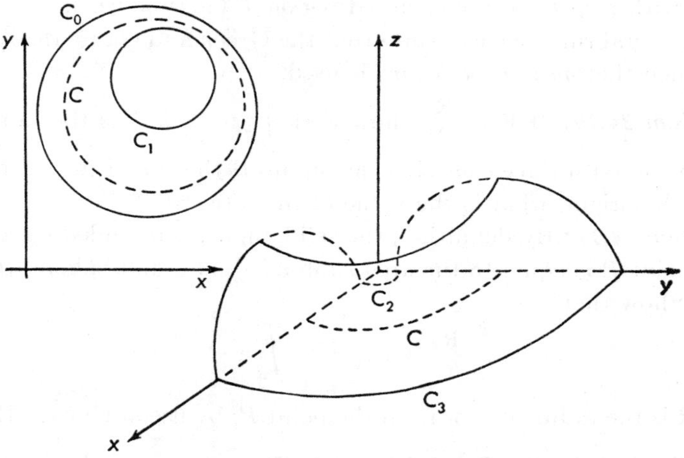

Figure 31: Multiply Connected Regions in the Plane and Space

of sharp points (such as conical points) where $\mathbf{n}$ does not exist and Gauss's formula will still be valid.[2] Further, a finite number of finite discontinuities in the derivatives of the field $\mathfrak{A}$ are permissible. In other words, we have derived formula (24.1) under conditions which are restrictive.

(b) ***Gauss's Theorem for Multiply Connected Regions.*** Another question which arises is the following: "Does Gauss's formula apply to multiply connected space regions?" In order to define such regions, we extend our previous definition of multiple connectivity in the plane to space (see Section 23). For example, the space region bounded by a torus (doughnut shaped surface) possesses one irreducible curve (the curve C in

[2] O. D. Kellog, *Foundations of Potential Theory,* J. Springer, Berlin, 1929.

Figure 31). Hence, this region has connectivity one. By inserting a plane cut across the surface, we obtain a simply connected region for which the previous form of Gauss's theorem is valid. Since the surface integrals over this cutting plane annul each other, we see that Gauss's theorem is applicable to the torus.

Another example of a more complicated region is the space region between two concentric spheres. Actually, this region is simply connected. By inserting a plane cut passing through the common center and applying Gauss's theorem to each of the two space regions obtained, we find that

$$\oint_S \mathbf{n} * \mathcal{A}\, d\sigma + \oint_{S'} \mathbf{n} * \mathcal{A}\, d\sigma = \int_T \nabla * \mathcal{A}\, d\tau,$$

where S and S' are the surfaces of the spheres. In each case, the exterior normal with respect to the enclosed region T must be used.

As a general rule, one can state that the Green and Gauss theorems are valid when the *complete boundary* is used.

Problem 24.10: If $\mathbf{F} = \dfrac{\mathbf{R}}{R^3}$, show that $\oint_S \mathbf{n} \cdot \mathbf{F}\, d\sigma$ has the same value over any closed surface enclosing the origin. If the closed surface does not enclose the origin, what is the value of the integral?

Problem 24.11: By definition, the solid angle ω subtended by a surface S at a point P is equal to the area subtended on a unit sphere with P as center. Show that

$$\omega = \int_S \frac{\mathbf{R}}{R^3} \cdot \mathbf{n}\, d\sigma = -\int_S \mathbf{n} \cdot \nabla \frac{1}{R}\, d\sigma,$$

where $\mathbf{R}$ is the radius vector from the point P, by use of Gauss's theorem.

25. Physical Applications of Gauss's Theorem. Consider a surface S (open or closed) in a fluid. Let $\mathbf{V}$ denote the velocity vector field of the fluid, and the scalar field ρ denote the density of the fluid. Then the mass of fluid crossing an element of surface in time Δt and in the direction of $\mathbf{n}$ is $\rho\mathbf{V} \cdot \mathbf{n}\, \Delta\sigma\, \Delta t$, except for terms of higher order. Hence, the time rate at which fluid mass leaves S is

$$\int_S \mathbf{n} \cdot \rho\mathbf{V}\, d\sigma.$$

Let S be the closed boundary of region T; then the time rate of increase of fluid mass within T is given by

$$\int_T \frac{\partial \rho}{\partial t}\, d\tau.$$

If we assume that matter is not created or destroyed in the fluid (this is the so-called continuity principle), then we obtain the continuity relation

$$\int_T \frac{\partial \rho}{\partial t}\, d\tau = -\oint_S \mathbf{n} \cdot \rho \mathbf{V}\, d\sigma. \tag{25.1}$$

Applying Gauss's theorem to the integral over S in (25.1), we find that the continuity relation reduces to

$$\int_T \left[\frac{\partial \rho}{\partial t} + \nabla \cdot \rho \mathbf{V}\right] d\tau = 0.$$

Since T is an arbitrary region, we may conclude that the integrand must vanish at all points P of T, or

$$\frac{\partial \rho}{\partial t} + \nabla \cdot \rho \mathbf{V} = 0. \tag{25.2}$$

The argument is as follows. Let us assume that (25.2) is not valid at a point $\bar{P}$ of T. Then, by continuity, the expression, $\frac{\partial \rho}{\partial t} + \nabla \cdot (\rho \mathbf{V})$, does not vanish and has a definite sign in some neighborhood $\bar{T}$ of $\bar{P}$ ($\bar{T}$ within T). If we integrate this expression over $\bar{T}$, we reach a contradiction. Equation (25.2) is known as the equation of continuity in hydrodynamics. If the fluid is incompressible, then ρ is constant and this relation reduces to $\nabla \cdot \mathbf{V} = 0$. Further, if $\mathbf{V}$ is the velocity of a potential field ($\mathbf{V} = \nabla \Omega$), then the continuity equation reduces to Laplace's equation, $\nabla^2 \Omega = 0$.

Our next application involves heat diffusion. Let θ denote the temperature (a scalar field) at any point P of a region T. Further, we introduce the terms:

k = conductivity of the material occupying region T;
ρ = density of the material occupying region T;
c = specific heat of the material occupying region T.

Finally, we note that the time rate at which heat crosses a surface S is proportional to the conductivity and the temperature gradient. That is, the time rate of heat loss is

$$\oint_S k\mathbf{n} \cdot \nabla \theta\, d\sigma = \int_T \nabla \cdot (k \nabla \theta)\, d\tau.$$

But, the time rate of heat increase within T is

$$\int_T c\rho \frac{\partial \theta}{\partial t}\, d\tau.$$

If we assume that heat behaves like a fluid mass and satisfies the continuity principle, then we may equate the last two expressions. By use of the same argument as was used in deriving (25.2), we find that

$$c\rho \frac{\partial \theta}{\partial t} = \nabla \cdot (k \nabla \theta). \tag{25.3}$$

In particular, if k is constant and the temperature is independent of time (steady state), we obtain the Laplace equation, $\nabla^2\theta = 0$.

Problem 25.1: Show that

$$\oint_S \mathbf{n} \cdot \psi \nabla \phi \, d\sigma = \int_T \nabla \psi \cdot \nabla \phi \, d\tau + \int_T \psi \nabla \cdot \nabla \phi \, d\tau.$$

Hint: Expand $\nabla \cdot (\psi \nabla \phi)$ and use Gauss's theorem.

Problem 25.2: By interchanging ψ and ϕ in the above problem and subtracting the resulting equations, verify Green's relation

$$\int_T (\psi \nabla^2\phi - \phi \nabla^2\psi) \, d\tau = \oint_S \mathbf{n} \cdot (\psi \nabla \phi - \phi \nabla \psi) \, d\sigma.$$

Problem 25.3: Consider the relation of Problem 25.1. Take $\phi = \psi$, and assume $\phi = 0$ on S, $\nabla^2\phi = 0$ in T. Show that $\phi = 0$ in the closed region $T + S$. This result is used in furnishing a uniqueness proof for the solutions of Laplace's equation.

Problem 25.4: Prove that $\oint_S \mathbf{n} \cdot \nabla \phi \, d\sigma = \int_T \nabla^2 \phi \, d\tau$, by assuming $\psi = 1$ in Problem 25.1. Hence, verify that for a harmonic function $(\nabla^2\phi = 0)$, $\oint_S \mathbf{n} \cdot \nabla \phi \, d\sigma = 0$.

Problem 25.5: If ϕ is harmonic in a closed region, prove that $\Omega = \frac{1}{4\pi r^2} \oint_S \phi \, d\sigma$, over any sphere of radius r, is independent of r. *Hint:* Use the result of Problem 25.4 on $\frac{\partial \phi}{\partial r} = \mathbf{n} \cdot \nabla \phi$.

Problem 25.6: (1) If $\phi = 1/R$ and ψ is a regular harmonic function $(\nabla^2\psi = 0)$ in a region T containing the origin, show that the value of ψ at the origin is given by

$$4\pi\psi = \oint_S \mathbf{n} \cdot \left(\psi \nabla \frac{1}{R} - \frac{1}{R} \nabla \psi\right) d\sigma$$

where S is a closed surface containing the origin.

(2) If the closed surface S does not contain the origin, prove that

$$0 = \oint_S \mathbf{n} \cdot \left(\psi \nabla \frac{1}{R} - \frac{1}{R} \nabla \psi\right) d\sigma$$

where ψ is regular in T and harmonic. The results of this problem are valuable in studying the solutions of Laplace's equation.

26. Some Elements of Surface Geometry. We shall define a surface S as a mapping of a region $\bar{S}$ in a two-dimensional u,v-plane into the three-dimensional Euclidean x,y,z-space. The equations

$$x = x(u, v), \qquad y = y(u, v), \qquad z = z(u, v) \tag{26.1}$$

which define the mapping are assumed to be continuous with continuous

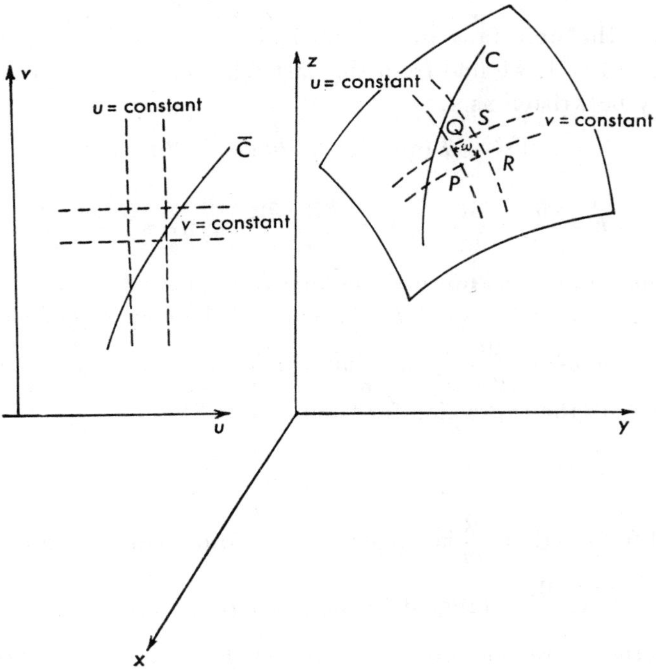

Figure 32: The Map of a Surface on the u, v Plane

second partial derivatives. Further, in order for S to represent a two-dimensional region and not a curve, it is necessary to assume that the following functional matrix

$$\begin{bmatrix} \dfrac{\partial x}{\partial u} & \dfrac{\partial y}{\partial u} & \dfrac{\partial z}{\partial u} \\[2ex] \dfrac{\partial x}{\partial v} & \dfrac{\partial y}{\partial v} & \dfrac{\partial z}{\partial v} \end{bmatrix}$$

contains at least one second order determinant which does not vanish.

First, we consider the theory of curves on S. Let

$$u = u(s), \qquad v = v(s) \tag{26.2}$$

define a curve $\bar{C}$ in $\bar{S}$ which possesses continuous second derivatives. Equations (26.1) and (26.2) determine the map of $\bar{C}$ (the curve C) on S. We assume that the parameter s of (26.2) is the arc length parameter along C. Let $\mathbf{R}(u, v) = \mathbf{i}x(u, v) + \mathbf{j}y(u, v) + \mathbf{k}z(u, v)$ denote the radius vector field from the origin to points of S. Then the vector

$$\mathbf{t} = \frac{d\mathbf{R}}{ds} = \frac{\partial \mathbf{R}}{\partial u}\frac{du}{ds} + \frac{\partial \mathbf{R}}{\partial v}\frac{dv}{ds}$$

represents the unit tangent vector field to C. By forming the scalar product, $\mathbf{t} \cdot \mathbf{t} = 1$, we find from this last relation that the element of arc on S may be written as

$$ds^2 = E(du)^2 + 2F\,du\,dv + G(dv)^2. \tag{26.3}$$

where

$$E = \frac{\partial \mathbf{R}}{\partial u} \cdot \frac{\partial \mathbf{R}}{\partial u}, \qquad F = \frac{\partial \mathbf{R}}{\partial u} \cdot \frac{\partial \mathbf{R}}{\partial v}, \qquad G = \frac{\partial \mathbf{R}}{\partial v} \cdot \frac{\partial \mathbf{R}}{\partial v}.$$

The formula (26.3) is known as the first fundamental form in differential geometry; the coefficients E, F, G are called the metric coefficients.

The vector fields $\frac{\partial \mathbf{R}}{\partial u}, \frac{\partial \mathbf{R}}{\partial v}$ are important in the theory which follows. When $dv = 0$, the expression for $\mathbf{t}$ reduces to

$$\mathbf{t} = \frac{\partial \mathbf{R}}{\partial u}\frac{du}{ds}.$$

Hence, it follows that $\frac{\partial \mathbf{R}}{\partial u}$ is tangent to the *parameter curves*, v = constant, on S; also, that $\frac{\partial \mathbf{R}}{\partial v}$ is tangent to the *parameter* curves, u = constant, on S. From the expressions for E, G, we see that the magnitudes of these vector fields are $\sqrt{E}$ and $\sqrt{G}$, respectively. Further, if ω denotes the angle between these two vector fields, then

$$\cos \omega = \left(\frac{\partial \mathbf{R}}{\partial u} \cdot \frac{\partial \mathbf{R}}{\partial v}\right) \Big/ \sqrt{EG} = F/\sqrt{EG},$$

and

$$\sin \omega = \sqrt{EG - F^2}/\sqrt{EG}.$$

In order to determine the element of surface area, $d\sigma$, we consider the area of the parallelogram whose sides are $PQRS$. From Figure 32 it follows that

$$\overrightarrow{\mathrm{PQ}} = \frac{\partial \mathbf{R}}{\partial v}\,dv, \qquad \overrightarrow{\mathrm{PR}} = \frac{\partial \mathbf{R}}{\partial u}\,du.$$

Since the magnitudes of the vector fields $\frac{\partial \mathbf{R}}{\partial v}, \frac{\partial \mathbf{R}}{\partial u}$ are $\sqrt{G}$, $\sqrt{E}$, respectively, and since sin ω is known, we find[3]

$$d\sigma = |\overrightarrow{PQ}|\,|\overrightarrow{PR}| \sin \omega = \sqrt{EG - F^2}\,du\,dv. \tag{26.4}$$

Further, the unit normal vector to S is determined by

$$\mathbf{n} = \pm\left(\frac{\partial \mathbf{R}}{\partial u} \times \frac{\partial \mathbf{R}}{\partial v}\right)\Bigg/\left|\frac{\partial \mathbf{R}}{\partial u}\right|\left|\frac{\partial \mathbf{R}}{\partial v}\right| \sin \omega.$$

Through use of the above relations, we find that this last equation reduces to

$$\mathbf{n} = \pm\left(\frac{\partial \mathbf{R}}{\partial u} \times \frac{\partial \mathbf{R}}{\partial v}\right)\Bigg/\sqrt{EG - F^2}.$$

Multiplying this expression for $\mathbf{n}$ by $d\sigma$, we obtain the important formula

$$\mathbf{n}\,d\sigma = \pm\left(\frac{\partial \mathbf{R}}{\partial u} \times \frac{\partial \mathbf{R}}{\partial v}\right) du\,dv. \tag{26.5}$$

Illustrative Example: Derive the relation, $dx\,dy = \pm(\mathbf{n}\cdot\mathbf{k})\,d\sigma$.

Solution: Let $u = x$, $v = y$, $z = z(x, y)$; then $\frac{\partial \mathbf{R}}{\partial u} = \mathbf{i} + \mathbf{k}\frac{\partial z}{\partial x}$, $\frac{\partial \mathbf{R}}{\partial v} = \mathbf{j} + \mathbf{k}\frac{\partial z}{\partial y}$. Thus, $\frac{\partial \mathbf{R}}{\partial u} \times \frac{\partial \mathbf{R}}{\partial v} = -\frac{\partial z}{\partial x}\mathbf{i} - \frac{\partial z}{\partial y}\mathbf{j} + \mathbf{k}$. Forming the scalar product of (26.5) with $\mathbf{k}$ and using the last relation, we obtain the desired result.

Problem 26.1: Compute the metric coefficients E, F, G when $x = u$, $y = v$, $z = z(x, y)$.

Problem 26.2: If the equation of a surface is given in the form $H(x, y, z) = 0$: (1) determine the expression for $\mathbf{n}$ in terms of the derivatives of $H(x, y, z)$; (2) determine $\cos \gamma$.

Problem 26.3: By use of the representation $u = y$, $v = z$, $x = x(y, z)$, derive the formula, $dy\,dz = \pm(\mathbf{n}\cdot\mathbf{i})\,d\sigma$.

Problem 26.4: By use of spherical coordinates, $u = \phi$, $v = \theta$, show that the element of area of a sphere of radius unity is $d\sigma = \sin\phi\,d\phi\,d\theta$.

Problem 26.5: Consider the surface, $x = r\cos\theta$, $y = r\sin\theta$, $z = c\theta$. Determine: (1) the metric coefficients E, F, G; (2) $\sin\omega$; (3) $\mathbf{n}$.

27. Stokes's Theorem (The Curl Theorem). We have verified a form of Stokes's formula [equation (22.3)] for the plane. Now we consider an orientable open surface S in three-space whose boundary is the closed curve C. In particular, we consider the case where $\bar{C}$ (the u,v-plane map of C) is an oval-shaped curve (see Figure 33). Further, if $\mathbf{n}$ is the unit normal vector field of S, then we can assign a sense to C by the right-hand screw

[3] An alternative approach is to *define* surface area by $\int \sqrt{EG - F^2}\,du\,dv$ and study the properties of the integral.

rule, as was used in the plane. The sense of C fixes the sense of $\bar{C}$; we assume that $\bar{C}$ is sensed as in Figure 33. This is valid, for instance, for the mapping $x = u$, $y = v$, and then the plus sign in (26.5) is the correct sign for $\mathbf{n}$. We shall prove the following form of Stokes's theorem:[4] *If $\mathfrak{A}$ is a*

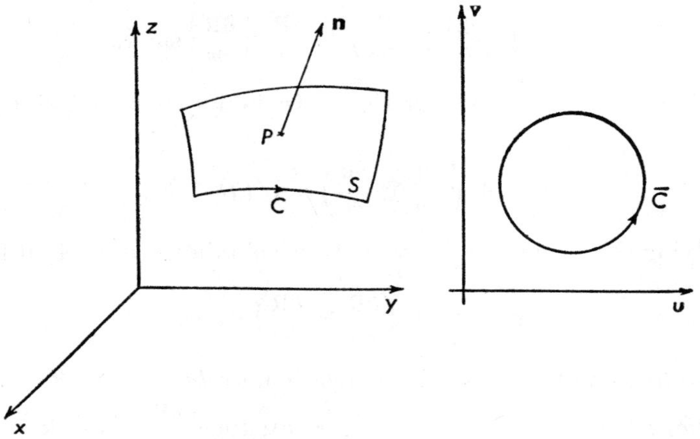

Figure 33: The Normal Vector of S at P, and the Sense of Transcription of the Boundary, C, in the x, y, z Space and in the u, v Plane

continuous field (scalar, vector, etc.) and if $\mathfrak{A}$ possesses continuous partial derivatives over the surfaces S, then

$$\int_S (\mathbf{n} \times \nabla) * \mathfrak{A} \, d\sigma = \oint_C \mathbf{t} * \mathfrak{A} \, ds. \tag{27.1}$$

In (27.1), $\mathbf{t}$ is the unit tangent vector to C and ds is the arc length element along C. We may view Stokes's formula (27.1) as a relation between integral operators. In this case, we write

$$\int_S (\mathbf{n} \times \nabla) * \, d\sigma = \oint_C \mathbf{t} * \, ds.$$

The proof of the theorem is very simple. By use of the expression for $\mathbf{n}$ (26.5) and the triple vector expansion, we find that

$$\begin{aligned} \int_S (\mathbf{n} \times \nabla) * \mathfrak{A} \, d\sigma &= \int_{\bar{S}} \left[\left(\frac{\partial \mathbf{R}}{\partial u} \times \frac{\partial \mathbf{R}}{\partial v} \right) \times \nabla \right] * \mathfrak{A} \, du \, dv \\ &= \int_{\bar{S}} \left[\frac{\partial \mathbf{R}}{\partial v} * \left(\frac{\partial \mathbf{R}}{\partial u} \cdot \nabla \right) \mathfrak{A} - \frac{\partial \mathbf{R}}{\partial u} * \left(\frac{\partial \mathbf{R}}{\partial v} \cdot \nabla \right) \mathfrak{A} \right] du \, dv. \end{aligned} \tag{27.2}$$

[4] An equivalent formulation of this proof will be found in: R. Courant (translated by E. J. McShane), *Differential and Integral Calculus*, Nordeman Publishing Co., New York, Vol. II, p. 392; L. Brand, *Vector and Tensor Analysis*, John Wiley and Sons, New York, p. 219.

With the aid of the fundamental property of the gradient [see (17.6)], with u replacing s, we find

$$\left(\frac{\partial \mathbf{R}}{\partial u} \cdot \nabla\right) \mathfrak{A} = \frac{\partial \mathfrak{A}}{\partial u}, \qquad \left(\frac{\partial \mathbf{R}}{\partial v} \cdot \nabla\right) \mathfrak{A} = \frac{\partial \mathfrak{A}}{\partial v}.$$

Thus, the formula for $\int_S (\mathbf{n} \times \nabla) * \mathfrak{A}\, d\sigma$ in (27.2) reduces to

$$\begin{aligned} \int_S (\mathbf{n} \times \nabla) * \mathfrak{A}\, d\sigma &= \int_{\bar{S}} \left(\frac{\partial \mathbf{R}}{\partial v} * \frac{\partial \mathfrak{A}}{\partial u} - \frac{\partial \mathbf{R}}{\partial u} * \frac{\partial \mathfrak{A}}{\partial v}\right) du\, dv, \\ &= \int_{\bar{S}} \left[\frac{\partial}{\partial u}\left(\frac{\partial \mathbf{R}}{\partial v} * \mathfrak{A}\right) - \frac{\partial}{\partial v}\left(\frac{\partial \mathbf{R}}{\partial u} * \mathfrak{A}\right)\right] du\, dv. \end{aligned} \tag{27.3}$$

To simplify the right-hand side of the last equation, we use Green's theorem in the u,v-plane. From (22.1), we see that the *general form of this theorem* is (see also Problem 22.8)

$$\oint \mathfrak{C}\, du + \mathfrak{B}\, dv = \int_{\bar{S}} \left(\frac{\partial \mathfrak{B}}{\partial u} - \frac{\partial \mathfrak{C}}{\partial v}\right) du\, dv,$$

where $\mathfrak{C}$, $\mathfrak{B}$ are both quantities of the same type (scalars, vectors or tensors of higher order). For our purposes, it is sufficient to identify $\mathfrak{C}$ with $\frac{\partial \mathbf{R}}{\partial u} * \mathfrak{A}$ and $\mathfrak{B}$ with $\frac{\partial \mathbf{R}}{\partial v} * \mathfrak{A}$. Then, (27.3) becomes

$$\int_S (\mathbf{n} \times \nabla) * \mathfrak{A}\, d\sigma = \oint_{\bar{C}} \frac{\partial \mathbf{R}}{\partial u} * \mathfrak{A}\, du + \frac{\partial \mathbf{R}}{\partial v} * \mathfrak{A}\, dv.$$

Since the $*$ product is distributive, the integrand of the right-hand side of the above relation may be replaced by $\frac{d\mathbf{R}}{ds} * \mathfrak{A}\, ds$, and we obtain Stokes's formula (27.1). Evidently the restriction that $\bar{C}$ be oval-shaped may be removed.

Before leaving this section, we make a few additional remarks. Stokes's formula shows that $\int_S (\mathbf{n} \times \nabla) * \mathfrak{A}\, d\sigma$ depends upon surface quantities. This result follows from the form of the right-hand side of (27.1). However, the del operator, ∇, involves derivatives with respect to quantities outside of the surface. The question arises, "Is there a contradiction here?" The answer is "No," since $\mathbf{n} \times \nabla$ is a surface differentiation operator. To verify this fact, one needs only to take the component of $\mathbf{n} \times \nabla$ along $\mathbf{n}$. This component $\mathbf{n} \cdot (\mathbf{n} \times \nabla)$ vanishes.

The theory of Stokes's theorem for multiply connected surfaces (see the discussion in Section 23) is very similar to that of Green's theorem in multiply connected plane regions. If C is the exterior boundary and C_1, etc., are interior boundaries of S, then (27.1) becomes

$$\int_S (\mathbf{n} \times \nabla) * \mathfrak{A}\, d\sigma = \oint_C \mathbf{t} * \mathfrak{A}\, ds + \oint_{C_1} \mathbf{t} * \mathfrak{A}\, ds + \text{etc.} \tag{27.4}$$

One form of Stokes's theorem

$$\int_S (\mathbf{n} \times \nabla) \cdot \mathbf{F}\, d\sigma = \oint \mathbf{t} \cdot \mathbf{F}\, ds. \tag{27.5}$$

is very useful in applications to mathematical physics. For instance, it is easily shown with the aid of (27.5) that *the necessary and sufficient condition that the line integral* $\oint \mathbf{F} \cdot d\mathbf{R}$ *shall vanish for every closed curve in a simply connected region,* T, *of space is that* $\nabla \times \mathbf{F} = 0$ *at all points of* T. [See Section 22(d) for the similar theorem in the plane.] When this condition is satisfied, the vector field $\mathbf{F}$ is said to be irrotational and $\mathbf{F}$ is the gradient of a scalar function Ω. It should be noted that T must be simply connected. In fact, if T is multiply connected and $\mathbf{F}$ is irrotational ($\nabla \times \mathbf{F} = 0$) throughout T, then (27.4) shows that (if the curve under consideration, C, is an exterior boundary and C_i are interior boundaries of some surface S in T),

$$\oint_C \mathbf{F} \cdot d\mathbf{R} + \oint_{C_1} \mathbf{F} \cdot d\mathbf{R} + \text{etc.} = 0.$$

Problem 27.1: If $\mathbf{F} = 2y\mathbf{i} - x\mathbf{j} + z\mathbf{k}$, find $\int_S (\mathbf{n} \times \nabla) \cdot \mathbf{F}\, d\sigma$ taken over the open surface, $x^2 + y^2 + z^2 = 1$, $z > 0$ by use of: (1) direct calculation; (2) Stokes's theorem. *Hint:* Use Green's theorem or direct calculation to evaluate the line integral in (2).

Problem 27.2: If $\mathbf{F} = x\mathbf{i} + 2y\mathbf{j} + (z + 2)\mathbf{k}$, find $\int_S (\mathbf{n} \times \nabla) \times \mathbf{F}\, d\sigma$ taken over the open surface, $x^2 + y^2 + z^2 = 1$, $z > 0$.

Problem 27.3: If $\mathbf{F} = (z^2 - 2)\mathbf{k}$, find $\int_S (\mathbf{n} \times \nabla) \times \mathbf{F}\, d\sigma$ taken over the open surface $x^2 + 4(y^2 + z^2) = 4$, $z > 0$.

Problem 27.4: If $\mathbf{F} = f(R)\mathbf{R}$ in the space region bounded by the two coaxial cylinders $x^2 + y^2 = 1$, $x^2 + y^2 = 25$, discuss by means of Stokes's theorem the value of $\oint \mathbf{F} \cdot d\mathbf{R}$ along: (1) the curve, $x^2 + y^2 = 4$, $z = 2$; (2) the curve, $(x - 3)^2 + y^2 = 1$, $z = 2$.

Problem 27.5: If $\mathbf{U}$ is irrotational, show that $\int_S \mathbf{n} \times \nabla\Omega \cdot \mathbf{U}\, d\sigma =$

$\oint_C \Omega\mathbf{U} \cdot d\mathbf{R}$, where S is any open surface and C is its closed boundary. *Hint:* Expand $\nabla \times (\Omega\mathbf{U})$.

Problem 27.6: Discuss $\oint_S (\mathbf{n} \times \nabla) * \mathfrak{A}\, d\sigma$ over any closed surface S.

Problem 27.7: If $\oint \mathbf{F} \times d\mathbf{R} = 0$ for every closed curve in a simply connected region T, show that $\mathbf{F}$ is a constant vector. *Hint:* By use of Stokes's theorem, one finds that $(\mathbf{n} \times \nabla) \times \mathbf{F} = 0$ at each point P for every unit vector $\mathbf{n}$. Show that $(\mathbf{N} \times \nabla) \times \mathbf{F} = 0$ for every vector $\mathbf{N}$ at P. By expanding in terms of components and use of the theory of linear equations, we obtain the desired result.

Problem 27.8: Assume that the following theorem is true: A vector field $\mathbf{V}$ is determined in a simply connected region T when the divergence and curl of $\mathbf{V}$ are known in T and the normal component of $\mathbf{V}$ is known on the closed surface, S, bounding T. Prove that a *unique* vector $\mathbf{V}$ is determined by these conditions.

ADDITIONAL PROBLEMS

1. If $\nabla \cdot \mathbf{V} = 0$ and $\mathbf{U} = \nabla\Omega$, where $\Omega = 0$ at infinity, prove that $\int_T \mathbf{V} \cdot \mathbf{U}\, d\tau = 0$. The integral is taken over a region bounded by a sphere of radius R, as R approaches infinity.
2. By vector methods, evaluate $\oint_S (a^2x^2 + b^2y^2 + c^2z^2)\, d\sigma$ over a closed sphere of radius unity and center at the origin.
3. Verify the formula

$$\int_S \mathbf{n} \cdot \nabla\alpha \times \nabla\beta\, d\sigma = \oint_C \alpha\, \nabla\beta \cdot \mathbf{t}\, ds.$$

   Discuss the properties of α, β for which this formula is valid.
4. Verify the formula

$$\oint_S \mathbf{v} \times \nabla\alpha \cdot \mathbf{n}\, d\sigma = \int_T \nabla\alpha \cdot (\nabla \times \mathbf{v})\, d\tau.$$

   Extend this formula to a multiply connected region T.
5. By use of Gauss's and Stokes's theorems (in this order) show that

$$\nabla \cdot \nabla \times \mathbf{v} = 0,$$

   for any vector field $\mathbf{v}$ which is twice differentiable in a simply connected closed region T.
6. Consider the points $P(x, y, z)$, $P'(x', y', z')$ of a space region T. Let $R(P, P')$ denote the distance between P and P'; ∇R^{-1} denote the

gradient of R^{-1} when P is variable and P' is fixed. Further, let $\rho(x', y', z')$ denote a scalar field and define the vector field $\mathbf{F}(x, y, z)$ by

$$\mathbf{F} = \int_T \rho \nabla \frac{1}{R}\, d\tau.$$

Show that:

(1) if ρ is continuous, then $\mathbf{F}$ exists;

(2) $\mathbf{F} = -\nabla\Omega$ where $\Omega = \int_T \frac{\rho}{R}\, d\tau$, is a scalar potential.

7. By use of the formula for solid angle (Problem 24.11), show that the vector field, $\mathbf{F}$, of the above problem satisfies the equation

$$\oint_S \mathbf{n} \cdot \mathbf{F}\, d\sigma = 4\pi \int_T \rho\, d\tau$$

where S is the closed surface bounding T. Hence, verify that the scalar potential, Ω, satisfies Poisson's equation, $\nabla^2\Omega = 4\pi\rho$. The results of these last two problems are of great importance in the theories of electrostatics and Newtonian potential.

8. Let the scalar potential Ω satisfy Poisson's equation. By use of Green's identity (see Problems 25.2 and 25.6), show that

$$4\pi\Omega(P) = \oint_S \mathbf{n} \cdot \left(\Omega\nabla \frac{1}{R} - \frac{1}{R}\nabla\Omega\right) d\sigma + 4\pi \int_T \frac{\rho\, d\tau}{R},$$

where S is a closed surface bounding a region, T, which contains the point P.

Chapter IV

VECTOR ANALYSIS IN APPLIED MATHEMATICS

28. The Range of Topics. In this chapter we shall briefly discuss two topics in applied mathematics. Our aim is to illustrate the use of vector methods. For this reason, we shall not offer a thorough treatment of any one subject. Rather, our purpose will be to show how vector methods unify the treatment of any subject and how these methods enable one to gain geometric insight in a subject with a minimum of calculations.

In the following sections, we shall show how vector methods may be used in rigid body dynamics and fluid dynamics. Further, we shall show why tensor methods are of even greater value. We shall not attempt to discuss the topic of elasticity, where one must immediately introduce tensors.

29. Rigid Body Dynamics. We shall discuss the rigid body concept, linear and angular momenta of a rigid body, and the relation of these quantities to the external forces and the moments of these forces.

(a) ***Kinematics of the Rigid Body.*** In order to define a rigid body, one must introduce two ideas: (1) a continuous distribution of matter in a region; (2) a group under which the density of the distribution of matter is invariant. We introduce a Cartesian orthogonal system with coordinate variables (X, Y, Z). It will be assumed that this reference frame is inertial in the sense of Newton's first law. The distribution of matter will be specified by a density function $m(X, Y, Z)$; the concept of a group will be discussed in Section 33.

Here we appeal to physical intuition to clarify the idea of the group to be considered—the group of translations and rotations about a point. It will be assumed that if this group of motions takes point $P(X, Y, Z)$ into point $P'(X', Y', Z')$, then $m(X, Y, Z) = m'(X', Y', Z')$. Further, we assume that it is evident that the distance between any two points $P_1(X_1, Y_1, Z_1)$ and $P_2(X_2, Y_2, Z_2)$ is unaltered by this group of motions. If we let $\mathbf{R}_1$, $\mathbf{R}_2$ denote the position vectors of P_1, P_2, and if $\mathbf{R}_1'$, $\mathbf{R}_2'$ are the position vectors of the transformed points, then we may formulate this condition as $(\mathbf{R}_1 - \mathbf{R}_2) \cdot (\mathbf{R}_1 - \mathbf{R}_2) = (\mathbf{R}_1' - \mathbf{R}_2') \cdot (\mathbf{R}_1' - \mathbf{R}_2')$ or

$$(\mathbf{R}_1 - \mathbf{R}_2) \cdot (\mathbf{R}_1 - \mathbf{R}_2) = \text{constant} \tag{29.1}$$

during the motion.

With the aid of (29.1), we can easily verify the following result: for a rigid body, *an infinitesimal rotation about a point is equivalent to an infinitesimal rotation about a line through the point.* If the word "infinitesimal" is replaced by the word "finite," the above result becomes Euler's theorem. In the study of the dynamics of a rigid body, the infinitesimal motion (or rate of motion) is of greater interest than the finite motion. Hence, we consider only infinitesimal motion. Further, one should note that in our definition of a rigid body, the concept of rotations *about a point* enters. Thus, the present result replaces the infinitesimal rotations *about a point* by infinitesimal rotations about a line.

First, we derive two fundamental geometric properties of the rigid body. Let P_0 denote the fixed point. If we replace $\mathbf{R}_2$ by $\mathbf{R}_0 = 0$, then (29.1) becomes $\mathbf{R}_1 \cdot \mathbf{R}_1 = \text{constant}$. Differentiating this equation with respect to time, we obtain the first important result of the theory

$$\dot{\mathbf{R}}_1 \cdot \mathbf{R}_1 = 0 \tag{29.2}$$

where $\dot{\mathbf{R}}_1$ denotes the time derivative of $\mathbf{R}_1$. If $\mathbf{R}_2$ is the radius vector of any other point of the rigid body, then by replacing the point P_1 by the point P_2, we obtain $\dot{\mathbf{R}}_2 \cdot \mathbf{R}_2 = 0$. Finally, by differentiation of (29.1) and use of these formulas, we obtain the second important relation,

$$\mathbf{R}_1 \cdot \dot{\mathbf{R}}_2 + \mathbf{R}_2 \cdot \dot{\mathbf{R}}_1 = 0. \tag{29.3}$$

To prove the infinitesimal form of Euler's theorem, we must show that if $\mathbf{R}$ is the radius vector of any point P, measured from the fixed point, then an angular velocity vector $\mathbf{\Omega}$ exists such that $\mathbf{\Omega} \times \mathbf{R} = \dot{\mathbf{R}}$. Consider the vector

$$\mathbf{\Omega} = (\dot{\mathbf{R}}_1 \times \dot{\mathbf{R}}_2)/(\dot{\mathbf{R}}_1 \cdot \mathbf{R}_2).$$

It is easily verified by use of the above relation and of (29.2) and (29.3) that $(\mathbf{\Omega} \times \mathbf{R}_1) = \dot{\mathbf{R}}_1$, and $(\mathbf{\Omega} \times \mathbf{R}_2) = \dot{\mathbf{R}}_2$. In order to show that $\mathbf{\Omega} \times \mathbf{R} = \dot{\mathbf{R}}$, we note that $\mathbf{R}_1$, $\mathbf{R}_2$ may be replaced by $\mathbf{R}$ in the rigid body conditions, or

$$\mathbf{R} \cdot \dot{\mathbf{R}} = 0, \qquad \mathbf{R}_1 \cdot \dot{\mathbf{R}} + \mathbf{R} \cdot \dot{\mathbf{R}}_1 = 0, \qquad \mathbf{R}_2 \cdot \dot{\mathbf{R}} + \mathbf{R} \cdot \dot{\mathbf{R}}_2 = 0.$$

Assume $\mathbf{R}$, $\mathbf{R}_1$, $\mathbf{R}_2$ are linearly independent. Evidently, if we can show that

$$[(\mathbf{\Omega} \times \mathbf{R}) - \dot{\mathbf{R}}] \cdot \mathbf{R} = [(\mathbf{\Omega} \times \mathbf{R}) - \dot{\mathbf{R}}] \cdot \mathbf{R}_1 = [(\mathbf{\Omega} \times \mathbf{R}) - \dot{\mathbf{R}}] \cdot \mathbf{R}_2 = 0,$$

then our theorem will be demonstrated. This verification is left to the problems. One question remains. Is $\mathbf{\Omega}$ unique? For instance, another permissible $\mathbf{\Omega}$ is

$$\mathbf{\Omega}' = (\dot{\mathbf{R}}_3 \times \dot{\mathbf{R}}_4)/(\dot{\mathbf{R}}_3 \cdot \mathbf{R}_4).$$

The question is whether $\mathbf{\Omega} = \mathbf{\Omega}'$. Since $\mathbf{\Omega}'$ has the property that $\mathbf{\Omega}' \times \mathbf{R} = \dot{\mathbf{R}}$, one sees that $(\mathbf{\Omega} - \mathbf{\Omega}') \cdot \mathbf{R} = 0$, for arbitrary $\mathbf{R}$. This is possible if and only if $\mathbf{\Omega} = \mathbf{\Omega}'$.

Consider the *general infinitesimal motion* of a rigid body. Let O be some point of the body and O' be the transformed point. If $\delta\mathbf{s}$ denotes the infinitesimal displacement from O to O', then referred to O, the motion of the rigid body consists of: (1) a translation, $\delta\mathbf{s}$; and (2) a rotation with angular velocity vector, $\mathbf{\Omega}$. We shall show that *if one changes the base point* O *to* Q, *then the motion consists of:* (1) *a translation,* $\delta\mathbf{s}'$; *and* (2) *the same rotation.* This means that the translation vector depends upon the base point but the angular velocity vector is independent of the base point. To verify this result, we note that the displacement of an arbitrary point P of the body is

$$\delta\mathbf{s} + \mathbf{\Omega} \times \mathbf{R}\, dt$$

where $\mathbf{R}$ is the position vector, $\overrightarrow{\mathrm{OP}}$. Similarly, one may represent the displacement of P by

$$\delta\mathbf{s}' + \mathbf{\Omega}' \times (\mathbf{R} + \overrightarrow{\mathrm{QO}})\, dt$$

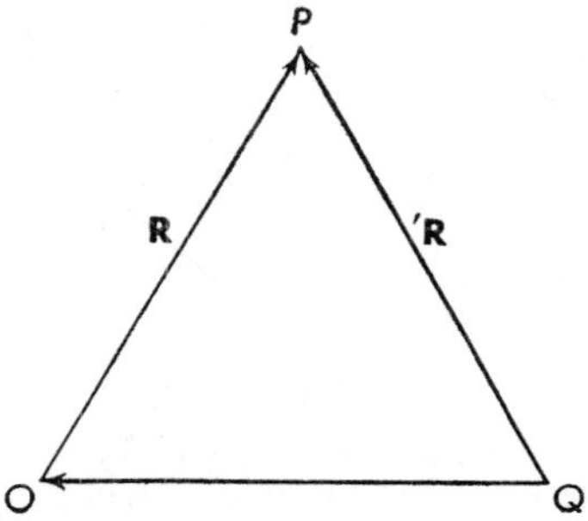

Figure 34: The Base Points O and Q in the Motion of P

where $\mathbf{\Omega}'$ represents the angular velocity vector when Q is the base point. Equating these two displacements, and noting that $\mathbf{R}$ is arbitrary and $\delta\mathbf{s}$, $\delta\mathbf{s}'$ are independent of $\mathbf{R}$, it follows that $(\mathbf{\Omega} - \mathbf{\Omega}') \times \mathbf{R} = 0$. Since this relation is valid for arbitrary $\mathbf{R}$, it follows that $\mathbf{\Omega} = \mathbf{\Omega}'$.

In order to discuss the general infinitesimal motion from an analytic viewpoint, we introduce the idea of moving frames (Section 16). We imagine an inertial frame XYZ fixed in space and a moving frame xyz, which is fixed in the rigid body. Since the frame xyz is fixed in the rigid body, the apparent velocity of any point P of the body vanishes. Thus, the velocity, $\mathbf{v}$, of point P with respect to the inertial frame is given by

$$\mathbf{v} = \mathbf{v}_0 + \mathbf{\Omega} \times \mathbf{R}, \tag{29.4}$$

where $\mathbf{v}_0$ is the "translational" velocity of the origin O of the xyz frame (see Figure 35). Finally, we recall that the time rate of change of an arbitrary vector **H**, which is measured in the moving frame, is

$$\frac{d\mathbf{H}}{dt} = \frac{\delta \mathbf{H}}{\delta t} + \mathbf{\Omega} \times \mathbf{H} \tag{29.5}$$

where $\delta\mathbf{H}/\delta t$ is the apparent rate of change of **H.**

(b) ***The Laws of Motion of a Rigid Body.*** There are two possible approaches to the theory of the laws of motion of a rigid body. One may

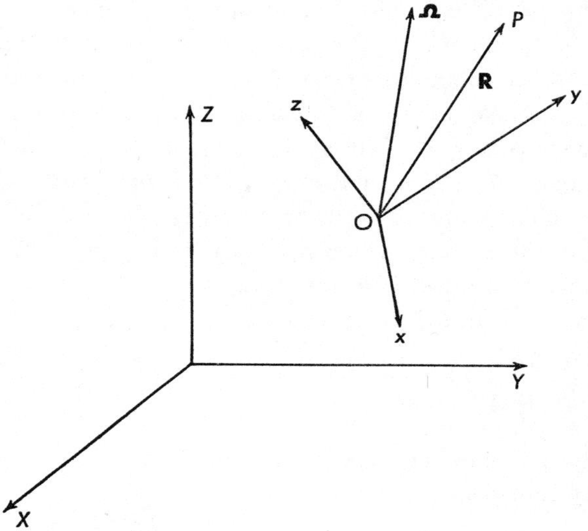

Figure 35: The Inertial Frame *XYZ* and the Moving Reference Frame *Oxyz* (This Last Frame Is Rigidly Attached to the Body)

assume the validity of Newton's three laws of particle dynamics and generalize to the rigid body by summation, or more properly by integration, over the particles. This approach involves several logical difficulties. One can most easily understand some of these difficulties by noticing that the external forces are usually concentrated forces. Hence, one would probably have to introduce Stieltjes's integrals. To avoid these and other difficulties, we adopt the second viewpoint. Here, we merely *assume that Newton's laws of motion for rigid bodies are given by*

$$\frac{dm}{dt} = 0, \tag{29.6}$$

$$\frac{d}{dt}\int_T m\mathbf{v}\, d\tau = \mathbf{F}, \tag{29.7}$$

$$\frac{d}{dt}\int_T m\mathbf{R} \times \mathbf{v}\, d\tau = \mathbf{G}, \tag{29.8}$$

where T is the region of space determined by the rigid body; $\mathbf{v}(x, y, z, t)$ is the velocity of any point of T with respect to an inertial frame; $m(x, y, z)$ is the mass distribution function; $\mathbf{F}$ is the sum of the external forces; $\mathbf{G}$ is the total moment of these forces with respect to O, the origin of the moving reference frame which is rigidly attached to the body; $\mathbf{R}$ is the radius vector from this origin O to any point P of the region T occupied by the rigid body; and $d\tau$ is the volume element of T. Our problem in this section will be to express the left-hand sides of the equations of motion, (29.7) and (29.8), in terms of quantities associated with the rigid body.

Before proceeding to the discussion of this problem, let us consider the significance of our assumptions (29.6) through (29.8). Evidently, the first equation is nothing but a restatement of the assumption that under the translation and rotation groups, the mass density is an invariant. That is, this equation is a form of the *equation of continuity* for rigid body motions. The second equation (29.7) states that the *total external force is equal to the rate of change of linear momentum.* This result is equivalent to Newton's second law. Finally, the equation (29.8) states that the *rate of change of angular momentum is equal to the moment of the external forces.* In particle dynamics, this result is a consequence of Newton's second law.

By use of the transformation properties of integrals, we may show that the time derivative in the basic equations (29.7) and (29.8) can be taken under the integral sign. To verify this result, we write the equations defining the group of motions in the form: $x = x(\bar{x}, \bar{y}, \bar{z}, t)$, $y = y(\bar{x}, \bar{y}, \bar{z}, t)$, $z = z(\bar{x}, \bar{y}, \bar{z}, t)$. In our later work [Section 33(a)], it will be shown that the Jacobian (here the determinant)

$$J = \begin{vmatrix} \frac{\partial x}{\partial \bar{x}} & \frac{\partial x}{\partial \bar{y}} & \frac{\partial x}{\partial \bar{z}} \\ \frac{\partial y}{\partial \bar{x}} & \frac{\partial y}{\partial \bar{y}} & \frac{\partial y}{\partial \bar{z}} \\ \frac{\partial z}{\partial \bar{x}} & \frac{\partial z}{\partial \bar{y}} & \frac{\partial z}{\partial \bar{z}} \end{vmatrix}$$

has the value 1 for the rotation group. In the case of the translation group, this result can be easily verified by writing the equations for a translation. Finally, we state a result of advanced calculus, which is valid for any field $\mathfrak{a}$ and will be verified in Section 49:

$$\int_T m\mathfrak{a}\, d\tau = \int_{\bar{T}} mJ\mathfrak{a}\, d\bar{\tau}$$

where $\bar{T}$ is the region of space determined by the rigid body at time $t = t_0$ (usually, $t_0 = 0$). It should be noted that x, y, z depend, when

$\bar{x}$, $\bar{y}$, $\bar{z}$ are fixed, upon the time variable t, and hence the region T also depends upon t. However, t, $\bar{x}$, $\bar{y}$, $\bar{z}$ are independent variables and hence $\bar{T}$ is independent of time. Thus, the equations of motion, (29.7) and (29.8), may be written as

$$\int_{\bar{T}} \frac{d}{dt} (Jm\mathbf{v})\, d\bar{\tau} = \mathbf{F}, \qquad \int_{\bar{T}} \frac{d}{dt} (Jm\mathbf{R} \times \mathbf{v})\, d\bar{\tau} = \mathbf{G}.$$

It should be noted that $\frac{d\mathbf{v}}{dt}$ is actually a partial derivative with respect to time with $\bar{x}$, $\bar{y}$, $\bar{z}$ constant. Since $J = 1$, $\frac{dm}{dt} = 0$, $\frac{d\mathbf{R}}{dt} = \mathbf{v} - \mathbf{v}_0$, where $\mathbf{v}_0$ is the velocity of O, we may rewrite the above equations in the T coordinates as

$$\int_T m \frac{d\mathbf{v}}{dt}\, d\tau = \mathbf{F} \tag{29.9}$$

$$\int_T m \left(\mathbf{R} \times \frac{d\mathbf{v}}{dt} - \mathbf{v}_0 \times \mathbf{v}\right) d\tau = \mathbf{G}. \tag{29.10}$$

First, we consider (29.9). If we rewrite (16.10) in terms of our present notation and note that the apparent velocity and acceleration are zero, since the coordinate frame is rigidly attached to the body, we obtain

$$\frac{d\mathbf{v}}{dt} = \frac{d\mathbf{v}_0}{dt} + \boldsymbol{\alpha} \times \mathbf{R} + \boldsymbol{\Omega} \times (\boldsymbol{\Omega} \times \mathbf{R}).$$

It should be noted that the vectors $\mathbf{v}_0$, $\boldsymbol{\alpha}$, $\boldsymbol{\Omega}$ are independent of the particular point P under consideration. Thus, we may write (29.9) as

$$\mathbf{F} = M \frac{d\mathbf{v}_0}{dt} + \boldsymbol{\alpha} \times \int_T m\mathbf{R}\, d\tau + \boldsymbol{\Omega} \times \left(\boldsymbol{\Omega} \times \int_T m\mathbf{R}\, d\tau\right)$$

where M is total mass of the rigid body. *If we require that O, the origin of the moving frame be at the center of mass,* then

$$\int_T m\mathbf{R}\, d\tau = 0$$

and equation (29.9) reduces to

$$\mathbf{F} = M \frac{d\mathbf{v}_0}{dt}.$$

That is, *if one replaces the rigid body by a particle of the same mass situated at the center of mass, then Newton's law of motion for particle dynamics is satisfied.* This last equation determines the path traced out by the center of mass. For this reason, we usually refer the motion to the center of mass as base point. The only exception is the case where the rigid body undergoes pure rotation about a fixed point. Then, one ignores the first relation, (29.9), and studies the second relation, (29.10), with the fixed point as base point.

Secondly, by choice of proper base point, we shall simplify the moment relation (29.8) or (29.10). Let us define the angular momentum (or moment of momentum) of the rigid body with respect to the base point O by

$$\mathbf{H} = \int_T m\mathbf{R} \times \mathbf{v}\, d\tau.$$

Then, the equation (29.8) may be written in the form

$$\frac{d\mathbf{H}}{dt} = \mathbf{G}. \tag{29.11}$$

It should be noted that this last relation may be written as [see (29.10)]

$$\mathbf{G} = \frac{d\mathbf{H}}{dt} = \int_T m\left(\mathbf{R} \times \frac{d\mathbf{v}}{dt} - \mathbf{v}_0 \times \mathbf{v}\right) d\tau.$$

Two cases of interest arise: (1) *the origin of the moving frame is a fixed point*, $\mathbf{v}_0 = 0$; (2) *the origin of the moving frame is the center of mass*, $\int_T m\mathbf{R}\, d\tau = 0$. Since $\mathbf{v} = \mathbf{v}_0 + \boldsymbol{\Omega} \times \mathbf{R}$, the second term in the right-hand side of the above formula for $\dfrac{d\mathbf{H}}{dt}$ reduces to

$$\int_T m\mathbf{v}_0 \times \mathbf{v}\, d\tau = \int_T m\mathbf{v}_0 \times (\boldsymbol{\Omega} \times \mathbf{R})\, d\tau.$$

It is easily verified that the above integral vanishes in either of the previously mentioned cases. Thus, the moment relation reduces to the simplified form

$$\mathbf{G} = \frac{d\mathbf{H}}{dt} = \int_T m\mathbf{R} \times \frac{d\mathbf{v}}{dt}\, d\tau.$$

(c) ***The Determination of* H; *The Limitations of Vector Analysis.*** By use of the velocity decomposition, (29.4), we find that the angular momentum, $\mathbf{H}$, may be expressed as

$$\mathbf{H} = \int_T m\mathbf{R} \times \mathbf{v}_0\, d\tau + \int_T m\mathbf{R} \times (\boldsymbol{\Omega} \times \mathbf{R})\, d\tau.$$

If we refer the motion to a base point: (1) which is fixed in space and in the body, $\mathbf{v}_0 = 0$ (the motion is one of rotation about a fixed point); (2) which is the center of mass, $\int_T m\mathbf{R}\, d\tau = 0$, then in either case, the first integral on the right-hand side of the expression for **H** vanishes. Thus, we see that the expression for angular momentum reduces to

$$\mathbf{H} = \int_T m\mathbf{R} \times (\boldsymbol{\Omega} \times \mathbf{R})\, d\tau.$$

In order to properly study this relation for **H,** one should introduce tensor analysis. For the present, we will work with the component expansion of $\mathbf{R} \times (\boldsymbol{\Omega} \times \mathbf{R})$ in terms of orthogonal Cartesian coordinates. We find that

$$\begin{aligned} \mathbf{H} = \mathbf{i} \int_T &[m(z^2 + y^2)\Omega_x - m(xy\Omega_y + xz\Omega_z)]\, d\tau \\ + \mathbf{j} \int_T &[m(z^2 + x^2)\Omega_y - m(yx\Omega_x + yz\Omega_z)]\, d\tau \\ + \mathbf{k} \int_T &[m(x^2 + y^2)\Omega_z - m(zx\Omega_x + zy\Omega_y)]\, d\tau. \end{aligned} \tag{29.12}$$

The quantities

$$\int_T m(z^2 + y^2)\, d\tau, \text{ etc.,} \qquad - \int_T mxy\, d\tau, \text{ etc.,}$$

are known as the moments and products of inertia, respectively. These quantities are completely specified when the particular rigid body, the base point O, and the reference frame xyz are known. Further, since the reference frame moves with the rigid body, these quantities are constants of the motion. Generally, we designate these quantities by

$$I_{xx} = \int_T m(z^2 + y^2)\, d\tau = \text{moment of inertia about } Ox,$$

$$I_{xy} = I_{yx} = - \int_T mxy\, d\tau = \text{product of inertia about } Ox,\ Oy.$$

With this notation, we may express the components of **H** in (29.12) by

$$\begin{aligned} H_x &= I_{xx}\Omega_x + I_{xy}\Omega_y + I_{xz}\Omega_z \\ H_y &= I_{yx}\Omega_x + I_{yy}\Omega_y + I_{yz}\Omega_z \\ H_z &= I_{zx}\Omega_x + I_{zy}\Omega_y + I_{zz}\Omega_z. \end{aligned} \tag{29.13}$$

The essential significance of the above formulas lies in the fact that the six quantities ($I_{xy} = I_{yx}$, etc.) *constitute the components of a second-order symmetric tensor.* As we shall show in the section on tensor analysis, these equations indicate that the angular momentum vector is formed by taking the scalar product of the moment of inertia tensor and the angular velocity vector.

In order to simplify (29.13), one must understand some of the properties of a second-order symmetric tensor. Here we merely quote some results. It can be shown that by proper choice of coordinate system (that is, by properly orienting the xyz system) that the *products of inertia may be made to vanish.* In this case, the coordinate system is said to coincide with the principal axes of inertia of the body. Then, the compoments of **H** reduce to

$$H_x = I_{xx}\Omega_x, \qquad H_y = I_{yy}\Omega_y, \qquad H_z = I_{zz}\Omega_z.$$

If we express the angular momentum equation (29.11) in terms of components associated with the frame xyz, rigidly attached to the moving body, then we obtain (see 29.5)

$$\frac{\delta \mathbf{H}}{\delta t} + \mathbf{\Omega} \times \mathbf{H} = \mathbf{G}.$$

By use of the preceding expressions for H_x, H_y, H_z, this last equation may be written as

$$I_{xx}\frac{d\Omega_x}{dt} + (I_{zz} - I_{yy})\Omega_y\Omega_z = G_x$$

$$I_{yy}\frac{d\Omega_y}{dt} + (I_{xx} - I_{zz})\Omega_x\Omega_z = G_y$$

$$I_{zz}\frac{d\Omega_z}{dt} + (I_{yy} - I_{xx})\Omega_x\Omega_y = G_z.$$

These equations are known as the *Euler equations for the motion of a rigid body.* They play a fundamental role in the study of the motion of a rigid body.

Problem 29.1: Prove that $\dfrac{(\dot{\mathbf{R}}_1 \times \dot{\mathbf{R}}_2)}{(\dot{\mathbf{R}}_1 \cdot \mathbf{R}_2)} \times \mathbf{R}_1 = \dot{\mathbf{R}}_1.$

Problem 29.2: If $\mathbf{\Omega} = \dfrac{(\dot{\mathbf{R}}_1 \times \dot{\mathbf{R}}_2)}{(\dot{\mathbf{R}}_1 \cdot \mathbf{R}_2)}$, show that

$$[(\mathbf{\Omega} \times \mathbf{R}) - \dot{\mathbf{R}}] \cdot \mathbf{R} = [(\mathbf{\Omega} \times \mathbf{R}) - \dot{\mathbf{R}}] \cdot \mathbf{R}_1 = [(\mathbf{\Omega} \times \mathbf{R}) - \dot{\mathbf{R}}] \cdot \mathbf{R}_2 = 0.$$

Problem 29.3: By use of the fact that the displacement of an arbitrary point of a rigid body is $\delta\mathbf{s} + \mathbf{\Omega} \times \mathbf{R}\, dt$, prove that the work due to an infinitesimal displacement of a rigid body is $\delta W = \mathbf{F} \cdot \delta\mathbf{s} + \mathbf{G} \cdot \mathbf{\Omega}\, dt$, where **F** is the resultant force and **G** is the total moment.

Problem 29.4: Since the velocity of any point in a rigid body is $\mathbf{v} = \mathbf{v}_0 + \mathbf{\Omega} \times \mathbf{R}$ show that if the base point O is a fixed point or is the center of mass, then the kinetic energy, T, of the body is $T = \dfrac{M}{2}(\mathbf{v}_0 \cdot \mathbf{v}_0) + \dfrac{1}{2}(I_{xx}\Omega_x^2 + I_{yy}\Omega_y^2 + I_{zz}\Omega_z^2)$. (Note, $\mathbf{v}_0 = 0$ if O is a fixed point. Further, it is assumed that the coordinate system coincides with the principal axes of inertia.)

Problem 29.5: If the total moment of the external forces is zero, show that two first integrals of the Euler equations are

$$'T = \frac{1}{2}(I_{xx}\Omega_x^2 + I_{yy}\Omega_y^2 + I_{zz}\Omega_z^2) = \text{constant},$$

$$H^2 = (I_{xx}\Omega_x)^2 + (I_{yy}\Omega_y)^2 + (I_{zz}\Omega_z)^2 = \text{constant}.$$

Problem 29.6: If the total moment of the external forces is zero and if $\Omega_x = \text{constant}$, show that $\Omega_y = \Omega_z = 0$. If instead of $\Omega_x = \text{constant}$, we assume $\Omega_y = \text{constant}$, then what are the permissible values of Ω_x, Ω_z? Interpret these results physically.

30. Fluid Dynamics (Perfect Fluids). There are two viewpoints that one may adopt in studying fluid dynamics: (1) the stationary observer or the Eulerian approach; (2) the moving observer or the Lagrangian approach. Here we shall briefly outline the Euler and Lagrange viewpoints for determining the relations between the pressure p, the density ρ, and the velocity vector **v**, at any point of the fluid. It should be noted that p and ρ are scalar fields and **v** is a vector field. In addition, one may introduce the temperature T, the entropy S, and the energy e, etc. This will be done when we study compressible fluids.

(a) ***The Lagrangian View.*** Let $\bar{x}$, $\bar{y}$, $\bar{z}$ denote the coordinates of a fluid particle at time $\bar{t}$. Usually we assume $\bar{t} = 0$. Further, let x, y, z denote the

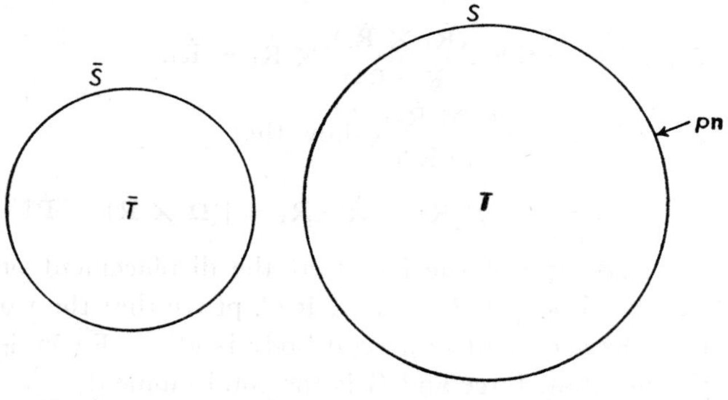

Figure 36: The Original Flow Space, $\bar{T}$, at Time, $\bar{t} = 0$, and the Flow Space, T, at Time, t

coordinates of the same fluid particle at time t. It is assumed that x, y, z are at least twice differentiable functions of the independent variables $\bar{x}$, $\bar{y}$, $\bar{z}$, t. If $\bar{\rho}(\bar{x}, \bar{y}, \bar{z})$ denotes the density at $\bar{x}$, $\bar{y}$, $\bar{z}$ at time $\bar{t} = 0$, then the mass $\bar{M}$ of fluid in a region $\bar{T}$ is

$$\bar{M} = \int_{\bar{T}} \bar{\rho}\, d\bar{\tau},$$

where $d\bar{\tau}$ is the volume element of $\bar{T}$. Due to the motion of the fluid, the region $\bar{T}$ is transformed into the region T with density $\rho(x, y, x, t)$ and mass, M, given by

$$M = \int_T \rho \, d\tau.$$

Since in the Lagrangian view, we follow the motion of the individual particles, the conservation of mass furnishes the relation $M = \bar{M}$, or

$$\int_T \rho \, d\tau = \int_{\bar{T}} \bar{\rho} \, d\bar{\tau}.$$

By the rule for transforming integrals, we know that

$$\int_T \rho \, d\tau = \int_{\bar{T}} \rho J \, d\bar{\tau},$$

where J is the Jacobian of the transformation from $\bar{x}, \bar{y}, \bar{z}$ to x, y, z [see Section 29(b)]. Equating the right-hand sides of the two above integrals, we obtain the relation

$$\int_{\bar{T}} \bar{\rho} \, d\bar{\tau} = \int_{\bar{T}} \rho J \, d\bar{\tau}.$$

Since the region $\bar{T}$ is arbitrary, a simple argument shows that this last equation is equivalent to

$$\rho J = \bar{\rho} \bar{J}, \qquad \bar{J} = 1. \tag{30.1}$$

Thus, ρJ *is an invariant of the motion;* equation (30.1) is the Lagrangian analogue of the conservation of mass equation, (29.6), for rigid bodies. One often refers to this equation as the *equation of continuity in Lagrangian form.*

According to whether ρJ is expressed in terms of $\bar{x}, \bar{y}, \bar{z}, t$ or in terms of x, y, z, t, two derivative formulations of this continuity relation are available. If ρJ is expressed in terms of x, y, z, t, then (30.1) may be written as

$$0 = \frac{d}{dt} \rho J = \frac{\partial}{\partial t} (\rho J) + \frac{\partial(\rho J)}{\partial x} \frac{\partial x}{\partial t} + \frac{\partial(\rho J)}{\partial y} \frac{\partial y}{\partial t} + \frac{\partial(\rho J)}{\partial z} \frac{\partial z}{\partial t}.$$

Since the velocity vector $\mathbf{v}$ is determined by

$$\mathbf{v} = \mathbf{i} \frac{\partial x}{\partial t} + \mathbf{j} \frac{\partial y}{\partial t} + \mathbf{k} \frac{\partial z}{\partial t},$$

we may express the above result in the form

$$0 = \frac{d}{dt} \rho J = \mathbf{v} \cdot \nabla(\rho J) + \frac{\partial}{\partial t} (\rho J).$$

One often denotes the derivative $\frac{d}{dt}$ by $\frac{D}{Dt}$ and states that this derivative denotes differentiation "following the fluid particle." On the other hand, if ρJ is expressed in terms of $\bar{x}$, $\bar{y}$, $\bar{z}$, t (by eliminating x, y, z), then the above equation must be replaced by

$$\frac{\partial}{\partial t}(\rho J) = 0. \tag{30.2}$$

This last form is the one adopted in the Lagrangian approach.

We turn to the derivation of the equations of motion. Let $\mathbf{F}$ denote the external force per unit mass. *If we restrict our theory to perfect fluids,* then at any point P the value of the pressure p is independent of the direction and this internal stress acts perpendicular to any surface element through P. That is, $p(x, y, z)$ is a scalar field. In viscous fluid theory, the scalar field p must be replaced by a tensor field. It is for this reason that we have restricted ourselves to perfect fluid theory for the present.

In order to obtain the equations of motion, we apply Newton's second law to the motion of a fluid mass which is enclosed in a moving closed surface S:

$$\frac{d}{dt}\int_T \rho\mathbf{v}\,d\tau = \int_T \rho\mathbf{F}\,d\tau - \int_S p\mathbf{n}\,d\sigma. \tag{30.3}$$

By use of Gauss's theorem (24.1), we see that

$$\int_S p\mathbf{n}\,d\sigma = \int_T \nabla p\,d\tau = \int_{\bar{T}} J\,\nabla p\,d\bar{\tau}.$$

Further, by exactly the same argument as was used in Section 29 for transforming integrals, we find through use of (30.2) that

$$\frac{d}{dt}\int_T \rho\mathbf{v}\,d\tau = \int_{\bar{T}} \rho J\,\frac{\partial\mathbf{v}}{\partial t}\,d\bar{\tau},$$

$$\int_T \rho\mathbf{F}\,d\tau = \int_{\bar{T}} \rho J\mathbf{F}\,d\bar{\tau}.$$

Substituting these expressions into (30.3), we obtain the relation

$$\int_{\bar{T}} J\left[\rho\,\frac{\partial\mathbf{v}}{\partial t} - \rho\mathbf{F} + \nabla p\right]d\bar{\tau} = 0. \tag{30.4}$$

Since this relation is valid for arbitrary regions $\bar{T}$, by use of the continuity of the integrand, we find that the *equations of motion* in Lagrangian form are

$$\rho \frac{\partial \mathbf{v}}{\partial t} = \rho \mathbf{F} - \nabla p \tag{30.5}$$

where $\mathbf{F}$, $\mathbf{v}$, p, ρ, are to be expressed in terms of the independent variables $\bar{x}$, $\bar{y}$, $\bar{z}$, t, and ∇ is to be expressed in terms of these variables.

The moment of momentum equation furnishes nothing new. This can be verified by recalling that $\nabla \times \mathbf{R} = 0$.

(b) ***The Eulerian View.*** It should be remarked that the so-called Lagrangian and Eulerian views are both due to Euler. In the Eulerian view, one considers the variables x, y, z, t as the independent variables of the theory and $\mathbf{v}$, p, $\mathbf{F}$, etc., as the dependent variables. By transforming (30.4) into the region T $\left(\text{and hence replacing } \frac{\partial \mathbf{v}}{\partial t} \text{ by } \frac{\partial \mathbf{v}}{\partial t} + (\mathbf{v} \cdot \nabla)\mathbf{v}\right)$, we find

$$\int_T \rho \left[\frac{\partial \mathbf{v}}{\partial t} + (\mathbf{v} \cdot \nabla)\mathbf{v} - \mathbf{F} + \frac{\nabla p}{\rho} \right] d\tau = 0.$$

Hence *in Eulerian form, the equations of motion* (30.5) become

$$\frac{\partial \mathbf{v}}{\partial t} + (\mathbf{v} \cdot \nabla)\mathbf{v} = \mathbf{F} - \frac{\nabla p}{\rho}. \tag{30.6}$$

The Lagrangian continuity relation (30.2) can be transformed into the Eulerian form when the rules for differentiating a determinant are known. We shall discuss this theory in Section 35e. Here we shall state the result:

$$\frac{\partial J}{\partial t} = J(\nabla \cdot \mathbf{v}) \tag{30.7}$$

where $\nabla \cdot \mathbf{v}$ represents the divergence of $\mathbf{v}$ in the Eulerian variables x, y, z, t. If we replace $\frac{\partial \rho}{\partial t}$ of (30.2) by its Eulerian equivalent, $\frac{\partial \rho}{\partial t} + (\mathbf{v} \cdot \nabla)\rho$, and use (30.7), we find the Lagrangian continuity equation must be replaced by the following *Eulerian equation of continuity*

$$\frac{\partial \rho}{\partial t} + (\nabla \cdot \mathbf{v})\rho + \mathbf{v} \cdot \nabla \rho = 0. \tag{30.8}$$

The formula (30.8) can be obtained in another manner by introducing some new physical principles. This method was used in Section 25 in the derivation of the continuity relation.

(c) ***The Bernoulli Relation.*** The Bernoulli relation is a first integral of the equations of motion, (30.6). To derive this relation, we use the vector identity

$$\nabla(\mathbf{V}\cdot\mathbf{W}) = (\mathbf{V}\cdot\nabla)\mathbf{W} + (\mathbf{W}\cdot\nabla)\mathbf{V} + \mathbf{V}\times(\nabla\times\mathbf{W}) + \mathbf{W}\times(\nabla\times\mathbf{V})$$

and find that for $\mathbf{v} = \mathbf{V} = \mathbf{W}$,

$$(\mathbf{v}\cdot\nabla)\mathbf{v} = \nabla\frac{v^2}{2} - \mathbf{v}\times\boldsymbol{\omega}$$

where $\boldsymbol{\omega}$ is the vorticity vector, $\boldsymbol{\omega} = \nabla\times\mathbf{v}$. Hence, the equation of motion becomes

$$\frac{\partial\mathbf{v}}{\partial t} + \nabla\frac{v^2}{2} - \mathbf{v}\times\boldsymbol{\omega} = \mathbf{F} - \frac{\nabla p}{\rho}. \tag{30.9}$$

The general first integral of (30.9) is unknown. However, if we require that $\mathbf{F}$ be a conservative field with potential Ω, $(\mathbf{F} = -\nabla\Omega)$, then some results can be obtained.

Case 1: $\mathbf{F} = -\nabla\Omega$; Steady Motion, $\dfrac{\partial\mathbf{v}}{\partial t} = \dfrac{\partial\rho}{\partial t} = \dfrac{\partial p}{\partial t} = 0$. Forming the scalar product of (30.9) with $\mathbf{v}$, we find that

$$-\frac{\partial}{\partial t}\frac{v^2}{2} = \mathbf{v}\cdot\nabla\left(\Omega + \frac{v^2}{2}\right) + \mathbf{v}\cdot\frac{\nabla p}{\rho}.$$

Since the motion is steady, the left-hand side of the above equation vanishes. Further, in steady motion the stream lines, which are the solutions of the ordinary differential equations

$$\mathbf{v} = \frac{d\mathbf{R}}{dl}, \qquad \mathbf{R} = \mathbf{i}x(l) + \mathbf{j}y(l) + \mathbf{k}z(l),\ l \text{ is a parameter},$$

are curves C which are independent of time (note, the direction numbers of these curves are determined by $\mathbf{v}$ at x, y, z and are independent of t). Thus, we obtain the result

$$0 = \frac{d}{dl}\left(\Omega + \frac{v^2}{2}\right) + \frac{1}{\rho}\frac{dp}{dl}.$$

In order to integrate this last equation, one could make some assumptions as to the nature of the density function $\rho(x, y, z)$. Actually, we need to know only the relation between p and ρ. This shows how thermodynamics enters into the theory.

If ρ = constant, the incompressible case, then the desired integral is the *Bernoulli relation*

$$\Omega + \frac{v^2}{2} + \frac{p}{\rho} = c, \tag{30.10}$$

where c is constant along a *given stream line* but may vary from stream line to stream line. In practice, the incompressible case arises in studying the flow of water and other liquids or in very low speed gas flows.

If $p = p(\rho)$, the flow is said to be isentropic (flow with constant entropy). In this case, it may be shown from thermodynamic considerations that the enthalpy (often called the heat content), h, is given by

$$h = \int \frac{dp}{\rho}.$$

The desired integral—the Bernoulli relation—becomes

$$\Omega + \frac{v^2}{2} + h = c, \tag{30.11}$$

where again *c is constant along a given stream line.* In practice, the isentropic case arises in the study of high speed gas flows in which viscosity effects can be neglected. This is due to the fact that viscosity effects usually involve heat dissipation. Since entropy is measured by the amount of heat dissipated, viscous flows are non-isentropic. If the gas is polytropic (internal energy proportional to the absolute temperature) then $p = c\rho^\gamma$, where c is a constant and γ is the ratio of the specific heat at constant pressure to the specific heat at constant volume. For air, $\gamma = 1.4$, approximately.

Case 2: $\mathbf{F} = -\nabla\Omega$; *Irrotational Motion,* $\boldsymbol{\omega} = 0$. Since the vorticity vector vanishes, $\boldsymbol{\omega} = \nabla \times \mathbf{v} = 0$, it follows from Stokes's theorem that a velocity potential function, $\phi(x, y, z, t)$, exists such that $\mathbf{v} = \nabla\phi$. If we restrict ourselves to isentropic flows, then (30.9) reduces to

$$\nabla\left(\frac{\partial\phi}{\partial t} + \Omega + h + \frac{v^2}{2}\right) = 0.$$

We consider two possible situations.

If the flow is steady, $\dfrac{\partial\phi}{\partial t} = 0$, and the above equation possesses as first integral the Bernoulli relation

$$\Omega + h + \frac{v^2}{2} = c$$

where c is *constant throughout the region of the flow.* The Bernoulli relation (30.11) is called the "weak" form; in the previous case, $\boldsymbol{\omega} \neq 0$, whereas in the present case, $\boldsymbol{\omega} = 0$.

If the flow is non-steady, $\frac{\partial \phi}{\partial t} \neq 0$, and the first integral of the above equation is

$$\frac{\partial \phi}{\partial t} + \Omega + h + \frac{v^2}{2} = c(t)$$

where $c(t)$ is a function of time. Evidently, if instead of the velocity potential, ϕ, we introduce a new potential, $'\phi$, such that

$$'\phi = \phi - \int^t c(t)\, dt$$

then $\mathbf{v} = \nabla '\phi$ and our new form of Bernoulli's relation is

$$\frac{\partial '\phi}{\partial t} + \Omega + h + \frac{v^2}{2} = 0.$$

(d) ***Kelvin's Theorem.*** We shall verify this theorem for a perfect, isentropic fluid with conservative force field. However, the theorem is valid under more general conditions. In short, the theorem states that: *The circulation, C, around any closed curve, C_o, moving with the fluid particles is constant.*

By definition the circulation at any time, t, is

$$C = \oint_{C_o} \mathbf{v} \cdot d\mathbf{R} = \oint_{C_o} \mathbf{v} \cdot \mathbf{t}\, d\alpha, \qquad \mathbf{t} = \frac{\partial \mathbf{R}}{\partial \alpha}.$$

Special attention must be paid to the choice of parameter α along C_o. In order to separate out the dependence of $\mathbf{R}(\alpha, t)$ on time, we require that: $0 \leq \alpha \leq 1$, $\mathbf{R}(0, t) = \mathbf{R}(1, t)$. That is, $\mathbf{R}(\alpha, t)$ spans a surface which for a fixed value of t determines the new locus of C_o which depends only upon the parameter α. We may now evaluate $\frac{dC}{dt}$ by differentiating under the integral sign and obtain

$$\frac{dC}{dt} = \oint_{C_o} \left(\frac{d\mathbf{v}}{dt} \cdot \mathbf{t} + \mathbf{v} \cdot \frac{\partial \mathbf{t}}{\partial t} \right) d\alpha.$$

Since $\frac{d\mathbf{v}}{dt} = \frac{\partial \mathbf{v}}{\partial t} + (\mathbf{v} \cdot \nabla)\mathbf{v}$, and $\mathbf{F} = -\nabla \Omega$, $\frac{\nabla p}{\rho} = \nabla h$, it follows from the equations of motion (30.6) that

$$\oint_{C_o} \frac{d\mathbf{v}}{dt} \cdot \mathbf{t}\, d\alpha = -\oint_{C_o} \mathbf{t} \cdot \nabla(\Omega + h)\, d\alpha = -\oint_{C_o} \frac{\partial}{\partial \alpha} (\Omega + h)\, d\alpha.$$

Evidently this integral vanishes. Now C_o moves with the fluid. Thus, the expression $\frac{\partial \mathbf{t}}{\partial t}$ is

$$\frac{\partial \mathbf{t}}{\partial t} = \frac{\partial}{\partial t}\frac{\partial \mathbf{R}}{\partial \alpha} = \frac{\partial}{\partial \alpha}\frac{\partial \mathbf{R}}{\partial t} = \frac{\partial \mathbf{v}}{\partial \alpha}$$

where $\mathbf{v}$ along C_o is considered to be a function of α and t. From this result, it follows that

$$\oint_{C_o} \mathbf{v} \cdot \frac{\partial \mathbf{t}}{\partial t}\, d\alpha = \oint_{C_o} \mathbf{v} \cdot \frac{\partial \mathbf{v}}{\partial \alpha}\, d\alpha = \frac{1}{2}\oint_{C_o} \frac{\partial v^2}{\partial \alpha}\, d\alpha.$$

Evidently, this integral vanishes, and dC/dt is zero.

(e) ***Helmholtz's Theorems on Vorticity.*** These theorems are concerned with rotational flow ($\boldsymbol{\omega} = \nabla \times \mathbf{v} \neq 0$) in a perfect fluid (zero viscosity). Further, it is assumed that the external body forces possess a potential ($\mathbf{F} = -\nabla \Omega$) and that the flow is steady and isentropic $\left(h = \int \frac{dp}{\rho}\right.$ exists or $\left.p = f(\rho)\right)$.

The *vortex lines* are the solutions of the differential equations

$$\boldsymbol{\omega}(x, y, z) = \frac{d\mathbf{R}}{d\beta}$$

where β is a parameter along the solution curves. Evidently, through each point (x, y, z) of the flow space, there passes one and only one vortex line.

The *vortex tubes* are defined as follows. Let C be a simple closed curve which is not a vortex line. The ∞^1 vortex lines through C form an open surface which is said to be a vortex tube, S.

Helmholtz's first result is that *vortex tubes move with the fluid.* In other words, a vortex tube always consists of the same fluid particles. To illustrate this, we have indicated the stream lines by L, $'L$, $''L$ in Figure 37, and shown how a vortex tube S is carried into a vortex tube $'S$ by the fluid motion. To verify the theorem, let C_o denote a simple closed curve on S, which is carried by the fluid motion into the simple closed curve $'C_o$. Further, let $'S$ denote the surface passing through $'C_o$ and generated by the original vortex tube. *Our problem is to show that $'S$ is a vortex tube.* If $\mathbf{n}$ denotes a unit vector perpendicular to S then the vortex tube is characterized by the property

$$\mathbf{n} \cdot \boldsymbol{\omega} = \mathbf{n} \cdot \nabla \times \mathbf{v} = 0, \text{ on } S. \tag{30.12}$$

We shall attempt to show that this relation is satisfied on $'S$. Consider the integral

$$\int_{'S} \mathbf{n} \cdot \nabla \times \mathbf{v}\, d\sigma$$

taken over an arbitrarily small surface region of $'S$, bounded by the closed simple curve $'C_o$. Let C_o on S (the vortex tube) correspond to $'C_o$ under the fluid motion. By Kelvin's theorem,

$$\oint_{'C_o} \mathbf{v} \cdot \mathbf{t}\, d\alpha = \oint_{C_o} \mathbf{v} \cdot \mathbf{t}\, d\alpha, \qquad \mathbf{t} = \frac{\partial \mathbf{R}}{\partial \alpha}.$$

But by Stokes's theorem,

$$\oint_{C_o} \mathbf{v} \cdot \mathbf{t}\, d\alpha = \int_S \mathbf{n} \cdot \nabla \times \mathbf{v}\, d\sigma$$

where S is that part of the vortex tube interior to C_o. From (30.12) and the above integrals, it follows that

$$\oint_{'C_o} \mathbf{v} \cdot \mathbf{t}\, d\alpha = 0.$$

Transforming this last integral by Stokes's theorem, we find

$$\int_{'S} \mathbf{n} \cdot \nabla \times \mathbf{v}\, d\sigma = 0$$

where $'S$ is the surface interior to $'C_o$. Since the surface interior to $'C_o$ was assumed to be arbitrarily small, it follows that $\mathbf{n} \cdot \nabla \times \mathbf{v}$ vanishes at each point of $'S$. Hence, $'S$ is a vortex tube.

Helmholtz's second result deals with the strength of vortex tubes. The strength of a tube is measured by

$$s(A) = \int_A \mathbf{n} \cdot \nabla \times \mathbf{v}\, d\sigma = \oint_C \mathbf{v} \cdot t\, d\alpha$$

where A is any surface cutting the vortex tube (see Figure 37). *The theorem to be shown is that*

$$s(A) = s(A_1) = s('A)$$

where A_1 is any other cross section of the original vortex tube and $'A$ is any cross section of the displaced tube, $'S$. If we apply Stokes's theorem for multiply connected regions to that section of S which is bounded by C, C_1, we find that

$$\oint_C \mathbf{v} \cdot \mathbf{t}\, d\alpha + \oint_{C_1} \mathbf{v} \cdot \mathbf{t}\, d\alpha = 0.$$

This equation shows that $s(A) = s(A_1)$. Again, let $'C$ denote the curve into which C is transformed by the fluid motion. From Kelvin's theorem, it follows that $s(A) = s('A)$. Thus, the second theorem of Helmholtz is demonstrated.

(f) ***Remarks on Viscous Fluids and Compressible Fluids.*** We have not attempted to introduce viscous fluid theory. The reason is that the viscous stresses can most easily be described by a tensor. Further, we have said very little about compressible flows. Although the introductory theory can be given without any reference to tensors, insight into the general theory of compressible flows (especially three-dimensional flows) does necessitate some knowledge of tensor analysis.

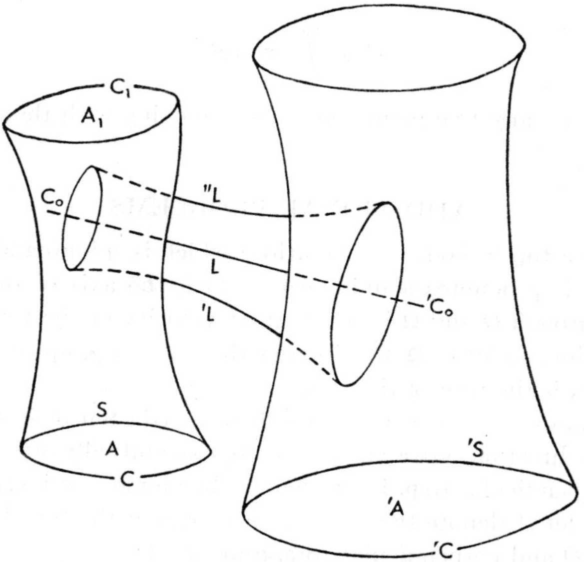

Figure 37: The Vortex Tube, S, through C, and the Vortex Tube, $'S$, through $'C$

Problem 30.1: If the fluid is incompressible (ρ = constant) and the fluid motion is two-dimensional, show that a stream function, $\psi(x, y)$ exists such that $u = \frac{\partial \psi}{\partial y}$, $v = -\frac{\partial \psi}{\partial x}$, where $\mathbf{v} = u\mathbf{i} + v\mathbf{j}$. (Note, $\psi = \int_A^B u\,dy - v\,dx$ is independent of the path and measures the volume of fluid crossing the path per unit time.)

Problem 30.2: If the fluid motion is two-dimensional, incompressible and irrotational, show that the stream function $\psi(x, y)$ and the velocity potential, $\phi(x, y)$ satisfy the Laplace equation,

$$\frac{\partial^2 \psi}{\partial x^2} + \frac{\partial^2 \psi}{\partial y^2} = \frac{\partial^2 \phi}{\partial x^2} + \frac{\partial^2 \phi}{\partial y^2} = 0.$$

Problem 30.3: If the velocity potential of a two-dimensional fluid motion is $\phi(x, y) = x^2 + y^2$, find $\mathbf{v}$. Then determine the equations of the stream lines, $\mathbf{v} = \frac{d\mathbf{R}}{dl}$.

Problem 30.4: Show that in two-dimensional motion, the vorticity vector, $\boldsymbol{\omega} = \nabla \times \mathbf{v}$, has the value $\boldsymbol{\omega} = \omega\mathbf{k}$, where

$$-\omega = \frac{\partial^2\psi}{\partial x^2} + \frac{\partial^2\psi}{\partial y^2}.$$

Problem 30.5: Determine the time rate of change of the partial circulation

$$C = \int_A^B \mathbf{v} \cdot d\mathbf{R}.$$

Note: A, B are any two points on a curve moving with the fluid.

ADDITIONAL PROBLEMS

1. Consider a top (a body of revolution) which is spinning about a fixed point O. If $\mathbf{p}$ denotes a unit vector along the axis of the top which passes through O and $\boldsymbol{\Omega}$ is the angular velocity of the top, show that the relation, $d\mathbf{p}/dt = \boldsymbol{\Omega} \times \mathbf{p}$ implies that $\boldsymbol{\Omega} = \mathbf{p} \times d\mathbf{p}/dt + s\mathbf{p}$, where $s = \boldsymbol{\Omega} \cdot \mathbf{p}$, is the spin of the top.
2. For the above problem, the moment of inertia tensor is such that its principal directions are along $\mathbf{p}$ and any two mutually orthogonal directions perpendicular to $\mathbf{p}$. Let C denote the moment of inertia of the top about $\mathbf{p}$; let A denote the moment of inertia of the top about any line through O and perpendicular to $\mathbf{p}$. Show that:

(1) $$\mathbf{H} = Cs\mathbf{p} + A\mathbf{p} \times \frac{d\mathbf{p}}{dt}$$

(2) $$\mathbf{G} = \frac{d\mathbf{H}}{dt} = C\frac{ds}{dt}\mathbf{p} + Cs\frac{d\mathbf{p}}{dt} + A\mathbf{p} \times \frac{d^2\mathbf{p}}{dt^2}$$

(3) if $\mathbf{G} = 0$, then $s =$ constant.

3. If a fluid is incompressible and has a constant vorticity vector, $\boldsymbol{\omega}$, show that $\nabla^2\mathbf{v} = 0$, where $\mathbf{v}$ is the velocity vector.
4. For an incompressible, irrotational fluid in a region T bounded by a closed surface S, show that the kinetic energy of the fluid, $\mathrm{K} = \frac{\rho}{2}\int_T \mathbf{v} \cdot \mathbf{v}\, d\tau$ may be expressed by, $\mathrm{K} = \frac{\rho}{2}\oint_S \phi\mathbf{n} \cdot \nabla\phi\, d\sigma$, where ϕ is the velocity potential.
5. Verify Kelvin's theorem that the irrotational motion of an incompressible fluid occupying a simply connected region has less kinetic energy than any other motion consistent with the same normal motion of the boundary.

Part II

TENSOR ANALYSIS

Chapter V

TENSORS IN CARTESIAN ORTHOGONAL COORDINATES

31. Introduction to Tensors. Up to the present time we have limited our considerations to scalar and vector quantities. Though we have indicated the possible existence of more general quantities, we have not had any real need for introducing such quantities. The two following examples will show the necessity for studying such new quantities.

Example 1: Three mutually orthogonal linear springs are joined at the fixed origin. Forces F_x, F_y, F_z are applied at the ends of the springs. Find

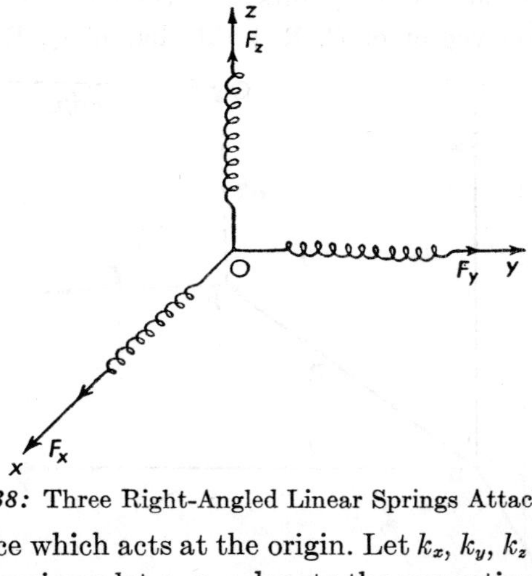

Figure 38: Three Right-Angled Linear Springs Attached at O

the resultant force which acts at the origin. Let k_x, k_y, k_z denote the spring constants of the springs; let x, y, z denote the respective displacements of the free ends of the springs. By Hooke's law

$$F_x = k_x x, \qquad F_y = k_y y, \qquad F_z = k_z z.$$

Hence, the resultant force, $\mathbf{F}$, acting at the common point, O, of the line of application of the forces is

$$\mathbf{F} = \mathbf{i}F_x + \mathbf{j}F_y + \mathbf{k}F_z = k_x x\mathbf{i} + k_y y\mathbf{j} + k_z z\mathbf{k}.$$

Let us ask whether any quantity, $\mathcal{A}$, exists such that if we form the scalar product of $\mathcal{A}$ and the displacement vector, $\mathbf{R} = \mathbf{i}x + \mathbf{j}y + \mathbf{k}z$, associated with the system, we obtain **F**. That is, does a quantity, $\mathcal{A}$, exist such that $\mathbf{F} = \mathcal{A} \cdot \mathbf{R}$? Consider the quantity

$$\mathcal{A} = k_x\mathbf{ii} + k_y\mathbf{jj} + k_z\mathbf{kk}. \tag{31.1}$$

Note: the product, **ii**, etc., is a new type of product which we shall investigate in detail shortly. Let us assume that the scalar product $\mathcal{A} \cdot \mathbf{R}$ is distributive. Then a simple computation shows that

$$\begin{aligned}\mathcal{A} \cdot \mathbf{R} &= (k_x\mathbf{ii} + k_y\mathbf{jj} + k_z\mathbf{kk}) \cdot (\mathbf{i}x + \mathbf{j}y + \mathbf{k}z) \\ &= k_xx\mathbf{i}(\mathbf{i} \cdot \mathbf{i}) + k_xy\mathbf{i}(\mathbf{i} \cdot \mathbf{j}) + k_xz\mathbf{i}(\mathbf{i} \cdot \mathbf{k}) \\ &\quad + k_yx\mathbf{j}(\mathbf{j} \cdot \mathbf{i}) + k_yy\mathbf{j}(\mathbf{j} \cdot \mathbf{j}) + k_yz\mathbf{j}(\mathbf{j} \cdot \mathbf{k}) \\ &\quad + k_zx\mathbf{k}(\mathbf{k} \cdot \mathbf{i}) + k_zy\mathbf{k}(\mathbf{k} \cdot \mathbf{j}) + k_zz\mathbf{k}(\mathbf{k} \cdot \mathbf{k}).\end{aligned}$$

By use of the well-known laws for the dot product, it is easily seen from the above that $\mathbf{F} = \mathcal{A} \cdot \mathbf{R}$ is valid. *The quantity $\mathcal{A}$ is known as a dyad or tensor of the second order.*

Example 2: This example is taken from linearized elasticity theory. Consider two neighboring points P, Q in a continuous medium. Let P', Q' denote the position of these points after the medium is strained; let $\mathbf{R}$ denote the position vector of P, $\mathbf{R} + d\mathbf{R}$ that of Q, $\mathbf{R} + \boldsymbol{\rho}$ that of P',

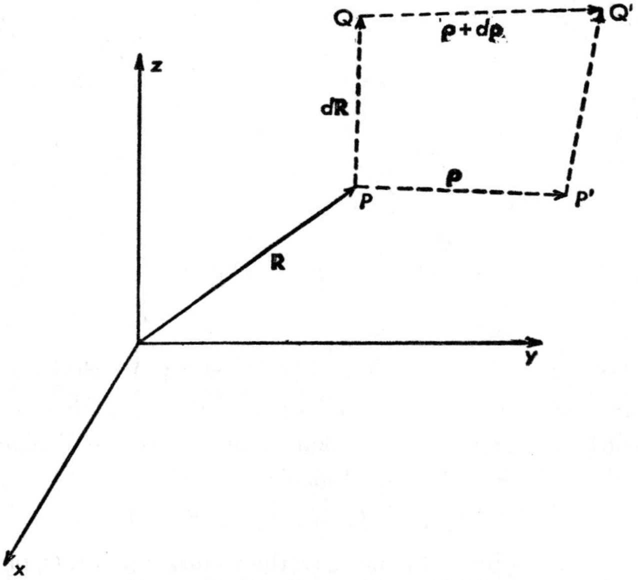

Figure 39: The Strain Vector Field, $\boldsymbol{\rho}$

$\mathbf{R} + d\mathbf{R} + \boldsymbol{\rho} + d\boldsymbol{\rho}$ that of Q'. A possible measure of strain appears to be the vector

$$\overrightarrow{\mathrm{P'Q'}} - \overrightarrow{\mathrm{PQ}} = (d\mathbf{R} + \boldsymbol{\rho} + d\boldsymbol{\rho} - \boldsymbol{\rho}) - d\mathbf{R} = d\boldsymbol{\rho}.$$

This strain vector may be expressed as

$$d\boldsymbol{\varrho} = \frac{\partial \boldsymbol{\varrho}}{\partial x}\,dx + \frac{\partial \boldsymbol{\varrho}}{\partial y}\,dy + \frac{\partial \boldsymbol{\varrho}}{\partial z}\,dz.$$

Now, $d\mathbf{R} = \mathbf{i}\,dx + \mathbf{j}\,dy + \mathbf{k}\,dz$. Hence, we may write the above vector, $d\boldsymbol{\varrho}$, in the form

$$d\boldsymbol{\varrho} = d\mathbf{R}\cdot\left(\mathbf{i}\,\frac{\partial \boldsymbol{\varrho}}{\partial x} + \mathbf{j}\,\frac{\partial \boldsymbol{\varrho}}{\partial y} + \mathbf{k}\,\frac{\partial \boldsymbol{\varrho}}{\partial z}\right).$$

Thus, again a new quantity enters the theory.

$$\mathcal{B} = \mathbf{i}\,\frac{\partial \boldsymbol{\varrho}}{\partial x} + \mathbf{j}\,\frac{\partial \boldsymbol{\varrho}}{\partial y} + \mathbf{k}\,\frac{\partial \boldsymbol{\varrho}}{\partial z}$$

is a *dyad or second-order tensor*. If we express $\boldsymbol{\varrho}$ in terms of its components $\boldsymbol{\varrho} = \mathbf{i}\rho_x + \mathbf{j}\rho_y + \mathbf{k}\rho_z$, then by direct expansion, we find that

$$\begin{aligned}\mathcal{B} = \nabla\boldsymbol{\varrho} = \mathbf{ii}\,\frac{\partial \rho_x}{\partial x} + \mathbf{ij}\,\frac{\partial \rho_y}{\partial x} + \mathbf{ik}\,\frac{\partial \rho_z}{\partial x}&\\ + \mathbf{ji}\,\frac{\partial \rho_x}{\partial y} + \mathbf{jj}\,\frac{\partial \rho_y}{\partial y} + \mathbf{jk}\,\frac{\partial \rho_z}{\partial y}&\\ + \mathbf{ki}\,\frac{\partial \rho_x}{\partial z} + \mathbf{kj}\,\frac{\partial \rho_y}{\partial z} + \mathbf{kk}\,\frac{\partial \rho_z}{\partial z}.&\end{aligned} \tag{31.2}$$

Note that $\mathcal{A}$ and $\mathcal{B}$ are quantities of the same type. Actually, $\nabla\boldsymbol{\varrho}$ is not the strain dyad (or tensor). One must eliminate that part of the displacement of $d\boldsymbol{\varrho}$ which is due to the simultaneous rotation of the elements $\overrightarrow{\mathrm{P'Q'}}$, $\overrightarrow{\mathrm{PQ}}$ before one can obtain the strain.

Next, we shall initiate a *brief formal* study of dyads. Consider the new multiplication table formed by "ordinary" multiplication of vectors.

	i	**j**	**k**
i	**ii**	**ij**	**ik**
j	**ji**	**jj**	**jk**
k	**ki**	**kj**	**kk**

(31.3)

These products are in general not commutative. That is, $\mathbf{ij} \neq \mathbf{ji}$, etc. Of course, **ii, jj, kk** are obviously commutative. We assume that these products have the following properties:

(1) they can be multiplied by a scalar, and such products are commutative, i.e., $(a)\mathbf{ii} = a\mathbf{ii} = \mathbf{ii}a$;

(2) they are associative, i.e., $a\mathbf{ii} + b\mathbf{ij} + c\mathbf{kj} + d\mathbf{ii} = (a + d)\mathbf{ii} + b\mathbf{ij} + c\mathbf{kj}$; this means that the addition can be performed in any order and corresponding dyads may be added;

(3) they are distributive under ordinary, scalar, or vector multiplication by scalars, vectors, etc.; we list a few types of such multiplications:

$$\begin{aligned}(a\mathbf{ij} + b\mathbf{jk}) \cdot \mathbf{d} &= a\mathbf{i}(\mathbf{j} \cdot \mathbf{d}) + b\mathbf{j}(\mathbf{k} \cdot \mathbf{d}) \\ \mathbf{d} \cdot (a\mathbf{ij} + b\mathbf{jk}) &= a(\mathbf{d} \cdot \mathbf{i})\mathbf{j} + b(\mathbf{d} \cdot \mathbf{j})\mathbf{k} \\ (a\mathbf{ij} + b\mathbf{jk}) \times \mathbf{d} &= a\mathbf{i}(\mathbf{j} \times \mathbf{d}) + b\mathbf{j}(\mathbf{k} \times \mathbf{d}) \\ (a\mathbf{ij} + b\mathbf{jk})\mathbf{d} &= a\mathbf{ijd} + b\mathbf{jkd}.\end{aligned}$$

The first two examples show that the order of multiplication must be preserved. This is due to the fact that our products are not commutative. The last example shows that "ordinary" multiplication of a dyad by a vector leads to a more general quantity—a third-order tensor. In fact, one can write even more complicated products such as $\mathbf{d} \cdot \mathcal{A} \cdot \mathbf{e}$ or $\mathbf{d} \cdot \mathcal{A} \times \mathbf{e}$, etc.

When one starts treating third-order or fourth-order tensors (which enter in relativity and other theories), the above notation becomes very complicated. In fact, the older texts on differential geometry in n-space abounded in notation such as $\overset{3}{\mathcal{A}} \overset{2}{\cdot} \overset{4}{\mathcal{B}}$, meaning that $\overset{3}{\mathcal{A}}$ is a third-order tensor, $\overset{4}{\mathcal{B}}$ is a fourth-order tensor, and the scalar product of the last two base vectors of $\overset{3}{\mathcal{A}}$ is to be taken with the first two base vectors of $\overset{4}{\mathcal{B}}$, (in order of last to first, next to last to second). Due to this difficulty, we now digress to a study of notation.

Problem 31.1: For Example (1) verify the relation, $\mathbf{F} = \mathcal{A} \cdot \mathbf{R}$.

Problem 31.2: In Example (2) show that $\mathcal{B}$ may be expressed by the right-hand side of (31.2).

Problem 31.3: Is $3\mathbf{ij} = \mathbf{ij}3$? Is $3\mathbf{ij} = 3\mathbf{ji}$?

Problem 31.4: Simplify $(3\mathbf{ii} + 4\mathbf{ij}) + (2\mathbf{ii} + 4\mathbf{ik})$.

Problem 31.5: Compute the vectors determined by: $(3\mathbf{ii} + 5\mathbf{ij}) \cdot \mathbf{i}$; $\mathbf{i} \cdot (3\mathbf{ii} + 5\mathbf{ij})$.

Problem 31.6: Compute the vectors determined by: $(4\mathbf{jj} + 6\mathbf{ik}) \times 2\mathbf{i}$; $2\mathbf{i} \times (4\mathbf{jj} + 6\mathbf{ik})$.

Problem 31.7: Compute the third-order tensors: $(4\mathbf{jj} + 3\mathbf{jk})\mathbf{i}$; $\mathbf{i}(4\mathbf{jj} + 3\mathbf{jk})$.

32. Tensor Notation; The Four Correspondence Principles in a Cartesian Orthogonal Coordinate System. In our future work, we shall deal with the *components of scalars, vectors, and tensors.* As we shall show, this device enables one to eliminate the awkwardness of notation indicated in the last section.

The work of this section is concerned with the methods for translating vector and dyad equations into component equations for a particular Cartesian orthogonal coordinate system. The methods will be based upon: (1) use of the *index notation* and *summation convention;* and (2) use of four *correspondence principles*.

(a) ***Index Notation.*** Evidently, a scalar has only one component. So our notation offers nothing new. Let us consider the case of vectors. As a first step in obtaining a simplified notation, we shall use the subscript or superscript notation (or index notation)

$$\mathbf{i} = \mathbf{e}_1 = \mathbf{e}^1, \qquad \mathbf{j} = \mathbf{e}_2 = \mathbf{e}^2, \qquad \mathbf{k} = \mathbf{e}_3 = \mathbf{e}^3.$$

Further, we indicate the components of $\mathbf{F}$ by the subscript or superscript notation

$$F_x = F_1 = F^1, \qquad F_y = F_2 = F^2, \qquad F_z = F_3 = F^3.$$

Note, F^2 means "the y component of $\mathbf{F}$" and not "the square of F." If one wishes to indicate the square of F, then an acceptable notation is $(F)^2$. In most of the work, there is very little possibility of confusion. The coordinate variables are denoted by

$$x = x_1 = x^1, \qquad y = x_2 = x^2, \qquad z = x_3 = x^3.$$

Similarly, we may represent tensors by their components. Let us consider our second example in Section 31 and write a particular component of the tensor $\mathfrak{B}$,

$$\frac{\partial \rho_x}{\partial y} = \frac{\partial \rho^1}{\partial x^2} = \frac{\partial \rho_1}{\partial x^2} = \rho_{21} = \rho^{21} = \nabla_2 \rho_1.$$

Careful attention must be paid to the ordering of the indices. Thus in writing ρ_{21} in the above, the first index (2) refers to the variable of the differentiation and the second index (1) refers to the component of the vector $\boldsymbol{\rho}$. There is no hard and fast rule, here. But, once a particular convention has been adopted, it should be consistently followed. In some respects, the notation $\nabla_2 \rho_1$ is most satisfactory, since it tells us that the partial derivative is formed with respect to the second coordinate variable. Symbolically, this corresponds to replacing the vector operator *del* by components: $\boldsymbol{\nabla} \leftrightarrow \nabla_j$. We have only written out one component of the above second-order tensor. This tensor has nine components. But the other components are formed in a similar manner.

(b) ***Summation Convention.*** As an additional short cut, we shall write

$$\mathbf{F} = F^1\mathbf{e}_1 + F^2\mathbf{e}_2 + F^3\mathbf{e}_3 = F^j\mathbf{e}_j$$
$$\mathbf{F} = F_1\mathbf{e}^1 + F_2\mathbf{e}^2 + F_3\mathbf{e}^3 = F_j\mathbf{e}^j \qquad j = 1, 2, 3.$$

The use *of the repeated index in a subscript and a superscript*, as in $F^i\mathbf{e}_j$ or $F_j\mathbf{e}^j$, to indicate a sum is called the summation convention. For the present we make no distinction between superscripts and subscripts. The index, j, in $F_j\mathbf{e}^j$ or $F^j\mathbf{e}_j$, is called a "*dummy*" *index*. That is, we may introduce an index i or k, and write: $F^j\mathbf{e}_j = F^i\mathbf{e}_i = F^k\mathbf{e}_k$.

By use of the index notation, and the above summation convention, we may express the tensor $\mathcal{B}$ of (31.2) in a very concise form. We obtain

$$\mathcal{B} = \boldsymbol{\nabla}\boldsymbol{\rho} = \rho_{ij}\mathbf{e}^i\mathbf{e}^j = \nabla_j\rho_k\mathbf{e}^j\mathbf{e}^k.$$

The student may verify this result by expanding the right-hand side of the above by use of the index notation explained in (a).

(c) ***The First and Second Correspondence Principles*** (***Tensor Addition***). In general, we shall represent a vector or a tensor by writing a typical component. Thus, we can set up a dictionary relating vectors and tensors with their components. We shall call the above procedure the *first correspondence principle*. In the following, we illustrate this procedure:

$$\mathbf{F} \leftrightarrow F^j \text{ or } F_j,$$
$$\mathcal{A} \leftrightarrow A^{ij} \text{ or } A_{ij} \text{ or } A_i^{\cdot j} \text{ or } A^i_{\cdot j},$$
$$\boldsymbol{\nabla} \leftrightarrow \nabla_i \text{ or } \nabla^i \text{ or } \frac{\partial}{\partial x^i}.$$

We can represent the sum of two vectors in our new notation by

$$\begin{array}{ccccc} \mathbf{A} & + & \mathbf{B} & = & \mathbf{C} \\ \updownarrow & & \updownarrow & & \updownarrow \\ A^j & + & B^j & = & C^j. \end{array}$$

The second equation states that the x, y, or z component of $\mathbf{A}$ plus the *corresponding* component of $\mathbf{B}$ equals the *corresponding* component of $\mathbf{C}$. This result was verified in Section 5. Note, the *corresponding components* of all three vectors must be used. That is, the expression $A^i + B^j = C^i$ is meaningless.

The rules following the table (31.3) show that two tensors of the same order (and hence the same number of indices) may be added by addition of *corresponding* components. Thus, we may express $\mathcal{A} + \mathcal{B} = \mathcal{C}$, where the tensors are of second order, by

$$A^{ij} + B^{ij} = C^{ij}, \qquad i, j = 1, 2, 3, \tag{32.1}$$

and similar expressions for higher order tensors. The indices i, j in the above relation are *called "free" indices. The same free indices must occur on both sides of the equation.* This rule merely states that corresponding components are being summed and generate the corresponding component of the sum. We call this rule *the second correspondence principle.*

(d) ***Scalar Products and the Third Correspondence Principle.*** The scalar product of two vectors may be expressed very simply by use of the summation convention. If $A^i = A_i$ denote the components of **A** and $B^i = B_i$ denote the components of **B** and if Ω is a scalar product of **A**, **B**, then

$$\Omega = \mathbf{A} \cdot \mathbf{B} = A_1B^1 + A_2B^2 + A_3B^3 = A_iB^i. \tag{32.2}$$

Note that Ω *has no index* and likewise, $A_iB^i = A^iB_i$ *has zero free indices.*

The following examples show how the scalar product of vectors and second-order tensors translate into index notation

$$\mathbf{F} = \mathcal{A} \cdot \mathbf{G}, \qquad \mathbf{H} = \mathbf{K} \cdot \mathcal{A}, \qquad \Omega = \mathbf{K} \cdot \mathcal{B} \cdot \mathbf{F},$$
$$F^i = A^{ij}G_j, \qquad H^i = K_jA^{ji}, \qquad \Omega = K_jB^{ji}F_i.$$

From these examples, we see that the rule is: *to express a scalar product, use the summation convention on the corresponding indices.* This rule is often called the *contraction of indices rule.* The reason for this name lies in the fact that by means of a scalar product between a second-order tensor and a vector, we reduce the tensor to a vector and hence "wipe out" one free index. Similarly, the scalar product of a vector by a vector reduces the vector to a scalar. Further, note that the same *free index, i,* occurs in both sides of the above equations. The fact that one may express the scalar product by means of the summation convention will be *called the third correspondence principle.*

As further examples, we translate the equations relating **F**, $\mathcal{A}$, and $d\boldsymbol{\varrho}$, $\nabla\boldsymbol{\varrho}$ of Section 31 into the new notation

$$\mathbf{F} = \mathcal{A} \cdot \mathbf{R} \leftrightarrow F^i = A^{ij}R_j = A^{ij}x_j, \tag{32.3}$$
$$d\boldsymbol{\varrho} = d\mathbf{R} \cdot \nabla\boldsymbol{\varrho} \leftrightarrow d\rho^i = dR^j\nabla_j\rho^i = dx^j\nabla_j\rho^i. \tag{32.4}$$

In order to verify these equations, one may expand the various components and compare them with the results of Section 31. For instance, the x-component of **F** is $F_x = (\mathcal{A} \cdot \mathbf{R})_x = k_xx$. Since $A^{11} = k_x$, $A^{22} = k_y$, $A^{33} = k_z$ and all other $A^{ij} = 0$ (see 31.1), and $R^1 = x$, $R^2 = y$, $R^3 = z$, a simple computation shows that F^1 of (32.3) reduces to F_x. In a similar manner, one may verify the second relation. It is of interest to note that the complicated appearing dyad relation for $d\boldsymbol{\varrho}$ in Section 31 is *nothing but the chain rule for forming the differential* $d\rho^j$. This follows by explicitly writing out the sum in (32.4).

To furnish one more example, let us verify the distributive law of scalar multiplication by means of components. It will be recalled this law was verified in Section 6(c) by use of the geometric idea of projection. In terms of our dictionary, we see that we wish to verify

$$\begin{aligned} \mathbf{A} \cdot (\mathbf{B} + \mathbf{C}) &= \mathbf{A} \cdot \mathbf{B} + \mathbf{A} \cdot \mathbf{C}, \text{ or} \\ A^i(B_i + C_i) &= A^iB_i + A^iC_i. \end{aligned} \tag{32.5}$$

The proof is very simple. The second relation of (32.5) follows immediately from the fact that the multiplication of numbers is distributive.

Finally, we shall verify a vector expansion involving ∇ by use of components. Earlier (Problem 19.1) we showed that

$$\nabla \cdot (\Omega \mathbf{V}) = \Omega \nabla \cdot \mathbf{V} + \mathbf{V} \cdot \nabla \Omega. \tag{32.6}$$

Now, the left-hand side of the above equation corresponds to

$$\nabla \cdot (\Omega \mathbf{V}) \leftrightarrow \nabla_j(\Omega V^j).$$

By definition, ∇_j is nothing but the partial differentiation operator $\partial/\partial x^j$. Thus, we find by differentiation that

$$\nabla_j(\Omega V^j) = \Omega \nabla_j V^j + V^j \nabla_j \Omega.$$

Since the right-hand side of this last relation corresponds exactly to the right-hand side of (32.6), we obtain a tensor verification for the vector expansion (32.6).

Problem 32.1: (1) By expanding $d\rho^i = dR^j \nabla_j \rho^i$, show that this equation is exactly the same as $d\boldsymbol{\varrho} = d\mathbf{R} \cdot \nabla \boldsymbol{\varrho}$; (2) Expand $H^i = I^{ij}\Omega_j$ and show that your results coincide with (29.13).

Problem 32.2: Expand $\nabla \boldsymbol{\varrho} \cdot d\mathbf{R}$ in terms of tensor components. Compare your result with $d\mathbf{R} \cdot \nabla \boldsymbol{\varrho}$ and show that a necessary and sufficient condition for $d\mathbf{R} \cdot \nabla \boldsymbol{\varrho} = \nabla \boldsymbol{\varrho} \cdot d\mathbf{R}$ (for arbitrary $d\mathbf{R}$) is that $\nabla_i \rho_j = \nabla_j \rho_i$. (A second-order tensor, h_{ij}, for which $h_{ij} = h_{ji}$ is called symmetric.)

Problem 32.3: In the component notation, it is usual to indicate the various components of a vector **A** by the row array (or row matrix): (A^1, A^2, A^3). Given the two vectors $(1, 2, -1)$, $(3, -1, 4)$. Find the sum of these vectors by use of the second correspondence principle.

Problem 32.4: Show that the vectors $(1, 4, 3)$, $(4, 2, -4)$ are orthogonal by use of the third correspondence principle.

Problem 32.5: Find the cosine of the angle between the vectors $(1, -2, -2)$ and $(2, 1, -2)$.

(e) ***Vector Products and the e and Kronecker Symbols; The Fourth Correspondence Principle.*** In order to treat vector products by component methods, we introduce the "e symbol," written as, $e^{ijk} = e_{ijk}$. We define this symbol as follows:

$$e^{123} = e^{312} = e^{231} = 1,$$
$$e^{132} = e^{213} = e^{321} = -1,$$
$$e^{112} = e^{233} = e^{111} = \cdots = 0.$$

The last line of the above means that all the e^{ijk} which have at least two equal indices are zero. This definition can be expressed in the language of permutation theory as follows:

$$\begin{aligned} e^{ijk} &= 1 && \text{when } i, j, k \text{ are an even permutation,} \\ e^{ijk} &= -1 && \text{when } i, j, k \text{ are an odd permutation,} \\ e^{ijk} &= 0 && \text{when } i, j, k \text{ contain two or more repeated indices.} \end{aligned} \tag{32.7}$$

In terms of the base vectors, $\mathbf{e}_i$, the above definitions imply that $e_{ijk} = \mathbf{e}_i \cdot \mathbf{e}_j \times \mathbf{e}_k$.

We shall now show that the cross product may be expressed in terms of the e^{ijk} symbol. To do this, we set up the correspondence

$$\mathbf{D} = \mathbf{A} \times \mathbf{B} \leftrightarrow D^i = e^{ijk}A_jB_k. \tag{32.8}$$

It should be noted that the indices on the components A_j, B_k are dummy indices. Further, the first index of the e symbol corresponds to the index on D^i; this is the free index. In order to verify that the correspondence of (32.8) furnishes the cross product, we expand one component and find by use of (32.7) that

$$D^1 = e^{123}A_2B_3 + e^{132}A_3B_2 = A_2B_3 - A_3B_2.$$

If we write this last relation in the more familiar language, $D_x = A_yB_z - A_zB_y$, then the validity of (32.8) becomes evident. The use of the e symbol to express the cross product will be called the *fourth correspondence principle.*

To facilitate the use of the e symbol, we introduce two other symbols. First, we define the Kronecker delta symbol, $\delta_{ij} = \delta^{ij} = \delta^i_j$ by

$$\begin{aligned} \delta^i_j &= 1, && \text{when} \quad i = j \ (\text{as } \delta^1_1 = 1), \\ \delta^i_j &= 0, && \text{when} \quad i \neq j \ (\text{as } \delta^1_2 = 0). \end{aligned} \tag{32.9}$$

From this definition we obtain three useful formulas:

$$\delta^j_j = 3, \qquad \delta^i_jA_i = A_j, \qquad \delta_{ij}\delta^{jl} = \delta^l_i. \tag{32.10}$$

Secondly, we *define the generalized Kronecker delta symbol,* δ^{ij}_{ln}, *by*

$$\begin{aligned} \delta^{ij}_{ln} &= 1, && \text{if } i = l, j = n, \text{ and } i \neq j \ (\text{as, } \delta^{12}_{12} = 1) \\ \delta^{ij}_{ln} &= -1, && \text{if } i = n, j = l, \text{ and } i \neq j \ (\text{as, } \delta^{12}_{21} = -1) \\ \delta^{ij}_{ln} &= 0, && \text{for all other combinations of indices.} \end{aligned} \tag{32.11}$$

Several useful results follow from the last definition. Evaluation of the various possible combinations of indices shows that

$$\begin{aligned} \delta^{ij}_{lj} &= -\delta^{ij}_{jl} = 2\delta^{i}_{l}, \\ \delta^{ij}_{ln} &= \delta^{i}_{l}\delta^{j}_{n} - \delta^{i}_{n}\delta^{j}_{l}, \\ \delta^{ij}_{ln} &= e^{ijk}e_{kln}. \end{aligned} \tag{32.12}$$

It is hoped that the student will actually verify representative samples of the above relations.

As an example of the use of the e symbol, we consider the triple scalar product. That is, we wish to express $\mathbf{C} \cdot (\mathbf{A} \times \mathbf{B})$ in terms of components. We do this in two steps. First, let $\mathbf{D} = \mathbf{A} \times \mathbf{B}$ [see (32.8)]. Then the triple scalar product, Ω, is given by

$$\Omega = C_i D^i = C_i e^{ijk} A_j B_k = e^{ijk} C_i A_j B_k. \tag{32.13}$$

In Section 8 we saw that the triple scalar product is a determinant. Thus, the equation (32.13) shows how one may express a *third-order determinant in the new notation.*

As an example of the utility of the e symbol and Kronecker symbol, we shall show how easily one may derive the triple vector expansion of Section 9. Again, we use (32.8) and find that $\mathbf{E} = \mathbf{C} \times \mathbf{D} = \mathbf{C} \times (\mathbf{A} \times \mathbf{B})$ may be expressed in terms of components by

$$E^i = e^{ijk} C_j D_k = e^{ijk} C_j (e_{kln} A^l B^n).$$

By use of the third relation in (32.12), we find that

$$E^i = \delta^{ij}_{ln} C_j A^l B^n.$$

Use of the second relation in (32.12) shows that the expression for $\mathbf{E}$ may be further simplified to read

$$E^i = (\delta^i_l \delta^j_n - \delta^i_n \delta^j_l) C_j A^l B^n.$$

Since $\delta^i_l A^l = A^i$, etc., the above expression for E^i reduces to

$$\begin{aligned} E^i &= \delta^j_n A^i C_j B^n - \delta^j_l B^i C_j A^l \\ &= A^i (C_n B^n) - B^i (C_l A^l). \end{aligned}$$

Translating this last relation into vector notation by the correspondence principles, we obtain the desired triple vector expansion.

Finally, we furnish an example of the use of components in deriving vector identities containing ∇ and the cross product. The *four correspondence principles* are the main tool. With this in mind, we attempt to determine $\nabla \times (\mathbf{V} \times \mathbf{W})$. For simplicity, we let $\mathbf{Z} = \mathbf{V} \times \mathbf{W}$. By use of

YORK JUNIOR COLLEGE LIBRARY
YORK, PENNA

the first and fourth correspondence principles, we may replace $\boldsymbol{\nabla} \times \mathbf{Z} = \boldsymbol{\nabla} \times (\mathbf{V} \times \mathbf{W})$ by

$$e^{ijk}\nabla_j Z_k = e^{ijk}\nabla_j(e_{kln}V^l W^n).$$

By use of the properties of e^{ijk}, δ^{ij}_{ln}, we find that the above expression may be written as

$$\begin{aligned} e^{ijk}e_{kln}\nabla_j(V^l W^n) &= \delta^{ij}_{ln}(V^l\nabla_j W^n + W^n\nabla_j V^l) \\ &= (\delta^i_l\delta^j_n - \delta^i_n\delta^j_l)(V^l\nabla_j W^n + W^n\nabla_j V^l) \\ &= V^i\nabla_n W^n - V^i\nabla_j W^i + W^i\nabla_j V^i - W^i\nabla_l V^l. \end{aligned}$$

Translating the above equation into vector form by means of the correspondence principles, we obtain (note: i is the free index)

$$\boldsymbol{\nabla} \times (\mathbf{V} \times \mathbf{W}) = \mathbf{V}(\boldsymbol{\nabla} \cdot \mathbf{W}) - (\mathbf{V} \cdot \boldsymbol{\nabla})\mathbf{W} + (\mathbf{W} \cdot \boldsymbol{\nabla})\mathbf{V} - \mathbf{W}(\boldsymbol{\nabla} \cdot \mathbf{V}).$$

Problem 32.6: The vectors from the origin to the points A, B, C are, respectively, (1, 2, 3), (1, −2, 1), (2, 1, −1). Find: (1) two vectors in the plane of ABC; (2) the normal to this plane by use of the fourth correspondence principle.

Problem 32.7: Show that $\mathbf{A} \times (\mathbf{B} \times \mathbf{C}) + \mathbf{B} \times (\mathbf{C} \times \mathbf{A}) + \mathbf{C} \times (\mathbf{A} \times \mathbf{B}) = 0$.

Problem 32.8: Verify the relations: (1) $\delta^i_i = 3$; (2) $\delta^i_j A_i = A_j$; (3) $\delta_{ij}\delta^{jl} = \delta^l_i$.

Problem 32.9: Verify the relations: (1) $\delta^{ij}_{kj} = 2\delta^i_k$; (2) $e^{ijk}e_{ijk} = \lfloor\underline{3}$.

Problem 32.10: Verify $\delta^{kj}_{ln} = \delta^k_l\delta^j_n - \delta^j_l\delta^k_n$. *Hint:* Consider the possible cases. First, if $j = k$ or $l = n$, then $\delta^{kj}_{ln} = 0$ (why?).

Problem 32.11: Find the expansion for $\boldsymbol{\nabla} \cdot (\mathbf{U} \times \mathbf{V})$ in terms of components.

Problem 32.12: Find the value of $\boldsymbol{\nabla} \times \boldsymbol{\nabla}\Omega$ by use of components.

Problem 32.13: Show that: (1) $\boldsymbol{\nabla} \cdot \mathbf{R} = 3$, (2) $\boldsymbol{\nabla} \times \mathbf{R} = 0$ by use of the component notation. The above refers to the space radial vector field $\mathbf{R}$, (x^1, x^2, x^3). If $\mathbf{r}$ is the plane radial vector field $(x^1, x^2, 0)$, find $\boldsymbol{\nabla} \cdot \mathbf{r}$, $\boldsymbol{\nabla} \times \mathbf{r}$.

Problem 32.14: Show that $\mathbf{U} \cdot (\boldsymbol{\nabla}\mathbf{V}) = (\mathbf{U} \cdot \boldsymbol{\nabla})\mathbf{V}$ by use of components.

Problem 32.15: Find $\mathbf{W} \cdot \boldsymbol{\nabla}\mathbf{R}$ in terms of components.

Problem 32.16: Let us reconsider Problem 32.2. If $\nabla_i\rho_j = \nabla_j\rho_i$, show that: (1) $\boldsymbol{\varrho}$ is irrotational; (2) $\boldsymbol{\varrho}$ is a gradient vector (see Stokes's theorem).

Problem 32.17: Show that the general second-order tensor h_{ij} can be written as a sum of a symmetric tensor $s_{ij} = s_{ji}$ and an alternating tensor, $a_{ij} = -a_{ji}$.

Problem 32.18: If s_{ij} is a symmetric tensor and a_{ij} is an alternating tensor, prove that $s^{ij}a_{ij} = 0$.

Problem 32.19: Prove that if s_{ij} is an arbitrary symmetric tensor and $s^{ij}a_{ij} = 0$, then a_{ij} is an alternating tensor.

Problem 32.20: Develop the theory of the e and delta symbols for $n = 2$ and $n = 4$.

Problem 32.21: By use of component notation, show that if $\nabla \cdot \mathbf{F} = 0$ then $\oint_S \mathbf{n} \times (\nabla \times \mathbf{F})\, d\sigma = -\int_T \nabla^2\mathbf{F}\, d\tau$ in a specified Cartesian orthogonal coordinate system, x^j.

33. Tensor Analysis as an Invariant Theory. In our previous work we have treated the components of a tensor in a particular Cartesian orthogonal coordinate system. The question arises, "How do the components of a tensor transform when the coordinate system is changed?" Actually, this question should have been raised before, but we have refrained from doing so. That is, we have represented vectors by arrows and talked of more general quantities, dyads, of similar nature. The essence of these tensors lies in the fact that they are independent of the coordinate system or are invariant under coordinate transformations. Notice that it is the vectors and dyads, not their components, that are invariant. Thus, two questions must be answered:

(1) What coordinate systems are to be considered?

(2) How do the components of tensors transform under the allowed coordinate transformations?

(a) ***The Allowable Coordinate Systems.*** Let us consider the case where the allowable coordinate systems are right-handed Cartesian orthogonal. To simplify matters, we consider a *particular* right-handed Cartesian orthogonal coordinate system with coordinate variables x^j, $j = 1, 2, 3$. Further, let $'x^j$, $j = 1, 2, 3$, denote the coordinate variables of any other right-handed Cartesian orthogonal coordinate system, whose origin coincides with that of the x^j system. Evidently, the x^j coordinate system may be made to coincide with the $'x^j$ coordinate system by a proper rotation. That is, the allowable coordinate systems are related by means of a rotation transformation. To determine explicit formulas for these transformations, we consider the invariant radius vector field, $\mathbf{R}$, in both systems of coordinates:

$$\mathbf{R} = x^j\mathbf{e}_j = {'x^j}\, {'\mathbf{e}_j} \tag{33.1}$$

where $\mathbf{e}_j$, $'\mathbf{e}_j$ are the base vectors of the systems (that is, **i, j, k,** etc.). Forming the scalar product of $\mathbf{R}$ with $\mathbf{e}^k = \mathbf{e}_k$ ($k = 1, 2, 3$), we obtain

$$x^k = (\mathbf{e}^k \cdot {'\mathbf{e}_j})'x^j.$$

Note that the quantities $(\mathbf{e}^k \cdot {}'\mathbf{e}_j) = a_j^k$ are the cosines of the angles between $\mathbf{e}^k$ and $'\mathbf{e}_j$. Since the sum of the squares of the direction cosines of any vector, $\mathbf{e}^k$, is plus one and the sum of the products of the direction cosines of two orthogonal vectors, $\mathbf{e}^k$, $\mathbf{e}^l$, is zero, it follows that the a_j^k satisfy the *orthogonality relations:*

$$\sum_{j=1}^{3} (a_j^k)^2 = 1, \qquad \sum_{j=1}^{3} a_j^k a_j^l = 0, \qquad l \neq k,\ j,\ l,\ k = 1, 2, 3. \qquad (33.2)$$

The symbol Σ in the above is the usual summation symbol. We cannot use the summation convention of Section 32(b), since we are not summing on an index which is repeated as both a subscript and superscript. In addition to the conditions (33.2), the coefficients a_j^k must be such that the x^i, $'x^i$ systems are both right-handed. It can be shown that this fact necessitates the condition that the determinant of the a_j^k is plus one. For future reference, we write the transformation equations in the form

$$x^k = a_j^k \, 'x^j. \qquad (33.3)$$

Conversely, if x^j are related to $'x^j$ by the above linear transformation where a_j^k satisfy (33.2), and the determinant of the a_j^k equals plus one, then the resulting transformation defines a rotation. This can easily be checked by showing that the lengths of vectors through the origin and the angle between vectors through the origin is not altered.

The transformations defined by (33.3), possessing the orthogonal properties (33.2), and having determinant plus one, form a *group*. This means that the set of rotation transformations has the following properties:

(1) the *succession of two rotation transformations is a rotation transformation;* that is, if $x^k = a_j^k \, 'x^j$, $'x^j = b_l^j \, ''x^l$ are rotations, then $x^k = (a_j^k b_l^j)''x^l$ is also a rotation; physically, the result is evident;
(2) the transformations are *associative;* we shall explain this term more fully later (see Problem 33.5);
(3) the transformations contain an *identity transformation;* in our case, this is the "zero" rotation, $x^k = {}'x^k$, $k = 1, 2, 3$;
(4) each transformation has an *inverse;* thus, by forming the scalar product of $\mathbf{R}$ in (33.1) with $'\mathbf{e}^k = {}'\mathbf{e}_k$, $k = 1, 2, 3$, we obtain

$$'x^k = ({}'\mathbf{e}^k \cdot \mathbf{e}_j)x^j = A_j^k x^j, \qquad A_j^k = {}'\mathbf{e}^k \cdot \mathbf{e}_j = a_k^j \qquad (33.4)$$

evidently, this transformation is the *inverse transformation* of (33.3); note, A_j^k satisfy (33.2).

To summarize: The allowable coordinate systems are those determined by the *rotation group of transformations*. The coordinate transformations are defined by (33.2), (33.3) and have determinant plus one. In a future section, we shall consider the case where the coordinate transformations are defined by a more general group. In particular, if the linear transformations (33.3) are such that *reflections* as well as rotations are permitted, then the determinant of the coefficients a_j^k is either minus or plus one. This follows from the fact that the transformation, $x = 'x$, $y = 'y$, $z = -'z$, changes a right-handed into a left-handed system. The coefficients a_j^k in this case are: $a_1^1 = a_2^2 = 1$, $a_3^3 = -1$, all other $a_j^k = 0$, and the determinant of these coefficients is -1. It can be shown that those linear transformations which permit both reflections and rotations form a group, the so-called *orthogonal group*.

Problem 33.1: Show the relations (33.2) follow from the equations $\mathbf{e}^k \cdot \mathbf{e}^k = 1$, $\mathbf{e}^k \cdot \mathbf{e}^j = 0$, $j \neq k$, when $\mathbf{e}^k$ are expressed in terms of $'\mathbf{e}_j$.

Hint: Use the relation $\mathbf{e}^k = \sum_{j=1}^{3} a_j^k \, '\mathbf{e}_j$.

Problem 33.2: By use of the triple scalar product, $'\mathbf{e}_1 \cdot '\mathbf{e}_2 \times '\mathbf{e}_3$, show that the determinant of the a_j^k is plus one for right-hand systems $\mathbf{e}_k$, $'\mathbf{e}_k$. What is the value of this determinant for left-hand systems $\mathbf{e}_k$, $'\mathbf{e}_k$? *Hint:* Form the triple scalar product by use of (32.13); note $e_{ijk} = \mathbf{e}_i \cdot \mathbf{e}_j \times \mathbf{e}_k$.

Problem 33.3: By considering two radius vector fields: $\mathbf{R} = \mathbf{i}x + \mathbf{j}y + \mathbf{k}z$, $\mathbf{R}^* = \mathbf{i}x^* + \mathbf{j}y^* + \mathbf{k}z^*$, show that the transformation relations of the last section imply that the lengths of these vectors and the angle between them is unaltered by the transformations.

Problem 33.4: An abstract group is defined as follows: A set of elements $A, B, C, \cdots$ exists and a group operation, called the product, exists such that:

(1) the product of any two elements is an element of the group, $AB = C$, say;
(2) the associative law is valid, $(AB)C = A(BC)$;
(3) an identity element exists such that $AI = IA = A$ for every element;
(4) each element, A, possesses an inverse, A^{-1}, so that $AA^{-1} = A^{-1}A = I$.

Show that the positive and negative integers form a group when ordinary addition is the group operation, called the product.

Problem 33.5: Prove that if $x^k = a_j^k \, 'x^j$, $'x^j = b_l^j \, ''x^l$, $''x^l = c_n^l \, '''x^n$ are three linear transformations, then the transformation relating x^k and $'''x^n$

is independent of the order in which the variables $'x^j$, $''x^l$ are eliminated. In other words, if A, B, C denote these transformations in a symbolic manner and multiplication corresponds to the elimination of the common variable in two transformations, then $(AB)C = A(BC)$. This is called the associative law for transformations.

Problem 33.6: Does the set of all translations form a group? Discuss this problem in relation to the four defining group properties. What is the identity?

Problem 33.7: Compute the transformation formulas corresponding to rotations about the origin in the x,y-plane of 0°, 45°, 90°, 135°, 180°, 225°, 270°, 315°. Show that these rotations form a group.

Problem 33.8: Prove that if $x^k = a_j^k \, 'x^j$, $'x^j = b_l^j \, ''x^l$ are rotations, then $x^k = a_j^k b_l^j \, ''x^l$ is a rotation. *Hint:* Determine the relation between the $''\mathbf{e}^k$ and $\mathbf{e}^k$ base vectors and use the procedure of Problem 33.1.

(b) ***Transformation Formulas for the Components of Vectors and Tensors.*** Now, we attempt to answer the second question raised at the beginning of this section. By substituting (33.3) into (33.1), we obtain: $a_j^k \, 'x^j \mathbf{e}_k = 'x^j \, '\mathbf{e}_j$. Since this equation is valid for all $'x^j$, we find that

$$'\mathbf{e}_j = a_j^k \mathbf{e}_k. \tag{33.5}$$

Similarly by use of the inverse transformation, we find

$$\mathbf{e}_i = A_i^j \, '\mathbf{e}_j = \sum_{j=1}^{3} a_j^i \, '\mathbf{e}_j. \tag{33.6}$$

where $A_j^k = a_k^j$. These formulas show how the unit base vectors transform under a coordinate transformation. By comparison of (33.3) with the last equation, we see that the *base vectors transform as do the coordinate variables under the rotation group.*

Now we determine the formula by which the components of a vector transform. Let us express the general vector $\mathbf{F}$ in terms of components in the coordinate systems x^i and $'x^i$

$$\mathbf{F} = F^j \mathbf{e}_j = 'F^j \, '\mathbf{e}_j.$$

By substituting first (33.5) and then (33.6) into the above, we obtain the formulas

$$F^k = a_j^k \, 'F^j \tag{33.7}$$

$$'F^k = A_j^k F^j. \tag{33.8}$$

Evidently, these last two transformations are inverse transformations. By comparison of (33.7) and (33.3), we see that the components of a vector transform as do the coordinate variables under the rotation group of transformations. It is very important to notice that the differentials of the coordinate variables also transform as the coordinate variables under the rotation group. Thus, one can say that the *components of a vector and the base vectors transform as do the differentials of the coordinate variables under the rotation group of transformations.*

By use of a similar procedure, we can determine how the components of a tensor transform. Corresponding to the expansion of **F** in terms of components, we write for the second-order tensor, $\mathfrak{A} = F^{ij}\mathbf{e}_i\mathbf{e}_j = {}'F^{ij}\,{}'\mathbf{e}_i\,{}'\mathbf{e}_j$. The transformation formulas for the components of the tensor $\mathfrak{A}$ are

$$F^{ij} = a^i_k a^j_l\,{}'F^{kl}, \qquad {}'F^{ij} = A^i_k A^j_l F^{kl}.$$

Thus, a second-order tensor transforms as does the product of two vectors, V^iW^j. Similarly, a third-order tensor transforms as the product of three vectors, etc. These results remain valid when the group of coordinate transformations is the orthogonal group.

In the next section, we shall generalize the group of coordinate transformations and determine how vectors, etc., transform under the new group.

Problem 33.9: Show that for any vector **F**, $F^iF_j = {}'F^i\,{}'F_j$.

Problem 33.10: Assume that $\delta_{ij} = \delta^{ij}$ is a second-order tensor. Show that the values of the new components of δ_{ij} are: $\delta_{ij} = 1$, if $i = j$; $\delta_{ij} = 0$, if $i \neq j$.

Problem 33.11: Assume that e^{ijk} are the components of a third-order tensor. What are the values of the new components of e^{ijk}? *Hint:* If two rows or columns of a determinant are equal, then the determinant has the value zero and if two rows or columns of a determinant are interchanged, then the determinant changes sign, hence $e^{ijk}A^1_iA^2_jA^3_k = {}'e^{123} = 1$, etc.

Problem 33.12: By use of the chain rule for differentiation, $\dfrac{\partial}{\partial x^l} = \dfrac{\partial\,{}'x^j}{\partial x^l}\dfrac{\partial}{\partial\,{}'x^j}$ show that the vector operator ∇_j transforms as follows under the rotation group: $\nabla_l = A^j_l\,{}'\nabla_j$.

Problem 33.13: Consider Figure 38 of Section 31. Introduce a new orthogonal coordinate system such that $O'z$ falls along Oz, $O'x$ bisects the angle between Ox, Oy. Determine the components of a vector **F** in the new coordinate system in terms of the components of **F** in the old system. Also, find the components of the second-order tensor $\mathfrak{A}$ in the new coordinate system.

ADDITIONAL PROBLEMS

1. The equation of a plane in tensor form is

$$a_j x^j + 1 = 0, \qquad j = 1, 2, 3.$$

Show that a_j are the components of a vector.

2. The equation of a quadric surface in tensor form is

$$a_{ij} x^i x^j + 1 = 0, \qquad i, j = 1, 2, 3.$$

Show that a_{ij} are the components of a second-order symmetric tensor.

3. Show that the six quantities, I_{jk}, of Section 29 are the components of a second-order symmetric tensor, the moment of inertia tensor. Hence, write Euler's equations of motion of a rigid body in tensor notation.

4. If F^i is a solenoidal vector ($\nabla_j F^j = 0$), show by use of tensor methods that, $\nabla \times \{\nabla \times [\nabla \times (\nabla \times \mathbf{F})]\} = \nabla^2\nabla^2\mathbf{F}$.

5. If $\mathfrak{A}$ is a third-order tensor, express Stokes's theorem

$$\oint_C \mathbf{t} * \mathfrak{A}\, ds = \int_S (\mathbf{n} \times \nabla) * \mathfrak{A}\, d\sigma$$

in tensor notation when the star multiplication is scalar multiplication. Show that in Cartesian orthogonal coordinates, the above formula has tensor character.

6. Express Maxwell's electromagnetic equations

$$\nabla \times \mathbf{H} = \frac{\epsilon}{c}\frac{\partial \mathbf{E}}{\partial t}, \qquad \nabla \cdot \mathbf{H} = 0,$$

$$\nabla \times \mathbf{E} = -\frac{\mu}{c}\frac{\partial \mathbf{H}}{\partial t}, \qquad \nabla \cdot \mathbf{E} = 0.$$

in tensor notation. Show that the standing wave solutions,

$$\mathbf{E} = {}'\mathbf{E}(x, y, z)e^{i\bar{k}t}, \qquad \mathbf{H} = {}'\mathbf{H}(x, y, z)e^{i\bar{k}t}, \qquad i^2 = -1,$$

satisfy the relations

$$e^{ijk}e_{lmi}\nabla^m\nabla_j\, {}'H_k - k^2\, {}'H_l = 0, \qquad \nabla_j\, {}'H^j = 0,$$

where $k^2 = \epsilon\mu\bar{k}^2/c^2$.

7. Let G_{lp} be a tensor solution of the standing wave equation

(1) $$e^{ijk}e_{lmi}\nabla^m\nabla_j G_{kp} - k^2 G_{lp} = 0.$$

Introduce the tensor H_{lp} defined by

(2) $$H^i_{\cdot p} = e^{ijk}\nabla_j G_{kp}$$

and show that the above equation and the equation

$$(3) \qquad k^2 G_{lp} = e_{lmi} \nabla^m H^i_{\cdot p}$$

are equivalent to (1) when H_{lp} satisfies the relation (1). By writing

$$H^{lp} = e^{lpi} \nabla_i \Omega$$

show that if Ω satisfies the scalar wave equation $\nabla^2 \Omega + k^2 \Omega = 0$ then[1] $G_{lp} = (\nabla_l \nabla_p - \nabla^2 \delta_{lp}) \Omega$ satisfies the relation (1). Discuss other methods of generating solutions of (1).

[1] This tensor was introduced by J. Schwinger and H. Levine, "On the Theory of Electromagnetic Wave Diffraction by an Aperture in an Infinite Plane Conducting Screen," *Communications on Pure and Applied Mathematics*, Vol. III, No. 4, Dec. 1950, p. 385.

Chapter VI

TENSORS IN GENERAL CARTESIAN COORDINATES

34. Survey of Topics. In this chapter, we shall be concerned with several topics which, at first glance, appear unrelated. Thus, we shall discuss: (1) the elements of determinant theory; (2) the two types of base vectors (covariant and contravariant); (3) the centered affine group of coordinate transformations; (4) the cross product of vectors under this group; (5) the definition of and transformation laws for the metric tensor and other tensors; (6) the geometric interpretation of the covariant and contravariant components of a vector; (7) the relation of complex numbers to vectors. These diverse topics are related as follows. To discuss the coordinate transformations of the centered affine group, one needs determinant theory; the discussion of the metric tensor depends upon a knowledge of the properties of the base vectors. Further, all of the remaining topics depend upon the properties of the centered affine group of coordinate transformations and the metric tensor.

35. Elements of Determinant Theory. We shall consider five important properties of third-order determinants:[1] (a) the interchange of two rows of a determinant; (b) the rule for determining the reduced cofactors; (c) the general formula for the expansion of a determinant by rows; (d) the rule for evaluating the elements of the product of two determinants; (e) the rule for differentiating determinants. Proofs of several other interesting properties of determinants are discussed in the problems. Further, the extensions of some of the above properties to second- and fourth-order determinants are considered in these problems.

(a) ***The Interchange of Two Rows of a Determinant.*** Through the use of the triple scalar expansion (32.13), we find that the determinant, a, may be written as

$$a = e^{kln}a_k^1 a_l^2 a_n^3, \qquad k, l, n = 1, 2, 3 \tag{35.1}$$

[1] An interesting exposition of the theory of Sections 35 and 37 will be found in A. J. McConnell, *Applications of the Absolute Differential Calculus*, Blackie and Son, London, 1931.

where the vectors **C**, **A**, **B** of (32.13)[2] are $\mathbf{a}^1$, $\mathbf{a}^2$, $\mathbf{a}^3$. Since the e symbol is antisymmetric ($e^{kln} = -e^{knl}$), the equation for the determinant, a, may be written in the form

$$a = -e^{knl}a_k^1 a_l^2 a_n^3 = -e^{knl}a_k^1 a_n^3 a_l^2. \tag{35.2}$$

The last term in the right-hand side of the above equation is the determinant formed by interchanging $\mathbf{a}^2$, $\mathbf{a}^3$. Thus, *if two rows of a determinant are interchanged, the determinant changes sign.* This result is also evident from the vector properties of the triple scalar product. Evidently, *if two rows of a determinant are equal or proportional, then the determinant vanishes.*

(b) ***The Reduced Cofactors,*** $A_j^i (a \neq 0)$. The formula (35.1) may be used to determine quantities A_j^i, called the reduced cofactors of the determinant. Dividing (35.1) by the determinant a, we obtain

$$\left(\frac{e^{kln}a_l^2 a_n^3}{a}\right) a_k^1 = 1.$$

We define the reduced cofactors, A_1^k, to be (see Appendix I)

$$A_1^k = (e^{kln}a_l^2 a_n^3)/a.$$

Similar formulas can be obtained for A_2^k, A_3^k.

(c) ***Expansion of a Determinant by Rows (or Columns).*** Another important formula in determinant theory can be found by writing the general formula of which (35.2) is a special case. This formula is

$$e^{pqr}a = e^{knl}a_k^p a_n^q a_l^r. \tag{35.3}$$

To verify the above, we need only to write out the various combinations for p, q, r and use the antisymmetric property of the e symbol. The expression (35.2) is obtained if $p = 1$, $q = 3$, $r = 2$ in (35.3). Similarly, one may expand a determinant by columns. We shall consider this topic in the problems. (See Problem 35.7.)

(d) ***The Product Rule for Determinants.*** We shall verify the following rule for multiplying determinants: *If b_l^k are the elements of a determinant, b, and A_l^k are the elements of a determinant, A, then*

$$c_j^k = b_l^k A_j^l \tag{35.4}$$

are permissible elements of the determinant, $c = bA$. This does not imply that the elements of a determinant are unique. It is merely one method for expressing the product of two determinants. Note that the upper index orders the rows of b_l^k, c_l^k and the lower index orders the rows of A_l^k, in their corresponding determinants.

[2] Here, $\mathbf{a}^1 = a_1^1\mathbf{i} + a_2^1\mathbf{j} + a_3^1\mathbf{k}$, etc.

The proof of the above result is fairly simple. Forming the determinant of the elements c^k_l, we may write, $c = e^{knl}c^1_k c^2_n c^3_l$. Eliminating the elements of c^k_l by use of (35.4), we obtain

$$c = e^{knl}(b^1_p A^p_k)(b^2_q A^q_n)(b^3_r A^r_l).$$

By rearranging the terms of the right-hand side of the above, we find that this equation may be written in the form

$$c = (e^{knl}A^p_k A^q_n A^r_l)(b^1_p b^2_q b^3_r).$$

If we assume that the determinant A can be expanded by columns and apply the formula (35.3) to the elements A^j_k, then the first parenthesis in the right-hand side of the above equation may be replaced by $e^{pqr}A$. Hence, our relation reduces to

$$c = A(e^{pqr}b^1_p b^2_q b^3_r).$$

Since the expression in the parenthesis in the right-hand side of this last relation is the determinant b, our result is verified.

(e) ***Differentiation of Determinants.*** Let us assume that the elements of a determinant are functions of some parameter α. It can be shown that the *derivative of the third-order determinant a with respect to α is given by a sum of three determinants C_1, C_2, C_3, where C_1 consists of a determinant in which the first row (or first column) is composed of the derived elements of the first row of a and the second and third rows contain the same element as in a, etc., for C_2, C_3.* This result follows directly by differentiation of the determinant, a, of (35.1).

It is interesting to verify the formula for the derivative of the Jacobian, J, of (30.7) by use of the above rule. Evidently we may express J by the formula

$$J = e^{knl}\frac{\partial x^1}{\partial \bar{x}^k}\frac{\partial x^2}{\partial \bar{x}^n}\frac{\partial x^3}{\partial \bar{x}^l}.$$

If we differentiate with respect to t, we obtain

$$\begin{aligned}\frac{\partial J}{\partial t} &= e^{knl}\frac{\partial}{\partial \bar{x}^k}\left(\frac{\partial x^1}{\partial t}\right)\frac{\partial x^2}{\partial \bar{x}^n}\frac{\partial x^3}{\partial \bar{x}^l} \\ &+ e^{knl}\frac{\partial x^1}{\partial \bar{x}^k}\frac{\partial}{\partial \bar{x}^n}\left(\frac{\partial x^2}{\partial t}\right)\frac{\partial x^3}{\partial \bar{x}^l} \\ &+ e^{knl}\frac{\partial x^1}{\partial \bar{x}^k}\frac{\partial x^2}{\partial \bar{x}^n}\frac{\partial}{\partial \bar{x}^l}\left(\frac{\partial x^3}{\partial t}\right).\end{aligned}$$

Now, $\dfrac{\partial x^1}{\partial t} = v^1$, $\dfrac{\partial x^2}{\partial t} = v^2$, etc. Further, by use of the chain rule for differentiation, we may write

$$\frac{\partial x^i}{\partial \bar{x}^n} = \frac{\partial x^i}{\partial x^j}\frac{\partial x^j}{\partial \bar{x}^n}.$$

Thus, the first determinant in the right-hand side of the expansion for $\frac{\partial J}{\partial t}$ is

$$C_1 = e^{knl} \frac{\partial v^1}{\partial x^i} \frac{\partial x^2}{\partial x^j} \frac{\partial x^3}{\partial x^p} \frac{\partial x^i}{\partial \bar{x}^k} \frac{\partial x^j}{\partial \bar{x}^n} \frac{\partial x^p}{\partial \bar{x}^l}.$$

Since $\frac{\partial x^2}{\partial x^j} = 0$ unless $j = 2$ and then $\frac{\partial x^2}{\partial x^2} = 1$, we may consider C_1 as the product of two determinants:

$$C_1 = \begin{vmatrix} \frac{\partial v^1}{\partial x^1} & \frac{\partial v^1}{\partial x^2} & \frac{\partial v^1}{\partial x^3} \\ 0 & 1 & 0 \\ 0 & 0 & 1 \end{vmatrix} J = \frac{\partial v^1}{\partial x^1} J.$$

Similar results are valid for the second and third expressions in the expansion for $\frac{\partial J}{\partial t}$. By this procedure, the formula for $\frac{\partial J}{\partial t}$ may be shown to reduce to

$$\frac{\partial J}{\partial t} = (\nabla \cdot \mathbf{v})\, J.$$

This last result is exactly the desired formula.

Problem 35.1: Evaluate the determinants

$$\begin{vmatrix} 2 & 1 & 4 \\ 4 & 0 & 2 \\ -1 & 2 & 2 \end{vmatrix}, \qquad \begin{vmatrix} 6 & 1 & 3 \\ 4 & 0 & 2 \\ -1 & 2 & 2 \end{vmatrix}$$

by determining the a_k^i and using the expansion formula (35.1).

Problem 35.2: Show by direct expansion that if the second and third rows of the determinants of Problem 35.1 are interchanged, then the determinants change sign.

Problem 35.3: Find the determinant which is the product of the two determinants of Problem 35.1. *Hint:* The element c_2^1 of the product determinant can be obtained by forming the sum of the products of the elements of the first row and the various columns of b_j^1 by the elements of the second row and corresponding columns of A_2^l. Thus, the element of the first row and second column in the product of the above determinants is $(2 \times 4) + (1 \times 0) + (4 \times 2) = 16$.

Problem 35.4: Show that if the rows and columns of the determinants of Problem 35.1 are interchanged then the determinants do not change their values.

Problem 35.5: Show that the value of a determinant is unaltered if one replaces any row of elements by the elements formed by the sum of that row and a scalar times the corresponding elements of another row. *Hint:* Replace a_k^1 in (35.1) by $a_k^1 + \mu a_k^2$.

Problem 35.6: (1) Show that if any row of a determinant, say a_k^1, is replaced by elements with proportional values, say μa_k^1, then the new determinant has the value μ times the old; (2) show that if one replaces any row by a linear combination of other rows, then the new determinant vanishes.

Problem 35.7: Show that a determinant may be expanded by columns instead of rows. This means that

$$a = e^{kln} a_k^1 a_l^2 a_n^3 = e_{pqr} a_1^p a_2^q a_3^r.$$

Hint: Let $b = e_{pqr} a_1^p a_2^q a_3^r$ and show that $e_{ijk} b = e_{pqr} a_i^p a_j^q a_k^r$; then multiply both sides by e^{ijk}.

Problem 35.8: Show that the determinant, a, of the a_k^i and the determinant, A, of the reduced cofactors A_k^i are reciprocals, or $aA = 1$.

Problem 35.9: Show that the orthogonality conditions (33.2) imply that $a^2 = 1$, where a is the determinant of a_k^i. *Hint:* Introduce $A_j^k = a_k^i$ and show that the orthogonality relations imply that $aA = 1$.

Problem 35.10: Show that if the orthogonality conditions characterize the two transformations $x^i = a_k^i\, 'x^k$, $'x^k = b_j^k\, ''x^j$, then these conditions also characterize the product transformation $x^i = (a_k^i b_j^k)''x^j$.

Problems 35.11: Extend the results of the theory of Section 35 to the second-order determinant, $a = e^{ij} a_i^1 a_j^2$, $i, j = 1, 2$.

Problem 35.12: Show that in the plane the quantities, $A^j = e^{ji} B_i$, have the orthogonality property, $A^j B_j = 0$, $i, j = 1, 2$.

Problem 35.13: If e^{ijkl} are defined by extending the definition of e^{ijk}, show that there are $\underline{|4} = 24$ nonzero symbols. Twelve of these have the value -1. How many nonzero symbols are there of the type e^{ijkln}?

Problem 35.14: If the fourth-order determinant is defined by $a = e^{ijkl} a_i^1 a_j^2 a_k^3 a_l^4$, show that the principle of interchange of rows is valid.

Problem 35.15: Verify the product rule for two fourth-order determinants.

Problem 35.16: Determine the formulas for the reduced cofactors of a fourth order non-vanishing determinant.

36. General Cartesian Coordinates. In order to clarify the transition in tensor theory from Cartesian orthogonal to general curvilinear coordinates, we shall study tensors in general Cartesian coordinates. First, we shall discuss the coordinate surfaces, and the coordinate lines or base vectors of such a coordinate system (see Section 14).

(a) ***The Coordinate Surfaces.*** The coordinate surfaces are three families of parallel planes. These planes are not necessarily orthogonal. As in the case of Section 14, we denote these planes by x = constant, y = constant, z = constant; or, more briefly, x^i = constant, $i = 1, 2, 3$.

(b) ***The Base Vectors.*** Again we use a system of base vectors to describe the coordinate lines, which are the intersections of the coordinate surfaces. The base vectors which are tangent to the coordinate lines are called the covariant base vectors and are denoted by $\mathbf{e}_j$, $j = 1, 2, 3$. *We shall not prescribe their magnitudes at present.* Our notation indicates that $\mathbf{e}_1$ is tangent to the coordinate line along which x^1 varies and x^2, x^3 are constant, etc. In addition, we introduce a system of contravariant base vectors, $\mathbf{e}^j$. These vectors are defined by the equations

$$\mathbf{e}^j \cdot \mathbf{e}_i = \delta^j_i \qquad (36.1)$$

where δ^j_i is the Kronecker delta symbol defined by (32.9) in the x^i coordinate system. The equation (36.1) implies that $\mathbf{e}^1$ is *orthogonal* to $\mathbf{e}_2$, $\mathbf{e}_3$ and normalized so that

$$|\mathbf{e}_1|\,|\mathbf{e}^1| \cos(\mathbf{e}^1, \mathbf{e}_1) = 1.$$

The vectors $\mathbf{e}^2$, $\mathbf{e}^3$ have similar properties. Figure 40 illustrates this situ-

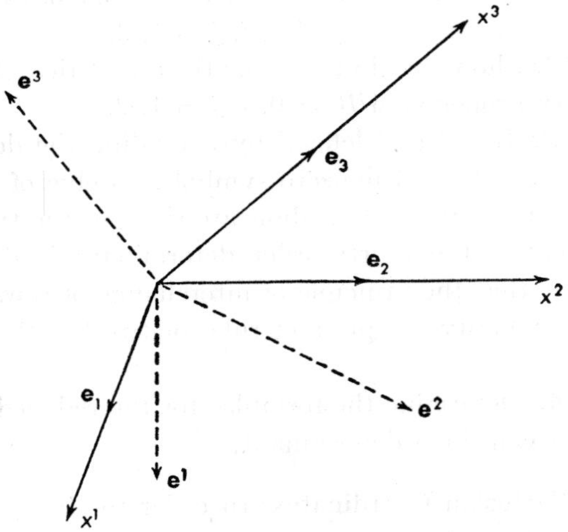

Figure 40: The Covariant Base Vectors, $\mathbf{e}_j$, and the Reciprocal System, $\mathbf{e}^j$

ation. The $\mathbf{e}^k$ *vectors are said to be reciprocal to the* $\mathbf{e}_k$, and conversely. *If* the $\mathbf{e}_k$ are unit orthogonal vectors, then they are self-reciprocal, $\mathbf{e}^i = \mathbf{e}_i$.

Problem 36.1: Let $'x$, $'y$ denote the Cartesian orthogonal coordinates in the plane. Consider the variables x, y which are defined by $(x = x^1, y = x^2)$

$$x = \sqrt{3}\,'x - 'y$$
$$y = 'x + 'y.$$

Show that the variables x, y define a system of general Cartesian coordinates of the plane. Describe the coordinate lines.

Problem 36.2: Let $'x$, $'y$, $'z$ denote Cartesian orthogonal coordinates in space. Describe the coordinate surfaces, $x =$ constant, $y =$ constant, $z =$ constant of the Cartesian system defined by

$$x = 'x - 'y$$
$$y = 'x + 2\,'y$$
$$z = 2\,'z.$$

Problem 36.3: Let $\mathbf{i}$, $\mathbf{j}$, $\mathbf{k}$ denote unit vectors along the Cartesian orthogonal coordinate lines. Show that

$$\mathbf{e}_1 = -\mathbf{i} + \mathbf{j}$$
$$\mathbf{e}_2 = 2\mathbf{i} + 2\sqrt{3}\,\mathbf{j}$$

are a permissible set of covariant base vectors for the general Cartesian coordinate system defined in Problem 36.1. Also, show that

$$\mathbf{e}_1 = 2\mathbf{i} - 2\mathbf{j}, \qquad \mathbf{e}_2 = \mathbf{i} + \sqrt{3}\,\mathbf{j}$$

are another set of permissible covariant base vectors. *Hint:* Compute the direction numbers of the coordinate line $y = 0$, and show that these direction numbers determine $\mathbf{e}_1$.

Problem 36.4: Find the two sets of contravariant base vectors, $\mathbf{e}^j$, which are reciprocal to the base vectors of Problem 36.3.

Problem 36.5: Show that

$$\mathbf{e}_1 = -4\mathbf{i} + 2\mathbf{j}, \qquad \mathbf{e}_2 = 3\mathbf{i} + 3\mathbf{j}, \qquad \mathbf{e}_3 = 2\mathbf{k}$$

are a system of covariant base vectors for the general Cartesian coordinates defined by Problem 36.2.

Problem 36.6: Find the set of contravariant base vectors which are reciprocal to the base vectors of Problem 36.5.

37. The Centered Affine Group. In this section we shall initiate our study of the centered affine group by considering: (a) the transformations of this group; (b) the transformation laws for vectors and tensors.

(a) ***The Allowable Group of Coordinate Transformations.*** We shall be concerned with coordinate transformations relating the variables:

x^i of a system of general Cartesian coordinates;

$'x^i$ of another system of general Cartesian coordinates;

$'y^i$ of a system of Cartesian orthogonal coordinates.

From the logical viewpoint, the $'y^i$ system is superfluous since it is a particular system $'x^i$. However, for pedagogical reasons, we retain this system. First, we relate the variables x^i (and $'x^i$) to $'y^i$. The equation of the family of parallel coordinate planes, $x^1 =$ constant, in Cartesian orthogonal coordinates must be of the form: $c^1 = a^1_j \, 'y^j, j = 1, 2, 3$, where c^1 takes on a constant value for each plane, $x^1 =$ constant. Hence by choice of a proper scale along the x^1 axis, we may write: $x^1 = a^1_k \, 'y^k$. In the same manner, we find that x^2, x^3 are related to $'y^i$ by linear equations. We write these equations as

$$x^i = a^i_k \, 'y^k. \tag{37.1}$$

It is easily seen that the *determinant of the* a^i_k *is not zero*. This follows from the fact that the vectors $\mathbf{a}^i$ are normal to the three families of coordinate planes, $x^i =$ constant. Since these normal vectors must be linearly independent, our result, $a \neq 0$, follows from the theory of Appendix I. Multiplying (37.1) by the reduced cofactors A^l_i introduced in Section 35(b), we find that

$$'y^l = A^l_k x^k. \tag{37.2}$$

Evidently this last relation is the inverse transformation to (37.1).

In a similar manner, we find that the variables $'x^k$, $'y^k$ are related by

$$'x^k = b^k_l \, 'y^l, \qquad 'y^l = B^l_k \, 'x^k \tag{37.3}$$

where B^l_k are the reduced cofactors of b^l_k, and the determinants of B^l_k and b^l_k are nonzero. Substituting (37.2) into (37.3), we obtain the relations between the coordinate variables, x^i and $'x^i$, of two general Cartesian coordinate systems. These relations are

$$'x^k = C^k_j x^j \tag{37.4}$$

where $C^k_j = b^k_l A^l_j$. Since the determinants of the b^k_l, A^k_l do not vanish, it follows that *the determinant of the* C^k_l *cannot vanish*. By introducing the reduced cofactors, c^k_l of C^k_l, we obtain the inverse transformation of (37.4)

$$x^k = c^k_j \, 'x^j. \tag{37.5}$$

It can easily be shown that the set of transformations of type (37.4) *with determinant of the* C^k_j *not zero form a group* (see the discussion in

Problem 33.4). This group, which is characterized by the property that the determinant of the C_j^k is not zero, is called the *centered affine group*. In view of the fact that the coefficients, C_j^k, need not satisfy the orthogonality relations, the centered affine group is much more general in nature than the rotation or orthogonal groups. In fact, the rotation and orthogonal groups are subgroups of the centered affine groups.

Problem 37.1: Let $'y^i$, $'x^i$, x^i have the significance of the above section. Give the geometric interpretation of the formulas

$$\begin{cases} x^1 = 'y^1 - 'y^2 \\ x^2 = 'y^1 + 2\,'y^2 \end{cases} \qquad \begin{cases} 'x^1 = 2\,'y^1 + 3\,'y^2 \\ 'x^2 = 'y^1 + 2\,'y^2 \end{cases}$$

by sketching the coordinate lines of the x^i, $'x^i$ system.

Problem 37.2: In the above problem, determine the $'y^i$ of the points, (0, 0), (1, 0), (0, 1) in the x^i coordinates and hence determine the relation of the scales along the x^1, x^2-axes to that of the ordinary Cartesian orthogonal coordinate axes $'y^1$, $'y^2$.

Problem 37.3: Determine the reduced cofactors of the coefficients a_k^i of the transformations in Problem 37.1 and hence find the A_k^i. Check your results by solving the equations of Problem 37.1 for $'y^i$.

Problem 37.4: Eliminate the variables $'y^i$ in Problem 37.1 and obtain the relation between x^k and $'x^k$. Check the result by determining C_j^k [see (37.4)].

(b) ***The Transformation Laws of Vectors and Tensors under the Centered Affine Group.*** In the following discussions, we shall assume that the p-th order tensor,

$$\mathfrak{A} = v^{i_1 \cdots i_p}\mathbf{e}_{i_1} \cdot \cdot \cdot \mathbf{e}_{i_p} = v_{j_1 \cdots j_p}\mathbf{e}^{j_1} \cdot \cdot \cdot \mathbf{e}^{j_p}$$

is an invariant under the centered affine group, (37.4). In particular, we shall assume that the radius vector, **R,** where

$$\mathbf{R} = x^j\mathbf{e}_j \tag{37.6}$$

is an invariant under this group. Further, we shall require that the relation $\mathbf{e}^j \cdot \mathbf{e}_i = \delta_i^j$, of (36.1), be valid in all general Cartesian coordinates.

The last two assumptions will determine the transformation laws of the covariant base vectors, $\mathbf{e}_j$, and the contravariant base vectors, $\mathbf{e}^j$. It should be noted that the coordinate variables, x^j *are not* to be written with subscripts, as x_j. When the transformation laws of the vectors, $\mathbf{e}_j$, $\mathbf{e}^j$ are known then the assumed invariance of $\mathfrak{A}$ will determine the transformation laws of the *covariant components,* $v_{i_1 \cdots i_p}$, and the *contravariant components,* $v^{i_1 \cdots i_p}$, of the tensor $\mathfrak{A}$. For the centered affine group, the covariant and contravariant components of a tensor *are not equal*. It will be recalled that in the Cartesian orthogonal coordinates (under the orthogonal group), these components of a tensor are equivalent.

Substituting the expression (37.5) for x^j in (37.6), we obtain $\mathbf{R} = c^j_k\, 'x^k \mathbf{e}_j = 'x^k\, '\mathbf{e}_k$, where $'\mathbf{e}_k$ are the covariant base vectors of the coordinate system $'x^k$. Since this equation is valid for arbitrary $'x^k$, we find that

$$'\mathbf{e}_k = c^j_k \mathbf{e}_j. \tag{37.7}$$

The last equation may be solved for $\mathbf{e}_j$ by multiplying by the reduced cofactors, C^j_k of the c^j_k: $\mathbf{e}_k = C^j_k\, '\mathbf{e}_j$. In invariant theory, the *variables*, $\mathbf{e}_j$, *which transform by the law* (37.7) [as opposed to the x^j which transform by the law (37.5)] are said to transform *contragrediently to the* x^j.

To obtain the transformation law of the contravariant base vectors, $\mathbf{e}^j$, we consider the defining relations of the $\mathbf{e}^j$, namely

$$\mathbf{e}^j \cdot \mathbf{e}_k = '\mathbf{e}^j \cdot '\mathbf{e}_k = \delta^j_k.$$

Replacing $'\mathbf{e}_k$ in the above by (37.7), we obtain

$$\mathbf{e}^j \cdot \mathbf{e}_k = '\mathbf{e}^j \cdot c^l_k \mathbf{e}_l.$$

Now, the $'\mathbf{e}^j$ vectors are related to the $\mathbf{e}^j$ by a linear transformation. This appears evident from the fact that any vector can be expressed as a linear combination of three independent vectors. Let us denote the relation between the $'\mathbf{e}^j$ and the $\mathbf{e}^j$ by

$$'\mathbf{e}^j = A^j_n \mathbf{e}^n.$$

Substituting this relation for $'\mathbf{e}^j$ into the preceding equation, we obtain by use of $\mathbf{e}^j \cdot \mathbf{e}_k = \delta^j_k$, that

$$\delta^j_k = A^j_l c^l_k.$$

But the last relation is of the type studied in Section 35. It is shown in Appendix I that corresponding to given c^l_k, the multipliers A^l_k are unique and are the reduced cofactors of c^l_k. Thus, we see that $A^l_k = C^l_k$ and the equation for $'\mathbf{e}^j$ in terms of $\mathbf{e}^j$ is

$$'\mathbf{e}^j = C^j_n \mathbf{e}^n. \tag{37.8}$$

By comparison of (37.8) with (37.4), we see that the two transformation laws are identical. In invariant theory, one says that the x^j *and* $\mathbf{e}^j$ *transform cogrediently*. By following the same procedure as was used in studying the transformation law of tensor components under the rotation group, we find that for the centered affine group

$$\begin{aligned} 'v^{i_1 \dots i_p} &= C^{i_1}_{j_1} \cdots C^{i_p}_{j_p} v^{j_1 \dots j_p} \\ 'v_{i_1 \dots i_p} &= c^{j_1}_{i_1} \cdots c^{j_p}_{i_p} v_{j_1 \dots j_p}. \end{aligned} \tag{37.9}$$

Comparing the last relations with (37.4), we obtain the result: *The contravariant base vectors and contravariant components of a tensor transform as do the coordinate variables or their differentials under the centered affine group.* Further, by comparing (37.7) and (37.9), we see that the *covariant base vectors and the covariant components of a tensor transform in the same manner.* The covariant and contravariant laws of transformation are inverse in the sense that $c^i_j C^j_k = \delta^i_k$ or $cC = 1$. The *essential difference between the transformation laws under the centered affine group and the rotation group lies in the fact that for the latter the inverse of a^i_j is a^j_i* (note, the relation $A^k_j = a^j_k$ of equation 33.4). That is, *for the rotation group, the covariant and contravariant laws of transformation are equivalent.* This is *not true* for the centered affine group. Hence, under this last group, an essential difference exists between the covariant and contravariant components of a tensor.

In addition to components which are covariant or contravariant, one may also introduce mixed components. Thus, for the second-order tensor, one may write

$$\mathfrak{A} = v^{ij}\mathbf{e}_i\mathbf{e}_j = v_{ij}\mathbf{e}^i\mathbf{e}^j = v_i^{\cdot j}\mathbf{e}^i\mathbf{e}_j = v^i_{\cdot j}\mathbf{e}_i\mathbf{e}^j.$$

The $v_i^{\cdot j}$, $v^j_{\cdot i}$ transform covariantly in (i) and contravariantly in (j).

The following problems all refer to the coordinate systems of the Problem 37.1.

Problem 37.5: Show that a permissible system of covariant base vectors for the coordinate system x^j is

$$\mathbf{e}_1 = 4\mathbf{i} - 2\mathbf{j}, \qquad \mathbf{e}_2 = 3\mathbf{i} + 3\mathbf{j}.$$

Hint: Do these vectors lie along the coordinate lines?

Problem 37.6: Show that the base vectors of Problem 37.5 do not satisfy the requirement that $\mathbf{R} = x^j\mathbf{e}_j = {'y^1}\,\mathbf{i} + {'y^2}\,\mathbf{j}$. Determine the desired base vectors. Note that these vectors are unique, but *are not unit vectors.*

Problem 37.7: Find the covariant base vectors in the $'x^j$ coordinates for which $\mathbf{R} = {'x^j}\,{'\mathbf{e}_j} = {'y^1}\,\mathbf{i} + {'y^2}\,\mathbf{j}$ is satisfied.

Problem 37.8: Determine the contravariant base vectors in the x^j, $'x^j$ systems. Verify the relation ${'\mathbf{e}^j} = C^j_n\mathbf{e}^n$.

Problem 37.9: If a vector has components $(1, -3)$ in the $'y^j$ system, find its covariant components and contravariant components in the x^j system.

Problem 37.10: Prove that $\mathbf{e}_j = \dfrac{\partial\mathbf{R}}{\partial x^j}$.

Problem 37.11: By use of the chain rule for differentiation, one finds that $\frac{\partial \mathbf{R}}{\partial\, 'x^k} = \frac{\partial \mathbf{R}}{\partial x^i}\frac{\partial x^i}{\partial\, 'x^k}$. Use this result to derive the formula, $'\mathbf{e}_k = c_k^i \mathbf{e}_i$.

38. The Invariance of the Correspondence Principles of Section 32. In Section 32, we introduced four correspondence principles for replacing vectors, **A**, and dyads, $\mathfrak{A}$ by their components in a *particular Cartesian orthogonal coordinate system.* The question arises whether these principles are independent of the coordinate system. We have refrained from discussing this question for the rotation group but now we shall discuss this question for the more general centered affine group.

(a) ***The First Correspondence Principle.*** In order to verify the first correspondence principle relating vectors and their components, we note that the transformation laws of the components of tensors were derived under the assumption that $\mathfrak{A}$ is an invariant. However, the *vector operator* $\boldsymbol{\nabla}$ must be treated in a different manner. Its components in a new coordinate system are known when the equations (37.4) defining the centered affine group are given. Thus, we find by use of the chain rule for differentiation,

$$\frac{\partial}{\partial\, 'x^j} = \frac{\partial x^k}{\partial\, 'x^j}\frac{\partial}{\partial x^k}.$$

Through use of (37.5), the above operator equation reduces to

$$\frac{\partial}{\partial\, 'x^j} = c_j^k \frac{\partial}{\partial x^k}.$$

From this relation, we see that *the operator components, $\partial/\partial x^j$, of $\boldsymbol{\nabla}$ transform as a covariant vector.* Thus, the first correspondence principle must be modified for the centered affine group so as to read

$$\boldsymbol{\nabla} \leftrightarrow \nabla_j = \frac{\partial}{\partial x^j}. \tag{38.1}$$

This result may be phrased as follows: The vector operator, $\boldsymbol{\nabla} = \mathbf{e}^i \frac{\partial}{\partial x^i}$, is invariant under the centered affine group. Note, one *cannot* write $\boldsymbol{\nabla} = \mathbf{e}_i \frac{\partial}{\partial x^i}$, except for the rotation group and the orthogonal group.

(b) ***The Second Correspondence Principle.*** The *second correspondence principle,* (32.1), *is invariant under coordinate transformation.* The result is obtained by multiplying this equation by $C_i^k C_j^l$ and using the transformation of tensor components (37.9). We find that

$$'A^{kl} + 'B^{kl} = 'C^{kl}. \tag{38.2}$$

(c) ***The Third Correspondence Principle.*** The *invariance of the third correspondence principle,* (32.2) follows by use of a similar procedure.

In fact, we can use the invariance of this principle to formulate a test for covariance or contravariance of a tensor. *This test states the following:* (1) if A^{ij}, $'A^{ij}$ denote the components of *some quantity* in the x^j, $'x^j$ coordinate systems, respectively; (2) if U_j, W_j denote the components of *two arbitrary vectors;* (3) if

$$A^{ij}U_iW_j = 'A^{ij}\,'U_i\,'W_j \tag{38.3}$$

then $'A^{ij} = C^i_kC^j_lA^{kl}$, and A^{ij}, $'A^{ij}$, etc., *denote the contravariant components of a second-order tensor,* $\mathfrak{A}$. Note that (38.3) must be valid in *all* coordinate systems, $'x^j$, x^j.

The proof of this result follows from the fact that U_j, W_j are arbitrary and are the components of a vector. From the vectorial character of U_j, W_j, it follows that $U_j = C^k_j\,'U_k$, $W_j = C^k_j\,'W_k$. Substituting these relations into the left-hand side of (38.3), and using the fact that U_j, W_k are arbitrary, one obtains the desired result. This result is one form of the *quotient rule.*

(d) ***The Fourth Correspondence Principle; Densities and Capacities.*** In equation (32.8), we introduced the *fourth correspondence principle.* This principle stated that if A_j, B_j are the components of two vectors, then $e^{ijk}A_jB_k$ represents the vector $\mathbf{A} \times \mathbf{B}$. We shall show that this correspondence is *not invariant* under the centered affine group. In fact, we shall show: (1) *if* e^{ijk} *have the values* 1, 0, -1 *in every coordinate system* x^j *of the centered affine group and if* A_j, B_j *are vectors, then* $e^{ijk}A_jB_k$ *is a vector density or pseudo-vector;* (2) *if and only if the group,* $x^k = c^k_j\,'x^j$, *is equivolumar* ($c = 1$) *does* $e^{ijk}A_jB_k$ represent a vector. Note that the rotation group has determinant $c = 1$, and is equivolumar.

To prove these results, we notice that $cC = 1$. By definition of the quantities $'e^{ijk}$ and e^{ijk}, we may write

$$'e^{ijk} = e^{ijk}(cC).$$

Expanding the determinant C according to its rows, we may express the above as

$$'e^{ijk} = ce^{rpq}C^i_rC^j_pC^k_q.$$

Since A_j, B_j are vectors, we know that

$$'A_j = c^l_jA_l, \qquad 'B_k = c^n_kB_n.$$

Hence, by multiplication of the above relations, we obtain

$$'e^{ijk}\,'A_j\,'B_k = cC^i_r(e^{rln}A_lB_n). \tag{38.4}$$

The last equation shows that the *quantity* $e^{rln}A_lB_n$ *does not transform as a vector unless* $c = 1$. A quantity which transforms according to the above law, that is, $'V^i = cC^i_jV^j$, is called a *vector density* of weight one or merely a vector density, since c occurs to the first power. If c occurs to the k-th power in the transformation law, then V^i is a *vector density* of weight k. *Tensor densities* of weight k are defined in a similar manner. One often denotes these quantities by the term "relative tensors of weight $(+k)$." It can be easily shown that e_{ijk} transforms according to the law

$$'e_{ijk} = c^{-1}e_{rpq}c^r_ic^p_jc^q_k.$$

Further, the quantity, $e_{ijk}A^jB^k$, transforms according to the law

$$'e_{ijk}\,'A^j\,'B^k = c^{-1}c^r_i(e_{rpq}A^pB^q). \tag{38.5}$$

The transformation law (38.5) represents a *vector capacity* of weight one[3]; the transformation law of *tensor capacities* of weight k is such that c occurs to the $-k$-th power. These quantities are often called "relative tensors of weight $(-k)$." We shall show how to generate a true vector from a vector density or capacity when we have introduced the metric tensor. From this, we shall be able to obtain the correct form of the fourth correspondence for the centered affine group.

By use of the transformation formulas for e^{ijk}, e_{ijk}, we find that

$$'e^{ijk}\,'e_{lmn} = e^{rpq}e_{stu}c^i_rc^j_pc^k_qC^s_lC^t_mC^u_n.$$

If we contract the indices i and l, we obtain by use of the defining relation for δ^{ij}_{lk} (32.12),

$$'\delta^{jk}_{mn} = \delta^{pq}_{tu}c^j_pc^k_qC^t_mC^u_n.$$

This equation shows that generalized Kronecker delta symbol δ^{jk}_{mn} is a tensor under the centered affine group. The tensor character of the Kronecker delta symbol, $\delta^{ij}_{lj} = 2\delta^i_l$, follows from a similar argument. However, the representations, δ^{ij} or δ_{ij}, *are not tensors unless* the group of transformations is rotational or orthogonal.

Problem 38.1: Show that if A_j are the covariant components of a vector, then ∇_lA_j transforms as the covariant components of a second-order tensor.

Problem 38.2: Show that if U^i, V^j, W^k are the contravariant components of three arbitrary vectors and if a quantity A_{ijk} is such that for all coordinate systems x^j, $'x^j$

$$A_{ijk}U^iV^jW^k = 'A_{ijk}\,'U^i\,'V^j\,'W^k,$$

[3] This term stems from the fact that e_{ijk} transforms in the same manner as the element of volume considered as a 3-vector (see Section 50).

then A_{ijk} are the covariant components of a third-order tensor.

Problem 38.3: Show that if the tensor A_{ij} is symmetric in one coordinate system (that is, $A_{ij} = A_{ji}$), then A_{ij} is symmetric in all coordinate systems.

Problem 38.4: Show that if the tensor A_{ij} is antisymmetric or skew symmetric or alternating, (that is, $A_{ij} = -A_{ji}$) in one coordinate system, then A_{ij} is skew symmetric in all coordinate systems.

Problem 38.5: Show that $e^{ijk}A_jB_kC_i$ is a scalar density.

39. The Metric Tensor. In this section, we shall define the metric tensor, $\mathcal{G}$, by introducing its covariant components, g_{ij}. After briefly studying the properties of g_{ij}, we shall introduce the contravariant components, g^{ij} of the metric tensor. Finally, we shall show how a vector capacity may be transformed into a true vector by use of the determinant, g, of g_{ij}.

(a) ***The Covariant Components, g_{ij}, of the Metric Tensor; The Lowering of Indices.*** Consider the invariant, $\mathbf{R} \cdot \mathbf{R}$, formed from $\mathbf{R} = x^i\mathbf{e}_i$,

$$\mathbf{R} \cdot \mathbf{R} = (\mathbf{e}_j \cdot \mathbf{e}_i)x^jx^i = ('\mathbf{e}_i \cdot '\mathbf{e}_j)'x^i\,'x^j.$$

Evidently a knowledge of the quantities $\mathbf{e}_i \cdot \mathbf{e}_j$ enables one to compute distances. Hence, we introduce the metric quantities g_{ij} defined by

$$g_{ij} = \mathbf{e}_i \cdot \mathbf{e}_j, \qquad 'g_{ij} = '\mathbf{e}_i \cdot '\mathbf{e}_j. \tag{39.1}$$

From Figure 40, we see that *if* $\mathbf{e}_i$ *are unit vectors, then*

$$g_{ij} = \cos(\mathbf{e}_i, \mathbf{e}_j) = \cos(x^i, x^j).$$

In particular, if the coordinate system, x^i, is Cartesian orthogonal, then $g_{ij} = \delta_{ij}$.

By use of the transformation laws of the $\mathbf{e}_j$ (37.7) and the invariance of $\mathbf{R} \cdot \mathbf{R}$, we find that

$$'g_{ij} = c_i^k c_j^l g_{kl}. \tag{39.2}$$

Thus, the g_{ij} are the covariant components of a second-order tensor, $\mathcal{G}$. This tensor is called the metric tensor and is defined by $\mathcal{G} = g_{ij}\mathbf{e}^i\mathbf{e}^j$. Since $g_{ij} = g_{ji}$, the *metric tensor is symmetric.*

Let us consider the role of the metric tensor in the scalar product. If $\mathbf{V} = V^i\mathbf{e}_i$, $\mathbf{W} = W^j\mathbf{e}_j$, then

$$\mathbf{V} \cdot \mathbf{W} = V^iW^j(\mathbf{e}_i \cdot \mathbf{e}_j) = g_{ij}V^iW^j.$$

By writing $\mathbf{V} = V^i\mathbf{e}_i$, $\mathbf{W} = W_j\mathbf{e}^j$, and using the relation $\mathbf{e}_i \cdot \mathbf{e}^j = \delta_i^j$, we find that

$$\mathbf{V} \cdot \mathbf{W} = V^iW_i.$$

Comparing the last two formulas for arbitrary V^i, we obtain the equation

$$W_i = g_{ij}W^j. \tag{39.3}$$

The formula (39.3) shows a very important property of the metric tensor, g_{ij}. *One may lower indices of a vector (or tensor) by use of the metric tensor.* In a Cartesian orthogonal system, $g_{ij} = \delta_{ij}$, the above equation reduces to $W_i = W^i$. Thus we see from another viewpoint that in a Cartesian orthogonal coordinate system, the covariant and contravariant components of a vector (or tensor) are equal.

The $\mathbf{e}_i$, $\mathbf{e}^j$ are related by a formula similar to (39.3). To obtain this formula, we use the relation, $\mathbf{e}^j \cdot \mathbf{e}_i = \delta^j_i$, and find

$$\mathbf{V} = V_j\mathbf{e}^j = (\mathbf{V} \cdot \mathbf{e}_j)\mathbf{e}^j.$$

If we replace $\mathbf{V}$ in the above by $\mathbf{e}_i$, then we obtain the desired result

$$\mathbf{e}_i = g_{ij}\mathbf{e}^j. \tag{39.4}$$

(b) ***The Contravariant Components, g^{ij}, of the Metric Tensor; The Raising of Indices.*** By definition, the g^{ij} will be the reduced cofactors of g_{ij}, or

$$g^{ij}g_{jk} = \delta^i_k, \qquad 'g^{ij}\,'g_{jk} = \delta^i_k. \tag{39.5}$$

We shall show that the g^{ij} are the contravariant components of the metric tensor. To do this, we must prove that: $\mathcal{G} = g_{ij}\mathbf{e}^i\mathbf{e}^j = g^{ij}\mathbf{e}_i\mathbf{e}_j$. First, *we show that the g^{ij} as defined by* (39.5) *are the components of a tensor.* By multiplying (39.4) by g^{ki} and using (39.5), we obtain

$$\mathbf{e}^k = g^{ki}\mathbf{e}_i. \tag{39.6}$$

Forming the scalar product of the last relation with $\mathbf{e}^i$ and using the invariant relations $\mathbf{e}^i \cdot \mathbf{e}_j = \delta^i_j$, we find that

$$g^{ki} = \mathbf{e}^k \cdot \mathbf{e}^i.$$

The last formula is the analogue of the corresponding formula (39.1) for g_{ij}. Since the $\mathbf{e}^j$ transform as contravariant vectors, it is evident from this relation that g^{ij} transform as the symmetric contravariant components of a tensor of the second order. Finally, in order to verify the result that g^{ik} are the contravariant components of $\mathcal{G}$ we substitute (39.6) into the formula for $\mathcal{G}$ and find by use of (39.5) that

$$\mathcal{G} = g_{ij}\mathbf{e}^i\mathbf{e}^j = g_{ij}g^{ik}g^{jl}\mathbf{e}_k\mathbf{e}_l = g^{kl}\mathbf{e}_k\mathbf{e}_l.$$

Similarly to the case for g_{ij}, one may show that

$$\mathbf{V} \cdot \mathbf{W} = g^{ij} V_i W_j \qquad \text{and} \qquad W^i = g^{ij} W_j. \tag{39.7}$$

Thus, the g^{ij} *may be used to raise indices.* By use of the various formulas for $\mathbf{V} \cdot \mathbf{W}$, one obtains for the angle, θ, between the vectors

$$\cos \theta = \frac{g_{ij} V^i W^j}{\sqrt{g_{ij} V^i V^j}\,\sqrt{g_{ij} W^i W^j}} = \frac{g^{ij} V_i W_j}{\sqrt{g^{ij} V_i V_j}\,\sqrt{g^{ij} W_i W_j}}.$$

(c) ***The Determinant, g, of the Metric Tensor, g_{ij}; Reduction of Vector Capacities and Densities to True Vectors.*** We shall show how one may use the determinant, g, of the g_{ij}, and the determinant, G, of the g^{ij}, to reduce vector capacities and densities to true vectors. The defining formulas for g^{ij}, (39.5), and the product rule for determinants show that

$$gG = 1 \qquad \text{or} \qquad G = g^{-1}.$$

Hence, we may consider either g or G in our future work. By the product rule for determinants, we may relate the determinants of the g_{ij}, $'g_{ij}$ by means of [see (39.2)]

$$'g = gc^2. \tag{39.8}$$

In particular, if the x^j coordinate system is Cartesian orthogonal, then $g_{ij} = \delta_{ij}$ and $g = 1$. Hence, *$'g$ is always positive.* Further, the formula (39.8) shows *that $\sqrt{g}$ transforms as a scalar density of weight one.* By division of the transformation law for the cross product (38.4) by $'g = gc^2$, we find that

$$\frac{'e^{ijk}\,'A_j\,'B_k}{\sqrt{'g}} = C^i_r \frac{e^{rln} A_l B_n}{\sqrt{g}}. \tag{39.9}$$

Thus, the quantity, $e^{rln} A_l B_n / \sqrt{g}$, transforms as a vector under the centered affine group. The fourth correspondence principle *must be modified* so that the *cross product is expressed by this quantity*. Similarly, it may be shown that $\sqrt{g}\, e_{rln} A^l B^n$ transforms as vector and represents the covariant components of the cross product. If the allowable coordinate systems are right-handed Cartesian orthogonal (rotation group), then $'g = g = 1$, and the formula (39.9) reduces to the fourth correspondence principle for expressing the cross product (32.8).

One further fact must be observed. Since $\sqrt{g}$, $\sqrt{'g}$ indicate positive numbers, it follows that for c positive, $\sqrt{'g} = c\sqrt{g}$. Thus if the determinant c is positive, then the above formula for $\mathbf{A} \times \mathbf{B}$ is correct. However, if c is negative, then (39.9) must be modified by replacing the left-hand side of this equation by its negative. Thus, $e^{rln} A_l B_n / \sqrt{g}$ transforms as a vector under the centered affine group with *positive determinant* (right-hand systems). If we consider the centered affine group as forming a *continuous group of transformations*, this restriction is a natural one. That, is, if transformations with positive determinant and negative determinant both belong to such a continuous group, then the transformation with zero determinant belongs to this group. This is not possible by the definition of the centered affine group.

Problem 39.1: Consider the coordinate transformation

$$x^1 = y^1 + y^2, \qquad x^2 = -y^1 + y^2, \qquad x^3 = 2y^3$$

relating the Cartesian orthogonal coordinates y^j and the general Cartesian coordinates x^j. Determine:

(1) The covariant base vectors $\mathbf{e}_i$ of x^j, which satisfy $\mathbf{R} = x^j \mathbf{e}_j$;
(2) The metric tensor's components in the x^j system;
(3) The contravariant components in the x^j system of the vectors $\mathbf{W}, \mathbf{V}$ whose components in the y^j system are $(3, 2, 0)$, $(2, -3, 0)$, respectively;
(4) Show that $\mathbf{W} \cdot \mathbf{V}$ is an invariant;
(5) Compute the determinant g of the tensor g_{ij};
(6) Compute $\mathbf{W} \times \mathbf{V}$ in the x^j system.

40. Other Groups of Coordinate Transformations. In the previous theory, we discussed the centered affine group of coordinate transformations. There exist many other groups of coordinate transformations. For instance, the projective group of transformations may be introduced into three-space by use of homogeneous coordinates (four coordinates). Again, the conformal group can be obtained by introducing five coordinates with proper significance into three space.

In concluding this section on groups, it should be noted that we have introduced the affine group into *Euclidean* three-space. Since *a Euclidean space has a metric*, this procedure does not determine the essential geometric properties of the affine group. In other words, a more general geometry is obtained if one introduces the affine group into a three space (not necessarily Euclidean), or into n-space. This point of view is discussed in more advanced texts.[4]

41. Geometric Interpretation of the Covariant and Contravariant Components of a Vector in General Cartesian Coordinates. We consider a

[4] J. A. Schouten, *Der Ricci Kalkül*, J. Springer, Berlin, 1929; L. Brillouin, *Les Tenseurs*, Dover Publications, New York, 1946.

general Cartesian coordinate system, x^j, for which the base vectors, $\mathbf{e}_j$, are *unit* vectors. This restriction implies that proper scale factors have been selected along the various coordinate lines. Further, let $\mathbf{u}_j$ denote the unit base vectors of a Cartesian orthogonal coordinate system, y^i. Figure 41 drawn below illustrates this situation where $\mathbf{e}_3 = \mathbf{u}_3$ and $\mathbf{e}_1$, $\mathbf{e}_2$

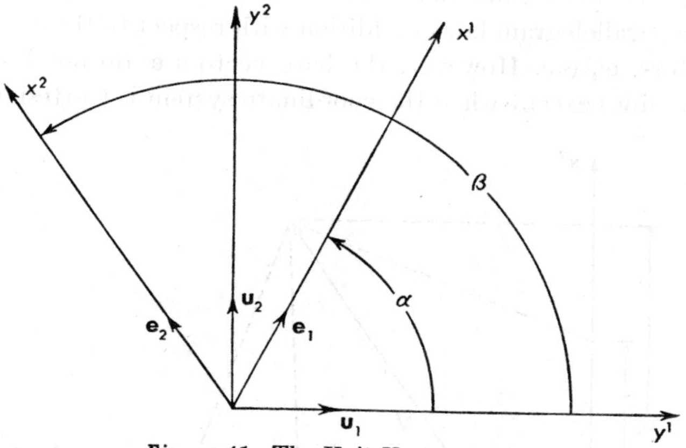

Figure 41: The Unit Vectors, $\mathbf{u}_j$, $\mathbf{e}_j$

lie in the plane of $\mathbf{u}_1$, $\mathbf{u}_2$. The angles between the Ox^1, Ox^2 axis and Oy^1 are denoted by α, β, respectively. From the figure, we see that

$$\mathbf{e}_1 = \cos\alpha\,\mathbf{u}_1 + \sin\alpha\,\mathbf{u}_2$$
$$\mathbf{e}_2 = \cos\beta\,\mathbf{u}_1 + \sin\beta\,\mathbf{u}_2. \tag{41.1}$$

By use of the assumed invariance of $\mathbf{R} = x^i\mathbf{e}_i = y^i\mathbf{u}_i$ and (41.1), we find that the coordinate transformation induced by the relation between $\mathbf{e}_j$, $\mathbf{u}_j$ is

$$y^1 = x^1\cos\alpha + x^2\cos\beta, \qquad y^2 = x^1\sin\alpha + x^2\sin\beta.$$

Now, we consider the geometric interpretation of the covariant and contravariant components, V_j and V^i of a vector in the x^j coordinates. First, we note that by assumption $\mathbf{V}$ is an invariant and hence

$$\mathbf{V} = V^j\mathbf{e}_j. \tag{41.2}$$

Since the vectors $\mathbf{e}_j$ are unit vectors along the coordinate axis, *the law* (41.2) *corresponds to parallelogram addition by segments parallel to the coordinate axis.* Figure 42 illustrates this when $\mathbf{V}$ lies in the x^1,x^2 plane. In terms of covariant components V_j, we may write $\mathbf{V}$ as

$$\mathbf{V} = V_j\mathbf{e}^j. \tag{41.3}$$

To interpret the covariant components V_j, we note that $\mathbf{e}^j \cdot \mathbf{e}_i = \delta^j_i$. Hence forming the scalar product of the above relation with $\mathbf{e}_i$, we obtain

$$\mathbf{e}_i \cdot \mathbf{V} = V_i. \tag{41.4}$$

Thus, the components V_i *are the projections of* **V** *on the coordinate axis* (see Figure 42). Similarly, one may show that the law (41.3) corresponds to use of the parallelogram law of addition with respect to the contravariant base vectors, $\mathbf{e}^j$, etc. However, the base vectors $\mathbf{e}^j$ do not lie along the coordinate lines except when the coordinate system is Cartesian orthogo-

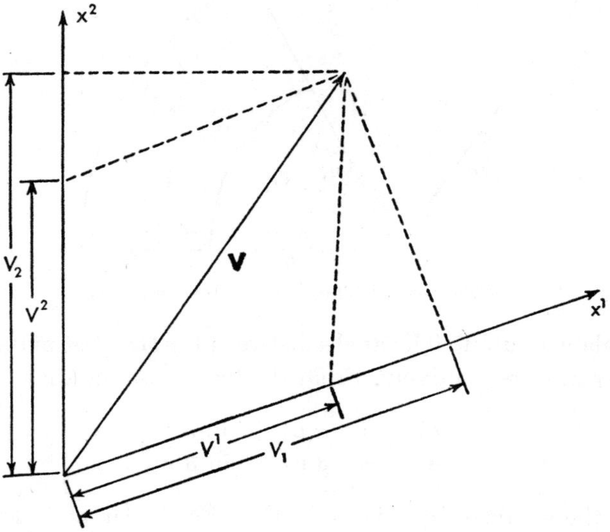

Figure 42: The Covariant and Contravariant Components of a Vector, **V**, in the x^j Coordinate System

nal. It is for this reason that the geometric interpretation of covariance and contravariance is usually given in terms of the vector $\mathbf{e}_j$.

Problem 41.1: Consider the case where $\alpha = 0$, $\beta \neq 0$ in Figure 41. Determine the formulas relating the y^j to the x^j variables.

Problem 41.2: Show that for the case when $\alpha = 0$, $\beta \neq 0$ of Figure 41:

$$V_2 = {'V_1} \cos \beta + {'V_2} \sin \beta, \qquad V_1 = {'V_1}$$

where $('V_1, 'V_2)$ are the components of **V** in the y^j system.

Problem 41.3: Consider a system of Cartesian coordinates in the plane with angle γ between Ox^1 and Ox^2. Let ξ, η denote the projections of a point P on Ox^1, Ox^2, respectively. Determine the covariant and contravariant components of the velocity vector.

Problem 41.4: Assume the vertical direction makes an angle of θ with Ox^1. Determine the equations of motion in terms of ξ, η (see Problem 41.3) when gravity is the only force acting.

42. Extension of the Previous Theory to Euclidean n-Space. The main body of the previous ideas can be immediately extended to Euclidean n-space. The single exception is the cross product of two vectors. In three-space, one can associate the vector perpendicular to two given vectors with those vectors. It is for this reason that one can define the cross product. In n-space, there are $(n - 2)$ vectors orthogonal to two given vectors. Hence, we cannot discuss the cross product. We shall consider n-dimensional e-systems and determinants as well as r-dimensional Kronecker deltas, $r < n$.

(a) ***n-Dimensional e-Systems; Determinants.*** We define the n-dimensional e-systems by generalizing the three-dimensional case. That is, we require that

$$\begin{aligned} e^{i_1\cdots i_n} &= 1, && \text{if } i_1 \cdots i_n \text{ is an even permutation;} \\ e^{i_1\cdots i_n} &= -1, && \text{if } i_1 \cdots i_n \text{ is an odd permutation;} \\ e^{i_1\cdots i_n} &= 0, && \text{if } i_1 \cdots i_n \text{ contains two or more repeated indices.} \end{aligned} \tag{42.1}$$

In order to clearly understand the above definition, it should be noted that: (1) even or odd permutations are to be formed from the ordered numbers $1, 2, \ldots, n$; (2) if an ordering, such as $2, 1, \ldots, n$ is obtained by an even number of permutations of $1, 2, \ldots, n$, then any other attempt to obtain $2, 1, \ldots, n$ will require an even number of permutations. It is because of the last result that one can consider an ordering as an even or an odd permutation. We shall not prove this result. The e-symbols, $e_{i_1\ldots i_n}$, are defined as in (42.1).

The n-th order determinant

$$\begin{vmatrix} a_1^1 & a_2^1 & \cdots & a_n^1 \\ a_1^2 & a_2^2 & \cdots & a_n^2 \\ \cdot & \cdot & & \cdot \\ \cdot & \cdot & & \cdot \\ \cdot & \cdot & & \cdot \\ a_1^n & a_2^n & \cdots & a_n^n \end{vmatrix}$$

will be defined by

$$a = e^{i_1\cdots i_n} a_{i_1}^1 a_{i_2}^2 \cdots a_{i_n}^n. \tag{42.2}$$

By use of the definition (42.2) and the skew symmetry of the e-symbol, one may extend the results obtained for third-order determinants to n-th order determinants. We list some of these results:

(1) The general expansion of an n-th order determinant by rows or by columns is furnished by

$$e^{i_1 \dots i_p} a = e^{j_1 \dots j_n} a^{i_1}_{j_1} a^{i_2}_{j_2} \cdots a^{i_n}_{j_n}$$

$$e_{i_1 \dots i_n} a = e_{j_1 \dots j_n} a^{j_1}_{i_1} a^{j_2}_{i_2} \cdots a^{j_n}_{i_n}.$$

(2) If two rows (or columns) of a determinant are interchanged, then the determinant changes sign.

(3) If two rows (or columns) of a determinant coincide, then the determinant vanishes. More generally, if one row of a determinant is a linear combination of the other rows, then the determinant vanishes.

(4) The elements $c^k_j = b^k_l A^l_j$ are the elements of the determinant $c = bA$.

(5) Any determinant may be expanded by *cofactors* $\bar{A}^k_j$, (signed minors) according to the formulas

$$\bar{A}^k_j = e^{i_1 \dots i_{j-1} k i_{j+1} \dots i_n} a^1_{i_1} \cdots a^{j-1}_{i_{j-1}} a^{j+1}_{i_{j+1}} \cdots a^n_{i_n}$$

$$a^l_k \bar{A}^k_j = a \delta^l_j, \qquad a^k_l \bar{A}^j_k = a \delta^j_l.$$

(6) If the *determinant, a, is not zero*, then one may define the *reduced cofactors*, A^k_j, by

$$A^k_j = \bar{A}^k_j / a \qquad \text{and} \qquad a^l_k A^k_j = \delta^l_j, \qquad a^k_l A^j_k = \delta^j_l.$$

(7) The derivative of a determinant is given by

$$\frac{da}{dt} = \frac{da^l_k}{dt} \bar{A}^k_l.$$

(b) ***r*-Dimensional Kronecker Deltas.** The r-dimensional Kronecker deltas, $\delta^{i_1 \dots i_r}_{j_1 \dots j_r}$, are defined by the equations

$$\underline{|n - r}\, \delta^{i_1 \dots i_r}_{j_1 \dots j_r} = e^{i_1 \dots i_r kl \dots n} e_{j_1 \dots j_r kl \dots n}. \tag{42.3}$$

One may easily verify several interesting properties of these symbols. Again, we merely list these properties.

$$\underline{|n - r}\, \delta^{i_1 \dots i_r}_{j_1 \dots j_r} = \delta^{i_1 \dots i_r kl \dots n}_{j_1 \dots j_r kl \dots n},$$

$$\delta^{ij}_{lj} = (n - 1) \delta^i_l, \qquad \delta^{ij}_{ij} = n(n - 1),$$

$$e^{i_1 \dots i_r kl \dots n} \delta^{j_{r+1} \dots j_n}_{k \dots \dots n} = \underline{|n - r}\, e^{i_1 \dots i_r j_{r+1} \dots j_n}.$$

A more complete discussion will be found in various texts.[5]

43. Are Complex Numbers Vectors? For any two vectors in the plane, the scalar and cross products have only one component each. Hence, such products cannot be in one-to-one correspondence with the product of

[5] O. Veblen, *Invariants of Quadratic Differential Forms*, Cambridge U. Tract Number 24, 1927.

complex numbers. It will be our task to attempt to define a new product of vectors which is in one-to-one correspondence with the product of the corresponding complex numbers. We shall show that such a correspondence can be preserved under a very restricted group of coordinate transformations.

We define the one-to-one correspondence between a vector, **V**, and the corresponding complex number, V, by

$$\mathbf{V} = V_x\mathbf{i} + V_y\mathbf{j} \leftrightarrow V = V_x + V_y i, \qquad i^2 = -1. \tag{43.1}$$

It is easily shown that this correspondence is preserved under addition. That is, if $\mathbf{V} + \mathbf{W} = \mathbf{U}$, then $V + W = U$ and conversely.

However, the correspondence (43.1) is not preserved under multiplication. Thus, by multiplying the complex numbers V, W, we obtain

$$U = VW = (V_xW_x - V_yW_y) + (V_xW_y + V_yW_x)i.$$

The components of the resulting complex number cannot be correlated with the scalar or vector products of **V**, **W**. By an examination of the complex product $U = VW$, we are led to the consideration of the vector **U** whose components are

$$\begin{aligned} U_x &= (V_xW_x - V_yW_y)A_x + (V_xW_y + V_yW_x)A_y \\ U_y &= (V_xW_y + V_yW_x)A_x - (V_xW_x - V_yW_y)A_y. \end{aligned} \tag{43.2}$$

Evidently, if **A** has the components (1, 0) then the vector **U** defined by (43.2) *is in one-to-one correspondence with the* complex number U. We must now show that (43.2) represents a vector determined by **V**, **W**, **A**. By rearranging terms in **U**, we obtain

$$\begin{aligned} U_x &= V_x(W_xA_x + W_yA_y) + V_y(W_xA_y - W_yA_x) \\ U_y &= V_y(W_xA_x + W_yA_y) - V_x(W_xA_y - W_yA_x). \end{aligned}$$

Evidently the first parentheses contain the scalar product of **W**, **A** and the second parentheses contain the cross product of **W**, **A**. Further, the vector whose components are $(V_y, -V_x)$ is orthogonal to the vector **V**. Let us denote this vector by $'\mathbf{V}$. Then **U** may be represented by

$$\mathbf{U} = \mathbf{V}(\mathbf{W} \cdot \mathbf{A}) + '\mathbf{V}(\mathbf{W} \times \mathbf{A} \cdot \mathbf{k}).$$

Now we translate the last equation into the index notation by means of the correspondence principles and the relation, $'V_j = \sqrt{g}\,(e_{jk}V^k)$, and obtain

$$U_j = V_j(W^kA_k) + ge_{jk}e_{ln}V^kW^lA^n.$$

Or, if one introduces the fourth-order tensor,

$$H^{i}_{\cdot kln} = \delta^{i}_{k} g_{ln} + g g^{hi} e_{hk} e_{ln}$$

then one may write the formula for U_j as

$$U_j = H_{jkln} V^k W^l A^n. \tag{43.3}$$

That is, the vector U_j of (43.3) formed from **V, W, A** (where **A** is a unit vector along the axis of reals) corresponds to the complex number product,[6] $U = VW$.

The group of coordinate transformations for which the vector **U** corresponds to the complex number U is a very restricted group; the vector **A** with components (1, 0) must be an invariant under this group. It is easily verified that this group is defined by

$$'x = x, \qquad 'y = dy, \qquad d \neq 0.$$

Hence, our correspondence of vectors and complex numbers is not preserved under the general affine group.

[6] A. W. Wundheiler, "Are Complex Numbers Vectors?" *Bulletin of the American Mathematical Society*, Vol. 46, 1940, p. 57, abstract. The above argument is equivalent to that used by Wundheiler. See also, A. Duschek and A. Hochrainer, *Grundzüge der Tensorrechnung in Analytischer Darstellung*, Teil II, Springer, Wein, 1950, p. 216.

Chapter VII

TENSORS IN GENERAL CURVILINEAR COORDINATES

44. General Curvilinear Coordinates; The Groups of Transformations. In this section, we shall discuss some of the properties of general curvilinear coordinates and the group of permissible coordinate transformations. Further, we shall introduce the concept of the *physical components* of a tensor.

(a) ***General Curvilinear Coordinates.*** Although our present developments are applicable to metric non-Euclidean spaces of n dimensions, we shall limit our study to Euclidean space of three dimensions. For the sake of concreteness, we shall follow the procedure of Section 37(a) and consider three coordinate systems:

$'y^j$, $j = 1, 2, 3$, a set of Cartesian orthogonal coordinates;
$'x^j$, $j = 1, 2, 3$, a set of curvilinear coordinates;
x^j, $j = 1, 2, 3$, another set of curvilinear coordinates.

First, we shall characterize the allowable coordinate systems x^j, $'x^j$. Consider the coordinates x^j and let us assume that these coordinates are related to the Cartesian orthogonal coordinates $'y^j$ by the equations

$$x^j = x^j('y^k), \qquad j, k = 1, 2, 3. \tag{44.1}$$

We shall require that the above equations possess the following properties at the points under discussion:

(1) the first and second derivatives of x^j with respect to $'y^k$ exist and are continuous;

(2) the Jacobian, J, of the transformation shall not vanish. By definition, J is the determinant

$$J = \begin{vmatrix} \dfrac{\partial x^1}{\partial\, 'y^1} & \dfrac{\partial x^1}{\partial\, 'y^2} & \dfrac{\partial x^1}{\partial\, 'y^3} \\ \dfrac{\partial x^2}{\partial\, 'y^1} & \dfrac{\partial x^2}{\partial\, 'y^2} & \dfrac{\partial x^2}{\partial\, 'y^3} \\ \dfrac{\partial x^3}{\partial\, 'y^1} & \dfrac{\partial x^3}{\partial\, 'y^2} & \dfrac{\partial x^3}{\partial\, 'y^3} \end{vmatrix}.$$

As illustrations of our conditions, we consider the cases of cylindrical coordinates ($'x^j = r, \theta, z$) and spherical coordinates ($x^j = R, \phi, \theta$). In Chapter II we found that for these coordinates the transformation relations are

$$r = \sqrt{x^2 + y^2}, \qquad \theta = \arctan \frac{y}{x}, \qquad z = z,$$

$$R = \sqrt{x^2 + y^2 + z^2}, \qquad \theta = \arctan \frac{y}{x}, \qquad \phi = \arctan \frac{\sqrt{x^2 + y^2}}{z}.$$

Any point of the Oz axis is a singular point of the first of the above transformations; the origin is the singular point of the second set.

It will be shown that the continuity of the second derivatives is needed in order to determine transformation laws of the derivatives of tensors. The question arises as to the significance of the assumption, $J \neq 0$. This question is answered by the following two theorems.

[1]***Theorem 1:*** If $'y^j_0, x^j_0$ satisfy $x^j = x^j('y^k)$ and J does not vanish at the point $'y^j_0$ then one may solve for the $'y^j$. These solutions, $'y^j = 'y^j(x^k)$, are such that at x^k_0, the values of y^k are y^k_0. Further, if the derivatives $\partial x^k / \partial\, 'y^j$ are continuous in the neighborhood of $'y^k_0$ then a unique inverse solution exists in the neighborhood of this point with continuous derivatives $\partial\, 'y^j / \partial x^k$.

[2]***Theorem 2:*** The necessary and sufficient condition for the non-existence of any (differentiable) relation of the type, $g(x^k) = 0$, among the variables x^k is that $J \neq 0$ through the region under discussion.

Thus, the condition that $J \neq 0$ insures the existence of an inverse transformation to (44.1). Further, the non-existence of a relation of the type, $g(x^k) = 0$, implies that the x^k are independent of each other. Both of these theorems are valid in spaces of n dimensions. In fact, the second theorem can be extended to the case of n variables x^k and m variables $'y^j$. For this case, the theorem reads: If the matrix of the system (44.1) is of rank r (Appendix II) then $(n - r)$ independent functional relations exist among the x^k.

If we assume that the variables $'x^j$ are related to $'y^j$ by a transformation for which $J \neq 0$, then one may solve these equations for $'y^j$ and by substituting into the equations, $x^j = x^j('y^k)$ obtain the transformation,

[1] Ch-J. de la Vallee Poussin, *Cours d'Analyse Infinitesimale*, Paris, Gautheir-Villars, 1941, Vol. I, p. 169.

[2] T. Levi-Civita, *The Absolute Differential Calculus*, Blackie and Son, London, 1929, p. 6.

$x^j = x^j('x^k)$. The following equations correspond to this relation for the case of spherical and cylindrical coordinates

$$R = \sqrt{r^2 + z^2}, \qquad \theta = \theta, \qquad \phi = \arctan \frac{r}{z}.$$

One can easily show that: If the transformations, $x^j = x^j('y^k)$, $'x^j = 'x^j('y^k)$ both satisfy the conditions (1) and (2), then the transformation $x^j = x^j('x^k)$ will satisfy these same conditions. To verify this result, one needs only to use the chain rule for differentiation:

$$\frac{\partial x^j}{\partial\, 'x^k} = \frac{\partial x^j}{\partial\, 'y^l} \frac{\partial\, 'y^l}{\partial\, 'x^k}, \qquad j, k, l = 1, 2, 3.$$

By use of the product rule for determinants (35.4), we see that the Jacobian of $\partial x^j/\partial\, 'x^k$ is the product of the Jacobians of $\partial x^j/\partial\, 'y^k$ and $\partial\, 'y^j/\partial\, 'x^k$. Since the latter Jacobians are non-vanishing, it follows that the Jacobian of $\partial x^j/\partial\, 'x^k$ is not zero. The continuity of the derivatives $\partial x^j/\partial\, 'x^k$ and $\partial^2 x^j/\partial\, 'x^k \partial\, 'x^l$ is easily established by the use of the above chain rule and its derivatives.

Finally, we introduce the covariant base vectors $\mathbf{e}_j$, $j = 1, 2, 3$. By definition, these vectors are tangent to the coordinate lines. However, these vectors are *not necessarily unit vectors*. Our reason for not specifying the magnitude of these vectors is that we wish to work with a centered affine group at any point P which is induced by the group of transformations $x^j = x^j('x^k)$ (see Section 37).

(b) ***The Allowable Groups of Transformations.*** We shall consider two groups of transformations. If x^k, $'x^k$ are permissible coordinate systems, then we require that the transformation $x^k = x^k('x^j)$ must possess the properties (1) and (2). In view of the discussion in (a), it can be shown that the allowed coordinate transformations form a group. We denote this group by G_3 and write

$$G_3\colon x^k = x^k('x^j). \tag{44.2}$$

At any point P of the space, the group G_3 induces a new group, A_3. *This group, A_3, is the centered affine group* and transforms the differentials of x^k, $'x^j$ according to the formula

$$A_3\colon dx^k = \frac{\partial x^k}{\partial\, 'x^j}\, d\, 'x^j. \tag{44.3}$$

At a given point P, the quantities $\partial x^k/\partial\, 'x^j$ are the constants, c_j^k of Section 37. We shall not stop to prove that the transformations A_3, which are induced by G_3, form a group. It is important to notice that our remaining discussion will deal with the induced group A_3 and not with G_3. That is, at each point P, of the space, one must determine how quantities transform under (44.3). For this reason, a great deal of the theory is equivalent to that discussed for the case of general Cartesian coordinates in Chapter VI. In fact, one often considers the variables dx^k as determining the local coordinates of a Euclidean space which is tangent to the original space at P. This last concept is very fruitful in the study of non-Euclidean or Riemannian spaces.

The dx^j will be *considered to behave as the contravariant components of a vector*. Hence, the formula (44.3) defines the group A_3 and *also the transformation law for contravariance*. Exactly the same procedure was used in Chapter VI, where the x^j were chosen as the contravariant components of **R**.

In order to determine the transformation law of the covariant base vectors and hence of covariant vectors, we shall require that $dx^j\mathbf{e}_j$ be an invariant under the group, A_3, or

$$dx^j\mathbf{e}_j = d\,'x^j\,'\mathbf{e}_j. \tag{44.4}$$

It should be noted that in Cartesian coordinates, $dx^j\mathbf{e}_j$ is $d\mathbf{R}$. Eliminating dx^k in the equation (44.4) through use of (44.3), we obtain

$$'\mathbf{e}_j = \frac{\partial x^k}{\partial\,'x^j}\,\mathbf{e}_k.$$

In order to solve for $\mathbf{e}_k$, we use the chain rule for differentiation,

$$\frac{\partial x^k}{\partial\,'x^j}\frac{\partial\,'x^j}{\partial x^l} = \frac{\partial x^k}{\partial x^l} = \delta^k_l.$$

That is, the partial derivatives $\partial\,'x^j/\partial x^l$ are the reduced cofactors of $\partial x^k/\partial\,'x^j$. Multiplying the equation for $'\mathbf{e}_j$ by $\partial\,'x^j/\partial x^l$ and using the above relation, we obtain

$$\mathbf{e}_k = \frac{\partial\,'x^l}{\partial x^k}\,'\mathbf{e}_l. \tag{44.5}$$

The transformation law (44.5) is contragredient to the transformation law for dx^k, (44.3).

To summarize: The contravariant components of vectors transform by the formula (44.3) and the covariant components of vectors transform by the formula (44.5). It is evident that the theories of: (1) covariant and contravariant components of a tensor; (2) the metric tensor; (3) the Kronecker tensors; and (4) the e^{ijk}, e_{ijk} tensor densities and capacities are exactly the same as that developed in Chapter VI for general Cartesian coordinates in three-space. Further, this theory is valid in metric n-dimensional non-Euclidean spaces. Hence, we leave the study of transformation theory.

The following problems will review some of these previous results. In solving these problems, the reader should compare his results with the theory of Chapter VI.

Problem 44.1: If we denote cylindrical coordinates according to the scheme, $x^1 = r$, $x^2 = \theta$, $x^3 = z$, show that the vectors whose contravariant components are (1, 0, 0), (0, $1/r$, 0), (0, 0, 1), are orthogonal unit vectors. (Assume that $g_{11} = 1$, $g_{22} = r^2$, $g_{33} = 1$, $g_{ij} = 0$, $i \neq j$.)

Problem 44.2: (1) From the invariance of $\mathbf{V} = V^j\mathbf{e}_j$, and the transformation law of the $\mathbf{e}_j$, derive the transformation formula for the contravariant components, V^j, of a vector; (2) Find the covariant and contravariant components of the vectors **i, j, k** in cylindrical coordinates.

Problem 44.3: Derive the transformation law for the contravariant components, V^{kj}, of a second-order tensor. Extend this law to the contravariant components $V^{j_1j_2\cdots j_r}$, of an r-th order tensor.

Problem 44.4: From the definition $\mathbf{e}^j \cdot \mathbf{e}_i = \delta^j_i$, derive the transformation formulas for the contravariant base vectors $\mathbf{e}^j$.

Problem 44.5: Derive the transformation law of the covariant components, $V_{k_1\ldots k_r}$ of an r-th order tensor. Notice that if $V_{k_1\ldots k_r}$ are zero in one coordinate system, then these components are zero in all coordinate systems.

Problem 44.6: If the quantities g_{ij} are defined in any curvilinear coordinate system by $g_{ij} = \mathbf{e}_i \cdot \mathbf{e}_j$, show that these quantities are the covariant components of a second-order tensor—the metric tensor.

Problem 44.7: If the space is Euclidean and $'x^j$ is a curvilinear coordinate system, show that the element of arc is given by $ds^2 = {'g_{ij}}d\,'x^id\,'x^j$. *Hint:* If R is the radius vector field, show that $d\mathrm{R} = dx^je_j$ in Cartesian coordinates, x^j; then use the definition $ds^2 = d\mathrm{R} \cdot d\mathrm{R}$. In the non-Euclidean spaces, one can proceed by one of two methods: (1) imbed the space in a Euclidean space of sufficiently high dimension; (2) *define* the element of arc, ds, by the formula, $ds^2 = g_{ij}\,dx^i\,dx^j$.

Problem 44.8: If the quantities g^{ij} are defined by the relations $g^{ij}g_{jk} = \delta^i_k$, show that: (1) the g^{ij} are the contravariant components of a second order tensor; (2) $g^{ij} = \mathbf{e}^i \cdot \mathbf{e}^j$; (3) the g^{ij} are the contravariant components of the metric tensor.

Problem 44.9: Show that $U^j = g^{jk}U_k$, $U_l = g_{lk}U^k$. This result is called "the principle of lowering or raising indices by means of the metric tensor."

Problem 44.10: Show that V^iW_j is an invariant under the group A_3, if V^i, W_j are the components of vectors.

Problem 44.11: If V_{kjl} are the covariant components of a third-order tensor, show that $V_{kjl}W^{jlnp}$, are the mixed components (covariant of order one and contravariant of order two) of a tensor, when W^{jlnp} are the contravariant components of a fourth-order tensor.

The results of Problems 44.10, 44.11 show that the third correspondence principle is invariant under the group A_3.

Problem 44.12: If V_j are the covariant components of a vector, show that $\partial V_j/\partial x^k$ are *not* the components of a tensor. *Hint:* Study the transformation law of $\partial V_j/\partial x^k$.

The result of Problem 44.12 shows that under the group A_3, the correspondence, $\nabla \leftrightarrow \partial/\partial x^j$, is not invariant. This means that this part of the first correspondence principle must be revised. Such a revision will be discussed in Section 46.

Problem 44.13: Show that the second correspondence principle is invariant under A_3.

Problem 44.14: Show that e^{ijk} is a third-order tensor density of weight one and e_{ijk} is a third-order tensor capacity of weight one under A_3.

Problem 44.15: Show that g, the determinant of the g_{ij}, is a scalar density of weight two.

Problem 44.16: If A_j, B_k are the covariant components of vectors, show that $e^{ijk}A_jB_k/\sqrt{g}$ is a vector.

The Problem 44.16 shows that the modification in Chapter VI of the fourth correspondence principle is necessary for the group A_3.

Problem 44.17: Consider the confocal plane coordinates, ϕ, ψ, defined by

$$x = c \cosh \phi \cos \psi$$
$$y = c \sinh \phi \sin \psi$$

where x, y are Cartesian orthogonal coordinates. Determine:

(1) The covariant base vectors $\mathbf{e}_\phi$, $\mathbf{e}_\psi$ of these coordinates in terms of the base vectors **i, j**;

(2) The covariant components, g_{ij} of the metric tensor.

Problem 44.18: Show that if X^i, Y^j are the components of arbitrary vectors and if $A^{ij}_{\cdot\cdot k}X^kY_j$ is a vector, then $A^{ij}_{\cdot\cdot k}$ are the components of a third-order tensor. This result can be extended to tensors of the p-th order and is often called the *quotient rule.*

Problem 44.19: Determine the covariant base vectors $\mathbf{e}_r$, $\mathbf{e}_\theta$, $\mathbf{e}_z$ for cylindrical coordinates in terms of: (1) **i, j, k**; (2) in terms of $\mathbf{r}_1$, $\boldsymbol{\theta}_1$, **k**. Verify the arc length formula in cylindrical coordinates by forming $g_{ij} = \mathbf{e}_i \cdot \mathbf{e}_j$.

Problem 44.20: Determine the covariant base vectors $\mathbf{e}_R$, $\mathbf{e}_\phi$, $\mathbf{e}_\theta$ for spherical coordinates in terms of the unit vectors $\mathbf{R}_1$, $\boldsymbol{\phi}_1$, $\boldsymbol{\theta}_1$. Verify that $ds^2 = (R\,d\phi)^2 + (dR)^2 + (R \sin \phi\, d\theta)^2$, by forming $g_{ij} = \mathbf{e}_i \cdot \mathbf{e}_j$.

Problem 44.21: (1) If $\mathbf{v}$, $\mathbf{w}$, $\mathbf{u}$ are three arbitrary vectors, show that

$$(\mathbf{v}, \mathbf{w}, \mathbf{u})^2 = \begin{vmatrix} v_jv^j & v_jw^j & v_ju^j \\ w_jv^j & w_jw^j & w_ju^j \\ u_jv^j & u_jw^j & u_ju^j \end{vmatrix}.$$

(2) Hence, prove that, $(\mathbf{e}_1, \mathbf{e}_2, \mathbf{e}_3) = \sqrt{g}$.

(c) ***The Physical Components of a Tensor.*** From the transformation law (44.3), we see that the differentials of the coordinate variables are the prototype of the contravariant components of a vector. Now, the coordinate variables may be angles. Hence, the contravariant components of a vector will not behave as displacements. Further, since the combination $dx^j\mathbf{e}_j$ does represent a displacement, the $\mathbf{e}_k$ will not be unit vectors, in general. In fact, any *specific* covariant base vector $\mathbf{e}_j$ is such that $dx^j\mathbf{e}_j$ (not summed on j) is a displacement. The magnitude of the $\mathbf{e}_k$ vectors is fixed by this requirement.

In general, the applied mathematician and the physicist are interested in quantities which behave as displacements. We shall call the components of this type of a vector or tensor, the *physical components*. Such components have desirable physical properties. However, their transformation formulas are very complicated. For this reason, all studies of such components are limited to a fixed coordinate system. If $\mathbf{u}_j$ denote unit vectors along the vectors $\mathbf{e}_j$ and $^*V_j$ denote the physical components of the first type of a vector $\mathbf{V}$, then in a *specified coordinate* system,

$$\mathbf{V} = V^k\mathbf{e}_k = \sum_k {}^*V_k\mathbf{u}_k. \tag{44.6}$$

Further, it is easily seen that in Cartesian orthogonal coordinates, the invariant $dx^j\mathbf{e}_j$ becomes

$$dx^j\mathbf{e}_j = dx\,\mathbf{i} + dy\,\mathbf{j} + dz\,\mathbf{k}.$$

Thus, this vector represents a displacement, and in a specified coordinate system x^k, we may write by analogy with (44.6)

$$dx^j\mathbf{e}_j = \sum_j {}^*(dx^j)\mathbf{u}_j$$

where $^*(dx^k)$ are the displacements corresponding to dx^k.

One may easily find the relations between $\mathbf{e}_k$, $\mathbf{u}_k$ and then between V^k,

$*V_k$, and dx^k, $*(dx^k)$. Since $\mathbf{e}_i \cdot \mathbf{e}_j = g_{ij}$, the magnitude of $\mathbf{e}_i$ is $\sqrt{g_{ii}}$. By definition, $\mathbf{u}_i$ lie along $\mathbf{e}_i$ and are unit vectors. Hence, we find that

$$\mathbf{e}_j = \sqrt{g_{jj}}\, \mathbf{u}_j \qquad \text{(not summed on } j\text{)}. \tag{44.7}$$

Since $V^k\mathbf{e}_k = *V_k\mathbf{u}_k$ (not summed on k) and similarly, $dx^k\mathbf{e}_k = *(dx^k)\mathbf{u}_k$ (not summed on k), we see that

$$*V_k = \sqrt{g_{kk}}\, V^k, \qquad *(dx^k) = \sqrt{g_{kk}}\, dx^k \qquad \text{(not summed on } k\text{)}. \tag{44.8}$$

The formula (44.8) refers to the components $*V_k$, which add by the *parallelogram law.* Instead, one may introduce physical components of the second type, $\tilde{V}_k$, which are *projections* of a vector on the unit vectors $\mathbf{u}_j$ along the coordinate lines. Let $\mathbf{w}_k$ denote the vectors of the system reciprocal to $\mathbf{u}_j$. We define $\tilde{V}_k$ by the relation

$$\mathbf{V} = V_k\mathbf{e}^k = \sum_k \tilde{V}_k\mathbf{w}_k. \tag{44.9}$$

or

$$\tilde{V}_k = \mathbf{V} \cdot \mathbf{u}_k.$$

Now, $\mathbf{w}_k$ lies along $\mathbf{e}^k$ and belongs to the system reciprocal to the unit vectors $\mathbf{u}_j$. In view of relation (44.7), it follows that

$$\sqrt{g_{jj}}\, \mathbf{e}^j = \mathbf{w}_j \qquad \text{(not summed on } j\text{)}.$$

From this last relation and the defining relation (44.9) for the components $\tilde{V}_k$, it follows that

$$V_k = \sqrt{g_{kk}}\, \tilde{V}_k \qquad \text{(not summed on } k\text{)}. \tag{44.10}$$

The defining relations for $*V_k$, $\tilde{V}_k$

$$\mathbf{V} = \sum_k *V_k\mathbf{u}_k, \qquad \tilde{V}_k = \mathbf{V} \cdot \mathbf{u}_k$$

where $\mathbf{u}_k$ are unit vectors along the coordinate lines should be compared with (41.2) and (41.4) respectively. Such a comparison will show that $*V_k$, $\tilde{V}_k$ are, respectively, the contravariant and covariant components of $\mathbf{V}$ in a local coordinate system in which the base vectors $\mathbf{e}_j$ have been unitized. Again, it should be noted that in an *orthogonal curvilinear coordinate system,* $*V_k = \tilde{V}_k$. This follows from (44.8) and (44.10), and the fact that, $V_k = g_{kk}V^k$ (not summed on k), in such a coordinate system. Finally, we note that two other types of physical components may be introduced.[3] These can be obtained by unitizing the vectors $\mathbf{w}_j$ of the system reciprocal to $\mathbf{u}_j$.

[3] This was called to the attention of the author by Mr. Robert Wasserman.

The previous theory of physical components for a vector can be immediately extended to obtain the physical components of a tensor. This is due to the fact that an arbitrary tensor of order m can be considered to be the sum of products of m vectors (see Section 47). Thus, corresponding to (44.8) and (44.10), we find that the physical components $^*V_{ij}$, $\tilde{V}_{ij}$ of a second-order tensor are

$$^*V_{jk} = \sqrt{g_{jj}g_{kk}}\, V^{jk}, \qquad \sqrt{g_{jj}g_{kk}}\, \tilde{V}_{jk} = V_{jk}.$$

Illustrative Example: Evaluate $\mathbf{e}_j$, $^*(dx^k)$, $^*V_k$ in cylindrical coordinates.

Solution: By use of the components of the metric tensor in cylindrical coordinates (Section 14), we see that if $\mathbf{e}_1 = \mathbf{e}_r$, $\mathbf{e}_2 = \mathbf{e}_\theta$, $\mathbf{e}_3 = \mathbf{e}_z$, then $g_{11} = 1$, $g_{22} = r^2$, $g_{33} = 1$. Thus, (44.7) becomes (with $\mathbf{u}_j = \mathbf{r}_1, \boldsymbol{\theta}_1, \mathbf{k}$)

$$\mathbf{e}_r = \mathbf{r}_1, \qquad \mathbf{e}_\theta = r\boldsymbol{\theta}_1, \qquad \mathbf{e}_z = \mathbf{k}.$$

Similarly, we find that

$$^*(dx^1) = dr, \qquad ^*(dx^2) = r\,d\theta, \qquad ^*(dx^3) = dz$$
$$^*V_1 = V^1, \qquad ^*V_2 = rV^2, \qquad ^*V_3 = V^3.$$

Problem 44.22: Consider the vector $\mathbf{V} = 2\mathbf{i}$. Determine: (1) the contravariant components of this vector in cylindrical coordinates; (2) the physical components of this vector in cylindrical coordinates.

Problem 44.23: Find the contravariant components and the physical components of the velocity vector $\mathbf{V} = \mathbf{i}\,\dfrac{dx}{dt} + \mathbf{j}\,\dfrac{dy}{dt} + \mathbf{k}\,\dfrac{dz}{dt}$ in cylindrical coordinates.

Problem 44.24: Evaluate $\mathbf{e}_j$, $^*(dx^k)$, $^*V_k$ in spherical coordinates.

Problem 44.25: Determine the contravariant components and the physical components of the velocity vector in spherical coordinates.

45. The Connection of Local Spaces. The covariant components, V_j, and the contravariant components, V^j, of the vector $\mathbf{V}$ are related to this vector by the equations: $\mathbf{V} = V^j\mathbf{e}_j = V_j\mathbf{e}^j$, where $\mathbf{e}_j$ and $\mathbf{e}^j$ are reciprocal systems of base vectors. If we form the differentials of $\mathbf{V}$, we obtain the equations

$$d\mathbf{V} = \mathbf{e}_j\,dV^j + V^j\,d\mathbf{e}_j, \qquad d\mathbf{V} = \mathbf{e}^j\,dV_j + V_j\,d\mathbf{e}^j. \tag{45.1}$$

In order to compute the $d\mathbf{V}$ vector, we must obtain formulas for $d\mathbf{e}^j$, $d\mathbf{e}_j$. As examples, we compute these formulas for the base vectors in cylindrical and spherical coordinates.

(a) ***The Differentials of the Covariant Base Vectors in Cylindrical and Spherical Coordinates.*** First, we consider cylindrical coordinates. From the illustrative example of Section 44, we see that

$$d\mathbf{r}_1 = d\mathbf{e}_r, \qquad d(r\boldsymbol{\theta}_1) = d\mathbf{e}_\theta, \qquad d\mathbf{k} = d\mathbf{e}_z.$$

Use of the rule for forming differentials and the table of Chapter II shows that

$$d\mathbf{r}_1 = \boldsymbol{\theta}_1\, d\theta, \qquad d\boldsymbol{\theta}_1 = -\mathbf{r}_1\, d\theta, \qquad d\mathbf{k} = 0.$$

By use of the above results, we obtain the desired formulas

$$d\mathbf{e}_r = \frac{\mathbf{e}_\theta}{r}\, d\theta, \qquad d\mathbf{e}_\theta = -r\mathbf{e}_r\, d\theta + \frac{\mathbf{e}_\theta}{r}\, dr, \qquad d\mathbf{e}_z = 0. \tag{45.2}$$

For spherical coordinates, the basic formulas are (see Section 14):

$$\begin{array}{lll} \mathbf{e}_1 = \mathbf{e}_R, & \mathbf{e}_3 = \mathbf{e}_\theta, & \mathbf{e}_2 = \mathbf{e}_\phi \\ \mathbf{u}_1 = \mathbf{R}_1, & \mathbf{u}_3 = \boldsymbol{\theta}_1, & \mathbf{u}_2 = \boldsymbol{\phi}_1 \\ g_{11} = 1, & g_{33} = R^2 \sin^2 \phi, & g_{22} = R^2. \end{array}$$

By use of (44.7), we obtain the formulas relating $\mathbf{u}_i$ and $\mathbf{e}_i$ for spherical coordinates. These are

$$\mathbf{R}_1 = \mathbf{e}_R, \qquad R \sin \phi\, \boldsymbol{\theta}_1 = \mathbf{e}_\theta, \qquad R\boldsymbol{\phi}_1 = \mathbf{e}_\phi.$$

Carrying through a computation similar to that for cylindrical coordinates, we derive the formulas which correspond to (45.2)

$$\begin{aligned} d\mathbf{e}_R &= \mathbf{e}_\theta\, d\theta/R \sin \phi + \mathbf{e}_\phi\, d\phi/R \\ d\mathbf{e}_\theta &= -\mathbf{e}_R R \sin^2 \phi\, d\theta + \mathbf{e}_\theta(\cot \phi\, d\phi + dR/R) \\ &\qquad - \mathbf{e}_\phi \sin \phi \cos \phi\, d\theta \\ d\mathbf{e}_\phi &= -\mathbf{e}_R R\, d\phi + \mathbf{e}_\theta \cot \phi\, d\theta + \mathbf{e}_\phi\, dR/R. \end{aligned} \tag{45.3}$$

(b) ***The Differentials of the Covariant Base Vectors in General Curvilinear Coordinates.*** In order to obtain general formulas for $d\mathbf{e}_j$, we notice that $d\mathbf{e}_j$ is a vector at any point P and hence it can be expressed as a linear combination of the base vectors $\mathbf{e}_j$ at P. Further, $d\mathbf{e}_j$ depends linearly upon dx^k [see (45.2) and (45.3)]. In view of these observations, we may write

$$d\mathbf{e}_j = \Gamma^l_{jk}\, dx^k \mathbf{e}_l \tag{45.4}$$

where Γ^l_{jk} are undetermined coefficients. One may also write this last relation in the form

$$\frac{\partial \mathbf{e}_j}{\partial x^k} = \Gamma^l_{jk} \mathbf{e}_l. \tag{45.5}$$

The undetermined coefficients Γ^l_{jk} are called the components of the connection; the Γ^l_{jk} *are not the components of a tensor* (as will be shown) but have vital geometric significance. This significance lies in the following fact: If Γ^l_{jk} are known, one may determine the derivatives of vectors and tensors. But this implies that one can compare tensors at two distinct points, P and $'P$. That is, the Γ^l_{jk} serve to *connect* tensor fields at two distinct points.

Let us consider the reciprocal base system, $\mathbf{e}^j$. As in the case of the covariant base vectors, we can express the $d\mathbf{e}^j$ as linear combinations of the $\mathbf{e}^j$ and dx^k. We write

$$d\mathbf{e}^j = U^j_{lm}\mathbf{e}^l\,dx^m \tag{45.6}$$

where the coefficients U^j_{lm} are to be determined. From the fundamental relations $\mathbf{e}^j \cdot \mathbf{e}_k = \delta^j_k$, for the reciprocal base vectors, we obtain by differentiation

$$d\mathbf{e}^j \cdot \mathbf{e}_k + \mathbf{e}^j \cdot d\mathbf{e}_k = 0.$$

Eliminating $d\mathbf{e}^j$, $d\mathbf{e}_k$ by use of (45.4) and (45.6), the above relation furnishes the result

$$U^j_{km} = -\Gamma^j_{km}. \tag{45.7}$$

Thus, there exists only one connection for Euclidean spaces. This same result is valid in Riemannian spaces (non-Euclidean spaces such as the surface of a sphere).

Problem 45.1: Show that for cylindrical coordinates with $\mathbf{e}_r = \mathbf{e}_1$, $\mathbf{e}_\theta = \mathbf{e}_2$, $\mathbf{e}_z = \mathbf{e}_3$, the components of Γ^l_{jk} are: $\Gamma^2_{12} = 1/r$, $\Gamma^1_{22} = -r$, $\Gamma^2_{21} = 1/r$, all others zero.

Problem 45.2: Show that for spherical coordinates with $\mathbf{e}_R = \mathbf{e}_1$, $\mathbf{e}_\theta = \mathbf{e}_3$, $\mathbf{e}_\phi = \mathbf{e}_2$, the components of Γ^l_{jk} are: $\Gamma^3_{13} = 1/R$, $\Gamma^2_{12} = 1/R$, $\Gamma^1_{33} = -R\sin^2\phi$, $\Gamma^3_{31} = 1/R$, $\Gamma^3_{32} = \cot\phi$, $\Gamma^2_{33} = -\sin\phi\cos\phi$, $\Gamma^1_{22} = -R$, $\Gamma^3_{23} = \cot\phi$, $\Gamma^2_{21} = 1/R$, all others zero.

(c) ***Expression for the Γ^i_{ln} in Terms of the Metric Tensor, g_{ij}.*** First, we shall prove that *the quantities Γ^i_{ln} are symmetric in the two lower indices, l, n.* If we restrict ourselves to Euclidean spaces and differentiate the equation $\mathbf{e}_j = (\partial\,'x^k/\partial x^j)'\mathbf{e}_k$ of (44.5), where $'\mathbf{e}_j$ are the fixed base vectors of a Cartesian coordinate system, we obtain

$$\frac{\partial \mathbf{e}_j}{\partial x^l} = \frac{\partial^2\,'x^k}{\partial x^j \partial x^l}\,'\mathbf{e}_k = \frac{\partial \mathbf{e}_l}{\partial x^j}.$$

Replacing the partial derivatives of the vectors $\mathbf{e}_j$ by (45.5) in the above, we obtain the desired result.

In non-Euclidean spaces which are Riemannian, the relation $\Gamma^{j}_{ln} = \Gamma^{j}_{nl}$ is still valid. However, the above proof fails because a system of fixed base vectors does not exist. The symmetry of Γ^{j}_{ln} for general curvilinear coordinates of such a space follows from the integrability conditions for the coordinate variables. We shall discuss the topic of integrability conditions in Section 48. For non-holonomic coordinate systems (systems in which the "differentials of the coordinate variables" are defined but not the coordinate variables) of Riemannian space, the symmetry property of Γ^{j}_{ln} is no longer valid. Further, for general non-Riemannian spaces (spaces which do not possess a metric tensor) the Γ^{j}_{ln} are not symmetric.

Secondly, we shall derive a formula for the Γ^{j}_{ln} in terms of the metric tensor. In Section 39, we defined the covariant components of the metric tensor to be $g_{ij} = \mathbf{e}_i \cdot \mathbf{e}_j$. By differentiation of this formula and use of (45.5) we obtain

$$\frac{\partial g_{ij}}{\partial x^k} = g_{lj}\Gamma^l_{ik} + g_{li}\Gamma^l_{jk}.$$

Further, by permuting the indices of the above, we find

$$\frac{\partial g_{ik}}{\partial x^j} = g_{lk}\Gamma^l_{ij} + g_{li}\Gamma^l_{kj}$$

$$\frac{\partial g_{jk}}{\partial x^i} = g_{lk}\Gamma^l_{ji} + g_{lj}\Gamma^l_{ki}.$$

Subtracting the first equation from the sum of the last two, and using the symmetry property of the Γ^l_{ij}, one finds that

$$2g_{lk}\Gamma^l_{ij} = \left[\frac{\partial g_{ik}}{\partial x^j} + \frac{\partial g_{jk}}{\partial x^i} - \frac{\partial g_{ij}}{\partial x^k}\right].$$

By multiplying the above equation by g^{kn} and dividing by 2, we obtain the desired formula

$$\Gamma^n_{ij} = \frac{1}{2}g^{nk}\left[\frac{\partial g_{ik}}{\partial x^j} + \frac{\partial g_{jk}}{\partial x^i} - \frac{\partial g_{ij}}{\partial x^k}\right]. \tag{45.8}$$

The combination of metric coefficients inside the bracket of the right-hand side of (45.8) is called a Christoffel symbol of the first kind. Further, the right-hand side itself is called a Christoffel symbol of the second kind. These symbols are generally denoted by $[ij, k]$, $\{ij, n\}$, respectively, in the literature:

$$[ij, k] = \frac{1}{2}\left[\frac{\partial g_{ik}}{\partial x^j} + \frac{\partial g_{jk}}{\partial x^i} - \frac{\partial g_{ij}}{\partial x^k}\right]$$

$$\{ij, k\} = \Gamma^k_{ij}.$$

Problem 45.3: The element of arc in cylindrical coordinates is $ds^2 = dr^2 + (r\,d\theta)^2 + dz^2$. Let $r = x^1$, $\theta = x^2$, $z = x^3$, and determine Γ^n_{ij} by use of the formulas of this section.

Problem 45.4: The element of arc in spherical coordinates is $ds^2 = dR^2 + R^2\,d\phi^2 + (R \sin\phi\,d\theta)^2$. Let $R = x^1$, $\theta = x^3$, $\phi = x^2$, and find Γ^n_{ij}.

Problem 45.5: Consider the confocal plane coordinates of Problem 44.17. Determine the components of Γ^n_{ij} in this coordinate system.

Problem 45.6: Determine the components of Γ^n_{ij} in a general system of *orthogonal* curvilinear coordinates. *Hint:* Determine which Γ^n_{ij} vanish.

(d) ***The Transformation Formulas of the*** Γ^n_{ij}. From (45.5) we obtain the result

$$\Gamma^l_{jk} = \mathbf{e}^l \cdot \frac{\partial \mathbf{e}_j}{\partial x^k}.$$

Since the $\mathbf{e}^l$, $\mathbf{e}_j$ transform according to the laws, $\mathbf{e}^l = (\partial x^l/\partial\,'x^i)'\mathbf{e}^i$ and $\mathbf{e}_j = (\partial\,'x^n/\partial x^j)'\mathbf{e}_n$ (see Section 44), the above formula furnishes the relation

$$\begin{aligned}\Gamma^l_{jk} &= \left(\frac{\partial x^l}{\partial\,'x^i}\,'\mathbf{e}^i\right)\cdot\left[\frac{\partial}{\partial x^k}\left(\frac{\partial\,'x^n}{\partial x^j}\,'\mathbf{e}_n\right)\right]\\ &= \frac{\partial x^l}{\partial\,'x^i}\,\frac{\partial\,'x^p}{\partial x^k}\,\frac{\partial\,'x^n}{\partial x^j}\,'\Gamma^i_{np} + \frac{\partial x^l}{\partial\,'x^n}\,\frac{\partial^2\,'x^n}{\partial x^k\,\partial x^j}.\end{aligned} \tag{45.9}$$

The last formula shows how the components of the connection transform under a change of coordinates. From this result, we see that the Γ^l_{jk} *are not the components of a tensor except when*

$$\frac{\partial x^l}{\partial\,'x^n}\,\frac{\partial^2\,'x^n}{\partial x^k\,\partial x^j} = 0.$$

By multiplying both sides of the above by $\partial\,'x^p/\partial x^l$ and summing on l, we obtain

$$\frac{\partial^2\,'x^p}{\partial x^k\,\partial x^l} = 0.$$

The general solution of these equations is

$$'x^p = a^p_q x^q + a^p_0.$$

where the coefficients are constants. These transformations define the non-centered affine group; *only for this group of coordinate transformations is the connection a tensor.* The connection is often called a *geometric object.*

46. The Covariant Derivative of a Tensor. It can be easily verified that the partial derivatives, $\partial V^i/\partial x^k$, $\partial V_j/\partial x^k$ do not transform as the components of tensors (see Problem 44.12). That is, the correspondence, $\nabla \leftrightarrow \partial/\partial x^i$, is *not invariant* under the group A_3. Our first problem is to obtain the correspondence which is invariant under A_3.

First, we consider the contravariant components, V^i of a vector. With the aid of the connection, we may write the differential of a vector (45.1), as

$$d\mathbf{V} = (dV^j + \Gamma^j_{lk} V^l \, dx^k)\mathbf{e}_j.$$

The expression δV^j defined by

$$\delta V^j = dV^j + \Gamma^j_{lk} V^l \, dx^k \tag{46.1}$$

must represent the contravariant components of the vector $d\mathbf{V}$. This vector, δV^i, is often called the *covariant differential* of V^i. Further, we define the quantities $\nabla_k V^j$ by means of

$$\nabla_k V^j = \frac{\partial V^j}{\partial x^k} + \Gamma^j_{lk} V^l. \tag{46.2}$$

A simple computation shows that

$$\delta V^j = dx^k \nabla_k V^j.$$

Since δV^j represents the contravariant components of a vector and dx^k are the contravariant components of an arbitrary vector, it is easily seen by use of the quotient rule that $\nabla_k V^j$ are the components of a second-order tensor; the tensor $\nabla_k V^j$ is called the *covariant derivative* of V^j.

Following a similar procedure, it may be verified that for the covariant components V_j of a vector, the δV_j and $\nabla_k V_j$ are determined by

$$\begin{aligned} \delta V_j &= dV_j - \Gamma^l_{jk} V_l \, dx^k \\ \nabla_k V_j &= \frac{\partial V_j}{\partial x^k} - \Gamma^l_{jk} V_l. \end{aligned} \tag{46.3}$$

By differentiation of the expression

$$\mathfrak{A} = A^{ij}_{\cdot\cdot k} \mathbf{e}^k \mathbf{e}_i \mathbf{e}_j$$

and use of the formulas for $d\mathbf{e}^k$, $d\mathbf{e}_j$ of Section 45 [for instance, (45.4)], we find that the covariant differential and derivative of the mixed components of this third-order tensor are

$$\begin{aligned} \delta A^{ij}_{\cdot\cdot k} &= dA^{ij}_{\cdot\cdot k} - \Gamma^l_{kn} A^{ij}_{\cdot\cdot l} \, dx^n + \Gamma^i_{ln} A^{lj}_{\cdot\cdot k} \, dx^n + \Gamma^j_{ln} A^{il}_{\cdot\cdot k} \, dx^n \\ \nabla_n A^{ij}_{\cdot\cdot k} &= \frac{\partial A^{ij}_{\cdot\cdot k}}{\partial x^n} - \Gamma^l_{kn} A^{ij}_{\cdot\cdot l} + \Gamma^i_{ln} A^{lj}_{\cdot\cdot k} + \Gamma^j_{ln} A^{il}_{\cdot\cdot k}. \end{aligned} \tag{46.4}$$

From this example, the general law for formulating the covariant differential and derivative of a p-th order mixed tensor is fairly evident.

Now, we return to the problem of determining the tensor operator which corresponds to ∇. Henceforth, we shall *write the desired correspondence as* $\nabla \leftrightarrow \nabla_j$, *where the covariant derivative,* ∇_j, *is determined by the general rule exemplified by* (46.4).

In the next few paragraphs, we shall discuss some of the interesting properties of the covariant derivatives. Some of the verifications will be left to the problems. All of these properties are valid in n-dimensional Riemannian space.

(a) ***The Operator*** ∇_j ***Is Distributive;*** $\nabla_j(A^k + B^k) = \nabla_j A^k + \nabla_j B^k$. This rule has been illustrated for the case of vectors but is valid for tensors of the p-th order. The result is verified by a simple computation.

(b) ***The Operator*** ∇_j ***Differentiates Products of Vectors and Tensors by the Ordinary Rule;*** $\nabla_j(A^l B_k) = (\nabla_j A^l)B_k + A^l(\nabla_j B_k)$. Again a simple computation will check this formula. That is, one merely expands the two sides of the above and compares the result.

(c) ***The Covariant Derivative of a Scalar Is the Ordinary Derivative;*** $\nabla_j\Omega = \partial\Omega/\partial x^j$. This result follows from the fact that $\partial\Omega/\partial x^j$ transforms as a covariant vector under the group A_3. Another method of verifying this result is to use (b) and prove that $\nabla_j(A^l B_l) = \partial(A^l B_l)/\partial x^j$, since the Γ^l_{ij}'s enter with plus sign in $\nabla_j A^l$ and minus sign in $\nabla_j B_l$.

(d) $\nabla_i g_{jk} = \nabla_i g^{jk} = 0$; ***Ricci's Lemma.*** By use of the theory for determining the covariant derivative, (46.4), we may express the covariant derivative of the metric tensor by the formula

$$\nabla_i g_{jk} = \frac{\partial g_{jk}}{\partial x^i} - \Gamma^l_{ji} g_{lk} - \Gamma^l_{ki} g_{lj}.$$

Use of the formula for Γ^n_{ij} (45.8) and a simple computation shows that the above covariant derivative vanishes. Conversely, one may show that if a second-order tensor has the property that its covariant derivative vanishes then Γ^n_{ij} can be expressed in terms of this tensor. The vanishing of the $\nabla_i g^{jk}$ is verified by a similar procedure. This general result is known as Ricci's Lemma.

(e) $\nabla_i V_j = g_{jl}\nabla_i V^l$. This formula states that the rule for raising or lowering indices of vectors and tensors (see Problem 44.9) is applicable to the covariant derivatives of vectors and tensors. The verification of the result follows from the vanishing of the covariant derivative of the metric tensor, rule (b), and the computation

$$\nabla_i V_j = \nabla_i(g_{jl}V^l) = g_{jl}\nabla_i V^l.$$

(f) ***The Covariant Derivative of the Kronecker Tensor,*** δ^i_k, ***Vanishes;*** $\nabla_i\delta^i_k = 0$. This result is verified by direct computation.

(g) ***Parallel Vector Fields;*** $\nabla_j V^k = 0$. If the vector V^k, is such that its covariant derivative vanishes, we *say that* V^k *is a parallel vector field.* We shall discuss some of the properties of these fields in the problems.

In order to understand the significance of the term, "parallel vector field," we consider a vector **V** at a point P, x^j, of space. Let C be a curve passing through P and defined by, $x^k = x^k(t)$, (see Figure 43) where t is a parameter. At a point P' of C whose coordinates are $(x^j + dx^j)$, we con-

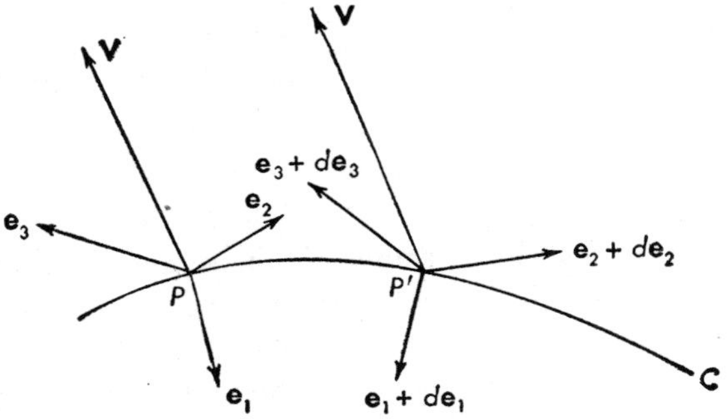

Figure 43: A Parallel Vector Field, **V**, along a Curve, C

struct the *same* vector **V**. Let V^k denote the components of **V** at P and $\mathbf{e}_j$ denote the covariant base vectors at P. Further, let $V^k + dV^k$ denote the components of V at P' and $\mathbf{e}_j + d\mathbf{e}_j$ denote the covariant base vectors at P'. From our construction, it follows that

$$\mathbf{V} = V^k\mathbf{e}_k = (V^k + dV^k)(\mathbf{e}_k + d\mathbf{e}_k).$$

Simplifying the above by use of the formula for $d\mathbf{e}_k$ (45.4), we obtain the result

$$dV^k + \Gamma^k_{jn}\, dx^n V^j + \Gamma^k_{jn}\, dV^j\, dx^n = 0.$$

If we consider only first-order terms in this equation or determine dV^k/dt along C, we find that $\delta V^k = 0$. *Thus, if a vector is parallel to itself* (*or moved by parallel transport*) *along a curve, then its covariant differential vanishes.*[4] In this sense, the covariant differential is a direct generalization of the ordinary differential. That is, in Cartesian orthogonal coordinates, the condition $dV^k = 0$ implies that **V** is defined by parallelism along C; in curvilinear coordinates, $\delta V^k = 0$ implies that **V** is defined by parallelism along C.

[4] Conversely, if $\delta V^k = 0$ then the vector field is transported by parallelism, since the ordinary differential equations $\delta V^k = 0$ possess unique solutions.

If **V** is a *parallel vector field in space*, then $\delta V^k = 0$ holds along every curve; that is, $\delta V^k = (\nabla_j V^k)\, dx^j = 0$ for every dx^j. Hence, $\nabla_j V^k = 0$, *is necessary and sufficient for parallelism of a vector field.* This result is valid for Euclidean spaces of n-dimensions as well as Riemannian spaces.

(h) ***The Covariant Derivative of the Determinant, g, and Densities and Capacities.*** By use of the rule for differentiating a determinant (see Section 42), we find that

$$\frac{\partial g}{\partial x^k} = g \frac{\partial g_{ij}}{\partial x^k} g^{ij}.$$

If we divide this equation by g and replace the partial derivatives of g_{jl} by Γ^n_{jl} through use of the theory of Section 45, we see that

$$\frac{\partial}{\partial x^k} \ln g = g^{ij}[g_{lj}\Gamma^l_{ik} + g_{li}\Gamma^l_{jk}] = 2\Gamma^i_{ik}.$$

By dividing by two, we obtain a well-known result, namely,

$$\frac{\partial}{\partial x^k} \ln \sqrt{g} = \Gamma^i_{ik}. \tag{46.5}$$

Since the covariant derivative of g_{ij} vanishes, by use of the product rule of (b), one obtains another formula involving the derivatives of g:

$$\nabla_k g = g g^{ij} \nabla_k g_{ij} = 0.$$

Next, we shall define the rule for the covariant derivative of a scalar density, A, of weight one. In order to motivate our definition, we proceed as follows. Since $\sqrt{g}$ is a scalar density of weight one, it follows that the quotient $A/\sqrt{g}$ is a true scalar. By the rule of (c), we find that

$$\nabla_j \left(\frac{A}{\sqrt{g}}\right) = \frac{\partial}{\partial x^j}\left(\frac{A}{\sqrt{g}}\right) = \frac{1}{\sqrt{g}} \frac{\partial A}{\partial x^j} - \frac{A}{g} \frac{\partial \sqrt{g}}{\partial x^j}.$$

If we assume that we can expand the left-hand side of this relation by use of the rule (b), we obtain

$$\nabla_j \left(\frac{A}{\sqrt{g}}\right) = \frac{1}{\sqrt{g}} \nabla_j A.$$

Combining these last two equations, we find that

$$\nabla_j A = \frac{\partial A}{\partial x^j} - A \frac{\partial}{\partial x^j} \ln \sqrt{g}$$

Finally, by use of (46.5), we obtain the desired formula

$$\nabla_j A = \frac{\partial A}{\partial x^j} - \Gamma^i_{ij} A. \tag{46.6}$$

If the above expression for $\nabla_j A$ is *defined to be the covariant derivative of the density of weight one*, it is easily shown that the covariant differentiation operator ∇_j acting on such a density multiplied by a scalar satisfies the product rule (b) of this section.

The following definitions are usually used for: $\overset{k}{A}$, a scalar density of weight k; $\underset{k}{A}$, a scalar capacity of weight k; $\overset{k}{V}{}^i_l$, a tensor density of weight k; $\underset{k}{V}{}^i_l$, a tensor capacity of weight k.

$$\begin{aligned}
\nabla_n \overset{k}{A} &= \frac{\partial \overset{k}{A}}{\partial x^n} - k\Gamma^i_{in}\overset{k}{A} \\
\nabla_n \underset{k}{A} &= \frac{\partial \underset{k}{A}}{\partial x^n} + k\Gamma^i_{in}\underset{k}{A} \\
\nabla_n \overset{k}{V}{}^i_l &= \frac{\partial \overset{k}{V}{}^i_l}{\partial x^n} + \Gamma^i_{jn}\overset{k}{V}{}^j_l - \Gamma^j_{ln}\overset{k}{V}{}^i_j - k\Gamma^j_{jn}\overset{k}{V}{}^i_l \\
\nabla_n \underset{k}{V}{}^i_l &= \frac{\partial \underset{k}{V}{}^i_l}{\partial x^n} + \Gamma^i_{jn}\underset{k}{V}{}^j_l - \Gamma^j_{ln}\underset{k}{V}{}^i_j + k\Gamma^j_{jn}\underset{k}{V}{}^i_l.
\end{aligned} \tag{46.7}$$

With the aid of these formulas, one may show that the previous distributive and product rules (a) and (b) of differentiation are still valid for tensor densities and capacities.

Problem 46.1: Prove that $\nabla_j \delta^k_l = 0$, where δ^k_j is the Kronecker tensor.

Problem 46.2: Determine the value of the covariant derivative of the generalized Kronecker tensor δ^{jk}_{ln}.

Problem 46.3: Prove the rule $\nabla_j(A^l B_k) = (\nabla_j A^l)B_k + A^l(\nabla_j B_k)$.

Problem 46.4: Find the covariant derivative of $\Omega = V^i W_i$, by use of the rules for $\nabla_j V^i$, $\nabla_j W_i$ and (b).

Problem 46.5: Consider the metric tensor g_{ij} in cylindrical coordinates. Using the results of Problem 45.1, show that $\nabla_k g_{ij} = 0$.

Problem 46.6: In spherical coordinates, the vector field, $\mathbf{V} = f(\theta, \phi)\mathbf{e}_R$ is parallel along the radial lines, ϕ = constant, θ = constant. Prove that $\delta V^k = 0$ along these radial lines.

Problem 46.7: Verify the formula, $\partial(\ln \sqrt{g})/\partial x^k = \Gamma^i_{ik}$, for cylindrical coordinates.

Problem 46.8: Derive the formula for the covariant derivative of the tensor density e^{ijk}.

Problem 46.9: Show that the scalar $\nabla_j V^j$, which is called the divergence of a vector, may be written as

$$\nabla_j V^j = \frac{1}{\sqrt{g}} \frac{\partial}{\partial x^j} (V^j \sqrt{g}).$$

Problem 46.10: Show that the tensor known as the "curl of a vector," $V_{jk} = \nabla_j V_k - \nabla_k V_j$, may be written as $\partial V_k/\partial x^j - \partial V_j/\partial x^k$. One often uses the notation, $2\nabla_{[j} V_{k]} = \nabla_j V_k - \nabla_k V_j$, to indicate this tensor.

Problem 46.11: The gradient of a scalar Ω may be written as $\nabla_j \Omega = \partial \Omega/\partial x^j$. Show that the *physical components* of the gradient, $\partial \Omega / {}^*(\partial x^j)$ are $\nabla_j \Omega / \sqrt{g_{jj}}$ in the coordinate system x^j. *Hint:* Use equation (44.8).

Problem 46.12: For an orthogonal coordinate system, the physical components of a tensor, ${}^*V_{ij}$, are related to the ordinary tensor components, V_{ij}, by means of ${}^*V_{ij} = V_{ij}/\sqrt{g_{ii}g_{jj}}$ (see Section 44). Using the result of Problem 46.10, show that the physical components of the curl of a vector are given by the formula

$${}^*V_{ij} = \frac{1}{\sqrt{g_{ii}g_{jj}}} \left[\frac{\partial}{\partial x^i} (\sqrt{g_{jj}}\, {}^*V_j) - \frac{\partial}{\partial x^j} (\sqrt{g_{ii}}\, {}^*V_i) \right].$$

Problem 46.13: Since the divergence of a vector is a scalar, the quantity $\nabla_j V^j$ represents the divergence of the vector in terms of its physical components. Hence, show that the right-hand side of

$$\nabla_j V^j = \sum_j \frac{1}{\sqrt{g}} \frac{\partial}{\partial x^j} \left(\frac{\sqrt{g}}{\sqrt{g_{jj}}}\, {}^*V_j \right)$$

represents the divergence in terms of the physical components of V^j. *Hint:* See Problem 46.9.

[5]***Problem 46.14:*** The vector, $\mathbf{W} = e^{ijk}(\nabla_j V_k)\mathbf{e}_i/\sqrt{g}$, is often called the "curl of a vector." In an orthogonal curvilinear coordinate system, $g = g_{11}g_{22}g_{33}$. Show that ${}^*W_3 = {}^*V_{12}$, ${}^*W_2 = {}^*V_{31}$, ${}^*W_1 = {}^*V_{23}$ where ${}^*W_i$ are the physical components of $\mathbf{W}$ and ${}^*V_{ij}$ are the physical components of the tensor $2\nabla_{[i} V_{j]}$ (see Problem 46.10).

Problem 46.15: A particle moves along a curve C. Compute the physical components in cylindrical coordinates of the vector, $d\mathbf{H}/dt$ and show that these components coincide with the components of the vector, $\delta \mathbf{H}/\delta t + \boldsymbol{\omega} \times \mathbf{H}$, where $\boldsymbol{\omega} = \mathbf{k}\, d\theta/dt$ and the apparent derivative, $\delta \mathbf{H}/\delta t$, has been discussed in Section 16.

[5] The results of Problems 46.13 and 46.14 should be compared with those of Problems 19.10 and 19.9. Note, the vectors $\mathbf{u}_j$, of the present section, and $\mathbf{e}_j$, of Section 19, coincide.

Problem 46.16: Show that the Gauss formula

$$\int_T \nabla_j V^j \, d\tau = \oint_S n_j V^j \, d\sigma$$

is valid in general curvilinear coordinates. Further, show that the Gauss formula

$$\int_T \nabla_j V_k \, d\tau = \oint_S n_j V_k \, d\sigma$$

is valid only in the general Cartesian coordinates discussed in Chapter VI.

(i) ***The Vector Operator,*** ∇. In Section 18 we defined the quantity, $\nabla * \mathcal{A}$. Our present work will relate $\nabla * \mathcal{A}$ to the components of tensors. We consider orthogonal curvilinear coordinates, x^j. If $\mathcal{A}$ is a vector $\mathbf{V}$, and $\mathbf{u}_i$ denote unit vectors along the coordinate lines, then the formula $\nabla * \mathcal{A}$ of (18.4) may be expressed in our present notation as

$$\nabla * \mathbf{V} = \sum_{i=1}^{3} \mathbf{u}_i * \frac{1}{\sqrt{g_{ii}}} \frac{\partial \mathbf{V}}{\partial x^i}.$$

For an orthogonal coordinate system, the equation relating the base vectors $\mathbf{e}^j$ and $\mathbf{u}_j$ (of Section 44) becomes $\mathbf{e}^j = \mathbf{u}_j/\sqrt{g_{jj}}$. Further, we may express $\mathbf{V}$ in terms of the covariant base vectors, $\mathbf{e}_j$, by the formula $\mathbf{V} = V^j \mathbf{e}_j$. Hence the relation for $\nabla * \mathbf{V}$ reduces to

$$\begin{aligned} \nabla * \mathbf{V} &= \mathbf{e}^i * \frac{\partial}{\partial x^i} (V^j \mathbf{e}_j) \\ &= \mathbf{e}^i * \left[V^j \frac{\partial \mathbf{e}_j}{\partial x^i} + \mathbf{e}_j \frac{\partial V^j}{\partial x^i} \right]. \end{aligned}$$

Replacing the derivative of $\mathbf{e}_j$ with respect to x^i by $\Gamma^l_{ji} \mathbf{e}_l$ of (45.5), we may write the above equation as

$$\nabla * \mathbf{V} = (\nabla_i V^j)(\mathbf{e}^i * \mathbf{e}_j). \tag{46.8}$$

If the star product denotes the scalar product, then from the relation $\mathbf{e}^i \cdot \mathbf{e}_j = \delta^i_j$, it follows that (46.8) reduces to

$$\nabla \cdot \mathbf{V} = \nabla_i V^i.$$

This verifies the formula (18.4) for the case of scalar products. If the star product denotes an "ordinary" product, then (46.8) reduces to

$$\nabla \mathbf{V} = (\nabla_i V^j) \mathbf{e}^i \mathbf{e}_j.$$

This result agrees with the formula for expressing the derivative of any tensor in terms of its base vectors.

Finally, we consider the case where the star product is the vector product. By lowering the index j of V^j, we may express (46.8) as

$$\nabla \times \mathbf{V} = (\nabla_i V_j)(e^i \times \mathbf{e}^j).$$

Introducing the unit vectors $\mathbf{u}_j = \sqrt{g_{jj}}\, \mathbf{e}^j$ (see Section 44 and note $\mathbf{u}_j = \mathbf{w}_j$) the above equation becomes

$$\nabla \times \mathbf{V} = \sum_{i,j=1}^{3} \frac{\nabla_i V_j}{\sqrt{g_{ii}g_{jj}}} (\mathbf{u}_i \times \mathbf{u}_j).$$

From the definition of the cross product, it follows that

$$\sum_{k=1}^{3} e^{kij}\mathbf{u}_k = \mathbf{u}_i \times \mathbf{u}_j.$$

Further, $\mathbf{u}_k = \mathbf{e}_k/\sqrt{g_{kk}}$, and $\sqrt{g_{11}g_{22}g_{33}} = \sqrt{g}$. Hence, $\nabla \times \mathbf{V}$ may be written as

$$\nabla \times \mathbf{V} = \frac{e^{kij}}{\sqrt{g}} \nabla_i V_j\, \mathbf{e}_k.$$

From the results of Problem 46.14, we see that this expression actually represents the curl of a vector.

For the case of an arbitrary tensor $\mathcal{A}$, the essential feature of the definition (18.4) is the invariance of $\nabla * \mathcal{A}$. This can be seen by determining the formula corresponding to (46.8) for such a tensor. We find

$$\nabla * \mathcal{A} = (\nabla_i A^{j_1 \cdots j_r})(\mathbf{e}^i * \mathbf{e}_{j_1}\mathbf{e}_{j_2} \cdots \mathbf{e}_{j_r}).$$

Thus, whenever the product $\mathbf{e}^i * \mathbf{e}_{j_1} \cdots \mathbf{e}_{j_r}$ has invariant significance, then $\nabla * \mathcal{A}$ has such significance.

47. The Orthogonal 3-Tuple and the Decomposition of Tensors. Consider three unit vector fields which are mutually orthogonal at any point P of Euclidean three-space. We denote these vector fields by

$$\underset{l}{i}^k, \ \underset{l}{i}_k, \quad k, l = 1, 2, 3.$$

Note that the index k denotes the contravariance or covariance of the vector but the subscript, l, is used to identify the various vectors. We assume that the coordinate system, x^k, is a general curvilinear system belonging to the group G_3. For the case of n-dimensional spaces, an n-tuple of unit orthogonal vector fields can be used instead of the above 3-tuple.

(a) ***The Decomposition of the Metric Tensor and the Kronecker Tensor.*** From the definition of the orthogonal 3-tuple, it follows that

$$\underset{l}{i^k}\,\underset{n}{i_k} = \underset{ln}{\delta} \tag{47.1}$$

where $\underset{ln}{\delta}$ is the Kronecker *symbol.* That is, $\underset{ln}{\delta} = 1$ if $l = n$, $\underset{ln}{\delta} = 0$ if $l \neq n$. Evidently, (47.1) implies that $\underset{n}{i_k}$ is the reduced cofactor of $\underset{l}{i^k}$. From the work of Appendix I, we see that

$$\delta_l^k = \sum_{n=1}^{3} \underset{n}{i^k}\,\underset{n}{i_l} \tag{47.2}$$

where δ_l^k is the Kronecker delta tensor. The above formula determines the *decomposition of the Kronecker delta tensor with respect to the orthogonal 3-tuple,* $\underset{n}{i^k}$.

Since the metric tensor may be used to lower indices, we may write

$$g_{kj}\underset{n}{i^j} = \underset{n}{i_k}.$$

Multiplying this relation by $\underset{n}{i^l}$ and summing on the index n, we find through use of (47.2) that

$$g_{kj} = \sum_{n=1}^{3} \underset{n}{i_k}\,\underset{n}{i_j}. \tag{47.3}$$

The last equation determines the *decomposition of the covariant components of the metric tensor with respect to the orthogonal 3-tuple,* $\underset{n}{i^k}$. Similarly, by use of the fact that the contravariant components of the metric tensor can be used to raise indices, one may show that

$$g^{kj} = \sum_{n=1}^{3} \underset{n}{i^k}\,\underset{n}{i^j}. \tag{47.4}$$

The above formula furnishes the *decomposition of the contravariant components of the metric tensor.*

(b) ***The Decomposition of a General Tensor.*** For the sake of clarity, we restrict ourselves to a second-order tensor, H_{ij}. The decomposition of a general tensor is obtained by an obvious generalization. Consider the scalar quantities

$$\underset{ln}{H} = H_{kj}\underset{l}{i^k}\,\underset{n}{i^j}.$$

If we multiply $\underset{ln}{H}$ by $\underset{l}{i_p}$, $\underset{n}{i_q}$ and sum on l, n, we obtain through use of the decomposition for δ^k_l (47.2)

$$H_{pq} = \sum_{l,n=1}^{3} \underset{ln}{H} \underset{l}{i_p} \underset{n}{i_q}. \tag{47.5}$$

The formula (47.5) determines the *decomposition of the second-order tensor* H_{pq} *with respect to the 3-tuple*, $\underset{n}{i_j}$.

(c) ***The Principal Directions of a Second-Order Symmetric Tensor,*** $h_{jk} = h_{kj}$. If h_{jk} is any symmetric second-order tensor field, then at each point $P(x^j)$ of Euclidean three-space one may associate with h_{jk} a quadric surface

$$h_{jk}X^jX^k = 1, \qquad j, k = 1, 2, 3.$$

At P, the h_{jk} are to be considered as known; the X^i, $i = 1, 2, 3$, may be interpreted as independent variables of a "local" Euclidean space with

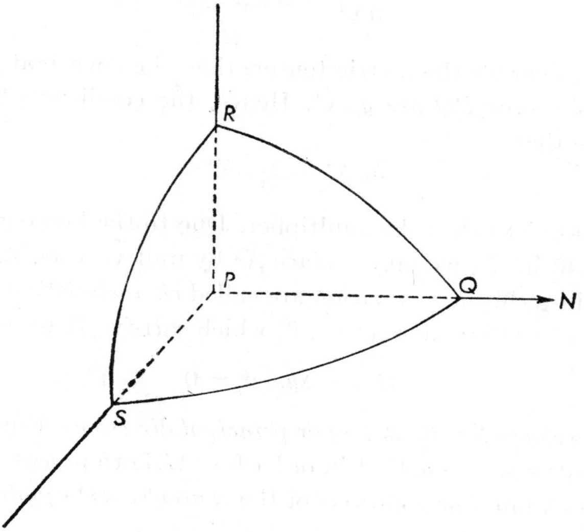

Figure 44: A Quadratic Surface at P

origin at P. With any quadric surface, one may associate principal directions. Thus, if the quadric surface is an ellipsoid, these principal directions are the directions of the major and the two minor axes. In order to obtain these directions, we note that their characteristic property is contained in the following geometric result: The radius vector, PQ, from the center of the quadric to the surface lies along the normal, QN, to the surface at Q. Thus, in Figure 44, PR, PS, PQ are the principal directions of the quadric. The quadric surface is to be considered as lying in the *tangent space* at P.

The concept of tangent spaces is of geometric nature. Essentially, we consider any space to be composed of "elementary" Euclidean spaces, the tangent spaces. In this sense, the surface of a sphere consists of elementary planes, its tangent spaces. In a given tangent space, the coordinates are always Cartesian. Hence, the theory of tensors is that of the last chapter. It should be noted that the above figure is considered as lying within the tangent space at P. The present theory of fibre bundles in topology is an attempt to develop the idea of tangent spaces in a rigorous fashion.

If we let the scalar Ω denote the quadratic form

$$\Omega = h_{ij}X^iX^j$$

then the covariant components of the normal vector to the quadric at Q are

$$\frac{\partial \Omega}{\partial X^j} = 2h_{jk}X^k.$$

Further, if g_{jk} denotes the metric tensor, then the covariant components of the radius vector PQ are $g_{jk}X^k$. Hence, the conditions for principal directions are that

$$h_{jk}X^k = \lambda g_{jk}X^k \tag{47.6}$$

where λ is an unknown scalar multiplier. Due to the homogeneity of the equation (47.6) in X^k, we may replace X^k by unit vectors, i^k. The scalars which enter into this new equation are called *characteristic values* or *characteristic numbers;* the unit vectors, i^k, which satisfy (47.6) or the relation

$$(h_{jk} - \lambda g_{jk})i^k = 0 \tag{47.7}$$

are called the *characteristic vectors* or *principal directions.* From the theory of linear equations, we see that in order for (47.7) to possess solutions for i^k, the scalars λ must be solutions of the *characteristic equation*

$$\|h_{jk} - \lambda g_{jk}\| = 0. \tag{47.8}$$

The double lines in the above denote the determinant. This equation is of the third degree in λ and has three roots, $\underset{1}{\lambda}, \underset{2}{\lambda}, \underset{3}{\lambda}$.

The significance of λ can be seen from the following geometric argument. Assume that a Cartesian orthogonal local coordinate system has been chosen so that the quadric is reduced to the canonical form

$$h_{11}(X^1)^2 + h_{22}(X^2)^2 + h_{33}(X^3)^2 = 1, \qquad h_{ii} > 0.$$

From this relation, we see that the magnitude of the radius vector PQ (see Figure 44) of the quadric is $1/\sqrt{h_{11}}$, if PQ denotes the X^1 axis. By our choice of coordinate system, $g_{jk} = \delta_{jk}$, at P. Further the vector $(X^1, 0, 0)$ lies along a principal direction. Hence, equation (47.6) reduces to: $h_{11}X^1 = \underset{1}{\lambda}X^1$, or $h_{11} = \underset{1}{\lambda}$. Thus, $\underset{1}{\lambda}$ *is the reciprocal of the square of the distance from the center,* P, *to the quadric along* $(X^1, 0, 0)$; *that is,* $\underset{1}{\lambda} = 1/(PQ)^2$. Similar characterizations are valid for $\underset{2}{\lambda}, \underset{3}{\lambda}$. Further, the case where $h_{11} < 0$ can be interpreted in a similar manner.

Another characterization of $\underset{i}{\lambda}$ $(i = 1, 2, 3)$ which is useful in differential geometry is given by the following: *The characteristic values,* $\underset{i}{\lambda}$, *are the relative maxima or minima of the ratio*

$$\lambda = h_{jk}X^jX^k/g_{jk}X^jX^k. \tag{47.9}$$

Differentiating the above equation with respect to X^j and letting $\partial\lambda/\partial X^j = 0$, one obtains the characteristic equation (47.6). This verifies the above statement. To determine the geometric significance of (47.9), we note that

$$\cos \alpha_j = X^j/\sqrt{g_{kl}X^kX^l}$$

where α_1 is the angle between the X^1 axis (the line PQ) and the general vector (X^1, X^2, X^3), etc. Hence, the above relation for λ may be written as[6]

$$\lambda = \sum_{j,k=1}^{3} h_{jk} \cos \alpha_j \cos \alpha_k \tag{47.10}$$

For a specified direction, determined by $\alpha_1, \alpha_2, \alpha_3$, the last equation furnishes a definite λ. In order to simplify this relation when $\lambda > 0$, we let

$$\lambda = \frac{1}{R^2}, \qquad R \cos \alpha_j = Y^j$$

where the geometric significance of R is to be determined. Then (47.10) reduces to

$$h_{ij}Y^iY^j = 1.$$

But this last equation determines the given quadric surface and R is the distance from the origin to any point of this surface. Hence, the scalar λ defined by (47.9) is the *reciprocal of the square of the radial distance from the*

[6] Equation (47.10) determines one component of an orthogonal decomposition of the tensor, h_{jk}.

center, P, to the quadric surface, $h_{ij}Y^iY^j = 1$. That is, our present characterization of the variable λ determines $\underset{j}{\lambda}$ whose geometric significance is the same as in the previous interpretation of $\underset{j}{\lambda}$.

From the first of the above interpretations, it can be seen that the problem of determining the characteristic values, $\underset{k}{\lambda}$, and the characteristic associated unit vectors, $\underset{k}{i^j}$, is equivalent to the problem of the simultaneous reduction to canonical or diagonal form of two quadric forms

$$\mathrm{I} = g_{ij}X^iX^j, \qquad \mathrm{II} = h_{ij}X^iX^j.$$

Since I is the positive definite metric form, it can be reduced to

$$\mathrm{I} = (X^1)^2 + (X^2)^2 + (X^3)^2$$

in infinitely many ways by use of Cartesian orthogonal local coordinates. If for one such coordinate system, II reduces to

$$\mathrm{II} = h_1(X^1)^2 + h_2(X^2)^2 + h_3(X^3)^2$$

then (47.6) furnishes the relations: $h_1X^1 = \underset{1}{\lambda}X^1$, $X^2 = X^3 = 0$. Hence, $\underset{1}{\lambda} = h_1$ and $(X^1, 0, 0)$ is the associated characteristic direction. Similar results are valid for $\underset{2}{\lambda}$, $\underset{3}{\lambda}$. We shall quote some algebraic results for n-dimensional Riemannian geometry in connection with this problem.[7]

Theorem 1: If the form I is positive definite (as in our work), the roots, $\underset{j}{\lambda}$, of the characteristic equation are real.

Theorem 2: If the form I is positive definite and $\underset{1}{\lambda}$ is a simple root, then the characteristic equations determine a unique characteristic vector, i^j; if $\underset{1}{\lambda}$ is a root of multiplicity μ ($\mu = 2, 3$) then the characteristic equation determines μ independent vectors, i^j. In this last case, any vector which is a linear combination of the μ independent vectors, i^j, is a characteristic vector. From this set of μ independent vectors, one may easily construct μ mutually orthogonal characteristic vectors belonging to this characteristic value.

Theorem 3: The characteristic vectors, $\underset{1}{i^j}$, $\underset{2}{i^j}$ corresponding to two distinct characteristic values $\underset{1}{\lambda}$, $\underset{2}{\lambda}$ are orthogonal. The proof of this result is

[7] T. J. P. A. Bromwich, *Quadratic Forms and Their Classification*, Cambridge Tracts, No. 3, Cambridge U. Press, 1906. T. Levi-Civita, *Absolute Differential Calculus*, Blackie and Son, London, 1929, p. 205.

very simple. By (47.7), the conditions of the theorem imply that

$$(h_{kj} - \underset{1}{\lambda} g_{kj})\underset{1}{i}^j = 0, \qquad (h_{kj} - \underset{2}{\lambda} g_{kj})\underset{2}{i}^j = 0. \tag{47.11}$$

Multiplying the first equations by $\underset{2}{i}^k$ and the second by $\underset{1}{i}^k$, and subtracting the resulting equations, we obtain the result $(\underset{1}{\lambda} - \underset{2}{\lambda}) g_{kj}\underset{1}{i}^k\underset{2}{i}^j = 0$. Since $\underset{1}{\lambda} \neq \underset{2}{\lambda}$, it follows that $g_{jk}\underset{1}{i}^j\underset{2}{i}^k = \underset{1}{i}_k\underset{2}{i}^k = 0$. Hence, the vectors $\underset{1}{i}^j$, $\underset{2}{i}^j$ are orthogonal.

Finally, we consider the decomposition of the symmetric tensor h_{jk} with respect to the 3-tuple formed by the unit characteristic vectors $\underset{m}{i}^j$. Let us write the equations (47.11) as

$$h_{kj}\underset{n}{i}^j = \underset{n}{\lambda} g_{kj}\underset{n}{i}^j, \qquad n = 1, 2, 3.$$

Multiplying this equation by $\underset{n}{i}_l$ and summing on n, we obtain

$$h_{kl} = \sum_{n=1}^{3} \underset{n}{\lambda}\underset{n}{i}_k\underset{n}{i}_l. \tag{47.12}$$

Note that the decomposition formula for δ^k_l (see 47.2) was used in deriving the above formula. Equation (47.12) furnishes the *decomposition of any symmetric tensor with respect to the 3-tuple formed by its principal directions.*

The above results can be generalized to n-dimensional Euclidean space. For Riemannian spaces, with indefinite first fundamental form I, the above results must be modified.[8] In this last case, the algebraic theory is similar to the above if the *elementary divisors* of the characteristic equation (47.8) are simple.

(d) ***Decomposition of a Bivector or Skew-Symmetric Second-Order Tensor,*** $H_{ij} = -H_{ji}$. In order to study this tensor, we consider the linear infinitesimal transformation in general Cartesian coordinates,

$$'x^k = x^k + \epsilon H^k_{\cdot l} x^l \tag{47.13}$$

where ϵ is an infinitesimal and $H^k_{\cdot l}$ is a tensor. If the transformation represents a rotation, then

$$g_{kl}\,'x^k\,'x^l = g_{kl}x^k x^l. \tag{47.14}$$

[8] L. P. Eisenhart, *Riemannian Geometry*, Princeton U. Press, Princeton, 1926, pp. 107–113. For an interesting exposition of elementary divisors, see A. J. McConnell, *Applications of the Absolute Differential Calculus*, Blackie and Son, London, 1931, p. 97.

Conversely, if the last equation is valid and if the determinant of (47.13) is positive, then that equation represents an infinitesimal rotation. Since (47.13) represents a transformation lying in the neighborhood of the identity transformation ($\epsilon = 0$), the determinant of the transformation is positive. By substituting (47.13) into (47.14), we obtain for the first-order terms

$$g_{jk}H^{k}_{\cdot l}x^{j}x^{l} + g_{jk}H^{j}_{\cdot l}x^{k}x^{l} = 0.$$

Lowering the indices in this last equation, we find that

$$(H_{jk} + H_{kj})x^{j}x^{k} = 0.$$

Since the above equation is valid for arbitrary x^{j}, *we see that* $H_{jk} + H_{kj} = 0$. *That is, the tensor,* H_{jk}, *is skew symmetric when the transformation (47.13) represents an infinitesimal rotation.*

Now, consider an arbitrary transformation

$$'x^{k} = x^{k} + \epsilon L^{k}_{\cdot j}x^{j}.$$

The tensor $L^{k}_{\cdot j}$ can be decomposed into a symmetric tensor, h_{ij}, and a skew-symmetric tensor, s_{ij}, according to the scheme

$$\begin{aligned} L_{ij} &= h_{ij} + s_{ij} \\ 2h_{ij} &= L_{ij} + L_{ji}, \qquad 2s_{ij} = L_{ij} - L_{ji}. \end{aligned} \tag{47.15}$$

By use of the above decomposition, we may consider the transformation as consisting of the succession of the two transformations

$$\begin{aligned} ''x^{k} &= x^{k} + \epsilon s^{k}_{\cdot j}x^{j}, \qquad & s^{k}_{\cdot j} &= g^{kl}s_{lj} \\ 'x^{k} &= ''x^{k} + \epsilon h^{k}_{\cdot j}\,''x^{j}, \qquad & h^{k}_{\cdot j} &= g^{kl}h_{lj}. \end{aligned}$$

The first of the above transformations is a rotation. Now, the general linear transformation is a combination of a rotation and a deformation. Thus, the second transformation ($''x^{k} \rightarrow {}'x^{k}$) represents a deformation. Note that this second transformation involves a symmetric tensor, h_{ij}.

It can be shown[9] that any skew-symmetric tensor, s_{ij}, can be decomposed with respect to an appropriate 3-tuple, $\underset{n}{i}^{j}$, into

$$s_{lj} = s\,(\underset{1}{i}_{l}\underset{2}{i}_{j} - \underset{2}{i}_{l}\underset{1}{i}_{j}). \tag{47.16}$$

(e) ***Orthogonal Components of a Tensor and Non-Holonomic Coordinates.*** The scalars $\underset{ln}{H}$ of (47.5) are called the orthogonal components of the tensor H_{jk}. These components are useful in the geometric and physical applications of tensor analysis.

[9] J. A. Schouten, *Der Ricci Kalkül*, J. Springer, Berlin, 1924, p. 8.

In order to understand the reason for the term "components," we shall develop the idea of non-holonomic coordinates. Under coordinate transformations, vectors and tensors transform by means of the quantities, $A_j^k = \partial x^k/\partial' x^j$. The quantities A_j^k satisfy the so-called integrability conditions

$$\frac{\partial A_j^k}{\partial\ 'x^l} = \frac{\partial A_l^k}{\partial\ 'x^j} \tag{47.17}$$

These relations are additional conditions on the coefficients determining the group A_3.

To obtain non-holonomic coordinates, we drop the integrability conditions. That is, we consider "local coordinate" transformations

$$dx^k = A_j^k\, d\,'x^j$$

where the A_j^k do not satisfy (47.17). Of course, the dx^k are no longer true differentials. In other words, the quantities dx^1, dx^2 no longer determine coordinate *surfaces*, x^3 = constant, etc. From the point of view of differential equations, we say that the Pfaffian equations

$$A_j^k\, d\,'x^j = 0$$

are not integrable.

If we consider the unit vectors $\underset{n}{i}{}^j$ as defining $\underset{n}{A}{}^j$, then the orthogonal components, $\underset{ln}{H}$, are defined by [see Section 47(a)]

$$\underset{ln}{H} = H_{kj}\underset{l}{i}{}^k\underset{n}{i}{}^j = H_{kj}\underset{n}{A}{}^j\underset{l}{A}{}^k. \tag{47.18}$$

Thus, the above relations may be considered as determining the behavior of the tensor, H_{kj}, under a non-holonomic coordinate transformation.

Non-holonomic quantities occur very frequently in physics. The work integral is a simple example. Such non-holonomic quantities depend on the path of the integration; they are not exact differentials. For a general theory of non-holonomic geometry, the reader should consult G. Vranceanu's work.[10]

Problem 47.1: By use of the contravariant and covariant components of the triad **i, j, k** in cylindrical coordinates, verify the relations:

$$g^{kl} = \sum_{n=1}^{3} \underset{n}{i}{}^k\underset{n}{i}{}^l, \qquad \delta_l^k = \sum_{n=1}^{3} \underset{n}{i}{}^k\underset{n}{i}{}_l.$$

[10] G. Vranceanu, *Etude des espaces non-holonomes, Journal de Math.*, tome XIII, Fasc II, 1934.

Note, the x^j coordinate system is assumed to be cylindrical coordinates.

Problem 47.2: Determine the characteristic values and the principal directions of the symmetric tensor, **ii** + (**ij** + **ji**) − **jj**.

Problem 47.3: Show that if $\underset{1}{\lambda}, \underset{2}{\lambda}, \underset{3}{\lambda}$ are the roots of the characteristic equation of a second-order symmetric tensor h_{ij} of Section 47(d), then

$$\sum_{j=1}^{3} \underset{j}{\lambda} = g^{lj}h_{lj}, \qquad \sum_{j=1}^{3} \underset{j}{\lambda}^2 = h^{lj}h_{lj}, \qquad \sum_{j=1}^{3} \underset{j}{\lambda}^3 = h^{lj}h_{jk}h^{k}_{\cdot l}.$$

Problem 47.4: The first law of thermodynamics for perfect gases may be written as

$$c_v\, dT + p\, dV = dQ$$

where the constant, c_v, is the molecular heat at constant volume, T is the absolute temperature, p is the pressure, V is the volume, and dQ is the heat added to the system. Further, the equation of state relates p, V, T. In the (V, T) plane, show that dQ defines a non-holonomic coordinate for the equation of state, $pV = kT$, where k is a constant.

48. Integrability Conditions. In the last section, we discussed the topic of integrability conditions very briefly [see (47.17)]. The work of this section will be concerned with furnishing a more complete theory in this direction. Let us introduce the coordinate variables, $'x^j$, $j = 1, 2, 3$ and assume that the coordinate variables, x^j, $j = 1, 2, 3$ are functions of the former variables. One possible interpretation of the functional relations, $x^j = x^j('x^k)$, is that these equations define a coordinate transformation in Euclidean three-space. Consider the nine functions, $f_j^k('x^p)$, $j, k = 1, 2, 3$, as known. We ask: "When do these functions determine a holonomic coordinate transformation in the sense that the first-order partial differential equations

$$\frac{\partial x^j}{\partial\, 'x^k} = f_k^j('x^p) \tag{48.1}$$

possess a solution?" We stated in the previous section that the necessary and sufficient conditions for a solution to exist are:

$$\frac{\partial f_k^j}{\partial\, 'x^l} = \frac{\partial f_l^j}{\partial\, 'x^k}. \tag{48.2}$$

These conditions are known as the *integrability conditions* of (48.1). When these conditions are satisfied, then the associated system of total differential equations (or Pfaffians)

$$dx^j = f_k^j('x^l)\, d\, 'x^k \tag{48.3}$$

can be integrated. This integration can be accomplished by use of the line integral in the Cartesian coordinates, $'x^k$. In fact, the conditions (48.2) are exactly the conditions that must be satisfied if the line integrals $\int f^i_k \, d\, 'x^k$, are to be independent of the path (Section 22) in a simply connected domain.

In the following, we shall consider various forms of (48.1) and the corresponding integrability conditions.

(a) ***The Quasi-Linear System;*** $\partial x^i/\partial\, 'x^k = f^i_k('x^p, x^p)$. This system of equations is the general system of type (48.1). The theory of this system is classical. For a complete discussion, the reader is referred to T. Levi-Civita's text.[11] Here, we shall briefly outline the results of the theory.

Necessary consequences of the system of equations

$$\frac{\partial x^i}{\partial\, 'x^k} = f^i_k('x^p, x^p) \tag{48.4}$$

are the relations

$$\frac{df^i_k}{d\, 'x^l} = \frac{df^i_l}{d\, 'x^k}.$$

Total derivatives must be formed in the above equations because f^i_k contain x^k. Expanding the above by the chain rule, we obtain

$$\frac{df^i_l}{d\, 'x^k} = \frac{\partial f^i_l}{\partial\, 'x^k} + \frac{\partial f^i_l}{\partial x^p}\frac{\partial x^p}{\partial\, 'x^k} = \frac{\partial f^i_l}{\partial\, 'x^k} + f^p_k \frac{\partial f^i_l}{\partial x^p}.$$

Hence, the integrability equations reduce to

$$\frac{\partial f^i_l}{\partial\, 'x^k} + f^p_k \frac{\partial f^i_l}{\partial x^p} = \frac{\partial f^i_k}{\partial\, 'x^l} + f^p_l \frac{\partial f^i_k}{\partial x^p}. \tag{48.5}$$

These equations belong to one of the following two types: (1) they are inconsistent; (2) they are consistent. In the first case, the system (48.4) does not possess a solution. For the second case, one can show that either the equations (48.5) are identically satisfied in the x^i, $'x^k$ or they can be solved for some of the x^i's in terms of the $'x^k$'s and the resulting system of (48.5) is identically satisfied in the remaining x^i's for all $'x^k$'s. Such a system is called *complete*. That is, any *consistent system of the type* (48.5) *can always be reduced to a complete system.* A complete system of equations has a unique set of solutions for x^i, except for at most three arbitrary constants. Thus, *the condition that* (48.5) *be complete is necessary and sufficient* in order for the given system to possess a unique solution. The proof of the sufficiency was given by Morera, and depends upon use of the line integral.

[11] T. Levi-Civita, *Absolute Differential Calculus*, Blackie and Son, London, 1929, pp. 13–32.

As an illustration of the value of the present theory, we consider the *problem of determining the necessary and sufficient conditions that a space be Euclidean.* These conditions are independent of the dimension of the space. Evidently, it is necessary and sufficient that a Cartesian coordinate system, x^k, exist in which the components, g_{jk}, of the metric tensor of the space be constant for the space to be Euclidean. But, from the formulas of Section 45(c), it follows that if and only if $\Gamma^i_{kp} = 0$, will the derivatives of the metric tensor vanish. Thus, we may write (45.9) in the form (after interchanging primed and unprimed variables)

$$\frac{\partial}{\partial\,'x^k}\left(\frac{\partial x^p}{\partial\,'x^j}\right) = {}'\Gamma^i_{jk}\frac{\partial x^p}{\partial\,'x^i}.$$

These equations are of the form (48.4) where f^j_k is replaced by ${}'\Gamma^i_{jk}(\partial x^p/\partial\,'x^i)$, which are *functions of* $'x^l$ *only*, and $i, j, k, p = 1, 2, 3$. Forming the integrability conditions, we obtain the relation

$$'R^{i}_{\cdot jkl}\frac{\partial x^p}{\partial\,'x^i} = 0$$

where

$$'R^{i}_{\cdot jkl} = \frac{\partial\,'\Gamma^i_{jk}}{\partial\,'x^l} - \frac{\partial\,'\Gamma^i_{jl}}{\partial\,'x^k} + {}'\Gamma^m_{jk}\,{}'\Gamma^i_{lm} - {}'\Gamma^m_{jl}\,{}'\Gamma^i_{km}.$$

In Section 54 [see (54.14)], it will be shown that $'R^{i}_{\cdot jkl}$ is a fourth-order tensor, called the curvature tensor (or the Riemann tensor or the Riemann-Christoffel tensor). Thus, *the necessary and sufficient condition that a space be Euclidean is that the curvature tensor vanish.* The curvature tensor plays an important role in n-dimensional differential geometry.[12]

(b) ***The Associated System of Equations;*** $A_k g = 0$. The equations (48.4) are equivalent to the system of Pfaff equations or total differential equations

$$dx^j = f^j_k\, d\,'x^k. \tag{48.6}$$

A function $g(x^j, 'x^k)$ which reduces to a constant, when *any* solution, $x^j = x^j('x^k)$, of (48.4) is used to eliminate the x^j in $g(x^j, 'x^j)$ is *called an integral of* (48.6). It can be shown that if the system (48.5) is complete, then the Pfaffian system (48.6) possesses exactly three independent integrals. Any integral, $g(x^k, 'x^k)$, can be shown to be a solution of the *associated system* of partial differential equations

$$A_k g \equiv \frac{\partial g}{\partial\,'x^k} + f^j_k\frac{\partial g}{\partial x^j} = 0.$$

[12] See T. Levi-Civita, *loc. cit.*, p. 175.

The three independent integrals of this last system of partial differential equations are the solutions of (48.4). When these integrals are solved for the three arbitrary constants, and any arbitrary function of these constants is formed, one obtains the general integral of (48.4).

Consider a homogeneous linear system of partial differential equations

$$A_k g \equiv \sum_{j=1}^{N} a_{kj} \frac{\partial g}{\partial z^j} = 0, \qquad k = 1 \cdots n, n < N. \tag{48.7}$$

Such systems may occur in problems in physics and applied mathematics. We ask: "When does (48.7) possess a solution, $g =$ constant?" In order to answer this question, the Poisson parenthesis operators $(A_k, A_j)g$ are introduced. These are defined by

$$\begin{aligned}(A_k, A_j)g &= (A_k A_j - A_j A_k)g \\ &= \sum_{l=1}^{N} a_{kl} \frac{\partial}{\partial z^l}\left(\sum_{p=1}^{N} a_{jp} \frac{\partial g}{\partial z^p}\right) - \sum_{l=1}^{N} a_{jl} \frac{\partial}{\partial z^l}\left(\sum_{r=1}^{N} a_{kr} \frac{\partial g}{\partial z^r}\right).\end{aligned}$$

It is easily shown that these operators are first-order operators, that is,

$$(A_k, A_j)g = \sum_{l,r=1}^{N} \left(a_{kl} \frac{\partial a_{jr}}{\partial z^l} - a_{jl} \frac{\partial a_{kr}}{\partial z^l}\right) \frac{\partial g}{\partial z^r}.$$

Now, the relation (48.7) implies that $(A_k, A_j)g = 0$. Further, by use of the Poisson parenthesis, we adjoin new equations to the given system. If one continues this process, two new cases arise: (1) $m \geq N$ equations of type (48.7) exist; (2) $m < N$ equations of this type exist, and the Poisson parenthesis of equations of this system furnishes only linear combinations of the existing equations of the system. In the first case, the system is over determined and possesses the trivial solution, $g \equiv 0$. When the second condition arises then one may write for a solution of (48.7)

$$(A_k, A_j)g = \sum_{l=1}^{m} \underset{kjl}{w} A_l g = 0 \tag{48.8}$$

and the *original system is called complete*. The $\underset{kjl}{w}$ are known functions of z^i.

It can be shown that a *complete system* possesses N-m independent integrals. This is accomplished by showing that with any complete system of the type (48.7), one can associate a complete system of the type (48.6). In other words, the procedure is just the reverse of that used in Section 48(a). In our work, we shall use the fact that the validity of (48.8) implies that the given system (48.7) is integrable. For this reason (48.8) *may be called the integrability conditions for the given system.*

(c) ***Tensor Formulation of the Integrability Conditions for the Complete System,***[13] $\underset{k}{v^j}\nabla_j\phi = 0,\ k = 1, \ldots, n.$ In this section we express the previous system (48.7) as

$$\underset{k}{v^j}\nabla_j\phi = 0, \qquad j = 1, 2, 3. \tag{48.9}$$

One can easily see the geometric significance of the equations. If $k = n = 1$, then the above equation possesses two independent integrals, $\phi_1(x^j) = c_1$, $\phi_2(x^j) = c_2$. Each integral determines a family of surfaces. From (48.9), it follows that $\underset{1}{v^j}$ lies in each surface of the family (that is, $\nabla_j\phi$ denotes a vector normal to the surface $\phi(x^j) = c$). Hence, $\underset{1}{v^j}$ lies along the intersection curves of the two families of surfaces, $\phi_1(x^j) = c_1$, $\phi_2(x^j) = c_2$; the vector $\underset{1}{v^j}$ is tangent to the ∞^2 curves determined by the simultaneous solutions $\phi_1(x^j) = c_1$, $\phi_2(x^j) = c_2$. One may often say that our system determines a *congruence of* ∞^2 *characteristic curves.* Characteristic curves are of considerable importance in applied mathematics and will be discussed in the section on compressible fluids. For the present, we notice these curves have the following geometric properties: (1) Any ∞^1 characteristic curves generate a surface which is an integral of the system (48.9); (2) through a given characteristic, ∞^1 integral surfaces of the system may be passed. If $n = 2$, $k = 1, 2$, then the original system possesses one independent integral, $\phi_1(x^j) = c_1$. Since (48.9) implies that $\underset{1}{v^j}$, $\underset{2}{v^j}$ lie on any such surface $\phi_1(x^j) = c_1$, one says that $\underset{1}{v^j}$, $\underset{2}{v^j}$ span or build the family of surfaces.

In our previous discussion, we noted that the necessary and sufficient condition for the completeness of (48.9) is that the Poisson parenthesis operators $(A_k, A_j)g$ be linear combinations of the equations of the given system. This means that

$$\underset{r}{v^j}\frac{\partial}{\partial x^j}\underset{t}{v^l} - \underset{t}{v^j}\frac{\partial}{\partial x^j}\underset{r}{v^l} = \sum_{s=1}^{n}\underset{rts}{w}\,\underset{s}{v^l}$$

where $\underset{rts}{w}$ are scalars. Due to the symmetry of the connection, Γ^l_{jk}, one may

[13] J. A. Schouten, *Der Ricci Kalkül*, J. Springer, Berlin, 1924; see Chap. 3. In this text, the theory of Section 48(*c*), (*d*), (*e*) is given for *n*-dimensional general space.

express the above integrability conditions in the tensor form

$$\underset{r}{v^j}\nabla_j \underset{t}{v^l} - \underset{t}{v^j}\nabla_j \underset{r}{v^l} = \sum_{s=1}^{n} \underset{rts}{w}\,\underset{s}{v^l}. \tag{48.10}$$

If N_j denotes a vector field orthogonal to the manifold determined by $\underset{r}{v^j}$, $r = 1, \ldots, n$, then

$$\underset{r}{v^l} N_l = 0.$$

By covariant differentiation of this last relation, we obtain

$$N_l \nabla_k \underset{r}{v^l} = -\underset{r}{v^l} \nabla_k N_l.$$

Forming the scalar product of (48.10) with N_l, and using the last two relations, we find that the integrability conditions reduce to

$$(\underset{r}{v^j}\underset{t}{v^l} - \underset{t}{v^j}\underset{r}{v^l})\nabla_j N_l = 0. \tag{48.11}$$

Conversely, by use of the relations, $N^i \underset{r}{v_j} = 0$, it is easily seen that the above equation (48.11) implies (48.10). Hence, *equations (48.11) are equivalent to (48.10) and furnish the integrability conditions for the given system of equations.*

Finally, we note that the equations

$$\underset{r}{v^j}\underset{t}{v^l}(\nabla_j N_l - \nabla_l N_j) = 0 \tag{48.12}$$

are equivalent to (48.11). These equations may be easily interpreted in terms of the orthogonal 3-tuple of Section 47. We consider the case where our original system (48.9) defines a family of surfaces ($n = 2$). Let $\underset{r}{i^j}$, $r = 1, 2$ denote a 2-tuple of orthogonal unit vectors lying in the tangent planes of any surface. By adjoining a unit vector normal to $\underset{r}{i^j}$, say N^j, to this 2-tuple, we obtain the desired 3-tuple, N^j, $\underset{r}{i^j}$. Since $\underset{r}{v^l}$ are linear combinations of $\underset{r}{i^l}$, equations (48.12) imply that

$$\underset{r}{i^j}\underset{s}{i^l}(\nabla_j N_l - \nabla_l N_j) = 0.$$

We may express $\nabla_j N_l$ in terms of this 3-tuple by introducing the scalars, $\underset{ln}{h}$, and writing:

$$\nabla_j N_l = \underset{33}{h} N_j N_l + \sum_{r=1}^{2} \underset{3r}{h} N_j \underset{r}{i_l} + \sum_{r=1}^{2} \underset{r3}{h}\,\underset{r}{i_j} N_l + \sum_{r,s=1}^{2} \underset{rs}{h}\,\underset{r}{i_j}\underset{s}{i_l}.$$

Substituting the above expression for $\nabla_j N_l$ into the preceding relation, we obtain the result

$$\underset{rs}{h} = \underset{sr}{h}, \qquad s, r = 1, 2. \tag{48.13}$$

That is, the integrability conditions imply that the *component of* $\nabla_j N_l$ *which lies in the surface is symmetric*. Further, since $N^l N_l = 1$, and $N^l \nabla_j N_l = 0$, we find that $\underset{33}{h} = \underset{r3}{h} = 0$. Hence, the above expression for $\nabla_j N_l$ may be written as

$$\nabla_j N_l = N_j u_l + h_{jl} \tag{48.14}$$

where u_l, h_{jl} *lie in the tangent planes of the surface and* h_{jl} *is symmetric*. It is easily verified that $u_l = N^j \nabla_j N_l$ and hence u_l *is the curvature vector of the curves determined by* N_l. The tensor, h_{jl}, is called the *second fundamental tensor* of the surfaces for which N_l is the unit normal vector.

(d) ***Tensor Formulation of the Integrability Conditions for the Equations;*** $\nabla_k \phi = w_k$. The equations

$$\nabla_k \phi = w_k, \qquad w_k = w_k(x^i)$$

are equivalent to (48.1) when $x^j = \phi$. From the previous results [Section 48(a)], we know that the integrability conditions of the above are

$$\frac{\partial w_k}{\partial x^j} = \frac{\partial w_j}{\partial x^k}.$$

Due to the symmetry of the connection, Γ^l_{jk}, we may write these last equations as

$$\nabla_j w_k - \nabla_k w_j = 0. \tag{48.15}$$

That is, the skew-symmetric part of the tensor, $\nabla_j w_k$, must vanish.

(e) ***Tensor Formulation of the Integrability Conditions for the Equations;*** $\nabla_k v^{j_1 \cdots j_r} = w_k^{\cdot j_1 \cdots j_r}$. In order to treat the general partial differential equations

$$\nabla_k v^{j_1 \cdots j_r} = w_k^{\cdot j_1 \cdots j_r} \tag{48.16}$$

we shall consider a simple case and extend our results by observation to the above general case. Thus, we consider the case of a second-order tensor, v^{jl}. Then, the given system may be written in the form

$$\nabla_k v^{jl} = w_k^{\cdot jl}. \tag{48.17}$$

The tensor v^{jl} is considered as unknown and the tensor $w_k^{\cdot jl}$ is considered to be known.

We now consider a 3-tuple of unit orthogonal vectors and the orthogonal components of v^{jl} with respect to this 3-tuple. That is, we shall study the scalar fields

$$\underset{nm}{v} = v^{jl}\underset{n}{i_j}\underset{m}{i_l}.$$

Forming the covariant derivatives of $\underset{nm}{v}$, we obtain

$$\frac{\partial \underset{nm}{v}}{\partial x^k} = (\nabla_k v^{jl})\underset{n}{i_j}\underset{m}{i_l} + v^{jl}\nabla_k(\underset{n}{i_j}\underset{m}{i_l}).$$

Replacing $\nabla_k v^{jl}$ by $w_k^{\cdot jl}$, we find that the original equation (48.17) has been *reduced to the equivalent system*

$$\frac{\partial \underset{nm}{v}}{\partial x^k} = w_k^{\cdot jl}\underset{n}{i_j}\underset{m}{i_l} + v^{jl}\nabla_k(\underset{n}{i_j}\underset{m}{i_l}).$$

These last equations are nine gradient equations of the type studied in Section 48(d). Hence, their integrability conditions are [see (48.15)]

$$\nabla_i(w_k^{\cdot jl}\underset{n}{i_j}\underset{m}{i_l}) - \nabla_k(w_i^{\cdot jl}\underset{n}{i_j}\underset{m}{i_l}) + \nabla_i[v^{jl}\nabla_k(\underset{n}{i_j}\underset{m}{i_l})] - \nabla_k[v^{jl}\nabla_i(\underset{n}{i_j}\underset{m}{i_l})] = 0.$$

Expanding the above, we obtain by use of our original equations (48.17)

$$(\nabla_i w_k^{\cdot jl} - \nabla_k w_i^{\cdot jl})\underset{n}{i_j}\underset{m}{i_l} + v^{jl}[\nabla_i\nabla_k(\underset{n}{i_j}\underset{m}{i_l}) - \nabla_k\nabla_i(\underset{n}{i_j}\underset{m}{i_l})] = 0.$$

In order to further simplify this relation, one must study the tensor in the brackets of the second term in this equation. For the present, we merely state that one may write[14]

$$(\nabla_k\nabla_i - \nabla_i\nabla_k)\underset{n}{i_j}\underset{m}{i_l} = R^{h}_{\cdot jki}\underset{n}{i_h}\underset{m}{i_l} + R^{h}_{\cdot lki}\underset{n}{i_j}\underset{m}{i_h}. \tag{48.18}$$

The tensor $R^{h}_{\cdot jki}$ is the curvature tensor of Section 48(a). Substituting (48.18) into the preceding equation and simplifying by changing dummy indices, we obtain

$$\underset{n}{i_j}\underset{m}{i_l}[\nabla_i w_k^{\cdot jl} - \nabla_k w_i^{\cdot jl} - R^{j}_{\cdot hki}v^{hl} - R^{l}_{\cdot hki}v^{jh}] = 0.$$

Since this last relation is valid for all $\underset{n}{i^j}$, $\underset{m}{i^k}$, n, $m = 1, 2, 3$, the tensor inside the bracket must vanish. Thus, we obtain the desired integrability conditions

$$\nabla_i w_k^{\cdot jl} - \nabla_k w_i^{\cdot jl} - R^{j}_{\cdot hki}v^{hl} - R^{l}_{\cdot hki}v^{jh} = 0. \tag{48.19}$$

In Euclidean three-space, $R^{j}_{\cdot hki} = 0$. Hence, the integrability conditions become

$$\nabla_i w_k^{\cdot jl} - \nabla_k w_i^{\cdot jl} = 0.$$

[14] See Section 54, Problem 54.3.

The above results can be extended to n-dimensional space. Further, the Euclidean character of the space was used only in deriving the final form of the integrability conditions. Hence, these results are valid for general Riemannian spaces. However, the space must possess a symmetric connection, Γ^l_{ij}. For spaces with unsymmetric connections, the above conditions must be modified.[15]

The results of this section are especially valuable in applied mathematics. In this subject, one encounters many problems involving systems of linear partial differential equations. As an example, we shall show, in the section on the theory of elasticity, that the compatibility relations are integrability relations and follow from the above theory.

Problem 48.1: Show that the condition

$$e^{ijk}P_k\nabla_jP_i = 0, \qquad i, j, k = 1, 2, 3,$$

is the integrability condition of the Pfaffian differential equation

$$P_k\, dx^k = 0.$$

Hint: Show that the above differential equation implies that a scalar multiplier exists so that $P_k = G\,\partial\phi/\partial x^k$; write the integrability conditions (48.15) and then eliminate G.

Problem 48.2: Discuss the integrability conditions and solutions of

$$x^1\frac{\partial\phi}{\partial x^1} + x^2\frac{\partial\phi}{\partial x^2} = 0, \qquad x^4\frac{\partial\phi}{\partial x^3} - x^3\frac{\partial\phi}{\partial x^4} = 0.$$

Hint: Show that this system is complete and *Jacobian* $(A_1, A_2)\phi \equiv 0$; the general integral of the first equation is $x^1 = cx^2$; find the general integral of the second equation by considering $dx^3/x^4 = -dx^4/x^3$; hence, find the general integral of the system.

Problem 48.3: Show that the integrability conditions of the equations $\nabla_jv_k - \nabla_kv_j = 2\omega_{jk}$, are (where ω_{jk} are known)

$$\nabla_j\omega_{ik} - \nabla_i\omega_{jk} + \nabla_k\omega_{ji} = 0.$$

Hint: Consider the equations, $\nabla_jv_k = H_{jk}$ and show that $\nabla_iH_{jk} - \nabla_jH_{ik} = 0$ are their integrability conditions [see (48.19)]; decompose H_{jk} into $H_{jk} = \omega_{jk} + h_{jk}$, where ω_{jk} is antisymmetric and h_{jk} is symmetric; show that

$$2\nabla_ih_{jk} = \nabla_i\nabla_jv_k + \nabla_i\nabla_kv_j$$
$$\nabla_ih_{jk} = \nabla_j\omega_{ik} + \nabla_kh_{ji}.$$

[15] See J. A. Schouten, *loc. cit.*

Note that the integrability conditions of $\nabla_j v_k = H_{jk}$ have been used in going from step one to two in the above computation. By cyclic permuting of the indices, i, j, k in the last relation and adding the resulting equations, the desired integrability conditions are obtained.

Problem 48.4: In Euclidean three-space, the integrability conditions of Problem 48.3 consist of a single equation, although the general formula is valid in a Euclidean space of n dimensions. Show that for three-space, this integrability relation is equivalent to the conditions, $\nabla \cdot \omega = 0$, where $\omega = \nabla \times \mathbf{V}$. *Hint:* We may write, $2\omega_{ik} = e_{ikl}\omega^l$, in Cartesian orthogonal coordinates; substitute this relation into the integrability condition of Problem 48.3; form the scalar product of the resulting equation with e^{ikn}. Note, for the plane problem, the integrability conditions are identically satisfied and the curl of a vector, v^k, may be arbitrarily prescribed.

The results of Problems 48.3 and 48.4 are of importance in the study of rotational compressible fluids in Chapter XI.

ADDITIONAL PROBLEMS

1. Let x, y, z denote Cartesian orthogonal coordinates and let u, v, ϕ denote curvilinear coordinates defined by

$$x = \sqrt{(u^2 - 1)(1 - v^2)} \sin \phi, \qquad y = \sqrt{(u^2 - 1)(1 - v^2)} \cos \phi,$$
$$z = uv.$$

Show that:

(1) u = constant are ellipsoids of revolution, v = constant are hyperboloids of revolution, ϕ = constant are planes;

(2) $g_{11} = \dfrac{u^2 - v^2}{u^2 - 1}, \; g_{22} = \dfrac{u^2 - v^2}{1 - v^2}, \; g_{33} = (u^2 - 1)(1 - v^2), \; g_{ij} = 0, i \neq j.$

Find the expressions for Γ^k_{ij}, $\nabla_j W^i$ where W^i is an arbitrary vector.

2. Let x^j denote Cartesian orthogonal coordinates and let $\bar{x}^j = \bar{x}^j(u, v)$ define a convex surface, S. Consider the curvilinear coordinates, u, v, w, defined by

$$x^j = \bar{x}^j(u, v) + w\bar{n}^j(u, v), \qquad j = 1, 2, 3,$$

where $\bar{n}^j$ is the unit normal vector of S. Determine the g_{ij} and Γ^l_{ij} for the u, v, w curvilinear coordinate system. Show that vectors tangent to the three coordinate curves are transported by parallelism along the coordinate curves, w = variable. (The surfaces, w = constant, are called parallel surfaces.)

3. If we define physical components by $\mathbf{V} = \sum_k \tilde{V}_k \mathbf{w}_k$, where $\mathbf{w}_k$ are reciprocal to $\mathbf{u}_j$ (and $\mathbf{w}_k$ are not necessarily unit vectors), then $\tilde{V}_k$ are the projections of $\mathbf{V}$ on the coordinate lines. Find these physical components of the velocity vector in the coordinate system of Problem 2.

4. Show that the covariant derivative of a weighed tensor is a tensor of the same weight.

5. Show that
$$\nabla^2\Omega = \frac{1}{\sqrt{g}}\frac{\partial}{\partial x^j}\left(\sqrt{g}\, g^{jk}\frac{\partial \Omega}{\partial x^k}\right).$$

6. (1) Prove that the transformations defined by
$$'h^i = h^j \frac{\partial\, 'x^i}{\partial x^j}\left|\frac{\partial x^l}{\partial\, 'x^p}\right|^k$$
form a group (the h^j is a vector density of weight k);
(2) Show that the sum of two vector densities of weight k is a vector density of the same weight.

7. If w^{jk} is an alternating (skew-symmetric) tensor of weight one, and v_l is the vector $v_l = e_{ljk}w^{jk}$, show that the curl of v_k is related to the divergence of w^{jk} by
$$\frac{\partial v_l}{\partial x^k} - \frac{\partial v_k}{\partial x^l} = e_{lkj}\frac{\partial w^{pj}}{\partial x^p}.$$
Is this a tensor equation?

8. If w^j is a vector density of weight one, show that $\partial w^j/\partial x^j$ is a scalar density of weight one.

9. If $Q^k_{\cdot l}$ is a second-order tensor, and v^k is a given vector, show that
$$v^j\frac{\partial Q^k_{\cdot l}}{\partial x^j} + Q^k_{\cdot n}\frac{\partial v^n}{\partial x^l} - Q^p_{\cdot l}\frac{\partial v^k}{\partial x^p}$$
is a second-order tensor. This tensor is called the Lie derivative of $Q^k_{\cdot l}$.

10. Show that the transformation law of the contravariant components of a skew-symmetric second-order tensor can be expressed as the transformation law of a covariant vector of weight one.

11. Prove that under parallel displacement, $0 = \delta(v^j w_j)$, and hence angles between vectors are unaltered by this type of displacement.

12. Show that when a vector v^j on a sphere of radius one is infinitesimally displaced by parallelism along a small circle, then the change in angle, $d\psi$, of the vector is
$$d\psi = \cos\phi\, d\theta$$
where ϕ is the colatitude and θ is the longitude.

Chapter VIII

THE THEOREMS OF GAUSS AND STOKES IN N-DIMENSIONAL EUCLIDEAN SPACE

49. Surface Area and the Content of N-Dimensional Space Regions. In order to develop the theory of discontinuities in compressible fluids, it will be necessary to formulate the theorems of Gauss and Stokes in the four-dimensional Euclidean manifold of space-time. Since these theorems can be developed for the case of n-dimensional Euclidean space, rather than just for four-dimensional space, with approximately the same amount of theory, we shall furnish this more general development.

To provide a gradual transition from the previous theory which was essentially for three-dimensional Euclidean space, we shall generalize our theory of surface area (Section 26) to volume of a region of three-space, and to content (generalized volume) in n-dimensional Riemannian space. It should be recalled that a Riemannian space is a metric space (possessing a metric tensor) which is curved (as the surface of a sphere).

(a) ***The Metric Tensor of a Surface in Euclidean Three-Space,*** $'g_{\lambda\mu}$. Let u^λ, $\lambda, \mu = 1, 2$ denote a coordinate system on the surface S; and let x^i, $j, k = 1, 2, 3$ denote a general curvilinear system of coordinates in Euclidean three-space. The theory of the metric tensor of the surface, S, can be developed as a theory of projection. That is, by projecting any vector field which is attached to S onto the tangent planes to S, we obtain a vector field in S. Similarly by projecting the base vectors of the Euclidean three-space, E_3, at S onto S, we obtain a family of base vectors for S. By this procedure, one may carry all of the previous theory for Euclidean three-space into a corresponding theory for a surface in this space. Rather than proceeding in this direction at present, we shall briefly introduce the surface metric tensor and mention some of its properties which are important for our purposes.

If g_{jk} denotes the metric tensor of Euclidean three-space, then we define $'g_{\lambda\mu}$, $\lambda, \mu = 1, 2$, the metric tensor of the surface, by

$$'g_{\lambda\mu} = g_{jk} \frac{\partial x^j}{\partial u^\lambda} \frac{\partial x^k}{\partial u^\mu} \tag{49.1}$$

where the equations of the surface in the x^i curvilinear coordinates are assumed to be, $x^k = x^k(u^\lambda)$. The metric coefficients, E, F, G of a surface (Section 26) are nothing but the components of the surface metric tensor, $'g_{\lambda\mu}$, when the x^i are Cartesian orthogonal coordinates ($g_{jk} = \delta_{jk}$). In fact, the relations

$$E = 'g_{11}, \qquad F = 'g_{12} = 'g_{21}, \qquad G = 'g_{22}$$

follow directly from our definition of $'g_{\lambda\mu}$.

In our theory, we will use one important property of the surface metric tensor. Let $\bar{u}^\lambda$, $\lambda = 1, 2$, denote a new system of surface coordinates, such that the transformations, $u^\lambda = u^\lambda(\bar{u}^\alpha)$ have continuous second derivatives and non-vanishing Jacobian, $'J$. By definition, $'J$ is the positive valued determinant

$$'J = \begin{vmatrix} \dfrac{\partial u^1}{\partial \bar{u}^1} & \dfrac{\partial u^1}{\partial \bar{u}^2} \\ \dfrac{\partial u^2}{\partial \bar{u}^1} & \dfrac{\partial u^2}{\partial \bar{u}^2} \end{vmatrix}.$$

Then, just as in the case of the space metric tensor, g_{jk}, one may show [see Section 39(c)] that

$$'\bar{g} = 'g('J)^2 \tag{49.2}$$

where $'\bar{g}$, $'g$ are the determinants of the metric tensors, $'\bar{g}_{\lambda\mu}$ (in the $\bar{u}^\lambda$ system) and $'g_{\lambda\mu}$, respectively. With these few remarks, we leave the theory of the surface metric tensor.

(b) ***Area of Surfaces in Euclidean Three-Space.*** The essential requirements for a proper definition of surface area are two in number:

(1) the adopted measure should agree with our intuitive concept of surface area; in particular, it should reduce to the well-known formulas for the area of a segment of a plane;

(2) the adopted measure should be independent of the coordinate systems by means of which the surface is defined; in particular, it should be independent of the particular surface and/or space coordinate systems used.

In order to discuss these points, we consider a coordinate system, u^λ, on a surface, S, and a coordinate system, x^i, in space. We define the surface area as

$$A = \int \sqrt{g}\, e_{ijk} n^i \frac{\partial x^j}{\partial u^1} \frac{\partial x^k}{\partial u^2} du^1\, du^2$$

where e_{ijk} is the e-tensor capacity, g is the determinant of the metric tensor of the space coordinates, n^i is the unit surface normal vector. From our previous discussion, we see that the right-hand side of the above equation is an invariant and is such that the element of area, dA, of the above formula represents the volume of a parallelepiped of altitude one (along n^j) and whose area of base is equal to that of the elementary parallelogram formed by the vectors $d\mathbf{R}_1$, $d\mathbf{R}_2$ (which lie along the surface coordinate

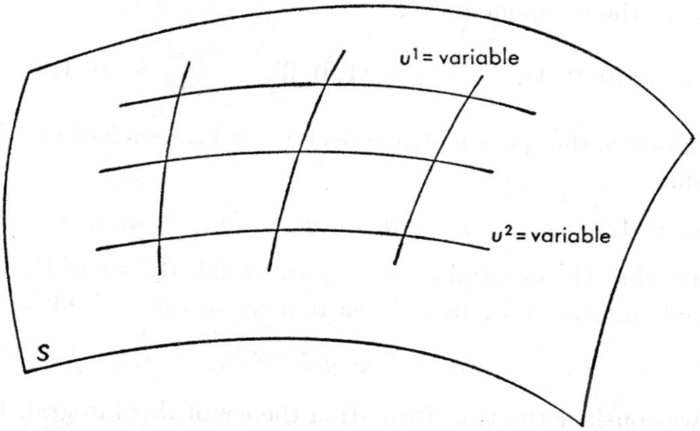

Figure 45: The u^1, u^2 Parameter Lines on a Surface in Euclidean Three-Space

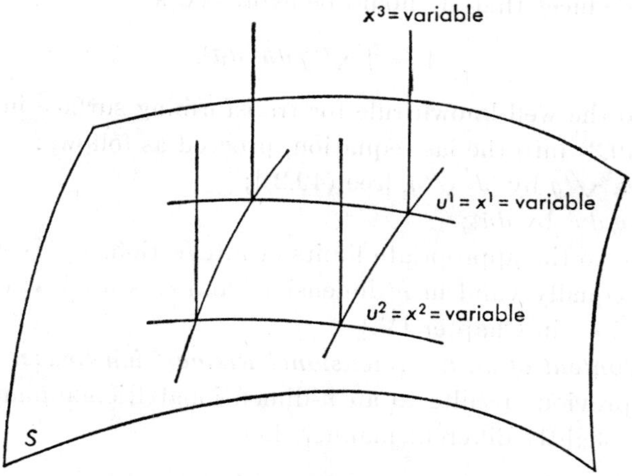

Figure 46: The Space Coordinate Lines, x^3 = Variable, and the Surface Coordinate Lines, x^1, x^2 = Variable along S

lines). Thus, this formula appears to satisfy the conditions (1) and (2). However, this formula has one major defect; it depends upon *space* quantities, such as n^j.

In order to write an expression for surface area in a form which is independent of the space quantities, we imagine a coordinate system *in space* which possesses the following properties along the surface, S: The x^1 =

variable and the x^2 = variable coordinate lines coincide with the u^1 = variable and the u^2 = variable coordinate lines of the surface, respectively; the x^3 = variable coordinate lines are lines orthogonal to the surface, S. It follows that along S, x^3 = constant.

In this type of coordinate system, on S, the space vectors n^i, $\partial x^i/\partial u^1$, $\partial x^i/\partial u^2$ have the components

$$n^i = (0, 0, 1), \qquad \frac{\partial x^i}{\partial u^1} = (1, 0, 0), \qquad \frac{\partial x^i}{\partial u^2} = (0, 1, 0).$$

Further, along S, the space metric tensor g_{ij}, and the surface metric tensor, $'g_{\lambda\mu}$, become

$$g_{33} = 1, \qquad g_{3\lambda} = g_{\lambda 3} = 0, \qquad g_{\lambda\mu} = {'g_{\lambda\mu}}, \qquad \lambda, \mu = 1, 2.$$

This means that the determinants g, $'g$ are equal. By use of these results, the original equation for surface area reduces to the desired formula

$$A = \int \sqrt{'g}\, du^1\, du^2. \tag{49.3}$$

Now, we consider the transformation theory of this integral. Let $\bar{u}^1$, $\bar{u}^2$ denote a new surface coordinate system. Then, by following the previous theory, one deduces that A should be expressed as

$$A = \int \sqrt{'\bar{g}}\, d\bar{u}^1\, d\bar{u}^2.$$

This leads to the well-known rule for transforming surface integrals. To transform (49.3) into the last equation, proceed as follows:

(1) replace $\sqrt{'g}$ by $'J\sqrt{'g}$, [see (49.2)];

(2) replace du^λ by $d\bar{u}^\lambda$;

(3) change to the appropriate limits of integration.

This rule is equally valid in n dimensions and was used extensively for three dimensions in Chapter IV.[1]

(c) ***The Content of an n-Dimensional Riemannian Space.*** In order to extend the previous results to an n-dimensional Riemannian space, we proceed in a slightly different manner. Let

$$\underset{1}{du^\lambda}, \underset{2}{du^\lambda}, \cdots \underset{n}{du^\lambda}, \lambda = 1, 2, \cdots n,$$

denote n independent differential vector fields of the n-space. The fact that $\underset{k}{du^\lambda}$ are *vector* fields means that the quantities must transform in the well-known manner (44.3) under coordinate transformation. If $g_{\lambda\mu}$ denotes

[1] In the work of Chapter IV we considered the transformation relations as point transformations in a given coordinate system; at present, we consider these relations as coordinate transformations for a given point.

the metric tensor of the space, g denotes the determinant of the metric tensor, and $e_{\lambda\mu\ldots\gamma}$ the n-dimensional e-tensor capacity, we *define the n-dimensional content of a region of the Riemannian space of n dimensions by*

$$C = \int \sqrt{g}\, e_{\lambda\mu\ldots\gamma}\, \underset{1}{du^\lambda}\, \underset{2}{du^\mu} \cdots \underset{n}{du^\gamma}. \tag{49.4}$$

The limits of integration are difficult to determine for arbitrary $\underset{k}{du^\lambda}$. But, if the differential fields lie along the coordinate lines, then

$$\underset{1}{du^\lambda} = (du^1, 0, 0, \cdots 0)$$
$$\underset{2}{du^\lambda} = (0, du^2, 0, \cdots 0), \text{ etc.};$$

and the formula for content reduces to

$$C = \int \sqrt{g}\, du^1\, du^2 \cdots du^n.$$

For $n = 2$, the above formula coincides with that of surface area (49.3). Further, for a Cartesian orthogonal coordinate system in three-space, the above reduces to the well-known formula, $V = \int dx^1\, dx^2\, dx^3$. Finally, the result that *C is independent of the coordinate system* follows directly from the transformation laws (where $\bar{u}^\lambda$ are the new coordinates):

$$\underset{1}{du^\lambda} = \frac{\partial u^\lambda}{\partial \bar{u}^\alpha}\, \underset{1}{d\bar{u}^\alpha}, \text{ etc.,}$$
$$e_{\lambda\mu\ldots\gamma}\, \underset{1}{du^\lambda}\, \underset{2}{du^\mu} \cdots \underset{n}{du^\gamma} = J \bar{e}_{\lambda\mu\ldots\gamma}\, \underset{1}{d\bar{u}^\lambda}\, \underset{2}{d\bar{u}^\mu} \cdots \underset{n}{d\bar{u}^\gamma}$$
$$\sqrt{g} = \sqrt{\bar{g}}/J.$$

In order to determine C in the new coordinate system, one follows the procedure outlined previously. It is important to note that (49.4) defines the n-dimensional content of an n-dimensional Riemannian space in terms of a coordinate system u^λ, $\lambda = 1, 2, \ldots, n$, which maps the n-space. Thus in an m-dimensional, $m < n$, subspace of the given space, one *cannot write*

$$C = \int \sqrt{g}\, e_{\lambda\ldots\mu}\, \underset{1}{du^\lambda} \cdots \underset{m}{du^\mu}, \qquad \lambda, \mu = 1, \cdots n.$$

The difficulty lies in the fact that $e_{\lambda\ldots\mu}$ is not a tensor capacity for the coordinate system, u^λ, $\lambda = 1, \ldots, n$. But, by introducing a class of coordinate systems in which

$$u^\lambda = \text{constant}, \qquad \lambda = m + 1, \ldots, n$$

define the m-dimensional subspace and the coordinate lines

$$u^\lambda = \text{variable} \qquad \lambda = 1, \ldots, m$$

lie in the m-dimensional subspace, one may apply the above formula. This procedure was adopted in deriving our formula for surface area in Section 49(b).

Problem 49.1: Find the content of that portion of a four-dimensional Euclidean space, E_4, which is bounded by the hyperplane, $a_j x^j = 1$ and the coordinate hyperplanes, $x^j = 0$. The coordinate variables, x^j, are assumed to be Cartesian orthogonal.

Problem 49.2: Find the content of the boundary hyperplane $a_j x^j = 1$, in Problem 49.1. *Hint:* Use the parameters, $x^1 = u^1$, $x^2 = u^2$, $x^3 = u^3$, as hyperplane parameters; notice that $'g_{11} = 1 + (a_1/a_4)^2$, etc.

Problem 49.3: Find the content of the hypersphere: $(x^1)^2 + (x^2)^2 + (x^3)^2 + (x^4)^2 = 1$. *Hint:* Introduce the generalized spherical coordinates in E_4, r, θ, ϕ, α;

$$x^1 = r \cos\theta \cos\phi \cos\alpha, \qquad x^3 = r \cos\theta \sin\phi$$
$$x^2 = r \cos\theta \cos\phi \sin\alpha, \qquad x^4 = r \sin\theta$$

and note that the equation of the hypersphere is $r = 1$.

Problem 49.4: Consider a coordinate surface, x^3 = constant, in a curvilinear coordinate system, x^j, $j = 1, 2, 3$. Let g denote the determinant of the metric tensor. Hence, the reduced cofactor, g^{33}, is [see Section 39(b)]

$$g^{33} = {'g}/g$$

where $'g$ is the determinant $[g_{11}g_{22} - (g_{12})^2]$ of the metric coefficients. Thus, (49.3) may be written as

$$dA_3 = \sqrt{gg^{33}}\, dx^1\, dx^2.$$

Verify this result by noting that

$$dA_3 = |d\mathbf{R}_1 \times d\mathbf{R}_2|$$

and that $d\mathbf{R}_j = \mathbf{e}_j\, dx^j$ (not summed on j). *Hint:* Use the result of Problem 44.21 and show that $\mathbf{e}_1 \times \mathbf{e}_2 = \sqrt{g}\, e_{j12}\mathbf{e}^j$.

Problem 49.5: By use of the methods of Problem 49.4, show that if $\mathbf{n}$ is the unit normal of the area bounded by $d\mathbf{R}_j$ ($j = 1, 2, 3$) and dA is the area of this piece of surface, then

$$\mathbf{n}\, dA = \sum_j \frac{\mathbf{e}^j}{\sqrt{g^{jj}}}\, dA_j.$$

Thus, if $\mathbf{n} = n_j \mathbf{e}^j$ then

$$\sqrt{g^{jj}}\, n_j\, dA = dA_j \qquad \text{(not summed on } j\text{)}.$$

50. Orientations and Coordinate Systems for an *m*-Dimensional Surface, S_m, in *n*-Dimensional Euclidean Space, E_n. The work of this section will lay the direct basis for generalizing the formulas of Gauss and Stokes.[2] Two concepts must be developed for this purpose: (1) orientations must be assigned to S_m and S_{m-1}; (2) a simplified coordinate system must be introduced in S_{m-1} and S_m in E_n. It should be noted that the "S_m in E_n" means an m-dimensional surface in an n-dimensional Euclidean space.

(a) ***Orientations of S_m and the m-Vectors of S_m.*** In order to assign an orientation to S_m, we introduce the m-vectors of S_m in E_n. By definition, an m-vector is an m-th order tensor which is *skew symmetric in all its indices.* It is easily verified that this skew symmetry property is invariant under coordinate transformation. In particular, a contravariant n-vector in n-dimensional space, $v^{\overset{\lambda}{1}\dots\overset{\lambda}{n}}$, is equivalent to a scalar capacity of weight one and a covariant n-vector, $v_{\underset{1}{\lambda}\dots\underset{n}{\lambda}}$, is equivalent to a scalar density of weight one. To verify this result, we proceed as follows. Evidently, the n-vector, $v^{\overset{\lambda}{1}\dots\overset{\lambda}{n}}$, consists of one distinct component (except for sign), $v^{12\dots n} = -v^{21\dots n}$, etc. Further, if J denotes the Jacobian (or the determinant) of the coordinate transformation from the u^λ to the $\bar{u}^\lambda$ variables, then

$$v^{12\dots n} = \frac{\partial u^1}{\partial \bar{u}^\lambda}\frac{\partial u^2}{\partial \bar{u}^\mu}\cdots\frac{\partial u^n}{\partial \bar{u}^\gamma}\bar{v}^{\lambda\mu\dots\gamma} = J\bar{v}^{12\dots n}.$$

The properties of the covariant n-vector are verified in a similar manner. It should be stressed that the contravariant n-vectors, $v^{\overset{\lambda}{1}\dots\overset{\lambda}{n}}$, $e^{\overset{\lambda}{1}\dots\overset{\lambda}{n}}$ transform as a scalar capacity and a tensor density, respectively. Similar results are valid for $e_{\underset{1}{\lambda}\dots\underset{n}{\lambda}}$, $v_{\underset{1}{\lambda}\dots\underset{n}{\lambda}}$, respectively.

One may construct m-vectors associated with a given m-dimensional manifold, S_m, $n \geq m$, in many ways. We list three examples:

(1) In an n-dimensional space, the e-tensor density, $e^{\overset{\lambda}{1}\dots\overset{\lambda}{n}}$, is an n-vector [for the corresponding three-dimensional theory, see Section 39(c)]; the symbol $e^{\overset{\lambda}{1}\dots\overset{\lambda}{m}}$ has no tensor significance in the n-dimensional coordinate system u^λ, $\lambda = 1, \dots, n$ but is of some value in constructing m-th order determinants in a *specified coordinate system.*

(2) If $\underset{1}{i}^\lambda, \dots, \underset{m}{i}^\lambda$ denote m independent vector fields in an n-dimen-

[2] J. A. Schouten, *loc. cit.*, p. 95.

sional space, then the alternating sum of $\underline{|m}$ terms (where $\underline{|m}$ is "m factorial")

$$v^{\lambda_1\ldots\lambda_m} = \frac{1}{\underline{|m}}\left(\underset{1}{i}^{\lambda_1}\underset{2}{i}^{\lambda_2}\cdots\underset{m}{i}^{\lambda_m} - \underset{1}{i}^{\lambda_2}\underset{2}{i}^{\lambda_1}\cdots\underset{m}{i}^{\lambda_m} + - - -\right)$$

is an m-vector. The omitted terms (in the dashes) are constructed by prefixing a plus sign if the ordering of the upper indices is an even permutation and by prefixing a minus sign if the ordering of the upper indices is an odd permutation of 1, 2, 3, . . . , m. In the literature, this m-vector is usually denoted by

$$v^{\lambda_1\ldots\lambda_m} = \underset{1}{i}^{[\lambda_1}\underset{2}{i}^{\lambda_2}\cdots\underset{m}{i}^{\lambda_m]}.$$

The brackets on the indices indicate the right-hand side of the last expression is to be evaluated by use of the right-hand side of the previous expression.

(3) By introducing m independent differential vector fields, $\underset{1}{du}^{\lambda}$, . . . , $\underset{m}{du}^{\lambda}$, one may construct the m-vector

$$\underset{1}{du}^{[\lambda_1}\cdots\underset{m}{du}^{\lambda_m]}. \tag{50.1}$$

The m-vector of (50.1) is of considerable value in our future work. Let the scalars, $\underset{m}{d\tau}$, denote the *contents* of any of the elementary parallelepipeds formed by any *displacements* which lie along the vectors $\underset{k}{du}^{\lambda}$. This definition does not determine a unique positive number $\underset{m}{d\tau}$ but rather a whole class of positive numbers. With any number of this class of scalars we associate an m-vector, $f^{\lambda_1\ldots\lambda_m}$, by means of the relation

$$f^{\lambda_1\ldots\lambda_m}\underset{m}{d\tau} = \underline{|m}\,\underset{1}{du}^{[\lambda_1}\cdots\underset{m}{du}^{\lambda_m]}. \tag{50.2}$$

If the vectors $\underset{k}{du}^{\lambda}$ are tangent to the m-dimensional subspace, S_m, the m-vectors, $f^{\lambda_1\ldots\lambda_m}$, are said to be tangent to S_m. It should be noted that any m-vector lying in an n-dimensional Euclidean space, E_n, has $\underline{|n}/(\underline{|m})(\underline{|n-m})$ components. Further, the m-vector, $f^{\lambda_1\ldots\lambda_m}$, assigns an orientation to the subspace, S_m, at each point P. This result follows from the fact that if any two vectors $\underset{k}{du^\lambda}$ are interchanged in (50.2) then the sign of $f^{\lambda_1 \cdots \lambda_m}$ is changed.[3]

(b) ***A System of Preferential Coordinates in E_n.*** In order to determine the desired coordinate systems, we return to the class of such systems introduced in Section 49. It will be recalled that in this class of preferential coordinates, the coordinate lines

$$u^\lambda = \text{variable}, \qquad \lambda = 1, 2 \cdots m \tag{50.3}$$

lie in the subspace, S_m, and the equations

$$u^\lambda = \text{constant}, \qquad \lambda = m + 1, \cdots n$$

define the subspace S_m in E_n. If we allow the vectors $\underset{k}{du^\lambda}$ to fall along the coordinate lines of S_m, then we may use the following representations for these vectors:

$$\begin{array}{rl} & \quad m \text{ positions} \qquad\qquad n - m \text{ positions} \\ \underset{1}{du^\lambda} = & (du^1, 0, 0, \cdots 0, 0, 0, \cdots\cdots 0) \\ \underset{2}{du^\lambda} = & (0, du^2, 0, \cdots 0, 0, 0, \cdots\cdots 0) \\ \cdot & \\ \cdot & \\ \cdot & \\ \underset{m}{du^\lambda} = & (0, 0, 0, \cdots du^m, 0, 0, \cdots\cdots 0). \end{array} \tag{50.4}$$

The formula (50.2) becomes in *any such particular coordinate system*

$$f^{1\cdots m} \underset{m}{d\tau} = du^1 \cdots du^m, \qquad f^{1\cdots i \cdots m} = 0 \tag{50.5}$$

if any index i, belongs to the set, $m + 1, \ldots, n$. In integrating over S_m it is customary to sum in such a manner that the increments along the coordinate lines (and hence du^k) are positive. This means that in writing the above formula we assume that $f^{1\cdots m}$ is positive.

(c) ***The $(m - 1)$—Vectors and Coordinates of S_{m-1}.*** Now, consider a subspace of $(m - 1)$ dimensions S_{m-1} lying in S_m. With this subspace one may associate $(m - 1)$—vectors, $f^{\lambda_1 \cdots \lambda_{m-1}}$ by means of the equation

$$f^{\lambda_1 \cdots \lambda_{m-1}} \underset{m-1}{d\tau} = \lfloor m - 1 \; \underset{1}{du}^{[\lambda_1} \cdots \underset{m-1}{du}^{\lambda_{m-1}]} \tag{50.6}$$

[3] It is not always possible to assign a unique sign to the m-vector of S_m. For the case of the Möbius strip (an S_2 in E_3), the sign is not unique and the surface is non-orientable.

where $\underset{m-1}{d\tau}$ denote the positive scalar *contents* of any of the elementary parallelepipeds formed by any *displacements* which lie along the vectors $\underset{k}{du^\lambda}$ $(k = 1, \ldots, m-1)$. The vectors $\underset{k}{du^\lambda}$ lie in S_{m-1} and do not necessarily coincide with the first $(m-1)$ vectors of (50.2).

Let us assume that the surface parameters of S_{m-1} are chosen to be u^λ, $\lambda = 1, \ldots, m-1$. This means that the S_{m-1} is defined by the relations

$$\begin{aligned} &u^\lambda = \text{constant}, && \lambda = m+1, \ldots, n \\ &u^m = u^m(u^1, \ldots, u^{m-1}), && u^m \neq \text{constant}. \end{aligned} \tag{50.7}$$

It should be noted that the term "u^1 = variable, coordinate line" has two meanings. First, this term may refer to a family of coordinate lines, u^2 = constant, $\ldots$, u^n = constant, of S_m. Secondly, this term may refer to a family of coordinate lines, u^2 = constant, $\ldots$, $u^m = u^m(u^1, \ldots, u^{m-1})$, u^{m+1} = constant, $\ldots$, u^n = constant, of S_{m-1}. In the following discussion the term u^1 = variable, coordinate line, will denote the coordinate lines of S_{m-1} and similarly for the u^2 = variable, $\ldots$ u^{m-1} = variable coordinate lines; but the u^m = variable, coordinate line, will denote a family of coordinate lines in S_m. If instead of the above parameterization, one adopts the parameterization of S_{m-1}

$$\begin{aligned} &u^\lambda = \text{constant}, && \lambda = m+1, \ldots, n \\ &u^1 = u^1(u^2, \ldots, u^m), && u^1 \neq \text{constant}, \end{aligned}$$

then the term, u^1 = variable coordinate line, refers to a family of coordinate lines of S_m but the u^α = variable, coordinate line, $\alpha = 2, \ldots, m$ refers to the coordinate lines of S_{m-1}. Figure 47 indicates the situation for the parameterization of (50.7). The well-known parameterization of a surface in three-space, $x^1 = u^1$, $x^2 = u^2$, $x^3 = x^3(u^1, u^2)$, provides the simplest example of the above parameterization of S_{m-1} in S_m. The x^1 = variable coordinate lines of the surface consists of the ∞^1 curves of intersection of the surface with planes, x^2 = constant; the x^1 = variable coordinate lines of space are straight lines, x^2 = constant, x^3 = constant.

By expressing the $\underset{k}{du^\lambda}$ $(k = 1, \ldots, m-1)$ in the form of coordinate differentials (50.4) we obtain the $(m-1)$-dimensional analogue of the m-vector (50.5). One should be a little careful. If we happened to choose $\underset{1}{du^\lambda}$ along the decreasing u^1 = variable coordinate line and $\underset{2}{du^\lambda}$ along the increasing u^2 = variable coordinate line, etc., then a negative sign is obtained. To allow for this freedom of choice we write this analogue as

$$f^{12\ldots m-1}\,\underset{m-1}{d\tau} = \pm du^1 \cdots du^{m-1} \tag{50.8}$$

The sign of the $(m-1)$-vector will be fixed when we have studied the *orientation of S_{m-1} relative to S_m*. For the present, we note that $f^{12,\ldots m}$ is always positive, but $f^{12\ldots m-1}$ may be either positive or negative.

(d) ***The Orientation of S_{m-1} Relative to S_m.*** In order to consider the orientation of S_{m-1} relative to S_m, we introduce the term "exterior normal" of S_{m-1} in S_m. The exterior normal is a vector which is: (1) orthogonal to S_{m-1}; (2) contained in S_m; (3) sensed toward that part of S_m which

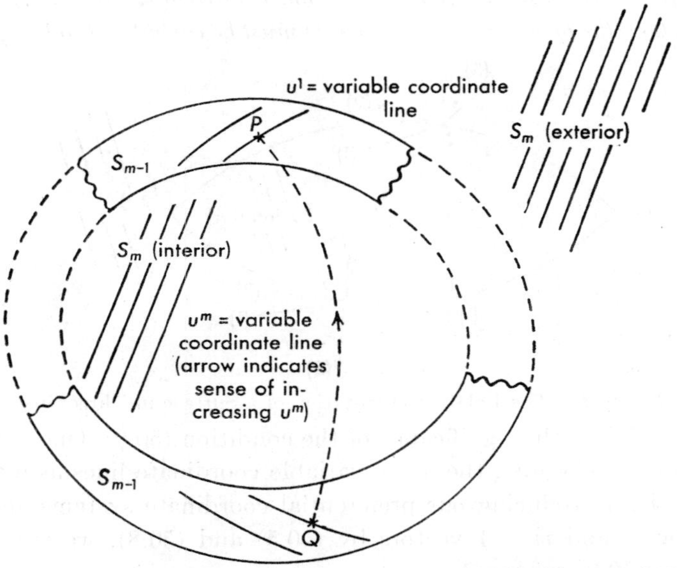

Figure 47: The u^m = Variable Coordinate Lines of S_m; the u^1 = Variable Coordinate Lines of S_{m-1}

is exterior to S_{m-1}. This definition implies that S_{m-1} has an interior and an exterior as a manifold in S_m (see Figure 47). The exterior normal may be associated with the sense in which the coordinate line, u^m = variable, increases or decreases. Thus, in Figure 47, at P the exterior normal is in the sense of increasing u^m, and at Q the exterior normal is in the sense of decreasing u^m. We shall fix the *orientation of S_{m-1} relative to S_m by requiring that*

$$f^{[\underset{1}{\lambda}\ldots\underset{m}{\lambda}]} = f^{[\underset{1}{\lambda}\ldots\underset{m-1}{\lambda}}k^{\underset{m}{\lambda}]} \tag{50.9}$$

where k^λ *is a vector along the exterior normal.*

One can best understand the problem of orientation by considering the S_{m-1} as an ordinary closed surface in a three-dimensional Euclidean space (S_2 in E_3). Let the vectors (1), (2), in Figure 48, lie on the surface and let the vector (3) lie along the exterior normal at P. We move the triad of vectors from P to Q along the space curve. If we preserve orientation in the three-space, we must use the triad consisting of heavy lines at the point Q. However, this triad contains the inward-drawn normal. If we move the triad, in a continuous fashion along the surface from P to Q, then the triad at Q is indicated by the dotted lines. The dotted and full (1), (2) vectors cannot be made to coincide by a rotation. A reflection is needed for the dotted and full (1), (2) vectors to coincide. That is, *if the orientation is to be preserved in the space S_m and if one desires to use the exterior normal to S_{m-1}, then the orientation of S_{m-1} at Q must be considered to be opposite to*

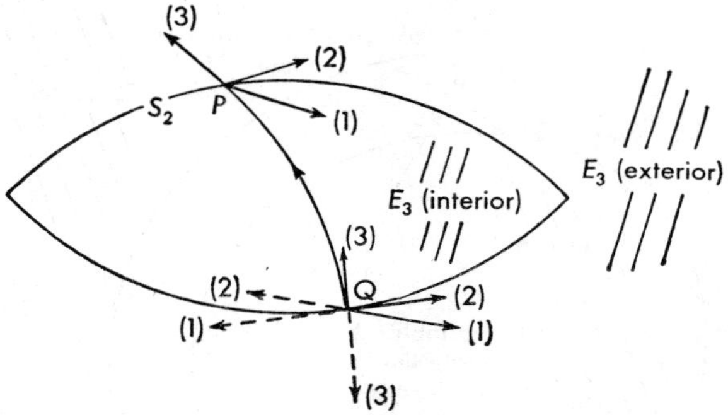

Figure 48: The Relative Orientation of a Surface in Three-Space

that at P. This is the significance of the condition (50.9). One may verify this result by choosing the u^m = variable coordinate lines as orthogonal to S_{m-1}. By introducing our preferential coordinate systems and evaluating the m and $m - 1$ vectors by (50.5) and (50.8), we see that the condition (50.9) reduces to

at P, $\quad f^{12\ldots m} = f^{12\ldots m-1}k^m$

at Q, $\quad f^{12\ldots m} = -f^{12\ldots m-1}k^m$

where k^m is a positive number. Thus, at P and Q, one must write:

at P, $\quad f^{12\ldots m-1} \underset{m-1}{d\tau} = du^1 \cdots du^{m-1}$

at Q, $\quad f^{12\ldots m-1} \underset{m-1}{d\tau} = -du^1 \cdots du^{m-1}. \qquad (50.10)$

51. The Theorems of Gauss and Stokes in n-Dimensional Euclidean Space. In this section, we shall derive a single formula relating an integral over S_m to an integral over its closed S_{m-1} boundary. This result will contain the formulas of Gauss and Stokes as special cases; this theorem is usually called the theorem of Stokes.[4]

[4] Our procedure is similar to that of J. A. Schouten, *Tensor Analysis for Physicists*, Clarendon Press, Oxford, 1951, p. 68. For a related and interesting exposition, see J. L. Synge and A. Schild, *Tensor Analysis*, U. of Toronto Press, Toronto, 1949, pp. 252–277.

(a) ***Conditions on the Tensor Fields and the Subspaces.*** We consider a p-th order tensor field $v_{\lambda\mu\ldots\gamma}$ defined over a subspace of m dimensions, S_m, in the Euclidean n-space, E_n. It is assumed that the tensor field is continuous and possesses continuous first partial derivatives in the m-dimensional subspace, S_m. We let S_{m-1} denote the closed boundary of S_m and assume that any coordinate line cuts this boundary in at most two points.

(b) ***The Fundamental Integration Formula.*** The formulas of Gauss and Stokes depend upon verifying the following type of integration formula for the p-th order tensor, $v_{\lambda\mu\ldots\gamma}$:

$$\int_{\underset{m}{\tau}} \left(\frac{\partial}{\partial u^m} v_{\lambda\mu\ldots\gamma}\right) f^{12\ldots m}\, d\underset{m}{\tau} = \int_{\underset{m-1}{\tau}} v_{\lambda\mu\ldots\gamma} f^{1\ldots m-1}\, d\underset{m-1}{\tau} \tag{51.1}$$

where the coordinate variables u^λ are chosen as in Section 50(b), (c). It should be noted that (51.1) is not a tensor formula and the repeated index "m" is not summed. Further, the regions $\underset{m}{\tau}, \underset{m-1}{\tau}$, are to be taken as follows. Let the parameter line, u^m = variable, of (50.7), cut S_{m-1} in the points

$$P_1\colon u^m = \underset{1}{u^m},$$
$$P_2\colon u^m = \underset{2}{u^m},$$

where all other u^λ of S_m are determined by $u^\lambda = \underset{0}{u^\lambda}$, $\lambda = 1, \ldots, m-1$. Then, we denote by $\underset{m}{\tau}$ that part of S_m which lies within the tube:

$$\underset{0}{u^\lambda} \le u^\lambda \le \underset{0}{u^\lambda} + du^\lambda, \qquad \lambda = 1, 2, \cdots m-1$$
$$\underset{1}{u^m} \le u^m \le \underset{2}{u^m}.$$

The region, $\underset{m-1}{\tau}$, in (51.1) denotes two boundaries of this tube. This region consists of two pieces:

$$\overset{1}{\underset{m-1}{\tau}}\colon u^m = \underset{1}{u^m}, \qquad \underset{0}{u^\lambda} \le u^\lambda \le \underset{0}{u^\lambda} + du^\lambda,$$
$$\overset{2}{\underset{m-1}{\tau}}\colon u^m = \underset{2}{u^m}, \qquad \underset{0}{u^\lambda} \le u^\lambda \le \underset{0}{u^\lambda} + du^\lambda, \qquad \lambda = 1, 2, \cdots m-1.$$

We shall assume that $\underset{2}{u^m} > \underset{1}{u^m}$. Since this assumption is no restriction, the above description corresponds to Figure 49.

To establish the integration formula, we consider the integral on the left-hand side of (51.1). By use of (50.5), we may replace this integral by

$$\int_{\underset{m}{\tau}} \left(\frac{\partial}{\partial u^m} v_{\lambda\ldots\gamma}\right) du^1 \cdots du^m.$$

If we replace the multiple integral by a repeated integral and integrate along the tube in the direction of the increasing u^m = variable coordinate line, we obtain

$$\int_{\underset{m-1}{\overset{2}{\tau}}} v_{\lambda\ldots\gamma}\, du^1 \cdots du^{m-1} - \int_{\underset{m-1}{\overset{1}{\tau}}} v_{\lambda\ldots\gamma}\, du^1 \cdots du^{m-1}.$$

Now we introduce the formulas for the $(m-1)$-vectors at P and Q, (50.10), into the above integral and obtain the right-hand side of (51.1).

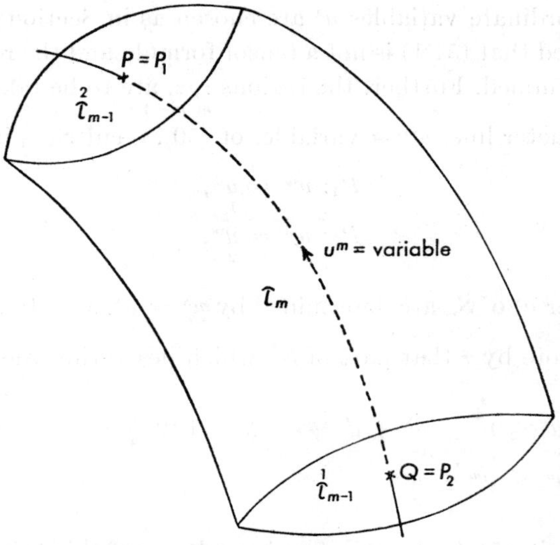

Figure 49: The Tubular Region for the Integration Formula (51.1)

By decomposing the space S_m into tubes and summing over all tubes, we obtain the general formula

$$\int_{S_m} \left(\frac{\partial}{\partial u^m} v_{\lambda\ldots\gamma}\right) f^{12\ldots m}\, d\underset{m}{\tau} = \int_{S_{m-1}} v_{\lambda\ldots\gamma} f^{12\ldots m-1}\, d\underset{m-1}{\tau}. \qquad (51.2)$$

(c) ***Tensor Formulations of the Theorems of Gauss and Stokes.*** If instead of the parameterization given by the second equation in (50.7), we use any other similar parameterization of S_{m-1}

$$u^1 = u^1(u^2, \ldots, u^m)$$

and repeat the previous calculations, we obtain[5]

$$\int_{S_m} \left(\frac{\partial}{\partial u^1} v_{\lambda\ldots\gamma}\right) f^{2\ldots m1} \underset{m}{d\tau} = \int_{S_{m-1}} v_{\lambda\ldots\gamma} f^{2\ldots m} \underset{m-1}{d\tau}.$$

Instead of the variable u^1 in the above, one may equally well use any other variable of the set $u^1, u^2, \ldots, u^m$ and write a formula corresponding to this one. Further, the m-vector, $f^{1\ldots m}$ vanishes if an index is repeated or coincides with any of the indices $m + 1, \ldots, n$. Thus, we may write

$$\int_{S_m} \left(\frac{\partial}{\partial u^\alpha} v_{\lambda\ldots\gamma}\right) f^{\underset{1}{\lambda}\ldots\underset{m-1}{\lambda}\alpha} \underset{m}{d\tau} = 0$$

where the index α is not summed and $\alpha = \underset{j}{\lambda}$, $j = 1, \ldots, m - 1$, or $m + 1, \ldots, n$. By addition of the proper n equations of the last two types, we obtain the relation

$$\int_{S_m} \left(\frac{\partial}{\partial u^\alpha} v_{\lambda\ldots\gamma}\right) f^{\underset{1}{\lambda}\ldots\underset{m-1}{\lambda}\alpha} \underset{m}{d\tau} = \int_{S_{m-1}} v_{\lambda\ldots\gamma} f^{\underset{1}{\lambda}\ldots\underset{m-1}{\lambda}} \underset{m-1}{d\tau} \qquad (51.3a)$$

where the index α is summed over the range $\alpha = 1, \ldots, n$.

We should like to write this *last formula in tensor form*. This replacement calls for considerable care. Two procedures are available: (1) We may express the integrands of (51.3a) as invariants; or (2) we may attempt to express the integrands in Cartesian coordinates. It is obvious that if the integrands are invariants then the resulting formula will be independent of the coordinate system. Further, it is obvious that if we use Cartesian coordinates for which the transformation coefficients, $\partial x^\mu / \partial\, 'x^\lambda$, are constants (Chapter VI) then

$$\frac{\partial x^\mu}{\partial\, 'x^\lambda} \int 'v^\lambda \underset{m}{d\tau} = \int \frac{\partial x^\mu}{\partial\, 'x^\lambda}\, 'v^\lambda \underset{m}{d\tau} = \int v^\mu \underset{m}{d\tau}$$

and the transform of an integral is the integral of the transformed quantity. We shall follow the second procedure and introduce Cartesian coordinates.

As a first step in this direction, we replace the tensor, $v_{\lambda\ldots\gamma}$, by an $(m - 1)$-order alternating or skew-symmetric tensor, $w_{\lambda\ldots\gamma}$, and sum on the proper number of equations of type (51.3a) in order to obtain

$$\int_{S_m} \left(\frac{\partial}{\partial u^\alpha} w_{\lambda\ldots\gamma}\right) f^{\lambda\ldots\gamma\alpha} \underset{m}{d\tau} = \int_{S_{m-1}} w_{\lambda\ldots\gamma} f^{\lambda\ldots\gamma} \underset{m-1}{d\tau}. \qquad (51.3b)$$

[5] The sign associated with $f^{2\ldots m1}$ may be positive or negative but by (50.9) a similar sign is associated with $f^{2\ldots m}$ at the point where du^1 is positive.

Since $w_{\lambda\ldots\gamma}$ has been chosen to be a skew symmetric tensor, it is easily verified by use of the rule for covariant differentiation (46.4) and the definition of the bracket used in Section 50(a) that

$$\underline{|m}\nabla_{[\alpha}w_{\lambda\ldots\gamma]} = \frac{\partial}{\partial u^\alpha} w_{\lambda\ldots\gamma} - \frac{\partial}{\partial u^\lambda} w_{\alpha\ldots\gamma} + - - -$$

The dashes in the above equation represent the alternating sum of the derivatives. Further, the integrand of the left-hand side of (51.3b) may be expressed in terms of this alternating product by noting that

$$\begin{aligned}\left(\frac{\partial}{\partial u^\alpha} w_{\lambda\ldots\gamma}\right) f^{\lambda\ldots\gamma\alpha} &= (-1)^m \left(\frac{\partial}{\partial u^\alpha} w_{\lambda\ldots\gamma}\right) f^{\alpha\lambda\ldots\gamma} \\ &= \frac{(-1)^m}{\underline{|m}}\left[\frac{\partial w_{\lambda\ldots\gamma}}{\partial u^\alpha} f^{\alpha\lambda\ldots\gamma} - \frac{\partial w_{\lambda\ldots\gamma}}{\partial u^\alpha} f^{\lambda\alpha\ldots\gamma} + - - -\right] \\ &= \frac{(-1)^m}{\underline{|m}}\left[\frac{\partial w_{\lambda\ldots\gamma}}{\partial u^\alpha} - \frac{\partial w_{\alpha\ldots\gamma}}{\partial u^\lambda} + - - -\right] f^{\alpha\lambda\ldots\gamma} \\ &= \nabla_{[\alpha}w_{\lambda\ldots\gamma]}f^{\lambda\ldots\gamma\alpha}.\end{aligned}$$

Thus, our integral may be replaced by an integral involving only *invariants*

$$\int_{S_m} \nabla_{[\alpha}w_{\lambda\ldots\gamma]} f^{\lambda\ldots\gamma\alpha}\, d\underset{m}{\tau} = \int_{S_{m-1}} w_{\lambda\ldots\gamma}f^{\lambda\ldots\gamma}\, d\underset{m-1}{\tau}. \tag{51.4}$$

Evidently, this last equation is valid in an arbitrary coordinate system and in particular in a Cartesian coordinate system, x^λ of E_n. In such a particular coordinate system, let us choose $w_{\lambda\ldots\gamma}$ so that $w_{1\ldots m-1} = \phi$, (ϕ, a scalar), and all other distinct components of $w_{\lambda\ldots\gamma}$ vanish. By use of our previous computation, we may write the integral (51.4) in Cartesian coordinates as

$$\int_{S_m} \frac{\partial\phi}{\partial x^\alpha} f^{1\ldots m-1\alpha}\, d\underset{m}{\tau} = \int_{S_{m-1}} \phi f^{1\ldots m-1}\, d\underset{m-1}{\tau}.$$

Replacing the indices $1, \ldots, m-1$ by any other set of $(m-1)$ indices and noting that $\partial\phi/\partial x^\alpha = \nabla_\alpha\phi$, we obtain the following tensor equation which is valid in all Cartesian coordinates, x^λ:

$$\int_{S_m} \nabla_\alpha\phi f^{\lambda\ldots\gamma\alpha}\, d\underset{m}{\tau} = \int_{S_{m-1}} \phi f^{\lambda\ldots\gamma}\, d\underset{m-1}{\tau}. \tag{51.5}$$

Next, we shall extend (51.5) to the case of tensors, $v_{\lambda\ldots\mu}$. First, we note that the covariant derivative of a vector, v^β, in the Cartesian coordinate systems of E_n is $\partial v^\beta/\partial x^\alpha = \nabla_\alpha v^\beta$. Now, write (51.5) for the case of three scalars, ϕ^1, ϕ^2, ϕ^3. By identifying these scalars with v^1, v^2, v^3, respectively, and replacing the derivatives of v^λ by $\nabla_\alpha v^\lambda$ we find that

$$\int_{S_m} (\nabla_\alpha v^\beta) f^{\lambda \cdots \gamma\alpha} \underset{m}{d\tau} = \int_{S_{m-1}} v^\beta f^{\lambda \cdots \gamma} \underset{m-1}{d\tau}. \tag{51.6}$$

Use of a similar technique shows that in a Euclidean space, E_n, which contains S_m and its closed boundary, S_{m-1}, we may write for any tensor, $v^{\beta \cdots \rho}$,

$$\int_{S_m} (\nabla_\alpha v^{\beta \cdots \rho}) f^{\lambda \cdots \gamma\alpha} \underset{m}{d\tau} = \int_{S_{m-1}} v^{\beta \cdots \rho} f^{\lambda \cdots \gamma} \underset{m-1}{d\tau}. \tag{51.7}$$

In case the n-dimensional space is non-Euclidean or the x^λ coordinate system is not Cartesian, these last formulas are no longer valid. Theorems for this general case are obtained by use of the basic relation (51.4).

(d) ***Reduction of the Formula (51.7) to the Theorems of Gauss and Stokes in Euclidean Three-Space.*** One may object to (51.7) on the grounds that the formula does not appear similar to the theorems of Gauss and Stokes as derived in Chapter III. We shall show that this formula reduces to the Gauss theorem (24.1), which in tensor notation is

$$\int_T (\nabla_\alpha v^{\beta \cdots \rho}) \, d\tau = \int_S n_\alpha v^{\beta \cdots \rho} \, d\sigma \tag{51.8}$$

for a space region, T, of Euclidean three-space and its closed boundary surface, S. Also, we shall show that our formula reduces to Stokes's theorem (27.1), which may be written as

$$\int_S e^{\alpha\beta\lambda} n_\beta \nabla_\lambda v^{\gamma \cdots \rho} \, d\sigma = \int_C t^\alpha v^{\gamma \cdots \rho} \, ds \tag{51.9}$$

where S is an open surface bounded by the closed curve, C.

To establish that the above results are consequences of our basic formula, we must calculate the pertinent (m) and $(m - 1)$ vectors, $f^{\lambda \cdots \mu}$, through use of the definition (50.2). First, we shall consider the m-vectors which enter into the Gauss equation. Here, we must assume that $n = m = 3$, $m - 1 = 2$. A permissible three-vector in three-space is $e^{\lambda\mu\gamma}$. Since any three-vector in three-dimensional space has only one component, the three-vector $f^{\lambda\mu\gamma}$ must be a multiple of $e^{\lambda\mu\gamma}$,

$$f^{\lambda\mu\gamma} = \omega e^{\lambda\mu\gamma}$$

where ω is a scalar or weighed scalar. To determine ω, we consider a Cartesian *orthogonal* coordinate system in three-space. If we allow the differential vectors of (50.2) to lie along the x, y, z coordinate lines of the coordinate system, then we find that $f^{123} \, d\tau = dx \, dy \, dz$. Since we may take $d\tau = dx\,dy\,dz$, the above relation shows that $f^{123} = 1$. Substituting this result into the formula for f^{123} we obtain the result, $\omega = 1$. Hence, $f^{\lambda\mu\gamma} = e^{\lambda\mu\gamma}$.

In order to determine the two-vector, $f^{\lambda\mu}$ of the surface, S_2, we use the orientation relation (50.9). By noting that $f^{\lambda\mu}$ lies in S_2 and forming the scalar product of the above three-vector (50.9) with the unit normal vector, n_λ, we obtain the result

$$f^{\lambda\mu\gamma}n_\gamma = \bar{\omega}f^{\lambda\mu} \tag{51.10}$$

where $\bar{\omega}$ is a new scalar. To evaluate $\bar{\omega}$, we allow the differential vectors of (50.6) to lie along the u,v-coordinate lines of the surface. We find that in terms of the x^λ, Cartesian orthogonal coordinates,

$$f^{\lambda\mu}\,d\sigma = \underline{|2}\, \underset{1}{dx}^{[\lambda}\, \underset{2}{dx}^{\mu]}.$$

Use of the area formula (49.3) and the theory of Section 49, shows that

$$d\sigma = \sqrt{'g}\,du\,dv,$$

$$\underset{1}{dx}^\lambda = \frac{\partial x^\lambda}{\partial u}\,du, \qquad \underset{2}{dx}^\lambda = \frac{\partial x^\lambda}{\partial v}\,dv$$

where $'g$ is the determinant of the surface metric tensor. Hence, we may reduce the above relation for $f^{\lambda\mu}$ to

$$\sqrt{'g}\,f^{\lambda\mu} = \frac{\partial x^\lambda}{\partial u}\frac{\partial x^\mu}{\partial v} - \frac{\partial x^\lambda}{\partial v}\frac{\partial x^\mu}{\partial u}.$$

Forming the scalar product of this last relation with $e_{\lambda\mu\gamma}n^\gamma$ and recalling that $e_{\lambda\mu\gamma}\dfrac{\partial x^\lambda}{\partial u}\dfrac{\partial x^\mu}{\partial v}n^\gamma\,du\,dv$ is the volume of a parallelepiped of altitude one and base area $\sqrt{'g}\,du\,dv$, we obtain

$$e_{\lambda\mu\gamma}f^{\lambda\mu}n^\gamma = 2.$$

Replacing $f^{\lambda\mu\gamma}$ in (51.10) by $e^{\lambda\mu\gamma}$ and forming the scalar product of the resulting relation with $e_{\lambda\mu\alpha}n^\alpha$, we obtain by use of the last formula the result, $\bar{\omega} = 1$.▌

To summarize: *A permissible 3-vector of three-space, in the Cartesian orthogonal coordinates x^λ, and a permissible associated 2-vector of a surface are given by the formulas*

$$f^{\lambda\mu\gamma} = e^{\lambda\mu\gamma}, \qquad f^{\lambda\mu} = e^{\lambda\mu\gamma}n_\gamma. \tag{51.11}$$

Finally, we consider the 1-vector of a closed curve C, bounding an *open* surface S, in Euclidean three-space. The determination of this vector is essential in order that one may write Stokes's theorem in the conventional form (51.9). In this case, the formula which corresponds to that for $f^{\lambda\mu}\,d\sigma$ is $f^\lambda\,ds = \underset{1}{dx^\lambda}$, where ds is the element of arc corresponding to the differential vector $\underset{1}{dx^\lambda}$ lying along the curve C. If t^λ denotes the unit tangent vector to C, then $t^\lambda = \underset{1}{dx^\lambda}/ds$ and f^λ may be written as

$$f^\lambda = t^\lambda.$$

To derive the Gauss formula from our basic relation (51.7), we substitute (51.11) into this formula. We find that

$$\int_T (\nabla_\alpha v^{\beta\cdots\rho})e^{\lambda\mu\alpha}\,d\tau = \int_S v^{\beta\cdots\rho}e^{\lambda\mu\alpha}n_\alpha\,d\sigma.$$

By forming the scalar product of the above with the constant 3-vector $e_{\lambda\mu\gamma}$ and noting that $e^{\lambda\mu\alpha}e_{\lambda\mu\gamma} = 2\delta^\alpha_\gamma$, we obtain the formula of Gauss (51.8).

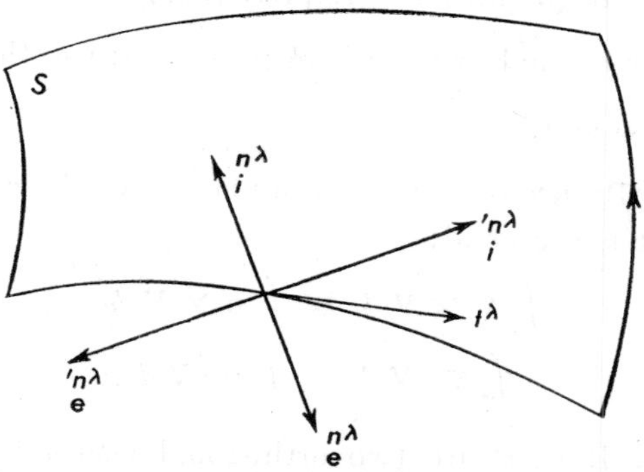

Figure 50: The Normals $\underset{i}{n^\lambda}$, $\underset{e}{n^\lambda}$ to S, and the Normals, $'\underset{i}{n^\lambda}$, $'\underset{e}{n^\lambda}$ to C in S

Similarly if we substitute the above formulas for $f^{\lambda\mu}$, f^λ into our basic formula, we obtain

$$\int_S e^{\lambda\alpha\gamma}n_\gamma\nabla_\alpha v^{\beta\cdots\rho}\,d\sigma = \int_C t^\lambda v^{\beta\cdots\rho}\,ds. \tag{51.12}$$

The last formula agrees with Stokes's formula (51.9) *except for sign.* However, this discrepancy is easily explained. Both the usual form of Stokes's formula (51.9) and our present form of this formula (51.12) contain n^λ, the unit normal vector to the surface S in Euclidean three-space. These two vectors *do not coincide but differ in sense.* To see the reason for this, we let $\underset{i}{n^\lambda}$ denote the normal vector of (51.9) and $\underset{e}{n^\lambda}$ denote this normal vector in (51.12). Further, we let $'\underset{i}{n^\lambda}$ denote the inward-drawn normal to C on S, and $'\underset{e}{n^\lambda}$ denote the outward-drawn normal to C on S. From the relations [see (51.11) and Problem 51.4]

$$f^{\lambda\mu} = e^{\lambda\mu\gamma} \underset{e}{n}_{\gamma}, \qquad f^{\lambda\mu} = 2t^{[\lambda} \,{}'\underset{e}{n}^{\mu]}$$

it follows that the *ordered* triads, t^λ, $'\underset{i}{n}^\lambda$, $\underset{i}{n}^\lambda$, and t^λ, $'\underset{e}{n}^\lambda$, $\underset{e}{n}^\lambda$ form right-hand systems when $\underset{i}{n}^\lambda$, $\underset{e}{n}^\lambda$ are sensed as in Figure 50. Thus, in (51.9), we must use one triad and in (51.12), the other. Since a basic assumption in our derivation of Stokes's formula (51.12) is that the *outward*-drawn normal, $'\underset{e}{n}^\lambda$, to C is being used, the ordered triad, t^λ, $'\underset{e}{n}^\lambda$, $\underset{e}{n}^\lambda$ is being used in (51.12). Similarly, the usual convention used in deriving the Stokes's formula of Chapter III or (51.9) is that the ordered triad, t^λ, $'\underset{i}{n}^\lambda$, $\underset{i}{n}^\lambda$ is being used (see Section 27).

Problem 51.1: Write the formula $t^\lambda = \omega f^\lambda$, where ω is a scalar, and show that $\omega = 1$ by use of (50.9). *Hint:* Express (50.9) as $f^{\lambda\mu} = 2\omega t^{[\lambda} \,{}'\underset{e}{n}^{\mu]}$ where $'\underset{e}{n}^\mu$ is the exterior normal of C with respect to S; use the relation $f^{\lambda\mu} = e^{\lambda\mu\gamma}\underset{e}{n}_\gamma$, and show $\omega = 1$.

Problem 51.2: By use of Gauss's formula (51.8), show that the following vector formulas are valid:

$$\int_T \nabla \times \mathbf{V}\, d\tau = \int_S \mathbf{n} \times \mathbf{V}\, d\sigma$$

$$\int_T \nabla \cdot \mathbf{V}\, d\tau = \int_S \mathbf{n} \cdot \mathbf{V}\, d\sigma.$$

Problem 51.3: If $\underset{1}{t}^\lambda$, $\underset{2}{t}^\lambda$ are two orthogonal vector fields on a closed surface S, express

$$\int_S v^{\beta\cdots\rho} \underset{1}{t}^{[\lambda} \underset{2}{t}^{\mu]}\, d\sigma$$

by means of an integral over the enclosed space region.

Problem 51.4: Show that a surface 2-vector may be expressed as

$$f^{\lambda\mu} = e^{\lambda\mu\gamma} n_\gamma = 2t^{[\lambda} \,{}'n^{\mu]}$$

Hence, express Stokes's formula (51.7) in terms of surface quantities t^λ, $'n^\lambda$, etc.

Problem 51.5: Show that the Gauss theorem

$$\int_{E_n} \nabla_\alpha v^{\beta\cdots\rho}\, d\tau = \int_{S_{n-1}} n_\alpha v^{\beta\cdots\rho}\, d\sigma$$

is valid for a multiply connected region, E_n, of Euclidean n-space and its closed boundary S_{n-1}.

Part III

APPLICATIONS OF TENSOR ANALYSIS

Chapter IX

THE DIFFERENTIAL GEOMETRY OF SURFACES

52. Introduction to the Theory of Surfaces in Euclidean Three-Space. In Section 26, we introduced the theory of surfaces by means of vector analysis. The present section will be concerned with a more extensive development of surface theory by use of tensor analysis. In particular, we shall be concerned with the imbedding theory. That is, we consider surfaces and their relations to the Euclidean three-dimensional space, in which these surfaces lie. Many of our results are easily generalized to $(m - 1)$-dimensional surfaces in m-dimensional Euclidean space.

(a) ***The Allowable Groups of Coordinate Transformations.*** We assume that a surface is defined by the equations[1]

$$x^k = x^k(u^\lambda), \qquad \lambda, \mu = 1, 2, \qquad k, j = 1, 2, 3 \tag{52.1}$$

whose matrix has rank two. The coordinates, x^k, are to be considered as general curvilinear coordinates in Euclidean three-space. Further, we require that the group of permissible coordinate transformations of x^k be the group G_3 [see (44.2)]. There remains the task of characterizing the allowable coordinates, u^λ, $\bar{u}^\lambda$. We shall require that the transformations

$$G_2\colon u^\lambda = u^\lambda(\bar{u}^\mu)$$

possess properties similar to those of (44.1). It can be easily verified that the coordinate transformations which possess the above properties form a group, G_2. The group G_2 induces a group A_2 [see (44.3)] with tensor analysis similar to that of A_3. That is, one can now apply the theory of Sections 44 through 45 to the study of tensors on the surface. We shall return to this study shortly.

[1] Greek indices will run from 1 through 2; Latin indices will run from 1 through 3. To distinguish between surface tensors and the *corresponding* space tensors, we shall prime such surface quantities. If it is apparent that a surface tensor (or other geometric quantity) will not be confused with the corresponding space tensor, then we *shall not prime* such a tensor. The space components of such a tensor will be denoted by Latin indices; the surface components of such a tensor will be denoted by Greek indices.

For the present, we note that imbedding theory necessitates a study of tensors under two groups: A_3 and A_2.

(b) ***The Projection Tensors, B^k_λ, B^μ_k; the Covariant and Contravariant Base Vectors, $\mathbf{e}_\lambda$, $\mathbf{e}^\lambda$; and the Metric Tensors, $'g_{\lambda\mu}$, $'g^{\lambda\mu}$.*** By differentiation of (52.1), we obtain the quantities

$$B^k_\lambda = \frac{\partial x^k}{\partial u^\lambda}. \tag{52.2}$$

It is easily seen that these quantities transform as the contravariant components of a vector (with index k) under A_3 and as the covariant components of a vector (with index λ) under A_2.

Corresponding to (37.6), our basic invariant in the present theory will be the displacement vector, $d\mathbf{R}$, *along the surface.* We assume that dx^k, $k = 1, 2, 3$ and du^λ, $\lambda = 1, 2$ correspond to this displacement. Next, we introduce covariant base vectors, $\mathbf{e}_\lambda$, along the coordinate lines, $u^\lambda =$ variable, of the surface. The magnitude of these base vectors will be specified by the condition

$$d\mathbf{R} = dx^k\mathbf{e}_k = du^\lambda\mathbf{e}_\lambda.$$

Note that the covariant base vectors, $\mathbf{e}_k$, lie along the x^k coordinate lines. Since $dx^k = B^k_\lambda\, du^\lambda$, the above equation furnishes the projection relation

$$B^k_\lambda\mathbf{e}_k = \mathbf{e}_\lambda. \tag{52.3}$$

Further, by use of the relations $\mathbf{e}_k \cdot \mathbf{e}^j = \delta^j_k$, we may solve this last equation for B^k_λ and show that

$$B^k_\lambda = \mathbf{e}_\lambda \cdot \mathbf{e}^k. \tag{52.4}$$

Corresponding to the reciprocal contravariant base vectors, $\mathbf{e}^k$, defined by (36.1), we may introduce the reciprocal contravariant base vectors, $\mathbf{e}^\lambda$, defined by

$$\mathbf{e}_\lambda \cdot \mathbf{e}^\mu = \delta^\mu_\lambda$$

where δ^μ_λ is the Kronecker delta tensor in two dimensions. The vectors, $\mathbf{e}^\lambda$, $\mathbf{e}_\lambda$, all lie in the tangent plane to the surface at a given point.

We define the tensor B^μ_k by the relations

$$B^\mu_k\mathbf{e}^k = \mathbf{e}^\mu. \tag{52.5}$$

Thus, the tensor B^μ_k represents the quantities by which $\mathbf{e}^k$ must be multiplied in order to represent $\mathbf{e}^\mu$. It should be noted that it is not possible to define a tensor, D_k^μ, such that $D_k^\mu \mathbf{e}_\mu = \mathbf{e}_k$. That is, linear combinations of the $\mathbf{e}_\mu$ will not determine all of the vectors $\mathbf{e}_k$. By forming the scalar product of (52.5) with $\mathbf{e}_j$ and using the formula $\mathbf{e}^k \cdot \mathbf{e}_j = \delta_j^k$, we obtain an explicit formula for B_k^μ,

$$B_k^\mu = \mathbf{e}^\mu \cdot \mathbf{e}_k. \tag{52.6}$$

The fact that B_k^μ is a tensor is obvious from this last relation. We have called B_λ^k, B_k^λ, projection tensors. The significance of this term can be found in equations (52.3) and (52.5). That is, *these tensors project* $\mathbf{e}_k$, $\mathbf{e}^k$ *onto the tangent plane to the surface.*

Let us consider some of the properties of these projection tensors. First, we note that B_λ^k, B_k^λ *are essentially reciprocal.* This result follows from the computation

$$B_k^\mu B_\lambda^k = \mathbf{e}^\mu \cdot \mathbf{e}_k B_\lambda^k = \mathbf{e}^\mu \cdot \mathbf{e}_\lambda = \delta_\lambda^\mu.$$

Secondly, we consider the properties of B_λ^k, B_k^λ with respect to vector and tensor fields lying on the surface. Let $\mathbf{V}$ be a vector field lying on the surface. In terms of the base vectors, we may write

$$\mathbf{V} = v^k \mathbf{e}_k = v^\lambda \mathbf{e}_\lambda, \qquad \mathbf{V} = v_k \mathbf{e}^k = v_\lambda \mathbf{e}^\lambda.$$

By use of (52.3) and (52.5), we may rewrite the above as

$$v^k \mathbf{e}_k = v^\lambda B_\lambda^k \mathbf{e}_k, \qquad v_k \mathbf{e}^k = v_\lambda B_k^\lambda \mathbf{e}^k.$$

Since the base vectors $\mathbf{e}_k$, $\mathbf{e}^k$ are independent, we obtain the formulas

$$v^k = B_\lambda^k v^\lambda, \qquad v_k = B_k^\lambda v_\lambda. \tag{52.7}$$

Further, by multiplying by B_k^μ and B_μ^k, we may express the above relations as

$$v^\mu = B_k^\mu v^k, \qquad v_\mu = B_\mu^k v_k.$$

Hence, if a vector field lies on the surface, then B_k^μ *converts the components* v^k *into* v^μ. This result is valid for tensor fields.

In order to extend this last result to vector fields lying in space and not necessarily in the tangent planes to the surface, we note that for a fixed u^λ (say u^1), the quantities, B_1^k, are the contravariant components of a vector tangent to the surface and lying along the u^2 = constant coordinate line. Similarly, the quantities, B_2^k, are the contravariant components of a vector tangent to the surface and lying along the u^1 = constant coordinate line. Hence if w_k is a vector normal to the surface at each point of the surface, then

$$w_k B_\mu^k = 0. \tag{52.8}$$

Now consider an arbitrary vector field, u_k, and let w_k denote that part of the field which is normal to the surface and let v_k denote that part of u_k which lies in the tangent plane of the surface. Evidently, we may write

$$u_k = v_k + w_k.$$

By multiplying by B^k_μ and using the results (52.7) and (52.8), we obtain

$$B^k_\mu u_k = v_\mu \tag{52.9}$$

or the *tensor* B^k_μ *projects* u_k *onto the tangent plane to the surface.*

Finally, we shall show that B^k_λ *projects the space metric tensor,* g_{jk}, *into the metric tensor,* $'g_{\lambda\mu}$, *of the surface.* By anology with (39.1), we define the covariant components of the metric tensor of the surface by

$$'g_{\lambda\mu} = \mathbf{e}_\lambda \cdot \mathbf{e}_\mu$$

where $\mathbf{e}_\lambda$ are the covariant base vectors of the surface. Eliminating $\mathbf{e}_\lambda$ from the above equation by use of (52.3) and using the result, $g_{jk} = \mathbf{e}_j \cdot \mathbf{e}_k$, we obtain the desired formula

$$'g_{\lambda\mu} = B^k_\lambda B^j_\mu g_{kj}. \tag{52.10}$$

Notice that formula (52.10) is an extension of (52.9) to tensor fields. Since $dx^k = B^k_\lambda\, du^\lambda$, we easily find that the element of arc on the surface is

$$ds^2 = g_{kj}\, dx^k\, dx^j = {}'g_{\lambda\mu}\, du^\lambda\, du^\mu.$$

The last equation plays exactly the same role in surface theory as the invariant $\mathbf{R} \cdot \mathbf{R}$ of Section 39 does in the geometry of Euclidean spaces. As in Section 39, one may define the contravariant components, $'g^{\lambda\mu}$, of the metric tensor and verify the rules for the raising and lowering of indices

$$v^\lambda = {}'g^{\lambda\mu} v_\mu, \qquad v_\lambda = {}'g_{\lambda\mu} v^\mu.$$

Further, one may easily verify the projection rule

$$'g^{\lambda\mu} = B^\lambda_k B^\mu_j g^{kj}.$$

Similarly to the theory in Section 47, one may introduce a 2-tuple consisting of two orthogonal unit vectors, $\underset{\rho}{i}^\mu$, $\rho = 1, 2$, which lie in the tangent plane to the surface at any point P, and the analogues of (47.1) and (47.2) are

$$\underset{\rho}{i}^\mu \underset{\gamma}{i}_\mu = \underset{\rho\gamma}{\delta},$$

$$\delta^\mu_\lambda = \sum_{\rho=1}^{2} \underset{\rho}{i}^\mu \underset{\rho}{i}_\lambda, \qquad \mu, \rho, \gamma = 1, 2. \tag{52.11}$$

Further, by proceeding in exactly the same manner as in Section 47, one finds the formulas

$$B^j_\mu = \sum_{\rho=1}^{2} \underset{\rho}{i^j}\underset{\rho}{i_\mu}, \qquad B^\mu_j = \sum_{\rho=1}^{2} \underset{\rho}{i^\mu}\underset{\rho}{i_j}$$

$$B^k_j = B^\mu_j B^k_\mu = \sum_{\rho=1}^{2} \underset{\rho}{i^k}\underset{\rho}{i_j} \tag{52.12}$$

$$'g_{\lambda\mu} = \sum_{\rho=1}^{2} \underset{\rho}{i_\lambda}\underset{\rho}{i_\mu}, \qquad 'g^{\lambda\mu} = \sum_{\rho=1}^{2} \underset{\rho}{i^\lambda}\underset{\rho}{i^\mu}.$$

Problem 52.1: If N^i is the unit vector normal to the surface, show that $\delta^i_k = B^i_k + N^i N_k$.

(c) ***Covariant Differentiation with Respect to the Surface.*** There are two available schemes for developing the theory. First, one may work by analogy with Sections 45 and 46. This would mean the introduction of a surface connection (a geometric object), $\Gamma^\lambda_{\mu\alpha}$, by use of which the $d\mathbf{e}_\lambda$ may be expressed in terms of $\mathbf{e}_\lambda$. Then, one could determine $\Gamma^\lambda_{\mu\alpha}$ in terms of the metric tensor of the surface, $'g_{\lambda\mu}$ [see (45.8)]. Finally, one could show that the covariant derivative [see (46.2)] defined in terms of the derivatives with respect to u^λ, and $\Gamma^\lambda_{\mu\alpha}$ possess the properties listed in Section 46(a) through (h), excluding (g). The second procedure is to attempt to generalize the notion of parallelism [of Section 46(g)] to surfaces. We shall follow Levi-Civita[2] and proceed in this second manner.

We consider two points, P and P', on a surface. Let C be some curve lying on the surface and joining P and P'. Further consider a vector $\mathbf{V}$ lying in the tangent plane to the surface at P. *Our problem is to define a vector* $\mathbf{V}'$ *at* P' *which lies in the tangent plane to the surface,* S, *at* P' *and which is parallel to* $\mathbf{V}$ *with respect to the surface.* In order to accomplish this, Levi-Civita considers the surface D which is generated by the tangent planes of S along the curve C. Consecutive tangent planes intersect in lines such as PQ which may be considered as generating the surface D. Evidently, the tangent planes to D along C coincide with the tangent planes to the surface S along C. Further, the surface D is a developable surface. That is, by rotations about successive generators (such as PQ), one may flatten D into a plane surface. If this is done, then the vector $\mathbf{V}$ will lie in this plane. Now, one may apply the well-known idea of parallelism in the plane and construct a vector $\mathbf{V}'$ at P' which is parallel to $\mathbf{V}$. By bending the plane into D, one finds the vector $\mathbf{V}'$ at P' which is parallel to $\mathbf{V}$.

[2] T. Levi-Civita, *loc. cit.*

We now carry out the analysis corresponding to the above geometric construction. Let $\boldsymbol{\omega}\, dt$ represent the infinitesimal rotation about PQ which flattens one element of the developable surface D into a plane. Evidently, $\boldsymbol{\omega}$ lies along PQ. Note, we consider P and P' sufficiently close so that the rotations about the successive generators are infinitesimal. Then by the theory of Section 7, $d\mathbf{V} = \boldsymbol{\omega} \times \mathbf{V}\, dt$. Thus, $d\mathbf{V}$, is perpendicular to both $\boldsymbol{\omega}$ and $\mathbf{V}$ and hence to the tangent plane to S at P. If δV^i

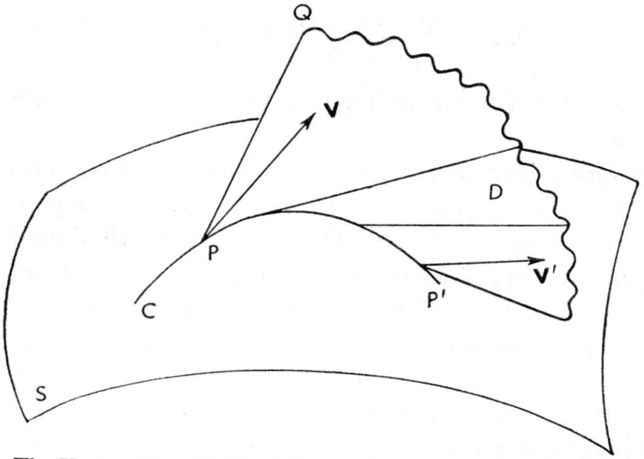

Figure 51: The Vector $\mathbf{V}'$ at P' Which Is Parallel with Respect to the Surface to the Vector $\mathbf{V}$ at P

denotes the covariant differential of the vector $\mathbf{V}$ which is tangent to S, then this condition may be expressed by

$$g_{jk}\, \delta V^j\, dx^k = 0$$

where dx^k is *any* displacement in the tangent plane. By use of (46.1) and the relation, $dx^k = B^k_\lambda\, du^\lambda$, the above equation may be written as

$$g_{jk}B^k_\lambda(dV^j + \Gamma^j_{ln}V^l\, dx^n) = 0. \tag{52.13}$$

Expressing V^j in terms of V^λ by means of $V^j = B^j_\mu V^\mu$ and substituting this result into (52.13), we find

$$g_{jk}B^k_\lambda B^j_\mu\, dV^\mu + g_{jk}B^k_\lambda V^\mu \frac{\partial B^j_\mu}{\partial u^\alpha}\, du^\alpha + \Gamma^j_{ln}B^l_\mu B^n_\alpha B^k_\lambda g_{jk} V^\mu\, du^\alpha = 0.$$

The above equation can be reduced by noting that $\Gamma^j_{ln}g_{jk} = [ln, k]$, $'g_{\lambda\mu} = g_{jk}B^k_\lambda B^j_\mu$, and hence

$$'g_{\lambda\mu}\, dV^\mu + g_{jk}B^k_\lambda V^\mu \frac{\partial B^j_\mu}{\partial u^\alpha}\, du^\alpha + [ln, k]B^l_\mu B^n_\alpha B^k_\lambda V^\mu\, du^\alpha = 0. \tag{52.14}$$

In order to further simplify, we differentiate (52.10) and find that

$$\frac{\partial\, 'g_{\lambda\mu}}{\partial u^\alpha} = B^k_\lambda g_{kj}\frac{\partial B^j_\mu}{\partial u^\alpha} + B^j_\mu g_{kj}\frac{\partial B^k_\lambda}{\partial u^\alpha} + B^k_\lambda B^j_\mu B^l_\alpha \frac{\partial g_{kj}}{\partial x^l}$$

$$\frac{\partial\, 'g_{\lambda\alpha}}{\partial u^\mu} = B^k_\lambda g_{kj}\frac{\partial B^j_\alpha}{\partial u^\mu} + B^j_\alpha g_{kj}\frac{\partial B^k_\lambda}{\partial u^\mu} + B^k_\lambda B^j_\alpha B^l_\mu \frac{\partial g_{kj}}{\partial x^l}$$

$$\frac{\partial\, 'g_{\alpha\mu}}{\partial u^\lambda} = B^k_\alpha g_{kj}\frac{\partial B^j_\mu}{\partial u^\lambda} + B^j_\mu g_{kj}\frac{\partial B^k_\alpha}{\partial u^\lambda} + B^k_\alpha B^j_\mu B^l_\lambda \frac{\partial g_{kj}}{\partial x^l}.$$

Adding the first two equations and subtracting the third equation, and noting that $\partial B^k_\alpha/\partial u^\lambda = \partial B^k_\lambda/\partial u^\alpha$, etc., we obtain

$$B^k_\lambda g_{kj}\frac{\partial B^j_\mu}{\partial u^\alpha} = [\mu\alpha, \lambda] - B^k_\lambda B^j_\mu B^l_\alpha [lj, k]. \qquad (52.15)$$

The first brackets in the right-hand side of (52.15) refer to the Christoffel symbols of the first kind for the surface variables. Eliminating $\partial B^j_\mu/\partial u^\alpha$ in (52.14) by use of (52.15), we find that

$$'g_{\lambda\mu}\, dV^\mu + [\mu\alpha, \lambda] V^\mu\, du^\alpha = 0. \qquad (52.16)$$

Multiplying (52.16) by $'g^{\beta\lambda}$, we obtain

$$dV^\beta + \Gamma^\beta_{\mu\alpha} V^\mu\, du^\alpha = 0.$$

Thus, our construction of **V** implies that $\delta V^\beta = 0$. That is, *the vanishing of the covariant differential of a vector field lying in the tangent planes to the surface implies that the vector field is defined by Levi-Civita's parallelism over the surface, and conversely.*

Since we have defined the covariant differential of a vector field lying in the tangent planes to the surface by $\delta V^\beta = dV^\beta + \Gamma^\beta_{\mu\alpha} V^\mu\, du^\alpha$, one can now consider the covariant differential of tensor fields, etc. Similarly to (46.2), one can introduce the covariant surface derivative defined by

$$'\nabla_\mu v^\lambda = \frac{\partial v^\lambda}{\partial u^\mu} + \Gamma^\lambda_{\alpha\mu} v^\alpha, \qquad \delta v^\lambda = du^\mu\, '\nabla_\mu v^\lambda.$$

The rest of this development would be exactly analogous to Section 46. Hence, we refer the reader to the problems.

Problem 52.2: Prove that the vector with surface components, $t^\alpha = du^\alpha/ds$ is a unit vector.

Problem 52.3: Consider the unit sphere with center at the origin. Let x^k denote a Cartesian orthogonal coordinate system in space and let u^λ denote the angle variables (θ, ϕ). Determine:

(1) B^k_λ;

(2) $\mathbf{e}_\lambda$, $\mathbf{e}^\lambda$;

(3) B^{μ}_{k};

(4) $'g_{\lambda\mu}$;

(5) the components of the orthogonal 2-tuple of unit vectors which lie along the base vectors $\mathbf{e}_{\lambda}$.

Problem 52.4: Determine the surface Christoffel symbols for the sphere of the above problem.

Problem 52.5: Show that the unit tangent vector field to a meridian curve of the sphere (θ = constant) is self-parallel in the sense of Levi-Civita.

Problem 52.6: Consider a surface of revolution, $z = f(r)$, and show that the tangent vector along a small circle is orthogonal to the tangent vector along a meridian curve at a given point and that the unit tangent vector field to a meridian curve is self-parallel in the sense of Levi-Civita.

Problem 52.7: Show that the space and surface components, v_{jk} and $v_{\alpha\beta}$, respectively, of a second-order tensor which lies in the tangent plane to a surface at any point P are related by: $v_{\alpha\beta} = B^j_\alpha B^k_\beta v_{jk}$.

(d) ***The Relation between the Covariant Derivatives,*** $'\nabla_\mu$, ∇_j. In this section, we shall show that *if v^j is a vector field tangent to the surface, then $'\nabla_\mu v^\lambda$ is the projection of $\nabla_j v^k$ onto the tangent planes of the surface.* That is,

$$'\nabla_\mu v^\lambda = B^j_\mu B^\lambda_k \nabla_j v^k. \tag{52.17}$$

To verify (52.17), we expand the right-hand side of this equation and find

$$B^j_\mu B^\lambda_k \nabla_j v^k = B^j_\mu B^\lambda_k \left(\frac{\partial v^k}{\partial x^j} + \Gamma^k_{jl} v^l\right) = B^\lambda_k \frac{\partial v^k}{\partial u^\mu} + \Gamma^k_{jl} B^j_\mu B^\lambda_k v^l. \tag{52.18}$$

If we differentiate $v^\lambda = B^\lambda_k v^k$, we obtain

$$B^\lambda_k \frac{\partial v^k}{\partial u^\mu} = \frac{\partial v^\lambda}{\partial u^\mu} - v^l \frac{\partial B^\lambda_l}{\partial u^\mu}.$$

Substituting this result into (52.18) and replacing v^l by $B^l_\alpha v^\alpha$, we find that

$$B^j_\mu B^\lambda_k \nabla_j v^k = \frac{\partial v^\lambda}{\partial u^\mu} - v^\alpha \left(B^l_\alpha \frac{\partial B^\lambda_l}{\partial u^\mu} - \Gamma^k_{jl} B^j_\mu B^l_\alpha B^\lambda_k\right). \tag{52.19}$$

Further, by differentiation of $B^l_\alpha B^\lambda_l = \delta^\lambda_\alpha$, we obtain

$$B^l_\alpha \frac{\partial B^\lambda_l}{\partial u^\mu} = -B^\lambda_l \frac{\partial B^l_\alpha}{\partial u^\mu}.$$

Hence, (52.19) reduces to

$$B^j_\mu B^\lambda_k \nabla_j v^k = \frac{\partial v^\lambda}{\partial u^\mu} + v^\alpha \left(B^\lambda_l \frac{\partial B^l_\alpha}{\partial u^\mu} + \Gamma^k_{jl} B^j_\mu B^l_\alpha B^\lambda_k\right).$$

From this equation, we see that the verification of (52.17) depends upon showing that

$$B_l^{\lambda} \frac{\partial B_\alpha^l}{\partial u^\mu} + \Gamma_{jl}^k B_\mu^j B_\alpha^l B_k^\lambda = \Gamma_{\mu\alpha}^\lambda. \tag{52.20}$$

To verify (52.20), we multiply (52.15) by $'g^{\lambda\nu}$ and replace $[lj, k]$ by $g_{kn}\Gamma_{lj}^n$. The resulting equation is

$$'g^{\lambda\nu} B_\lambda^k g_{kj} \frac{\partial B_\mu^j}{\partial u^\alpha} = \Gamma_{\mu\alpha}^\nu - {'g^{\lambda\nu}} B_\lambda^k B_\mu^j B_\alpha^l g_{kn} \Gamma_{lj}^n. \tag{52.21}$$

Evidently, if we can show that $'g^{\lambda\nu}B_\lambda^k g_{kj} = B_j^\nu$ then the last equation will reduce to (52.20). By multiplying the first formula of (52.12) by the last formula of (52.12), we obtain

$$'g^{\lambda\nu} B_\lambda^k = \sum_{\rho=1}^{2} \underset{\rho}{i^k} \underset{\rho}{i^\nu}.$$

Multiplying the above equation by g_{kj} and noting that $\underset{\rho}{i^k} g_{kj} = \underset{\rho}{i_j}$, we obtain through use of the second formula of (52.12)

$$'g^{\lambda\nu} B_\lambda^k g_{kj} = \sum_{\rho=1}^{2} \underset{\rho}{i_j} \underset{\rho}{i^\nu} = B_j^\nu.$$

Thus (52.21) reduces (52.20), and the verification of (52.17) is completed. The formula (52.20) should be noted since it is one of the principal formulas in the theory. In addition, it should be noted that (52.17) implies that

$$'\nabla_\mu v_\lambda = B_\mu^j B_\lambda^k \nabla_j v_k. \tag{52.22}$$

This result may be verified by noting that $v^\lambda = {'g^{\lambda\alpha}} v_\alpha$, $v^k = g^{kl} v_l$, $'g_{\lambda\mu} B_k^\lambda g^{kl} = B_\mu^l$.

With the aid of (52.17), one can immediately extend the theory relating $'\nabla_\mu$ and ∇_j to tensor fields. One method for doing this is by means of the orthogonal components [Section 47(b)] of a tensor. That is, we may express a general second-order tensor, H_{jk}, which is assumed to be tangent to the surface, by

$$H_{jk} = \sum_{\rho=1}^{2} \underset{\rho}{v_j} \underset{\rho}{w_k}$$

where $\underset{\rho}{v_j} = \sum_{\gamma=1}^{2} \underset{\rho\gamma}{H} \underset{\gamma}{i_j}$, $\underset{\rho}{w_k} = \underset{\rho}{i_k}$. Hence

$$\nabla_l H_{jk} = \sum_{\rho=1}^{2} (\nabla_l \underset{\rho}{v_j}) \underset{\rho}{w_k} + \underset{\rho}{v_j} (\nabla_l \underset{\rho}{w_k}).$$

Multiplying this last equation by $B^l_\alpha B^j_\beta B^k_\gamma$ and using (52.22), we obtain

$$B^l_\alpha B^j_\beta B^k_\gamma \nabla_l H_{jk} = \sum_{\rho=1}^{2} ('\nabla_\alpha \underset{\rho}{v_\beta}) \underset{\rho}{w_\gamma} + \underset{\rho}{v_\beta}('\nabla_\alpha \underset{\rho}{w_\gamma}).$$

But the right-hand side of the above is $'\nabla_\alpha H_{\beta\gamma}$. This leads us to the desired generalization of (52.22),

$$'\nabla_\alpha H_{\beta\gamma} = B^l_\alpha B^j_\beta B^k_\gamma \nabla_l H_{jk}.$$

The theory may be extended to tensors of any order by a similar procedure.

Again, the above theory of the relation between $'\nabla_\mu$ and ∇_j can be generalized. We shall not treat this general theory, which is due to R. Lagrange, B. L. van der Waerden, E. Bortolotti, J. A. Schouten and E. R. van Kampen. Instead, we refer the reader to some of the problems and to the literature.[3]

Problem 52.8: Prove that $'\nabla_\alpha\, 'g_{\lambda\mu} = 0$.

Problem 52.9: If the vector differentiation operator D_α is defined by $D_\alpha = B^j_\alpha \nabla_j$ (note, $D_\alpha \equiv {}'\nabla_\alpha$, when $B^j_\alpha \nabla_j$ operates on vectors in the tangent plane), show that

$$D_\alpha B^k_\lambda = \frac{\partial B^k_\lambda}{\partial u^\alpha} + \Gamma^k_{ln} B^l_\lambda B^n_\alpha - \Gamma^\gamma_{\lambda\alpha} B^k_\gamma = B^j_\alpha B^l_\lambda \nabla_j B^k_l$$

where Γ^k_{ln}, $\Gamma^\gamma_{\lambda\alpha}$ are the Christoffel symbols formed with respect to g_{jk}, $'g_{\alpha\beta}$, respectively. *Hint:* Use the orthogonal decomposition of B^k_β.

Problem 52.10: Determine $D_\alpha H^{jk\mu}_{\lambda l}$ for an arbitrary tensor $H^{jk\mu}_{\lambda l}$.

53. The Geometry of Surfaces in Euclidean Three-Space. This section will deal with some of the fundamental theorems for surfaces in Euclidean three-space. For further details, the reader should consult texts in differential geometry.

(a) ***The Frenet Formulas for Curves on a Surface.*** In Section 12, we derived the Frenet formulas for a curve C in Euclidean three-space by use of vector analysis. A similar derivation can be given by use of tensor analysis. Hence, we shall merely list these formulas in terms of our tensor notation:

$$\frac{\delta t^j}{ds} = \kappa n^j, \qquad \frac{\delta n^j}{ds} = -\kappa t^j + \tau b^j, \qquad \frac{\delta b^j}{ds} = -\tau n^j. \tag{53.1}$$

In the above formulas, t^j, is the unit vector tangent to C; n^j is the unit vector along the principal normal; b^j is the unit vector along the binormal;

[3] J. A. Schouten and D. J. Struik, *Einfuhrung in die Neueren Methoden der Differentialegeometrie*, Vol. I, P. Noordhoff, Groningen, Batavia, 1936.

κ and τ are the curvature and torsion, respectively. Further, it should be noted that the symbol, δ/ds, represents the covariant derivative along the curve. That is, $\delta/ds = (dx^k/ds)\nabla_k = t^k\nabla_k$.

If the curve C lies on a surface S, then one may determine the *Frenet formulas with respect to S of C*. To do this, we represent the unit tangent vector with respect to the surface coordinates by t^μ, $\mu = 1, 2$. Further, we represent the covariant derivative with respect to the surface and taken along the curve by

$$\frac{'\delta}{ds} = \frac{dx^\mu}{ds}\,'\nabla_\mu = t^\mu\,'\nabla_\mu.$$

Finally, we denote the unit normal vector of C, with respect to the surface, by $'n^\mu$. Note that $'n^\mu$ lies on the surface but n^j is a vector in space. Both vectors are perpendicular to t^j at any point P of C.

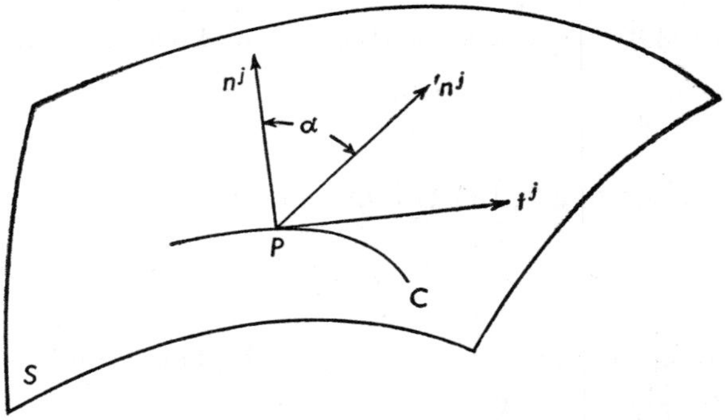

Figure 52: The Tangent Vector t^j to Curve C at P and the Unit Normal Vectors n^j, $'n^j$

Since t^μ is a unit vector, it follows that $t^\mu t_\mu = 1$. Forming the covariant derivative, $'\delta/ds$, of this relation, we obtain

$$t_\mu \frac{'\delta t^\mu}{ds} + t^\mu \frac{'\delta t_\mu}{ds} = 0.$$

Since indices may be raised or lowered through the operator, $'\delta/ds$ [see Section 46(e)], we may write the above equation as

$$t^\mu \frac{'\delta t_\mu}{ds} = 0.$$

That is, the vector $'\delta t^\mu/ds$ is orthogonal to t^μ. Hence, this vector must lie along $'n^\mu$. This may be expressed by

$$\frac{'\delta t^\mu}{ds} = {'\kappa}\,{'n^\mu} \tag{53.2}$$

where $'\kappa$ is the scalar multiplier representing the magnitude of $'\delta t^\mu/ds$. The scalar $'\kappa$ is called the *surface curvature* or the *geodesic curvature* of C and (53.2) is the first of the two Frenet formulas.

To complete the Frenet formulas with respect to the surface, we must determine $'\delta\ 'n^\mu/ds$. Since $'n^\mu$ is a unit vector, an argument similar to the above shows that the vector $'\delta\ 'n^\mu/ds$ is orthogonal to $'n^\mu$. That is, $'\delta\ 'n^\mu/ds$ lies along t^μ. Further, since $'n^\mu$ is orthogonal to t^μ, we know that $'n^\mu t_\mu = 0$. By covariant differentiation of this last relation, we obtain

$$'n^\mu \frac{'\delta t_\mu}{ds} + t_\mu \frac{'\delta\ 'n^\mu}{ds} = 0. \tag{53.3}$$

Forming the scalar product of $'n_\mu$ with (53.2), we find that

$$'n_\mu \frac{'\delta t^\mu}{ds} = {'\kappa}.$$

The equation (53.3) becomes by virtue of the above relation

$$t^\mu \frac{'\delta\ 'n_\mu}{ds} = -{'\kappa}. \tag{53.4}$$

Since $'\delta\ 'n^\mu/ds$ lies along t^μ, (53.4) implies that

$$\frac{'\delta\ 'n^\mu}{ds} = -{'\kappa} t^\mu. \tag{53.5}$$

The formula (53.5) is the second of the two Frenet formulas.

We shall now show that (see Figure 52)

$$'\kappa = \kappa \cos \alpha \tag{53.6}$$

where α is the angle between n^j and $'n^j$. That is, the *surface curvature* (*or geodesic curvature*) *of C is the projection of the space curvature, κ, onto the surface.*

To verify this result, we note that the first formula of (53.1) may be written as

$$t^k \nabla_k t_j = \kappa n_j.$$

Multiplying this equation by B^j_λ, replacing t^k by $t^\mu B^k_\mu$, and using the projection relation (52.22), we obtain

$$t^\mu\ '\nabla_\mu t_\lambda = \kappa n_j B^j_\lambda. \tag{53.7}$$

Since the left-hand side of (53.7) is $'\kappa\ 'n_\lambda$ (see 53.2), we find that

$$'\kappa\ 'n_\lambda = \kappa n_j B^j_\lambda.$$

Forming the scalar product of the last relation with $'n^\lambda$ and using the formulas: $B^j_\lambda\, 'n^\lambda = 'n^j$, $'n^j n_j = \cos\alpha$, we obtain the curvature relation (53.6).

(b) ***The Second Fundamental Tensor,*** h_{jk}. In Section 48, we showed that [see equation (48.14)]

$$\nabla_j N_l = N_j u_l + h_{jl} \tag{53.8}$$

where u_l is the curvature vector of the curves along N_j and lies in the tangent plane of the surface at a point P, and h_{jl} is a symmetric tensor which lies in the tangent plane of the surface at any point P. *The tensor,* h_{jl}, *is called the second fundamental tensor. Essentially, this tensor determines the curvature of the surface with respect to the imbedding space.*

In order to determine the properties of the tensor, h_{jl}, we consider a unit vector t^j lying on the surface and note that $N^l t_l = 0$. By covariant differentiation, we obtain

$$t^l \nabla_j N_l + N^l \nabla_j t_l = 0.$$

Forming the scalar product of the above equation with t^j and using the relations (53.1) and (53.8), we find that

$$h_{jl} t^j t^l = -\kappa N^l n_l. \tag{53.9}$$

The above equation is the basis for Meusnier's theorem: *The curvature of a normal section,* κ_N, *is related to the curvature,* κ, *of all other curves passing through a given point P of the surface and possessing the same tangent vector,* t^j, *by the relation*

$$\kappa_N = \kappa \cos\theta$$

where θ *is the angle between the normal,* n^j, *of the curve and the normal,* N^j, *of the surface.*

Before verifying this result, we shall discuss its significance. First, we consider the term, "normal section." At any point P of the surface, we introduce a unit tangent vector, t^j, to the surface. If we pass a plane through t^j and N^j, this plane will cut the surface in a curve C_N. The curve C_N is the "normal section"; κ_N is the curvature of this curve. Now, consider the family of all possible curves, C, through P with the *same* unit tangent vector, t^j. Meusnier's theorem relates the curvature, κ, of any such curves to κ_N.

To verify Meusnier's theorem, we note that the left-hand side of (53.9) depends only upon the point P under consideration and the unit vector t^j; the components, h_{jk}, of the second fundamental tensor are determined by the point P and hence, the scalar $h_{jk} t^j t^k$ is an invariant for the family of curves C. Thus, if we apply this equation to the curve C_N and a curve C, we obtain Meusnier's theorem:

$$h_{jl}t^jt^l = -\kappa \cos \theta = -\kappa_N. \tag{53.10}$$

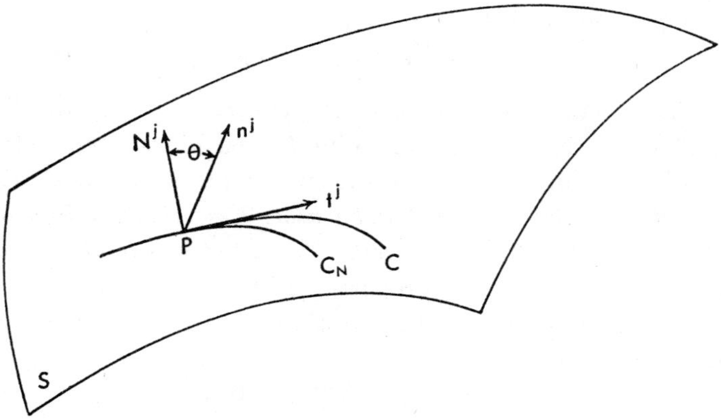

Figure 53: The Curve C and the Normal Section Curve C_N

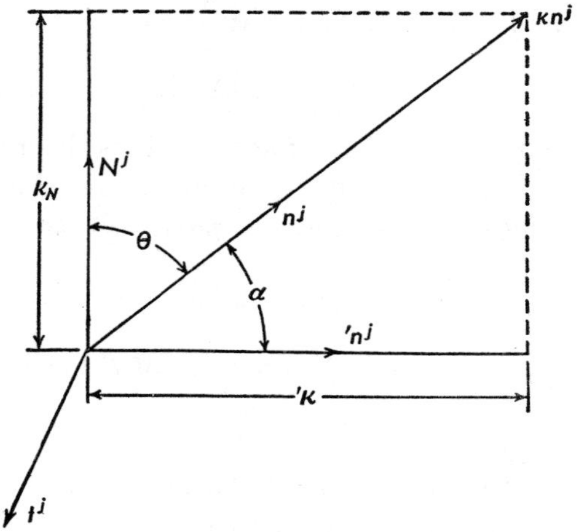

Figure 54: The Curvatures κ, $'\kappa$, κ_N

By combining equations (53.6) and (53.10), we obtain an interesting result. First, we note that the unit vector, $'n^j$, which is the principal normal of C with respect to the surface, lies on the surface and is orthogonal to t^j. Secondly, the unit vectors, N^j, n^j are both orthogonal to t^j and N^j is orthogonal to $'n^j$. Hence, the angle α between n^j and $'n^j$ is complementary to θ, the angle between N^j and n^j. Figure 54 shows the geometry of the various vectors and also the curvature relations (53.6) and (53.10). In words, *the projection of the curvature vector, κn^j, of C on $'n^j$ is the geodesic* *curvature, $'\kappa$ of C, and the projection of κn^j on N^j is the normal curvature, κ_N.* Note, the geodesic curvature depends on the curve C; the normal curvature is the same for *all curves* C with a given tangent vector, t^j.

Earlier, we found that κ_N is the curvature of the normal section, C_N. The question arises whether $'\kappa$ can be interpreted as the space curvature of some curve $'C$ passing through P and tangent to t^j. In order to determine the desired curve, $'C$, we consider the curve C, which is under discussion and lies on the surface, and project this curve into the tangent plane to the surface, S, at P. The projection is obtained by drawing lines from C parallel to N^j. We shall show that *the projected curve has the curvature $'\kappa$ and hence is the desired curve $'C$.* To do this, we note that the curve C and

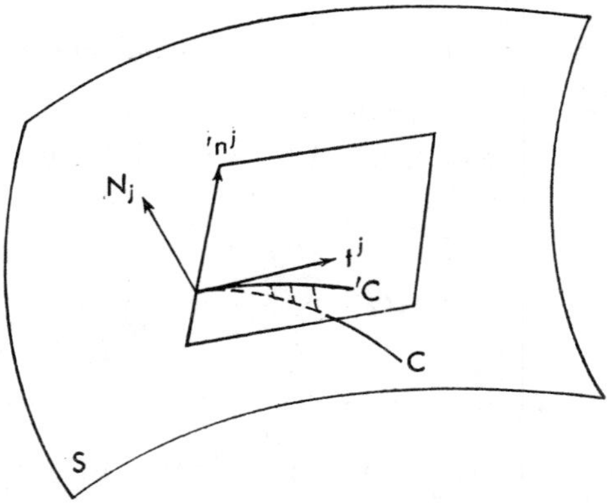

Figure 55: The Curve, C, and Its Projection, $'C$, onto the Tangent Plane

the projected curve both have the same tangent vector, t^j, and both lie on the cylindrical surface formed by the projections (see Figure 55). Further, the projected curve is a normal section of the cylindrical surface. This fact follows from: (1) The projected curve is a plane curve and hence has its curvature vector along $'n^j$; (2) $'n^j$ is normal to the cylindrical surface. Applying Meusnier's theorem to the curve C and the projected curve, we see that the curvature of the projected curve is $\kappa \cos \alpha$, where α is the angle between $'n^j$ and n^j. From (53.6), we see that this curvature is $'\kappa$ and our result is verified.

Next, we shall study the normal curvature locus, κ_N. That is, we shall allow t^j to vary through all possible positions and study the resulting curvatures, κ_N. To do this, we let $\underset{n}{i^j}$, $n = 1, 2$, denote unit vectors in the two principal directions of the symmetric second fundamental tensor, h_{jl}, and $\underset{n}{h}$, $n = 1, 2$, denote the characteristic values of this tensor. By analogy with (47.12), we may write

$$h_{jk} = \sum_{n=1}^{2} \underset{n}{h}\,\underset{n}{i_j}\,\underset{n}{i_k}. \tag{53.11}$$

Forming the scalar product of h_{jk} with $\underset{n}{i^j}\,\underset{n}{i^k}$, we obtain

$$\underset{n}{h} = h_{jk}\underset{n}{i^j}\,\underset{n}{i^k}, \qquad n = 1, 2.$$

From (53.10) and the above equation, we see that the $\underset{n}{h}$ are the negatives of the normal curvatures in the directions $\underset{n}{i^j}$. But from the theory of Section 47 we know that $\underset{n}{h}$ are the relative maxima and minima of $h_{jk}t^j t^k$. For this reason, the $\underset{n}{h}$'s are called the principal normal curvatures or, more simply, the principal curvatures.

Forming the scalar product of (53.11) with the unit tangent vector t^j, we obtain the equation

$$-\kappa_N = h_{jk}t^j t^k = \sum_{n=1}^{2} \underset{n}{h}(\underset{n}{i_j}t^j)(\underset{n}{i_k}t^k). \tag{53.12}$$

Since $\underset{n}{i^j}$, t^j are unit vectors, we may denote $\underset{1}{i_j}t^j$ by $\cos\theta$, where θ is the angle between $\underset{1}{i^j}$ and t^j. Further, $\underset{2}{i^j}$ is orthogonal to $\underset{1}{i^j}$. Hence, $\underset{2}{i_j}t^j = \sin\theta$. With the aid of this simplification, we obtain the *Euler formula*,

$$-\kappa_N = \underset{1}{h}\cos^2\theta + \underset{2}{h}\sin^2\theta. \tag{53.13}$$

This formula shows how the normal curvature varies with the angle that the unit vector, t^j, makes with the $\underset{1}{i^j}$ vector along a principal direction. Three cases arise:

$$\underset{1\,2}{hh} > 0; \text{ elliptic points,}$$

$$\underset{1\,2}{hh} < 0; \text{ hyperbolic points,}$$

$$\underset{1\,2}{hh} = 0; \text{ parabolic points.}$$

The normal curvature graphs for these cases are shown in Figure 56. It should be noted that the normal curvatures in the directions θ and $\theta + \pi$ are identical. For this reason, the graphs are plotted in the interval, $0 \leq \theta < \pi$. The principal directions are given by $\theta = 0$, $\theta = \pi/2$.

The directions for which κ_N vanishes have geometric significance. They are called *asymptotic directions* and are characterized by the condition

$$h_{jk}t^j t^k = 0. \tag{53.14}$$

From the graphs of κ_N versus θ, we see that the three cases are characterized by the following:

(1) elliptic points, no asymptotic directions;

(2) hyperbolic points, two distinct asymptotic directions which are distinct from the principal directions;

(3) parabolic points, one asymptotic direction which coincides with one of the principal directions.

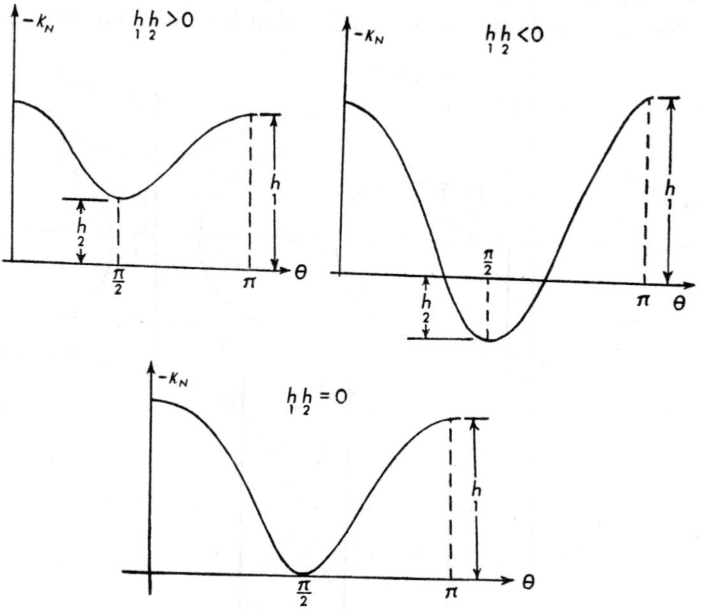

Figure 56: The Normal Curvature Locii

Finally, we introduce *conjugate pairs of directions,* $\underset{1}{t^j}$ and $\underset{2}{t^j}$. These directions are defined by the condition

$$h_{jk}\underset{1}{t^j}\underset{2}{t^k} = 0. \tag{53.15}$$

By use of (53.11), we may express the above condition as

$$\underset{1}{h}\cos\theta\cos{}'\theta + \underset{2}{h}\sin\theta\sin{}'\theta = 0$$

where θ is the angle between $\underset{1}{t}^j$ and $\underset{1}{i}^j$, and $'\theta$ is the angle between $\underset{2}{t}^j$ and $\underset{1}{i}^j$. By comparing (53.14) and (53.15), we see that *asymptotic directions are self-conjugate* ($\theta = {'\theta}$). Let us ask: Which direction is conjugate to a principal direction, say $\theta = 0$? From the equation for conjugate directions, we see that

(1) for elliptic or hyperbolic points, $'\theta = \pi/2$ is conjugate to $\theta = 0$;
(2) for parabolic points, $\underset{1}{h} = 0$, $\underset{2}{h} \neq 0$, every direction is conjugate to $\theta = 0$.

In order to obtain additional insight into the significance of the terms: *elliptic point, hyperbolic point,* and *parabolic point,* we reinterpret equation (53.13). First, we note that the negative sign before κ_N has no geometric

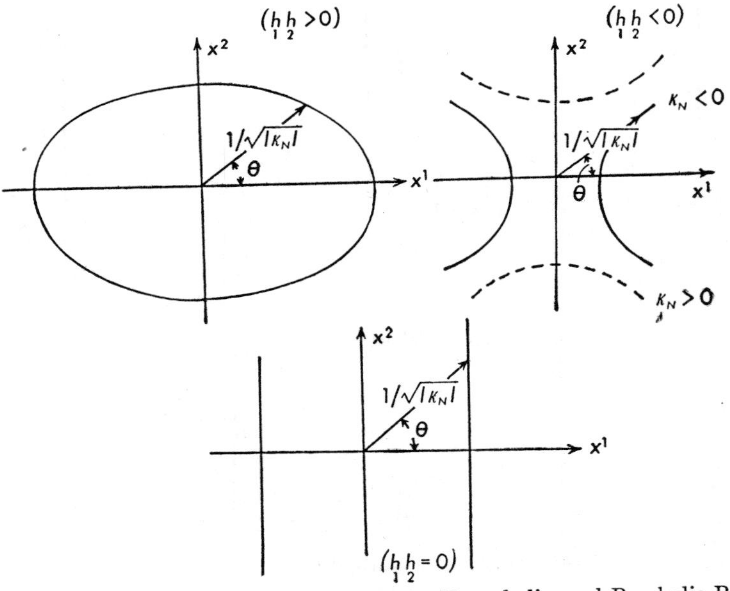

Figure 57: The Dupin Indicatrix for Elliptic, Hyperbolic, and Parabolic Points

significance. That is, if one replaces h_{jk} by $-h_{jk}$ then the negative sign disappears. Hence, let us consider the situation for $\kappa_N < 0$. If we interpret $-\kappa_N$ as the reciprocal of the square of a radial distance and form the polar coordinate analogue of (53.13), we obtain

$$1 = \underset{1}{h}(R \cos \theta)^2 + \underset{2}{h}(R \sin \theta)^2, \qquad -\kappa_N = 1/R^2.$$

Transforming to local rectangular coordinates, where $X^1 = R \cos \theta$,

$X^2 = R \sin \theta$, the equation for the curvature locus becomes

$$1 = \underset{1}{h}(X^1)^2 + \underset{2}{h}(X^2)^2. \tag{53.16}$$

Equation (53.16) is known as the *Dupin indicatrix*. The indicatrix is, evidently, a conic in the X^1,X^2-plane. It is easily seen that the three types of points mentioned previously correspond to the loci of Figure 57 (see Problem 53.3).

Problem 53.1: Show that the small circles on a sphere of radius R have geodesic curvature, $R^{-1} \cot \phi$, where ϕ is the angle between Oz and the radius vector, **R**. *Hint:* Use (53.6).

Problem 53.2:

(1) Show that the normal curvature is determined by

$$-\kappa_N = t^j t^l \nabla_j N_l;$$

(2) Show that the surface components of the second fundamental tensor satisfy the equations

$$h_{\alpha\beta} = B^l_\beta \frac{\partial N_l}{\partial u^\alpha} = g_{kl} \frac{\partial x^l}{\partial u^\beta} \frac{\partial N^k}{\partial u^\alpha};$$

(3) Hence, determine the second fundamental tensor for the surface

$$x^1 = u^1 \cos(u^2), \qquad x^2 = u^1 \sin(u^2), \qquad x^3 = f(u^1).$$

What type of surface is defined by these equations?

Problem 53.3: Show that a section of the surface by a plane parallel to the tangent plane at P and sufficiently close to this latter plane intersects the surface in a conic which is the Dupin indicatrix.

Problem 53.4 (The Theorem of Beltrami-Enneper): Show that the torsion of the two curves in the asymptotic directions at a hyperbolic point are equal in magnitude and opposite in sign.

Problem 53.5: If N^i denotes the unit normal to the surface, show that the following Gauss formula is valid:

$$D_\alpha B^j_\beta = -h_{\alpha\beta} N^j \qquad \text{or} \qquad \frac{\partial B^j_\beta}{\partial u^\alpha} + \Gamma^j_{ln} B^l_\alpha B^n_\beta - \Gamma^\gamma_{\alpha\beta} B^j_\gamma = -h_{\alpha\beta} N^j.$$

Hint: Use the result of Problem 52.1 and the definition of D_α in Problem 52.9. Further, verify the formula

$$D_\alpha N^j = h^j_{\cdot\alpha}.$$

54. Intrinsic Geometry of the Surface. We shall consider a few intrinsic surface properties. That is, the properties to be studied depend only upon the metric tensor, $'g_{\lambda\mu}$, of the surface and not upon how the surface is imbedded in three-space. As we have seen, the imbedding or curvature properties of a surface depend upon both $'g_{\lambda\mu}$ and $h_{\lambda\mu}$. However, in our present work, we shall *not* differentiate between the plane and the cylinder. Both of these surfaces are characterized by the same metric tensor, $'g_{\lambda\mu}$, and hence are equivalent. In fact, any surface is deformed by bending (without tearing) into a metrically equivalent surface. For this reason, *those tensors and invariants of the surface which depend upon* $'g_{\lambda\mu}$ *are often called bending invariants.* In the following work, we shall study two bending invariants: (1) the geodesic curvature; (2) the Riemann tensor.

(a) ***The Geodesic Curvature of a Curve and Geodesic Curves.*** In Section 53 [equation (53.2)], we introduced the surface curvature or geodesic curvature $'\kappa$ of a curve C lying on a surface. By forming the scalar product of (53.2) with the vector $'n^\mu$ which is normal to C and lies on the surface S, we find that

$$'\kappa = 'n_\mu \frac{'\delta t^\mu}{ds}.$$

Since the right-hand side of the above equation depends only upon the metric tensor, $'g_{\lambda\mu}$, and the tangent vector fields, t^μ, $'n^\mu$, *the geodesic curvature of C is a bending invariant* of the surface.

Those curves on a surface for which the *geodesic curvature,* $'\kappa$, *vanishes are called geodesics.* Such curves are the "straight lines" (curves of zero curvature) of the surface on which they lie. From Figure 54, it follows that the *space principal normal of such a curve falls along the normal to the surface.* This property can be used to define geodesics. We have refrained from doing so because of the fact that quantities external to the surface are involved in this definition. As an example of the value of this property, we note that: The meridian curves of surfaces of revolution are geodesics on these surfaces.

Another approach to geodesics is provided *by equation (53.2) when we require,* $'\kappa = 0$. This equation shows that a *geodesic curve is characterized by the condition that the unit tangent vector to the curve is moved along the curve by parallelism with respect to the surface.* That is, geodesics are self-parallel curves. It should be noted that the straight line in a plane is generated by the self-parallel displacement of a unit vector, the unit tangent vector.

Geodesic curves may be characterized by a "minimum distance" property. The exact statement of this property is the following: *Along a geodesic, the first variation of the arc length vanishes.* Roughly speaking, this result means that the distance between two points of a surface is least when taken along a geodesic joining these points. In order to verify this result, we consider the arc length integral along any curve C

$$s = \int_{t_0}^{t_1} \sqrt{'g_{\lambda\mu} \frac{du^\lambda}{dt} \frac{du^\mu}{dt}}\, dt.$$

This integral is of the type

$$s = \int_{t_0}^{t_1} f(u^\lambda, \dot{u}^\lambda)\, dt \tag{54.1}$$

where $\dot{u}^\lambda$ denotes du^λ/dt. Let $\bar{C}$ denote the curves

$$\bar{u}^\lambda = u^\lambda + \epsilon a^\lambda$$

where ϵ is a parameter and a^λ is a continuous differentiable vector function of t. This last equation defines a deformation of C. We shall require that the deformed curves $\bar{C}$ coincide with C at the initial and terminal points; that is,

$$a^\lambda(t_0) = a^\lambda(t_1) = 0.$$

If we evaluate (54.1) along a curve of the family $\bar{C}$, we obtain

$$\bar{s} = \int_{t_0}^{t_1} f(\bar{u}^\lambda, \dot{\bar{u}}^\lambda)\, dt. \tag{54.2}$$

By use of Taylor's series, we find that

$$f(\bar{u}^\lambda, \dot{\bar{u}}^\lambda) = f(u^\lambda, \dot{u}^\lambda) + \epsilon \left(\frac{\partial f}{\partial u^\lambda} a^\lambda + \frac{\partial f}{\partial \dot{u}^\lambda} \dot{a}^\lambda \right) + \cdots$$

where the dots denote terms of the second and higher order in ϵ. Substituting the Taylor series into (54.2) and ignoring the higher order terms in ϵ, we obtain the result

$$\bar{s} - s = \epsilon \int_{t_0}^{t_1} \left(\frac{\partial f}{\partial u^\lambda} a^\lambda + \frac{\partial f}{\partial \dot{u}^\lambda} \dot{a}^\lambda \right) dt. \tag{54.3}$$

If we integrate by parts and use the end-point conditions on a^λ, we see that

$$\int_{t_0}^{t_1} \frac{\partial f}{\partial \dot{u}^\lambda} \dot{a}^\lambda\, dt = - \int_{t_0}^{t_1} \frac{d}{dt} \left(\frac{\partial f}{\partial \dot{u}^\lambda} \right) a^\lambda\, dt.$$

Thus, (54.3) may be written in the form

$$\bar{s} - s = \epsilon \int_{t_0}^{t_1} \left[\frac{\partial f}{\partial u^\lambda} - \frac{d}{dt} \left(\frac{\partial f}{\partial \dot{u}^\lambda} \right) \right] a^\lambda\, dt. \tag{54.4}$$

The quantity $\bar{s} - s$ is known as the first variation of s and is usually written as $\delta s = \bar{s} - s$. Let us assume that a^λ is an arbitrary vector field. In this case, it seems reasonable to suppose that (54.4) implies *the vanishing of*

$$\frac{\partial f}{\partial u^\lambda} - \frac{d}{dt}\left(\frac{\partial f}{\partial \dot{u}^\lambda}\right) = 0 \tag{54.5}$$

is both sufficient and necessary for the vanishing of δs. This result can be derived in a rigorous manner. We refer the reader to the various texts in the calculus of variations. In fact, (54.5) are the Euler-Lagrange equations, or the first necessary condition for the minimization of the integral (54.1).

It remains to be shown that (54.5) is equivalent to the condition $'\delta t^\lambda/ds = '\kappa = 0$. We note that the function f of (54.1) is $\sqrt{'g_{\alpha\mu}\dot{u}^\alpha\dot{u}^\mu}$. Hence, the Euler-Lagrange equations reduce to

$$\frac{\dot{u}^\alpha\dot{u}^\mu}{\sqrt{'g_{\alpha\mu}\dot{u}^\alpha\dot{u}^\mu}}\frac{\partial\, 'g_{\alpha\mu}}{\partial u^\lambda} - 2\frac{d}{dt}\left(\frac{'g_{\alpha\lambda}\dot{u}^\alpha}{\sqrt{'g_{\alpha\mu}\dot{u}^\alpha\dot{u}^\mu}}\right) = 0. \tag{54.6}$$

In order to simplify the above, we note that

$$\frac{ds}{dt} = \dot{s} = \sqrt{'g_{\lambda\mu}\dot{u}^\lambda\dot{u}^\mu}$$

$$\frac{d}{dt}\left(\frac{'g_{\alpha\lambda}\dot{u}^\alpha}{\dot{s}}\right) = \frac{\left['g_{\alpha\lambda}\ddot{u}^\alpha + \frac{\partial\, 'g_{\alpha\lambda}}{\partial u^\mu}\dot{u}^\mu\dot{u}^\alpha\right]\dot{s} - 'g_{\alpha\lambda}\dot{u}^\alpha\ddot{s}}{\dot{s}^2}.$$

Substituting these relations into (54.6), we obtain

$$-2\, 'g_{\alpha\lambda}\ddot{u}^\alpha\dot{s} + \left(\frac{\partial\, 'g_{\alpha\mu}}{\partial u^\lambda} - 2\frac{\partial\, 'g_{\alpha\lambda}}{\partial u^\mu}\right)\dot{u}^\alpha\dot{u}^\mu\dot{s} + 2\, 'g_{\alpha\lambda}\dot{u}^\alpha\ddot{s} = 0. \tag{54.7}$$

Now, the surface Christoffel symbols are defined in the same manner as the space Christoffel symbols. Hence, we find that

$$\begin{aligned} 2\, 'g_{\beta\lambda}\Gamma^\beta_{\alpha\mu}\dot{u}^\alpha\dot{u}^\mu &= \left(\frac{\partial\, 'g_{\alpha\lambda}}{\partial u^\mu} + \frac{\partial\, 'g_{\mu\lambda}}{\partial u^\alpha} - \frac{\partial\, 'g_{\alpha\mu}}{\partial u^\lambda}\right)\dot{u}^\alpha\dot{u}^\mu \\ &= -\left(\frac{\partial\, 'g_{\alpha\mu}}{\partial u^\lambda} - 2\frac{\partial\, 'g_{\alpha\lambda}}{\partial u^\mu}\right)\dot{u}^\alpha\dot{u}^\mu. \end{aligned}$$

From this calculation, it follows that (54.7) is expressible as

$$['g_{\alpha\lambda}\ddot{u}^\alpha + 'g_{\beta\lambda}\Gamma^\beta_{\alpha\mu}\dot{u}^\alpha\dot{u}^\mu]\dot{s} - 'g_{\alpha\lambda}\dot{u}^\alpha\ddot{s} = 0.$$

Multiplying the above equation by $'g^{\lambda\nu}$, we obtain

$$\ddot{u}^\nu + \Gamma^\nu_{\alpha\mu}\dot{u}^\alpha\dot{u}^\mu - \dot{u}^\nu(\ddot{s}/\dot{s}) = 0. \tag{54.8}$$

The equations (54.8) are the equations of a geodesic expressed in terms of an arbitrary parameter, t. If we assume that t is the arc length parameter s, then the above equations reduce to

$$\frac{d^2u^\nu}{ds^2} + \Gamma^\nu_{\alpha\mu}\frac{du^\alpha}{ds}\frac{du^\mu}{ds} = 0. \tag{54.9}$$

Since the unit tangent vector, t^μ, to a geodesic is du^μ/ds, it follows that (54.9) may be written as $'\delta t^\mu/ds = 0$, and *the equations (54.9) determine a geodesic.*

An examination of the equations (54.9) of the geodesics reveals some further information. These equations are second-order ordinary differential equations. Hence, through each point of a surface, ∞^1 geodesics pass. Or, through any two points (sufficiently close), one may draw a single unique geodesic.

(b) ***The Riemann Tensor (the Curvature Tensor).*** In this discussion, we shall follow the treatment of Levi-Civita. First, we consider two independent vectors of the surface, $'du^\lambda$, du^λ at any point P. We shall show that *if these vectors are transferred by parallelism then they form an infinitesimal parallelogram* (see Figure 58). To verify this result, we compute

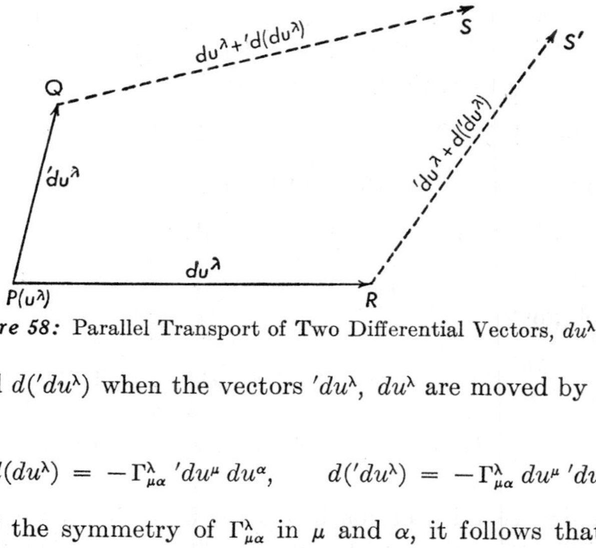

Figure 58: Parallel Transport of Two Differential Vectors, du^λ, $'du^\lambda$

$'d(du^\lambda)$ and $d('du^\lambda)$ when the vectors $'du^\lambda$, du^λ are moved by parallelism. We find

$$'d(du^\lambda) = -\Gamma^\lambda_{\mu\alpha}\,'du^\mu\,du^\alpha, \qquad d('du^\lambda) = -\Gamma^\lambda_{\mu\alpha}\,du^\mu\,'du^\alpha. \tag{54.10}$$

In view of the symmetry of $\Gamma^\lambda_{\mu\alpha}$ in μ and α, it follows that $'d(du^\lambda) = d('du^\lambda)$. Thus,

$$du^\lambda + ['du^\lambda + d('du^\lambda)] = 'du^\lambda + [du^\lambda + 'd(du^\lambda)]$$

and the point S coincides with S'. This verifies our result.

Now we consider a vector field $V^\lambda(u^\alpha)$ at $P(u^\alpha)$. We transport this field by parallelism from P to R to S and then from P to Q to S. Our problem is to determine the change in V^λ over one path as compared to the change in V^λ over the other path (see Figure 59). From the formulas for parallel transport, we find

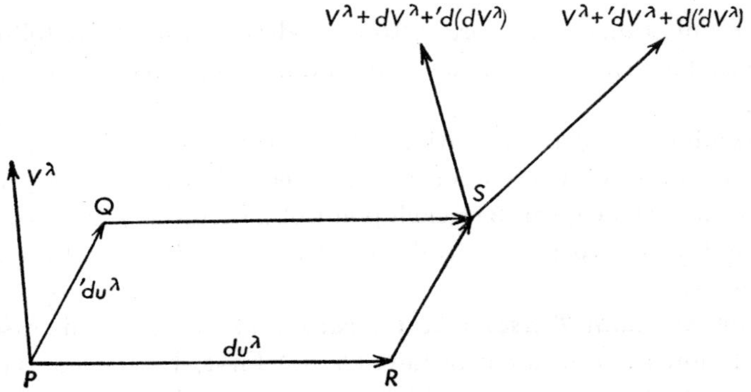

Figure 59: Parallel Transport of an Arbitrary Vector, V^λ, from P to Q to S and from P to R to S

$$dV^\lambda = -\Gamma^\lambda_{\mu\beta} V^\mu \, du^\beta; \qquad 'dV^\lambda = -\Gamma^\lambda_{\mu\beta} V^\mu \, 'du^\beta. \tag{54.11}$$

Thus at Q, the vector field V^λ becomes $V^\lambda + dV^\lambda = V^\lambda - \Gamma^\lambda_{\mu\alpha} V^\mu \, du^\alpha$, and at R, the field V^λ becomes $V^\lambda + 'dV^\lambda = V^\lambda - \Gamma^\lambda_{\mu\alpha} V^\mu \, 'du^\alpha$. If we move the vector field from Q to S, the field becomes

$$V^\lambda + dV^\lambda + 'd(V^\lambda + dV^\lambda) = V^\lambda + dV^\lambda + 'dV^\lambda + 'd(dV^\lambda).$$

Similarly, upon transporting the field from R to S, we obtain

$$V^\lambda + 'dV^\lambda + d(V^\lambda + 'dV^\lambda) = V^\lambda + 'dV^\lambda + dV^\lambda + d('dV^\lambda).$$

Hence, the difference vector of the above is $'d(dV^\lambda) - d('dV^\lambda)$. From (54.11) we obtain

$$\begin{aligned} 'd(dV^\lambda) &= -\frac{\partial \Gamma^\lambda_{\mu\alpha}}{\partial u^\beta} \, 'du^\beta \, du^\alpha V^\mu - \Gamma^\lambda_{\mu\alpha} \, 'dV^\mu \, du^\alpha - \Gamma^\lambda_{\mu\alpha} V^\mu \, 'd(du^\alpha), \\ d('dV^\lambda) &= -\frac{\partial \Gamma^\lambda_{\mu\alpha}}{\partial u^\beta} \, du^\beta \, 'du^\alpha V^\mu - \Gamma^\lambda_{\mu\alpha} \, dV^\mu \, 'du^\alpha - \Gamma^\lambda_{\mu\alpha} V^\mu d('du^\alpha). \end{aligned} \tag{54.12}$$

Subtracting the second equation in (54.12) from the first equation and simplifying with the aid of (54.10) and (54.11) we find that

$$'d(dV^\lambda) - d('dV^\lambda) = \left[\frac{\partial \Gamma^\lambda_{\mu\alpha}}{\partial u^\beta} - \frac{\partial \Gamma^\lambda_{\mu\beta}}{\partial u^\alpha} - \Gamma^\lambda_{\gamma\alpha}\Gamma^\gamma_{\mu\beta} + \Gamma^\lambda_{\gamma\beta}\Gamma^\gamma_{\mu\alpha} \right] 'du^\alpha \, du^\beta V^\mu. \tag{54.13}$$

By use of transformation theory, we can show that the expression inside the brackets in (54.13) is a fourth-order tensor. We call this tensor the Riemann tensor or the curvature tensor, and write [see Section 48(a)]

$$R^{\lambda}_{\cdot\mu\alpha\beta} = \frac{\partial \Gamma^{\lambda}_{\mu\alpha}}{\partial u^{\beta}} - \frac{\partial \Gamma^{\lambda}_{\mu\beta}}{\partial u^{\alpha}} - \Gamma^{\lambda}_{\gamma\alpha}\Gamma^{\gamma}_{\mu\beta} + \Gamma^{\lambda}_{\gamma\beta}\Gamma^{\gamma}_{\mu\alpha}. \tag{54.14}$$

The significance of the term "curvature tensor" becomes evident from the following considerations. Assume that the surface S is a plane. Then, from the geometric significance of parallel transport, it follows that

$$'d(dV^{\lambda}) - d('dV^{\lambda}) = 0.$$

This means that $R^{\lambda}_{\cdot\mu\alpha\beta}$ *vanishes for the plane*. Further, $R^{\lambda}_{\cdot\mu\alpha\beta}$ depends upon $'g_{\alpha\mu}$ and its surface derivatives. Hence, $R^{\lambda}_{\cdot\mu\alpha\beta}$ *is a bending invariant* and *vanishes for the cone, cylinder or any other surface which can be bent into a plane (the developable surfaces)*. From this argument, it seems reasonable to suppose that $R^{\lambda}_{\cdot\mu\alpha\beta}$ measures the intrinsic curvature of a surface. In some respects, the curvature tensor is a generalization to a surface of the curvature of a curve. For instance, if we draw the principal unit normals to a space curve and lay off these vectors from a common vertex, then these vectors generate a curve on a sphere. Essentially, the *ratio of the element of arc of this last curve to the element of arc of the space curve is the curvature of the curve*. If we draw the unit normals to a surface, and measure off these vectors from a common vertex, we obtain the spherical representation of the surface. *The ratio of the area of this representation to the corresponding area of the surface is related to the curvature tensor*. The verification of this result depends upon the study of the unit normal vector field of the surface.

The Riemann tensor has several interesting symmetry properties. In order to study these properties, we shall consider the Riemann tensor

$$R_{\gamma\mu\alpha\beta} = {}'g_{\gamma\lambda}R^{\lambda}_{\cdot\mu\alpha\beta}.$$

From the above relation and (54.14), it follows that this tensor is *skew-symmetric in the last two indices*. That is,

$$R_{\gamma\mu\alpha\beta} = -R_{\gamma\mu\beta\alpha}. \tag{54.15}$$

In n-dimensional space, there are n^4 possible distinct components for the tensor $R_{\gamma\mu\alpha\beta}$. However, the condition (54.15) implies that $R_{\gamma\mu\alpha\beta}$ vanishes when $\alpha = \beta$ and that only the *combinations* of α, β with $\alpha \neq \beta$ furnish different components. There are $n(n-1)/2$ distinct combinations of two indices. In virtue of (54.15), there exists at most $n^3(n-1)/2$ distinct components for the Riemann tensor. Another *skew-symmetry property of these components* is contained in the relation

$$R_{\gamma\mu\alpha\beta} = -R_{\mu\gamma\alpha\beta}. \tag{54.16}$$

To verify this relation, we note that the operator $('dd - d\,'d)$ of (54.13) behaves as an ordinary differential operator. That is,

$$('dd - d\,'d)(V^\lambda W_\lambda) = W_\lambda('dd - d\,'d)V^\lambda + V^\lambda('dd - d\,'d)W_\lambda. \tag{54.17}$$

Since $V^\lambda W_\lambda$ is a scalar, it follows from the geometric meaning of our operator that $('dd - d\,'d)(V^\lambda W_\lambda) = 0$. Further, it is easily shown by the previous methods that $('dd - d\,'d)W_\lambda = R_{\lambda\mu\alpha\beta}W^\mu\, du^\beta\, 'du^\alpha$. Hence (54.17) reduces to

$$0 = (R_{\lambda\mu\alpha\beta} + R_{\mu\lambda\alpha\beta})V^\mu W^\lambda\, 'du^\alpha\, du^\beta.$$

Since the vectors in the above equation are arbitrary, the validity of (54.16) is established. By arguing as in the previous case, we can show that now *at most* $[n(n-1)/2]^2$ *distinct components exist*. Further, it can be shown that additional relations of the type

$$R_{\gamma\mu\alpha\beta} + R_{\gamma\beta\mu\alpha} + R_{\gamma\alpha\beta\mu} = 0 \tag{54.18}$$

exist among the components. Note, (54.18) is formed by fixing the first index and cyclically permuting the remaining three indices. We shall omit the verification of this result. Finally, (54.18), (54.16), and (54.15) imply another interesting formula,

$$R_{\alpha\beta\gamma\mu} = R_{\gamma\mu\alpha\beta}. \tag{54.19}$$

That is, the components are *symmetric in the pairs of indices* α, β *and* γ, μ. This last result follows by writing (54.18) four times with cyclic permutation of the indices in each new equation. By use of (54.15) and (54.16), and by addition (or subtraction) of the four equations, one may establish this last relation.

We saw that as a consequence of (54.15) and (54.16), there exist $[n(n-1)/2]^2$ distinct components. In fact, we may imagine these components as forming a square matrix of $n(n-1)/2$ rows and columns. The relations (54.19) imply that only those components which lie on the main diagonal or to the right of this diagonal of the matrix are distinct components. The number of such terms is the sum of the arithmetic progression:

$$1 + 2 + 3 + \cdots + \frac{n(n-1)}{2} = \frac{(n^2 - n + 2)n(n-1)}{8}.$$

Further, (54.18) will contribute a new linear relation among these "distinct" components whenever γ, μ, α, β are distinct indices. There are $n(n-1)(n-2)(n-3)/\underline{|4}$ equations of this type. Hence, the number of distinct components reduces to

$$N = \frac{(n^2-n+2)(n-1)n}{8} - \frac{n(n-1)(n-2)(n-3)}{24} = \frac{n^2(n^2-1)}{12}.$$

For a surface, $n = 2$, $N = 1$; for a non-Euclidean three-space, $n = 3$, $N = 6$; for $n = 4$, $N = 20$. One might raise the question, "Are there additional linear relations between the components of $R_{\gamma\mu\alpha\beta}$?" For $n = 2$, there cannot be any other relations. This can be shown by computing $R_{\gamma\mu\alpha\beta}$ for the sphere. A simple computation shows that

$$R_{1212} = -'g/a^2, \text{ all other distinct } R_{\gamma\mu\alpha\beta} \text{ vanish},$$

where a is the radius of the sphere. In order to study $R_{\gamma\mu\alpha\beta}$ for arbitrary n, one must simplify the formula (54.14). It is evident that the terms

$$-\Gamma^{\lambda}_{\gamma\alpha}\Gamma^{\gamma}_{\mu\beta} + \Gamma^{\lambda}_{\gamma\beta}\Gamma^{\gamma}_{\mu\alpha}$$

are the complicating terms. Hence the problem arises whether a coordinate system $\bar{u}^\lambda$ exists such that at an arbitrary point, $\Gamma^{\lambda}_{\mu\alpha} = 0$. This question is treated below in Section 54(c).

(c) ***Geodesic Coordinates.*** Consider the coordinate transformation

$$u^\lambda = u^\lambda_0 + \bar{u}^\lambda + \frac{l^\lambda_{\alpha\beta}}{\underline{|2}}\bar{u}^\alpha\bar{u}^\beta + \frac{l^\lambda_{\alpha\beta\gamma}}{\underline{|3}}\bar{u}^\alpha\bar{u}^\beta\bar{u}^\gamma + \cdots \tag{54.20}$$

where $l^\lambda_{\alpha\beta}$, $l^\lambda_{\alpha\beta\gamma}$, etc., are constants which are symmetric in the lower indices and u^λ_0 are the coordinates of a point P_0 in the u^λ coordinate system. From (54.20), it follows that the coordinates of P_0 in the $\bar{u}^\lambda$ system are $\bar{u}^\lambda = 0$. Further, from this same equation we see that at P_0,

$$\frac{\partial u^\lambda}{\partial \bar{u}^\mu} = \delta^\lambda_\mu, \qquad \frac{\partial^2 u^\lambda}{\partial \bar{u}^\alpha\,\partial \bar{u}^\beta} = l^\lambda_{\alpha\beta}.$$

Evidently, we may write the formula for the transformation of $\Gamma^{\lambda}_{\alpha\beta}$ as [see (45.9)]

$$\bar{\Gamma}^{\lambda}_{\alpha\beta}\frac{\partial u^\gamma}{\partial \bar{u}^\lambda} = \Gamma^{\gamma}_{\mu\rho}\frac{\partial u^\mu}{\partial \bar{u}^\alpha}\frac{\partial u^\rho}{\partial \bar{u}^\beta} + \frac{\partial^2 u^\gamma}{\partial \bar{u}^\alpha\,\partial \bar{u}^\beta}.$$

Evaluating the above formula at P_0, we find that

$$\bar{\Gamma}^{\gamma}_{\alpha\beta} = \Gamma^{\gamma}_{\alpha\beta} + l^{\gamma}_{\alpha\beta}.$$

If we choose $l^\gamma_{\alpha\beta} = -\Gamma^\gamma_{\alpha\beta}$ then the Christoffel symbols, $\bar{\Gamma}^\gamma_{\alpha\beta}$ *will vanish at* P_0 in the $\bar{u}^\lambda$ coordinate system. In fact, this choice of $l^\gamma_{\alpha\beta}$ is both necessary and sufficient for the vanishing of $\bar{\Gamma}^\gamma_{\alpha\beta}$, and the coordinate transformation

$$u^\lambda = u^\lambda_0 + \bar{u}^\lambda - \frac{\Gamma^\lambda_{\alpha\beta})_0}{\lfloor 2} \bar{u}^\alpha \bar{u}^\beta + \cdots$$

defines a coordinate system $\bar{u}^\lambda$ with the following properties at P_0:

$$\frac{\partial u^\lambda}{\partial \bar{u}^\mu} = \delta^\lambda_\mu, \qquad \bar{\Gamma}^\lambda_{\alpha\beta} = 0. \tag{54.21}$$

In particular, the equations of Section 45 for the derivative of the metric tensor in terms of the Christoffel symbols show that at P_0 in the $\bar{u}^\lambda$ system, $\partial\, '\bar{g}_{\lambda\mu}/\partial \bar{u}^\alpha = 0$. The coordinate transformations of the type (54.21) define coordinates $\bar{u}^\lambda$ *which are called geodesic coordinates.* Since $\bar{\Gamma}^\lambda_{\alpha\beta}$ vanishes at P_0, we see that in a geodesic coordinate system, the covariant derivatives reduce to ordinary derivatives at the point P_0. The concept of geodesic coordinates may be extended in various manners. For instance, one can introduce Riemann coordinates at P, which possess the property that the equations of all geodesics through P_0 are linear in the arc length. Another extension is obtained by showing that geodesic coordinates may be introduced along a curve. That is, at all points of the curve, $\bar{\Gamma}^\lambda_{\alpha\beta} = 0$.

By use of geodesic coordinates and a simple computation, one may verify that at P_0,

$$2R_{\gamma\mu\alpha\beta} = \frac{\partial^2\, 'g_{\mu\beta}}{\partial u^\gamma\, \partial u^\alpha} + \frac{\partial^2\, 'g_{\gamma\alpha}}{\partial u^\mu\, \partial u^\beta} - \frac{\partial^2\, 'g_{\mu\alpha}}{\partial u^\gamma\, \partial u^\beta} - \frac{\partial^2\, 'g_{\gamma\beta}}{\partial u^\alpha\, \partial u^\mu}.$$

From this relation, the identities of Section 54(b) may be verified. Further, through use of geodesic coordinates, one can show that the covariant derivatives of the Riemann tensor *satisfy an identity known as Bianchi's identity*. This relation is

$$'\nabla_\gamma R^{\cdot\nu}_{\cdot\mu\alpha\beta} + {}'\nabla_\beta R^{\cdot\nu}_{\cdot\mu\gamma\alpha} + {}'\nabla_\alpha R^{\cdot\nu}_{\cdot\mu\beta\gamma} = 0.$$

To verify the Bianchi identity, we introduce geodesic coordinates at an arbitrary point P_0. Since the components of the connection $\Gamma^\lambda_{\mu\alpha}$ vanish at P_0 for these coordinates, the covariant derivative of $R^{\cdot\nu}_{\cdot\mu\alpha\beta}$ may be expressed as [see (54.14)]

$$'\nabla_\gamma R^{\cdot\nu}_{\cdot\mu\alpha\beta} = \frac{\partial^2 \Gamma^\nu_{\mu\alpha}}{\partial u^\gamma\, \partial u^\beta} - \frac{\partial^2 \Gamma^\nu_{\mu\beta}}{\partial u^\gamma\, \partial u^\alpha}.$$

By cyclically permuting the indices, γ, α, β and adding the resulting equations, we obtain the Bianchi relation.

Problem 54.1: Show that for a surface in Euclidean three-space, all $R_{\alpha\beta\lambda\mu}$ vanish except $R_{1212} = R_{2121} = -R_{2112} = -R_{1221}$. If we let $K = -R_{1212}/'g$, where $'g$ is the determinant of $'g_{\lambda\mu}$, show that

$$R_{\alpha\beta\lambda\mu} = -K\ 'g e_{\alpha\beta} e_{\lambda\mu}.$$

Determine the formula for K in terms of the metric coefficients, $'g_{\lambda\mu}$.

Problem 54.2: The integrability conditions of the Gauss formulas of Problem 53.5 are: $D_\gamma D_\alpha B^j_\beta - D_\alpha D_\gamma B^j_\beta = R^{\cdot\nu}_{\cdot\beta\gamma\alpha} B^j_\nu$. This result follows by expressing D_α in terms of $B^k_\alpha \nabla_k$ and using (48.19). Hence, show that

$$-h_{\alpha\lambda} h_{\beta\mu} + h_{\alpha\mu} h_{\beta\lambda} = R_{\alpha\beta\lambda\mu}.$$

This result is equivalent to Gauss's "Theorema Egregrium"; it shows that a specific combination of the second fundamental tensor's components are intrinsic surface invariants.

Problem 54.3: By use of geodesic coordinates, show that

$$('\nabla_\beta\ '\nabla_\alpha - '\nabla_\alpha\ '\nabla_\beta) v_{\mu\gamma} = R^{\cdot\rho}_{\cdot\mu\beta\alpha} v_{\rho\gamma} + R^{\cdot\rho}_{\cdot\gamma\beta\alpha} v_{\mu\rho}$$

where $v_{\mu\gamma}$ is a second-order tensor.

The integrability conditions of Problem 54.2 consist of the Gauss relation (as noted) and also the Mainardi-Codazzi relation

$$'\nabla_\alpha h_{\beta\mu} - '\nabla_\beta h_{\alpha\mu} = 0.$$

The importance of these relations is evident from the following fundamental theorem of surface theory: *If a positive definite fundamental tensor $'g_{\lambda\mu}$ and a symmetric tensor $h_{\lambda\mu}$ are given which satisfy the Gauss and Mainardi-Codazzi relations, then a surface is determined except for a rigid body motion.*[4]

(d) ***The Gauss-Bonnet Formula.*** We shall now derive a result which is of great importance in the theory of integral geometry and differentiable manifolds. Our method will depend upon the decomposition of a tensor [Section 48(c)] and the formula of Stokes [Section 51(c)].

Let C denote a closed curve on a surface S. Further, let t^λ (λ, $\mu = 1, 2$) denote the unit tangent vector along C; the sense of t^λ is determined by

[4] A. Duschek und A. Hochrainer, *Grundzüge der Tensorrechnung in Analytischer Darstellung*, Springer, Wein, 1950, pp. 290–293; V. Hlavaty, *Differential-geometrie der Kurven und Flächen und Tensorrechnung*, übersetzung von M. Pinl, Noordhoff, Groningen, 1939, p. 426.

the usual convention that the interior of C be on the left of an observer who moves around C (for a fuller discussion, see Chapter VIII). Finally, let $\underset{1}{i}^\lambda$, $\underset{2}{i}^\lambda$ denote unit tangent vectors along the positive directions of the orthogonal coordinate lines, u^1 = variable and u^2 = variable, respectively. Thus, along C, we may write

$$t^\lambda = \sum_{j=1}^{2} \underset{j}{a}\underset{j}{i}^\lambda, \qquad t^\lambda = \frac{du^\lambda}{ds} \tag{54.22}$$

where $\underset{j}{a}$ $(j = 1, 2)$ are the direction cosines

$$\underset{1}{a} = \cos\theta, \qquad \underset{2}{a} = \sin\theta,$$

and the variable θ is the angle between t^λ, $\underset{1}{i}^\lambda$. From (54.22), it is seen that the interior principal normal, $'n^\lambda$, to C on S is determined by

$$'n^\lambda = \sum_{j=1}^{2} \underset{j}{b}\underset{j}{i}^\lambda \tag{54.23}$$

where

$$\underset{1}{b} = -\sin\theta, \qquad \underset{2}{b} = \cos\theta.$$

With the aid of the Frenet formulas for C on S (53.2), it follows that the geodesic curvature, $'\kappa$, is determined by

$$'n^\lambda t^\mu \, '\nabla_\mu t_\lambda = '\kappa. \tag{54.24}$$

Eliminating the vectors $'n^\lambda$, t_λ in the relation (54.24) by use of (54.22) and (54.23), we obtain the equation

$$\sum_{j=1}^{2} \underset{j}{b}\frac{d\underset{j}{a}}{ds} + t^\mu \sum_{j,k=1}^{2} \underset{j}{a}\underset{k}{b}\underset{k}{i}^\lambda \, '\nabla_\mu \underset{j}{i}_\lambda = '\kappa.$$

From the definition of $\underset{j}{a}$, $\underset{j}{b}$ in terms of the angle θ, and the fact that $\underset{j}{i}^\lambda \, '\nabla_\mu \underset{j}{i}_\lambda$ vanishes and $\underset{k}{i}^\lambda \, '\nabla_\mu \underset{j}{i}_\lambda$ is skew-symmetric in j, k, the last equation becomes

$$\frac{d\theta}{ds} - t^\mu \underset{1}{i}^\lambda \, '\nabla_\mu \underset{2}{i}_\lambda = '\kappa. \tag{54.25}$$

In order to complete our derivation of the Gauss-Bonnet formula, we shall need to know formulas for the decomposition of $'\nabla_\mu \underset{1}{i}_\lambda$, $'\nabla_\mu \underset{2}{i}_\lambda$. Since the vectors $\underset{1}{i}_\lambda$, $\underset{2}{i}_\lambda$ are orthogonal to ∞^1 curves, respectively, the formula (53.8) leads to

$$\begin{aligned} {}'\nabla_\mu \underset{1}{i}_\lambda &= -\underset{2}{'\kappa}\underset{2}{i}_\mu \underset{2}{i}_\lambda + \underset{1}{'\kappa}\underset{1}{i}_\mu \underset{2}{i}_\lambda, \\ {}'\nabla_\mu \underset{2}{i}_\lambda &= -\underset{1}{'\kappa}\underset{1}{i}_\mu \underset{1}{i}_\lambda + \underset{2}{'\kappa}\underset{2}{i}_\mu \underset{1}{i}_\lambda, \end{aligned} \tag{54.26}$$

where $\underset{1}{'\kappa}$, $\underset{2}{'\kappa}$ are the geodesic curvatures of the congruences $\underset{1}{i}_\lambda$, $\underset{2}{i}_\lambda$, respectively. The relations (54.26) can be verified by noting that

$$\underset{2}{i}^\lambda\, {}'\nabla_\mu \underset{1}{i}_\lambda = -\underset{1}{i}^\lambda\, {}'\nabla_\mu \underset{2}{i}_\lambda, \qquad \underset{1}{i}^\lambda\, {}'\nabla_\mu \underset{1}{i}_\lambda = \underset{2}{i}^\lambda\, {}'\nabla_\mu \underset{2}{i}_\lambda = 0.$$

By use of (54.26), it follows that

$$(\underset{2}{i}^\beta\, {}'\nabla_\beta \underset{1}{i}_\lambda)(\underset{1}{i}^\mu\, {}'\nabla_\mu \underset{2}{i}^\lambda) = (\underset{1}{i}^\beta\, {}'\nabla_\beta \underset{1}{i}_\lambda)(\underset{2}{i}^\beta\, {}'\nabla_\beta \underset{2}{i}^\lambda) = 0. \tag{54.27}$$

Now, we integrate equation (54.25) around the curve C, evaluating the second term of the left-hand side by Stokes's theorem, and obtain the result

$$\oint d\theta + 2 \int\!\!\int_S \underset{1}{i}^{[\mu}\underset{2}{i}^{\beta]}\, {}'\nabla_\beta(\underset{1}{i}^\lambda\, {}'\nabla_\mu \underset{2}{i}_\lambda)\, d\sigma = \oint {}'\kappa\, ds. \tag{54.28}$$

By use of (54.27), we find that

$$\underset{1}{i}^{[\mu}\underset{2}{i}^{\beta]}\, {}'\nabla_\beta(\underset{1}{i}^\lambda\, {}'\nabla_\mu \underset{2}{i}_\lambda) = \frac{1}{2} R_{\alpha\lambda\beta\mu} \underset{2}{i}^\alpha \underset{1}{i}^\lambda \underset{2}{i}^\beta \underset{1}{i}^\mu.$$

Since on a surface (Problem 54.1)

$$R_{\alpha\lambda\beta\mu} = -K\, {}'g e_{\alpha\lambda} e_{\beta\mu}$$

and from the cross product relation

$$e_{\alpha\lambda} \underset{1}{i}^\alpha \underset{2}{i}^\lambda = 1/\sqrt{'g}$$

it follows that (54.28) reduces to the Gauss-Bonnet formula

$$\oint d\theta - \int\!\!\int_S K\, d\sigma = \oint {}'\kappa\, ds.$$

Problem 54.4: Show that if $\underset{j}{\phi}$ $(j = 1, 2, 3)$ represent the exterior angles of a geodesic triangle on the surface S, then

$$\int\!\!\int_S K\, d\sigma = -\sum_{j=1}^{3} \underset{j}{\phi} + 2\pi.$$

This result is usually called the Gauss-Bonnet theorem.

Problem 54.5: Show that if θ_j $(j = 1, 2, 3)$ represent the interior angles of a geodesic triangle on a surface S, then

$$\int\int_S K\, d\sigma = \sum_{j=1}^{3} \theta_j - \pi.$$

Problem 54.6: Show that for a sphere

$$\int\int_S K\, d\sigma = 4\pi,$$

and for a torus

$$\int\int_S K\, d\sigma = 0.$$

These results are of topological significance.

Problem 54.7: If l^λ is a unit vector at a point P of a surface S, and lies in the tangent plane to S at P, then if l^λ is transformed by surface parallelism around a closed curve C passing through P, the change in the angle, ϕ, between l^λ and the unit tangent vector t^λ to C is

$$\int\int_S K\, d\sigma.$$

Chapter X

INTRODUCTION TO THE THEORIES OF ELASTICITY AND VISCOUS FLUIDS

55. Introduction to the Theory of Elasticity. The theory of elasticity deals with the deformation of a continuous distribution of matter upon which external forces act. We shall discuss the theory of *finite deformations*. This means that there is only one limitation on the size of the deformations; the material must remain elastic. The following topics will be considered: the strain tensor; the stress tensor; the stress-strain relations; the equilibrium and compatibility conditions; the modifications in the theory when the gradients of the deformation vector are so "small" that a linearized theory is valid.[1] For further details, we refer the reader to the paper and text of F. D. Murnaghan[2] and the paper of A. E. Green and W. Zerna.[3] Our treatment will follow that of the latter paper.

(a) ***The Strain Tensor.*** Consider two Cartesian orthogonal coordinate systems, in which $Y^j, j = 1, 2, 3$ denote the position of the particles of the *unstrained* (or initial) material,[4] and y^j, $j = 1, 2, 3$ denote the position of the particles of the *strained* (or deformed) material. In particular, we let $\mathbf{R}(Y^j)$ denote the position vector of any particle in the unstrained state and $\mathbf{r}(y^j)$ denote the position vector of the *same* particle in the strained state. Let $\mathbf{v}(Y^j, y^j)$ denote the deformation vector

$$\mathbf{v} = \mathbf{r} - \mathbf{R} + \mathbf{C} \tag{55.1}$$

where $\mathbf{C}$ is the vector joining the origins of the Y^j, y^j systems (Figure 60). Now, we introduce curvilinear coordinates, x^α, $\alpha = 1, 2, 3$ which are attached to the body. Thus, the coordinates, x^α, of a particle in the

[1] It is more common to assume that the deformation vector and also the gradients of this vector are small.

[2] F. D. Murnaghan, "Finite Deformations of an Elastic Solid," *American Journal of Math.*, 59, 1937; *idem.*, John Wiley & Sons, New York, 1951.

[3] A. E. Green and W. Zerna, "Theory of Elasticity in General Coordinates," *London Phil. Magazine*, Seventh Series, 41, 1950.

[4] Although we shall refer to the *unstrained* material, this matter may be strained already.

unstrained material will not differ from the coordinates, x^α, of the *same* particle in the strained state. That is, we shall *assign fixed coordinates,* x^α, *to a given particle, and associate different tensors of a given type with the unstrained state (capital letters) and strained state (small letters).* This device can be explained as follows. Suppose, we wish to study the func-

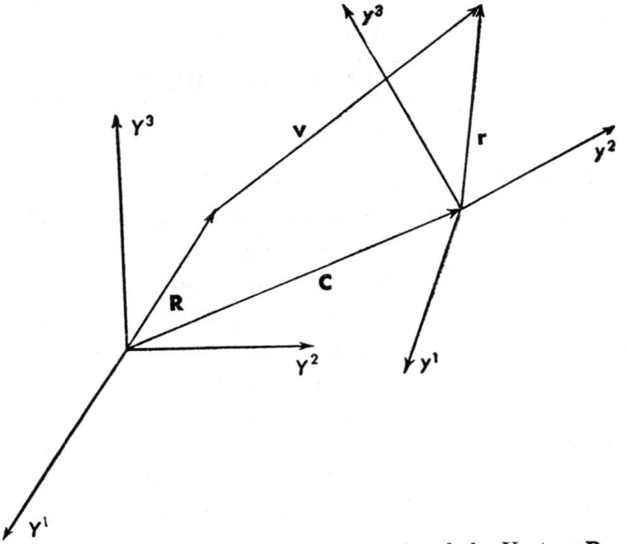

Figure 60: The Coordinate Systems, Y^i, y^i and the Vectors **R**, **r**, **C**, **v**

tion, x^2, in the two ranges, $0 \leq x \leq 1$, $1 \leq x \leq 2$. Instead, we may study the two functions, $F(x) = x^2$, $f(x) = (1 + x)^2$ in the single range, $0 \leq x \leq 1$.

Let $G_{\lambda\mu}$, $g_{\lambda\mu}$ denote the first fundamental tensors of the unstrained and the strained material, respectively. Then, if dS, ds denote the elements of arc in the two states, we may write

$$(dS)^2 = G_{\lambda\mu}\, dx^\lambda\, dx^\mu, \qquad (ds)^2 = g_{\lambda\mu}\, dx^\lambda\, dx^\mu.$$

We define the strain tensor, $e_{\lambda\mu}$, to be

$$2e_{\lambda\mu} = g_{\lambda\mu} - G_{\lambda\mu}. \tag{55.2}$$

Thus, it follows from the preceding relations that

$$(ds)^2 - (dS)^2 = 2e_{\lambda\mu}\, dx^\lambda\, dx^\mu.$$

The symmetric tensor, $e_{\lambda\mu}$, can be easily expressed in terms of the deformation vector, **v**, by use of (55.1). If $\mathbf{E}_\lambda$, $\mathbf{e}_\lambda$ denote the covariant base vectors of the coordinate system, x^λ, in the unstrained and strained states, respectively, then by use of (44.4), in the new notation, we find that

$$\mathbf{E}_\lambda = \frac{\partial \mathbf{R}}{\partial x^\lambda}, \qquad \mathbf{e}_\lambda = \frac{\partial \mathbf{r}}{\partial x^\lambda}.$$

Thus, (55.1) leads to the relation

$$e_\lambda = \mathbf{E}_\lambda + \frac{\partial \mathbf{v}}{\partial x^\lambda}. \tag{55.3}$$

Since, $g_{\lambda\mu} = \mathbf{e}_\lambda \cdot \mathbf{e}_\mu$, $G_{\lambda\mu} = \mathbf{E}_\lambda \cdot \mathbf{E}_\mu$ (see Problem 44.6), the dot product of the relation (55.3) with itself leads to the result

$$g_{\lambda\mu} = G_{\lambda\mu} + \mathbf{E}_\lambda \cdot \frac{\partial \mathbf{v}}{\partial x^\mu} + \mathbf{E}_\mu \cdot \frac{\partial \mathbf{v}}{\partial x^\lambda} + \frac{\partial \mathbf{v}}{\partial x^\lambda} \cdot \frac{\mathbf{v}\,\partial}{\partial x^\mu}. \tag{55.4}$$

By use of (46.2) and the formula preceding (46.1), we see that

$$\frac{\partial \mathbf{v}}{\partial x^\mu} = (\bar{\nabla}_\mu v^\beta)\mathbf{E}_\beta$$

where $\bar{\nabla}_\mu$ is the covariant derivative formed with respect to the metric tensor, $G_{\lambda\mu}$ of the unstrained state. Thus, from (55.4), we find that

$$g_{\lambda\mu} = G_{\lambda\mu} + \bar{\nabla}_\lambda v_\mu + \bar{\nabla}_\mu v_\lambda + (\bar{\nabla}_\mu v_\beta)(\bar{\nabla}_\lambda v^\beta). \tag{55.5}$$

By introducing the strain tensor, $e_{\lambda\mu}$, of (55.2), the above relation becomes

$$2e_{\lambda\mu} = \bar{\nabla}_\lambda v_\mu + \bar{\nabla}_\mu v_\lambda + (\bar{\nabla}_\mu v_\beta)(\bar{\nabla}_\lambda v^\beta). \tag{55.6}$$

This is the desired relation between the strain tensor and the deformation vector. If we solve (55.3) for $\mathbf{E}_\lambda$ and form the scalar product of the resulting equation with itself, we obtain

$$2e_{\lambda\mu} = \nabla_\lambda v_\mu + \nabla_\mu v_\lambda - (\nabla_\mu v_\beta)(\nabla_\lambda v^\beta) \tag{55.7}$$

instead of equation (55.6). It should be noted that in (55.7), ∇_λ is the covariant derivative formed with respect to the metric tensor, $g_{\lambda\mu}$, of the deformed state. Further, we have assumed that a vector, $\mathbf{v}$, is assigned to each point of the new medium.

So far the strain tensor has been written in general form. Let us assume that the x^α coordinate system reduces to the Y^i Cartesian orthogonal coordinate system. Then (55.6) becomes

$$2e_{ij} = \frac{\partial v_i}{\partial Y^j} + \frac{\partial v_j}{\partial Y^i} + \frac{\partial v_k}{\partial Y^i}\frac{\partial v^k}{\partial Y^j}.$$

Since $e_{\lambda\mu}$ is a symmetric tensor, one may associate with this tensor a quadric surface at any point P, $\Omega =$ constant, where [see Section 47(c)]

$\Omega = e_{\lambda\mu}X^\lambda X^\mu$. This quadric surface is called the strain quadric of Cauchy. In addition, one may introduce the principal directions of strain and the principal strains.

Problem 55.1: Determine the physical components, $^*v_\lambda$ of the displacement vector v_λ and the physical components, $^*e_{\lambda\mu}$, of the strain tensor, $e_{\lambda\mu}$, in an orthogonal curvilinear coordinate system, x^λ, [see Section 44(c)] in terms of v_λ. Show that for $\lambda \neq \mu$ in the linearized theory

$$2^*e_{\lambda\mu} = \frac{1}{\sqrt{g_{\lambda\lambda}g_{\mu\mu}}}\left[g_{\lambda\lambda}\frac{\partial}{\partial x^\mu}\left(\frac{^*v_\lambda}{\sqrt{g_{\lambda\lambda}}}\right) + g_{\mu\mu}\frac{\partial}{\partial x^\lambda}\left(\frac{^*v_\mu}{\sqrt{g_{\mu\mu}}}\right)\right].$$

Problem 55.2: Find $^*e_{\lambda\mu}$ in terms of $^*v_\lambda$ for the non-linear theory.

(b) ***The Stress Tensor.*** Consider a small curvilinear tetrahedron, of the deformed matter, which is determined by the differentials dx^α, $\alpha = 1, 2, 3$ of the coordinate lines (see Figure 61). Let $\mathbf{F}_\alpha$, $\mathbf{F}$, $\alpha = 1, 2, 3$ denote

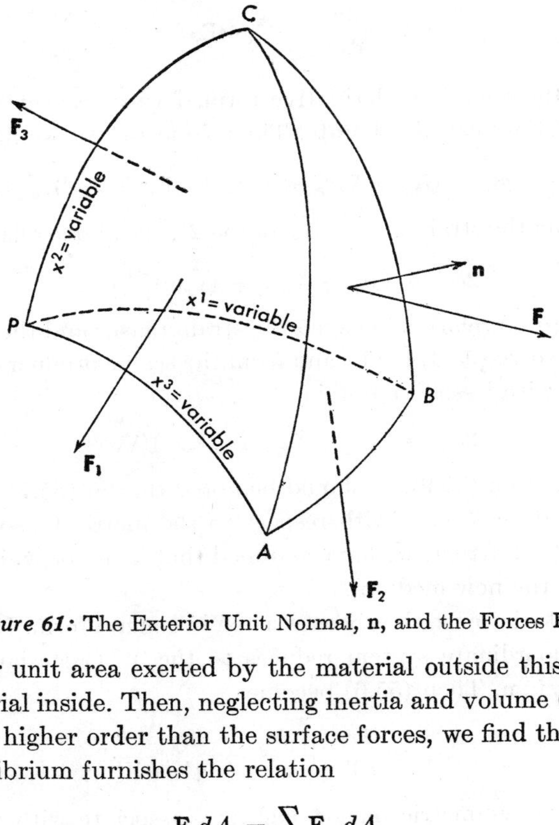

Figure 61: The Exterior Unit Normal, **n**, and the Forces **F**, $\mathbf{F}_\alpha$ ·

the force per unit area exerted by the material outside this tetrahedron on the material inside. Then, neglecting inertia and volume (body) forces which are of higher order than the surface forces, we find that the condition of equilibrium furnishes the relation

$$\mathbf{F}\,dA = \sum_\alpha \mathbf{F}_\alpha\,dA_\alpha$$

where dA, dA_α are the areas of the faces of the tetrahedron. In view of the results of Problem 49.5, we may write the above relation as

$$\mathbf{F} = \sum_\alpha n_\alpha \mathbf{F}_\alpha \sqrt{g^{\alpha\alpha}}$$

where n_α are the covariant components of the unit vector orthogonal to the face ABC, in the direction of the exterior normal (see Figure 61). Thus, it follows that $\mathbf{F}_\alpha \sqrt{g^{\alpha\alpha}}$ (not summed on α) is a *contravariant vector* and we may introduce a second order tensor, $\sigma^{\alpha\beta}$, such that

$$\sqrt{g^{\alpha\alpha}}\, \mathbf{F}_\alpha = \sigma^{\alpha\beta}\mathbf{e}_\beta \text{ (not summed on } \alpha). \tag{55.8}$$

The tensor, $\sigma^{\alpha\beta}$, is known as *the stress tensor*. From the last two equations, it follows that

$$\mathbf{F} = \sigma^{\alpha\beta} n_\alpha \mathbf{e}_\beta.$$

Thus, the components of $\mathbf{F}$, the force per unit area on face ABC, are

$$F^\beta = \sigma^{\alpha\beta} n_\alpha. \tag{55.9}$$

Equation (55.9) *shows the relation between the stress tensor and the components of the force (per unit area), F^β, acting over a surface orthogonal to the unit normal vector, n_α.*

It is easily shown that the stress tensor, $\sigma^{\alpha\beta}$, is *a symmetric tensor*. Let us determine the moments with respect to the point P of the forces acting over the various surfaces of the y^i coordinate tetrahedron. Again, we shall neglect the body and inertia forces since these forces constitute terms of order ϵ^3 whereas the surface forces are of order ϵ^2 (ϵ being the length of a side of the tetrahedron). Hence, the equilibrium of the tetrahedron necessitates that the total moment of these surface forces vanish. That is, if P is taken as the origin of the Cartesian orthogonal coordinate system, y^i, then by use of (55.9), we find that

$$\int_S e_{ijk} y^j F^k \, d\sigma = \int_S e_{ijk} y^j n_l \, \sigma^{lk} \, d\sigma = 0$$

where S is the complete surface of the tetrahedron, and y^j denotes the radius vector from P to any point of the surface. If we apply the Gauss theorem to this relation, we find that

$$\int_T e_{ijk} \left(\delta^j_l \sigma^{lk} + y^j \frac{\partial \sigma^{lk}}{\partial y^l} \right) d\tau = 0.$$

Since the derivatives of the stresses are of the same order as the stresses, for "small" y^j, the terms $y^j \, \partial\sigma^{lk}/\partial y^l$ are of higher order than σ^{lk} and may be neglected. Thus, our equation reduces to

$$\int_T e_{ijk}\sigma^{jk}\, d\tau = 0.$$

The above relation is valid for a tetrahedron whose sides are as small as we please. If the integrand is continuous, this result implies that

$$e_{ijk}\sigma^{jk} = 0$$

at each point P of the material. From this last equation, it follows that the *stress tensor is symmetric* in the y^i system and hence in all coordinate systems. One could now introduce the stress quadric of Cauchy, the principal stresses, and the principal directions of stress.

(c) ***The Equations of Motion and the Equilibrium Relations.*** By applying Newton's second law of motion to an arbitrary region of elastic material, we obtain the equations of motion of the elastic material. These equations will represent the manner in which a disturbance propagates through the material. This assumes that the displacement vector, **v**, is a function of time as well as of position. We shall use the Lagrangian approach; that is, we consider the variables Y^i, which specify the unstrained position of the body and t as the independent variables. Consider a region T of the deformed body which is bounded by a closed surface S.

We shall assume that the following forces act on T and S: (1) the body forces G^i (the external force per unit mass of T); (2) the inertia forces due to the acceleration of T; (3) the surface stresses. By differentiation of the transformation equations relating y^i and the fixed Y^i (55.1), we find that the velocity at any point P is

$$u^i = \frac{\partial y^i}{\partial t} = \frac{\partial v^i}{\partial t}.$$

Let ρ denote the density of the deformed material. From Newton's law of motion (see Section 30), we obtain in the Cartesian orthogonal coordinate system y^i

$$\frac{d}{dt}\int_T \rho\,\frac{\partial v^i}{\partial t}\, d\tau = \int_T \rho G^i\, d\tau + \int_S F^i\, d\sigma \tag{55.10}$$

where F^i represents the force per unit area exerted by the material outside of T on the surface S. If we replace F^i by an $n_k\sigma^{ik}$ and use Gauss's theorem, the right-hand side of (55.10) reduces to

$$\int_T \left(\rho G^i + \frac{\partial \sigma^{ik}}{\partial y^k}\right) d\tau.$$

Now, we transform the integrals over T in (55.10) to integrals over $\bar{T}$ in the unstrained medium [see Section 30, equations (30.3) through (30.4)]. By use of the equations of continuity (that is, $\partial(\rho J)/\partial t = 0$), we find that

$$\int_{\bar{T}} J\left[\rho\,\frac{\partial^2 v^j}{\partial t^2} - \rho G^j - \frac{\partial \sigma^{jk}}{\partial y^k}\right] d\bar{\tau} = 0.$$

In view of the fact that the region $\bar{T}$ is arbitrary, and the integrand is continuous, we may reduce these last equations to the *equations of motion*

$$\rho\,\frac{\partial^2 v^j}{\partial t^2} = \rho G^j + \frac{\partial \sigma^{jk}}{\partial y^k}. \tag{55.11}$$

It should be noted that in the left-hand side of (55.11), Y^j, t are the independent variables and in the right-hand side, y^j, t are the independent variables [see (30.5), where a similar situation arose]. To change the left-hand side of (55.11) from Lagrangian Y^j, t to Eulerian y^j, t variables, we use the chain rule of differentiation

$$\left.\frac{\partial v^j}{\partial t}\right)_{Y^j,t} = \left.\frac{\partial v^j}{\partial t}\right)_{y^j,t} + u^k\,\frac{\partial v^j}{\partial y^k}.$$

By forming $\partial^2 v^j/\partial t^2$ in terms of Eulerian variables, we obtain the desired form of the left-hand side of (55.11). The resulting relation is quite complicated. For this reason, most authors merely write ρa^j where a^j is the acceleration vector for the left-hand side of (55.11).

In curvilinear coordinates, x^λ, *the equilibrium relation* [when the left-hand side of (55.11) vanishes] becomes

$$\rho G^\lambda + \nabla_\mu \sigma^{\mu\lambda} = 0. \tag{55.12}$$

The reason for this is that (55.12) is a tensor equation which reduces to (55.11) in the case of a Cartesian orthogonal coordinate system. An alternative method for obtaining (55.11) and (55.12) is to use *tensor densities* and by this scheme to avoid using cumbersome relations such as (55.8). This is the procedure used by J. A. Schouten[5] and L. Brillouin[6], who note that the "element" of area dA_β determined by the vectors $\underset{1}{dx^\lambda}$, $\underset{2}{dx^\lambda}$ is a vector *capacity*

$$dA_\beta = e_{\beta\lambda\mu}\,\underset{1}{dx^\lambda}\,\underset{2}{dx^\mu}.$$

[5] J. A. Schouten, *Tensor Analysis for Physicists*, Oxford U. Press, New York, 1951, p. 140.

[6] L. Brillouin, *Les Tenseurs en Mecanique et en Elasticite*, Dover, New York, 1946, p. 215.

Thus, a tensor *density*, $\tau^{\alpha\beta}$ must exist such that

$$dF^{\alpha} = \tau^{\alpha\beta}\, dA_{\beta}$$

where dF^{α} is the force vector acting over dA_{β}. Then, these authors find the equilibrium relations in terms of the tensor density, $\tau^{\alpha\beta}$. We have followed the treatment of Green and Zerna which is more intuitive.

Problem 55.3: Compute the physical components $^*\sigma_{\alpha\beta}$ of the stress tensor, $\sigma_{\alpha\beta}$ in a system of orthogonal curvilinear coordinates, x^{β} and show that the equilibrium relations reduce to

$$\frac{\partial}{\partial x^{\alpha}}\,(g^*\sigma_{\alpha\alpha}) - \frac{1}{2}\sum_{\gamma=1}^{3} \frac{g^*\sigma_{\gamma\gamma}}{g_{\gamma\gamma}}\frac{\partial g_{\gamma\gamma}}{\partial x^{\alpha}} + \sum_{\alpha\neq\beta=1}^{3} \frac{\partial}{\partial x^{\alpha}}\left(\frac{g g_{\alpha\alpha}{}^*\sigma_{\alpha\beta}}{\sqrt{g_{\alpha\alpha}g_{\beta\beta}}}\right) = 0$$

where $\alpha = 1, 2, 3$ and g is the determinant of $g_{\alpha\beta}$.

Problem 55.4: In the problem of plane stress, $\sigma^{3j} = 0$, $j = 1, 2, 3$ for the case of orthogonal Cartesian coordinates y^i. Show that the equilibrium relations are satisfied by introducing the Airy stress function ϕ, where

$$\sigma^{ij} = e^{ik}e^{jl}\,\frac{\partial^2\phi}{\partial y^k\,\partial y^l}.$$

The tensor e^{ik} is the permutation tensor of two-space.

(d) ***The Stress-Strain Relations.*** One of the fundamental relations in elasticity is the law connecting the stress tensor $\sigma_{\alpha\beta}$ and the strain tensor $e_{\alpha\beta}$. *This is the generalized Hooke's law*[7]

$$\sigma_{\alpha\beta} = C_{\alpha\beta\lambda\mu}e^{\lambda\mu} \tag{55.13}$$

where $C_{\alpha\beta\lambda\mu}$ is a fourth-order tensor which is necessarily symmetric in α, β and λ, μ respectively. Due to this symmetry, it is easily shown that $C_{\alpha\beta\lambda\mu}$ has at most thirty-six distinct components. Further, $C_{\alpha\beta\lambda\mu} = C_{\lambda\mu\alpha\beta}$ and thus only twenty-one components are independent. Consider the orthogonal components of $C_{\alpha\beta\lambda\mu}$ when this tensor is referred to a triad of unit mutually orthogonal vectors at any point P (see Section 47). Evidently, this tensor has twenty-one distinct orthogonal components. By imposing the condition that $C_{\alpha\beta\lambda\mu}$ is invariant under various groups operating on the triad, one obtains various conditions on the twenty-one orthogonal components. The choice of the group depends upon the assumed symmetry of the crystal structure of the material. It has been

[7] J. A. Schouten, *Tensor Analysis for Physicists*, Oxford U. Press, London, 1951, p. 144 (3.8); I. S. Sokolnikoff, *Tensor Analysis*, John Wiley & Sons, New York, 1951, p. 318 (112.16). Sokolnikoff discusses some non-linear laws.

shown that the crystal structure can be subdivided into five main types.[8] In particular, if the crystal structure (or triad) is such that the orthogonal group (rotations plus reflections) is the operating group, then it can be shown that $C_{\alpha\beta\lambda\mu}$ has only two independent orthogonal components. The elastic materials possessing this property are said to be *isotropic.*[9] For these materials $C_{\alpha\beta\lambda\mu}$ has the form

$$C_{\alpha\beta\lambda\mu} = \lambda g_{\alpha\beta}g_{\lambda\mu} + \mu(g_{\alpha\lambda}g_{\beta\mu} + g_{\alpha\mu}g_{\beta\lambda}).$$

The scalar quantities λ, μ are constants for homogeneous materials and are called the constants of Lamé. Then equations (55.13) furnish the desired form of Hooke's law:

$$\sigma_{\alpha\beta} = \lambda(g^{\nu\rho}e_{\nu\rho})g_{\alpha\beta} + 2\mu e_{\alpha\beta}. \qquad (55.14)$$

The scalar $g^{\nu\rho}e_{\nu\rho}$ reduces to $e_{11} + e_{22} + e_{33}$ in Cartesian orthogonal coordinates and is called the dilation (change in volume per unit volume). In passing, it might be noted that in the theory of homogeneous turbulence, (see Chapter XII), a problem analogous to the determination of $C_{\alpha\beta\lambda\mu}$ arises.

Equations (55.14) can be easily solved for the strain tensor. By contracting with $g^{\alpha\beta}$ we obtain

$$g^{\alpha\beta}\sigma_{\alpha\beta} = (3\lambda + 2\mu)(g^{\alpha\beta}e_{\alpha\beta}).$$

Hence, replacing the dilation of $e_{\alpha\beta}$ by the mean stress $g^{\alpha\beta}\sigma_{\alpha\beta}$ multiplied by $(3\lambda + 2\mu)^{-1}$ in (55.14), we obtain (if $3\lambda + 2\mu \neq 0$)

$$e_{\alpha\beta} = -\frac{\lambda}{2\mu(3\lambda + 2\mu)}(g^{\nu\rho}\sigma_{\nu\rho})g_{\alpha\beta} + \frac{1}{2\mu}\sigma_{\alpha\beta}.$$

It is customary to introduce the scalar E, Young's modulus, and the scalar α, the ratio of Poisson, into this result. These scalars are defined by

$$E = \frac{\mu(3\lambda + 2\mu)}{\lambda + \mu}, \qquad \alpha = \frac{\lambda}{2(\lambda + \mu)}.$$

A simple algebraic computation shows that Hooke's law reduces to

$$e_{\gamma\beta} = \frac{1 + \alpha}{E}\sigma_{\gamma\beta} - \frac{\alpha}{E}(g^{\nu\rho}\sigma_{\nu\rho})g_{\gamma\beta}. \qquad (55.15)$$

(e) ***The Compatibility Relations.*** *The strain tensor satisfies certain relations which are called the compatibility relations.* This is due to the fact that

[8] A. E. H. Love, *Elasticity,* 4th Rev. Edition, Dover Publications, New York, p. 158.
[9] H. Jeffreys, *Cartesian Tensors,* Cambridge U. Press, London, 1931, pp. 66–70 (see formula 20).

the relations for $\nabla_\lambda v_\mu$ of (55.7) are a system of partial differential equations for v_μ. Such a system is solvable if and only if the tensor quantities, $e_{\lambda\mu}$ satisfy certain integrability conditions which are discussed in detail in Section 48. We have shown there [see Section 48(a)] that *the necessary and sufficient condition that the metric tensor, $g_{\lambda\mu}$, of a medium (say, the deformed one) determine a Euclidean space is that the Riemann tensor (54.14) of $g_{\lambda\mu}$ vanish.* Let us assume that the coordinate system x^λ in the undeformed state[10] is the *Cartesian orthogonal system, Y^i*. Hence, the components of G_{ij} in this system are

$$G_{ij} = \begin{cases} 1 \text{ if } i = j \\ 0 \text{ if } i \neq j \end{cases}. \tag{55.16}$$

If we write (55.2) in the form

$$g_{ij} = G_{ij} + 2e_{ij}$$

and form the Riemann tensor of g_{ij} using (55.16), we find after a tedious but straightforward computation that

$$R_{ijkl} = \frac{\partial^2 e_{jl}}{\partial Y^i\,\partial Y^k} + \frac{\partial^2 e_{ik}}{\partial Y^j\,\partial Y^l} - \frac{\partial^2 e_{jk}}{\partial Y^i\,\partial Y^l} - \frac{\partial^2 e_{il}}{\partial Y^j\,\partial Y^k} + g^{mn}(e_{ml,i}e_{jk,n} - e_{mk,i}e_{jl,n}) \tag{55.17}$$

where

$$e_{mk,i} = \frac{\partial e_{ik}}{\partial Y^m} + \frac{\partial e_{mi}}{\partial Y^k} - \frac{\partial e_{mk}}{\partial Y^i}.$$

The reduced cofactor, g^{mn}, can be expressed in terms of G_{ij} and e_{ij}. If we require that the Riemann tensor, R_{ijkl}, vanish then *(55.17) furnishes the six necessary and sufficient conditions that the strain tensor, e_{ij}, determines a deformed medium which is Euclidean.* Hence, there exists a deformation vector **v** which defines a mapping from a Euclidean space into a Euclidean space. In the linearized case, the terms in the parentheses in (55.17) vanish since they are of higher order than the terms involving the second derivatives of the strain tensor. The resulting *six compatibility equations* can be expressed in tensor form in the x^λ coordinates as

$$\bar\nabla_\rho\bar\nabla_\alpha e_{\mu\beta} + \bar\nabla_\mu\bar\nabla_\beta e_{\alpha\rho} - \bar\nabla_\rho\bar\nabla_\beta e_{\mu\alpha} - \bar\nabla_\mu\bar\nabla_\alpha e_{\rho\beta} = 0. \tag{55.18}$$

If, in addition, we assume that the deformation vector is small, then we may replace $\bar\nabla_\mu$ by ∇_μ in the last form of the compatibility relations.

By substituting Hooke's law for $e_{\lambda\mu}$, (55.15), into the compatibility relations, (55.17) or (55.18), we find the form of these relations in terms of the

[10] In order to show the sufficiency of this condition, we must drop the assumption that y^i determine an orthogonal Carteisan coordinate system.

stresses. These resulting equations are known as the *Beltrami-Mitchell compatibility relations.* Thus, the six stresses, $\sigma_{\lambda\mu}$, must satisfy nine relations; the three equilibrium relations and the six compatibility relations. This system of equations over-determines the stresses. For this reason, most mathematical problems in three-dimensional elasticity are stated as follows: to determine the nine quantities, $\sigma_{\lambda\mu}$, v_μ which satisfy the three equilibrium relations (55.12) and the six stress-strain relations (55.15), where the strain tensor is defined by equations of the type (55.6). However, in the case of plane strain, only one of the six compatibility relations is not identically zero. This relation and the two equilibrium relations furnish three equations for the determination of the three stress components.

Problem 55.5: Derive the compability relations (55.18) by examining the integrability conditions for (when v_μ is small)

$$2e_{\lambda\mu} = \nabla_\lambda v_\mu + \nabla_\mu v_\lambda.$$

Hint: The above relation implies that a skew-symmetric tensor, $s_{\lambda\mu}$, exists such that

$$\nabla_\lambda v_\mu = e_{\lambda\mu} + s_{\lambda\mu}.$$

Hence, we can examine the integrability conditions of

$$\nabla_\alpha \nabla_\lambda v_\mu = \nabla_\alpha e_{\lambda\mu} + \nabla_\alpha s_{\lambda\mu}.$$

Show that from the definition, $2s_{\lambda\mu} = \nabla_\lambda v_\mu - \nabla_\mu v_\lambda$, it follows that

$$\nabla_\alpha s_{\lambda\mu} = \nabla_\lambda e_{\alpha\mu} - \nabla_\mu e_{\lambda\alpha}.$$

Substituting this relation into the equation for $\nabla_\alpha \nabla_\lambda v_\mu$ and determining the the integrability condition of the latter, the compatibility relations are obtained.

(f) ***The Physical Significance of the Strain Tensor.*** Here, we consider the meaning of the strain tensor as defined by (55.2).

First, we consider the components of the type, $e_{\lambda\lambda}$, $\lambda = 1, 2, 3$, (not summed). Let the coordinate system, x^λ, coincide with the initial Cartesian orthogonal system Y^i. Consider an element with components $(dY^1, 0, 0)$. Then $dS = dY^1$ and from (55.2) and the relation

$$(ds)^2 - (dS)^2 = 2e_{\lambda\mu}\, dx^\lambda\, dx^\mu$$

we find that

$$(ds)^2 - (dS)^2 = 2e_{11}(dS)^2. \qquad \textbf{(55.19)}$$

Now, the elongation per unit length of the above element, dS, is

$$\frac{ds - dS}{dS}.$$

Hence, to a first approximation, we find from (55.19) that e_{11} *is this elongation per unit length of an element in the direction of the* Y^1 *coordinate line.* Similar interpretations are valid for e_{22}, e_{33}.

To determine the meaning of e_{12}, we proceed in a different manner. Consider the two orthogonal elements of the undeformed state:

$$(dY^1, 0, 0), \qquad (0, \delta Y^2, 0).$$

These are the orthogonal vectors, $d\mathbf{R}$, $\delta\mathbf{R}$ respectively. For these vectors, the elements of arc are, respectively,

$$dS = dY^1, \qquad \delta S = \delta Y^2.$$

Forming the corresponding differentials of (55.1), we find that

$$d\mathbf{r} = d\mathbf{v} + d\mathbf{R}, \qquad \delta\mathbf{r} = \delta\mathbf{v} + \delta\mathbf{R}.$$

If we form the scalar product of the above vectors, we obtain the relation (since $\delta\mathbf{R} \cdot d\mathbf{R} = 0$)

$$d\mathbf{r} \cdot \delta\mathbf{r} = d\mathbf{v} \cdot \delta\mathbf{v} + d\mathbf{v} \cdot \delta\mathbf{R} + \delta\mathbf{v} \cdot d\mathbf{R}. \tag{55.20}$$

The left-hand side of the above equation is

$$d\mathbf{r} \cdot \delta\mathbf{r} = \cos\theta \, ds \, \delta s$$

where ds, δs are the arc lengths of the deformed elements and θ is the angle between these elements. Since $\theta = \dfrac{\pi}{2} - \alpha$, where α is a small angle, the above relation becomes

$$d\mathbf{r} \cdot \delta\mathbf{r} = \alpha \, ds \, \delta s.$$

Let us evaluate the terms of the right-hand side of (55.20) in terms of the original Y^i orthogonal Cartesian coordinates. We find that

$$d\mathbf{v} \cdot \delta\mathbf{v} = \frac{\partial v_k}{\partial Y^i}\frac{\partial v^k}{\partial Y^j} dY^i \, \delta Y^j = \frac{\partial v_k}{\partial Y^1}\frac{\partial v^k}{\partial Y^2} dS \, \delta S,$$

$$d\mathbf{R} \cdot \delta\mathbf{v} = \frac{\partial v_k}{\partial Y^l} \delta Y^l \, dY^k = \frac{\partial v_1}{\partial Y^2} dS \, \delta S,$$

$$\delta\mathbf{R} \cdot d\mathbf{v} = \frac{\partial v_k}{\partial Y^l} dY^l \, \delta Y^k = \frac{\partial v_2}{\partial Y^1} dS \, \delta S.$$

By evaluating (55.6) when the x^λ, Y^i coordinate systems coincide or by use of the last equation of Section 55(a), we find that (55.20) reduces to

$$\alpha \, ds \, \delta s = 2e_{12} \, dS \, \delta S.$$

We have found in (55.19) that

$$ds = (1 + e_{11}) \, dS, \qquad \delta s = (1 + e_{22}) \, \delta S.$$

Thus, assuming that the strain tensor is small, $e_{ij} \ll 1$, we see that

$$\alpha = 2e_{12}.$$

That is, e_{12} *is half the change of angle between the orthogonal directions* $(dY^1, 0, 0)$, $(0, \delta Y^2, 0)$. For this reason, this component of the strain tensor is called a shearing strain. Similar interpretations are valid for the other $e_{\alpha\beta}(\alpha \neq \beta)$.

56. An Introduction to the Theory of Viscous Fluids. We have discussed briefly, in Section 30, the theory of perfect fluids. Here, we shall furnish a derivation of the equations of motion (the Navier-Stokes equations) of a viscous fluid in tensor form.

(a) ***The Navier-Stokes Equations.*** The theory of viscous fluids is more closely related to the theory of plasticity rather than to the linearized theory of elasticity. However, there are numerous analogies with elasticity theory. As in elasticity, it is assumed that due to the viscosity of the fluid, viscous symmetric stresses, $\sigma_{\alpha\beta}$, act at each point of the fluid. These stresses replace the hydraulic pressure, p. In the theory, it is customary to consider the "pressure" as the mean of the normal (tensions or compressions) viscous stresses. That is,

$$-3p = g^{\alpha\beta}\sigma_{\alpha\beta}.$$

The scalar, p, need not coincide with the pressure of the gas law, $pv = kT$, but usually one assumes that the identification is possible. In rectangular Cartesian coordinates, the above equation reduces to $-3p = \sigma_{11} + \sigma_{22} + \sigma_{33}$. As in plasticity theory, it is the over-stress tensor, $\theta_{\alpha\beta}$,

$$\theta_{\alpha\beta} = \sigma_{\alpha\beta} + pg_{\alpha\beta} \tag{56.1}$$

which plays the fundamental role in the theory. Similarly, we are concerned with the rate of strain rather than the strain, as in elasticity. This tensor is defined by [see Section 55(a)]

$$2\dot{e}_{\alpha\beta} = \nabla_\alpha v_\beta + \nabla_\beta v_\alpha \tag{56.2}$$

where v_α is the velocity vector.

The basic assumption of viscous fluid theory which replaces the Hooke's law (55.13) is that *the symmetric over-stress tensor,* $\theta_{\alpha\beta}$, *is a linear function of the rate of strain tensor,* $\dot{e}_{\alpha\beta}$. In particular, by the previously noted arguments, it can be shown that *if the fluid is homogeneous and isotropic then two constants,* λ *and* μ, *exist such that*

$$\theta_{\alpha\beta} = \lambda(g^{\nu\rho}\dot{e}_{\nu\rho})g_{\alpha\beta} + 2\mu\dot{e}_{\alpha\beta}. \tag{56.3}$$

The above relation is one of the fundamental equations for viscous fluids. This equation can be simplified by noting that the previous equations for p and $\theta_{\alpha\beta}$ imply that $g^{\nu\rho}\theta_{\nu\rho} = 0$. Forming the scalar product of (56.3) with $g^{\alpha\beta}$ and using the last result, we see that the scalar constants λ, μ are dependent, $3\lambda + 2\mu = 0$. It should be noted that this is exactly the case *not considered* in elasticity theory. If we eliminate λ from (56.3) through use of the relation between λ, μ, we obtain

$$\sigma^{\alpha\beta} = \left[-p - \frac{2}{3}\,\mu(g^{\nu\rho}\dot{e}_{\nu\rho})\right] g^{\alpha\beta} + 2\mu\dot{e}^{\alpha\beta}. \tag{56.4}$$

The scalar μ is known as the coefficient of viscosity.

A direct derivation of the equations of motion can be obtained by using the procedure of Section 30 [see equations (30.3) and (30.6)] where the tensor $g^{\alpha\beta}p$ is replaced by $-\sigma^{\alpha\beta}$. We obtain

$$\frac{\partial v^{\alpha}}{\partial t} + v^{\beta}\nabla_{\beta}v^{\alpha} = F^{\alpha} + \frac{1}{\rho}\,\nabla_{\nu}\sigma^{\nu\alpha} \tag{56.5}$$

where F^{α} is the body force (external force per unit mass). In addition, ρ and v^{α} must satisfy the equation of continuity (30.8). Expressed in tensor form, this equation is

$$\frac{\partial\rho}{\partial t} + \rho\nabla_{\alpha}v^{\alpha} + v^{\alpha}\nabla_{\alpha}\rho = 0. \tag{56.6}$$

It is customary to introduce the coefficient of kinematic viscosity, $\nu = \mu/\rho$, and replace $\sigma^{\alpha\beta}$ in the equations of motion by its expression in terms of $\dot{e}^{\alpha\beta}$ (56.4). The equations of motion become, under this substitution

$$\frac{\partial v^{\gamma}}{\partial t} + v^{\beta}\nabla_{\beta}v^{\gamma} = F^{\gamma} - \frac{g^{\gamma\beta}}{\rho}\,\nabla_{\beta}p - \frac{2}{3}\,\nu\,\nabla_{\beta}(g^{\nu\rho}\dot{e}_{\nu\rho})g^{\gamma\beta} + 2\nu\,\nabla_{\beta}\dot{e}^{\gamma\beta}.$$

To simplify the above, we must evaluate $\nabla_{\alpha}\dot{e}_{\lambda\mu}$. From the definition of $\dot{e}_{\lambda\mu}$ (56.2), it follows that $2\nabla_{\alpha}\dot{e}_{\lambda\mu} = \nabla_{\alpha}\nabla_{\lambda}v_{\mu} + \nabla_{\alpha}\nabla_{\mu}v_{\lambda}$. Forming the scalar product of this last equation with $(g^{\gamma\lambda}g^{\mu\alpha})$, we obtain

$$2\nabla_{\alpha}\dot{e}^{\gamma\alpha} = 2g^{\gamma\lambda}g^{\mu\alpha}\nabla_{\alpha}\dot{e}_{\lambda\mu} = g^{\gamma\lambda}\nabla_{\lambda}(g^{\mu\alpha}\nabla_{\alpha}v_{\mu}) + \nabla^{2}v^{\gamma}$$

where ∇^2 is the generalized Laplacian operator, $g^{\mu\alpha}\nabla_{\mu}\nabla_{\alpha}$. Since $g^{\alpha\beta}\nabla_{\alpha}v_{\beta} = g^{\alpha\beta}\dot{e}_{\alpha\beta}$, we find through use of the above relation for $\nabla_{\alpha}\dot{e}^{\gamma\alpha}$ that the equations of motion reduce to

$$\frac{\partial v^{\gamma}}{\partial t} + v^{\beta}\nabla_{\beta}v^{\gamma} = F^{\gamma} - \frac{g^{\gamma\beta}}{\rho}\,\nabla_{\beta}p + \frac{\nu}{3}\,\nabla_{\beta}(g^{\nu\rho}\dot{e}_{\nu\rho})g^{\beta\gamma} + \nu\,\nabla^{2}v^{\gamma}. \tag{56.7}$$

This last equation is called *the Navier-Stokes equation.* In particular if the fluid is incompressible ($\rho = c$) then the continuity relation shows that $\nabla_\alpha v^\alpha = g^{\alpha\beta}\dot{e}_{\alpha\beta} = 0$. Hence, the Navier-Stokes equation reduces to

$$\frac{\partial v_\alpha}{\partial t} + v^\beta \nabla_\beta v_\alpha = F_\alpha - \frac{\nabla_\alpha p}{\rho} + \nu\, \nabla^2 v_\alpha. \tag{56.8}$$

Another useful form of this relation is obtained by use of the identity [see Section 30(c)]

$$v^\beta \nabla_\beta v_\alpha = \nabla_\alpha \left(\frac{v_\beta v^\beta}{2}\right) - \sqrt{g}\, e_{\alpha\beta\gamma} v^\beta \omega^\gamma.$$

where ω^γ is the vorticity vector, $\omega^\gamma = e^{\gamma\lambda\mu}\nabla_\lambda v_\mu/\sqrt{g}$. Substitution of the above relation into (56.8) furnishes

$$\frac{\partial v_\alpha}{\partial t} - \sqrt{g}\, e_{\alpha\beta\gamma} v^\beta \omega^\gamma = F_\alpha - \nabla_\alpha \frac{(v_\beta v^\beta)}{2} - \frac{\nabla_\alpha p}{\rho} + \nu\, \nabla^2 v^\sigma.$$

Since the curl operator in tensor notation is $e^{\sigma\rho\alpha}\nabla_\rho(\ )/\sqrt{g}$, we find that the curl operating on the above equation furnishes the following relation for the vorticity vector

$$\frac{\partial \omega^\sigma}{\partial t} - \delta^{\sigma\rho}_{\lambda\mu}\nabla_\rho(v^\lambda \omega^\mu) = \frac{e^{\sigma\rho\alpha}}{\sqrt{g}}\nabla_\rho F_\alpha + \nu\, \nabla^2 \omega^\sigma. \tag{56.9}$$

Let us assume that F_α is a conservative vector field and hence the gradient of a scalar, θ, $F_\alpha = -\nabla_\alpha \theta$. Thus, the curl of F_α must vanish ($e^{\sigma\rho\alpha}\nabla_\rho\nabla_\alpha\theta = 0$). By use of the generalized Kronecker tensor (32.12) we find that

$$\delta^{\sigma\rho}_{\lambda\mu}\nabla_\rho(v^\lambda \omega^\mu) = \omega^\beta \nabla_\beta v^\sigma - \omega^\sigma \nabla_\beta v^\beta + v^\sigma \nabla_\beta \omega^\beta - v^\beta \nabla_\beta \omega^\sigma.$$

In this equation, two terms vanish. First, due to the incompressibility condition, $\nabla_\beta v^\beta = 0$. Secondly, the divergence of a curl must vanish: $\nabla_\beta \omega^\beta = 0$. Thus, (56.9) reduces to

$$\frac{\partial \omega^\sigma}{\partial t} + v^\beta \nabla_\beta \omega^\sigma = \omega^\beta \nabla_\beta v^\sigma + \nu \nabla^2 \omega^\sigma. \tag{56.10}$$

The two terms of the left-hand side of this equation measure the rate of change of the vorticity vector as one follows a fluid particle. In Cartesian orthogonal coordinates, the first term of the right-hand side becomes

$$\omega^\beta \nabla_\beta v^\sigma = \omega \frac{dv^\sigma}{ds_\omega}$$

where ds_ω is the element of arc along a vortex line. If dv^σ/ds_ω is positive, we can say that the velocity is increasing along the vortex line. *Thus, these vortex lines are being stretched when $\omega^\beta \nabla_\beta v^\sigma$ is positive.* Finally, we consider the significance of the second term on the right-hand side of (56.10). This term shows *that viscosity increases the vorticity*. This last increase follows the same general law as heat diffusion.

It is of some interest to compare the results in the previously discussed three-dimensional case with that of the two-dimensional case. For simplicity, we consider a Cartesian orthogonal coordinate system such that the plane flow region is $x^3 = 0$. Then we may write, $v^\alpha = v^\alpha(x^1, x^2, t)$, $\alpha = 1, 2$, $v^3 = 0$. From the definition of the vorticity, $\omega^\gamma = e^{\gamma\alpha\beta}\nabla_\alpha v_\beta/\sqrt{g}$, it follows that, $\omega^\gamma = 0$, $\gamma = 1, 2$, $\omega^3 = \omega^3(x^1, x^2, t)$. Hence, the term $\omega^\beta\nabla_\beta v^\sigma$ of (56.10) vanishes.

If we neglect the viscosity term for the present, then from Helmholtz's theorems, we know that vortex lines move with the fluid and have constant strength. Since $\omega^\beta\nabla_\beta v^\sigma = 0$, the vorticity vector ω^γ is constant as we follow the fluid [see (56.10)]. Further, the strength of a vortex tube for our two-dimensional case is the product of the area of the cross section of a tube by the magnitude of the vorticity. Due to the constancy of the vorticity, the *area of cross section of the tube is not changed as we follow the fluid*. The effect of viscosity is similar to that of the three-dimensional case; viscosity diffuses the vorticity.

Thus, in three-dimensional flows the vortex tubes convolve and distort due to the non-vanishing of the term $\omega^\beta\nabla_\beta v^\sigma$. In two-dimensional flows, this is no longer true. It is for this reason that one often says that "a three-dimensional theory of turbulence is possible but a two-dimensional theory is impossible."

Problem 56.1: Show that the velocity in a fluid at any point P, v_α, may be expressed in terms of the velocity at P_0, $\underset{0}{v_\alpha}$, by

$$v_\alpha = \underset{0}{v_\alpha} + \frac{1}{2}\,(e_{\alpha\beta\gamma}\omega^\beta)_0 x^\gamma + (\dot{e}_{\alpha\beta})_0 x^\beta$$

where x^α are the Cartesian orthogonal coordinates of P relative to P_0, ω^α is the curl of v^α, $\omega^\alpha = e^{\alpha\beta\gamma}\nabla_\beta v_\gamma$, and $\dot{e}_{\alpha\beta}$ is the rate of strain tensor. This result shows that the velocity of a fluid particle at P consists of three terms: a translational velocity, a rotational velocity, and a deformation velocity. *Hint:* Expand v_α in a Taylor series about P_0; decompose $\nabla_\beta v_\gamma$ into the sum of a symmetric and antisymmetric tensor [see Section 47, equation (47.15)]; show that the antisymmetric tensor may be written as $e_{\alpha\beta\gamma}\omega^\beta$.

Problem 56.2: Express the Navier-Stokes equations and the continuity relation in terms of the physical components of the velocity vector in: (1) cylindrical coordinates; (2) spherical coordinates.

Problem 56.3: Consider the steady motion of a viscous fluid through a circular tube. Assume cylindrical coordinates are being used with z-axis along the axis of the tube and that $*u_r = *u_\theta = 0$, $*u_z = w = f(r)$. Also, assume a constant pressure gradient, $p = p_0 z$. Show that for the resulting Poiseiulle flow

$$w = \frac{p_0}{4\mu}(a^2 - r^2)$$

where a is the radius of the tube.

(b) ***The Equation of Energy.*** We assume that the body force field, F_α, is conservative[11] ($F_\alpha = -\nabla_\alpha \theta$) and define the kinetic energy, K, and the potential energy, V, of the fluid occupying the region T by

$$2K = \int_T \rho v_\beta v^\beta \, d\tau, \qquad V = \int_T \rho\theta \, d\tau.$$

Multiplying the equations of motion (56.5) by, ρv_α, we obtain

$$\frac{\rho}{2}\frac{d}{dt}(v_\alpha v^\alpha) = -\rho v^\alpha \nabla_\alpha \theta + v_\alpha \nabla_\beta \sigma^{\alpha\beta}. \tag{56.11}$$

Assuming that the force potential, θ, is independent of time ($\partial\theta/\partial t = 0$), we find that the Eulerian derivative $d\theta/dt$ is, $d\theta/dt = v^\beta \nabla_\beta \theta$. Further, we may write

$$\begin{aligned} v_\alpha \nabla_\beta \sigma^{\alpha\beta} &= \nabla_\beta(\sigma^{\beta\alpha} v_\alpha) - \sigma^{\beta\alpha}\nabla_\beta v_\alpha \\ &= \nabla_\beta(\sigma^{\beta\alpha} v_\alpha) - \sigma^{\beta\alpha}\dot{e}_{\beta\alpha}. \end{aligned}$$

With the aid of these simplifications, equation (56.11) reduces to

$$\frac{\rho}{2}\frac{d}{dt}(v_\beta v^\beta) = -\rho\frac{d\theta}{dt} + \nabla_\alpha(\sigma^{\alpha\beta} v_\beta) - \sigma^{\alpha\beta}\dot{e}_{\alpha\beta}. \tag{56.12}$$

Now, we integrate this equation over the region, T. In view of the continuity relation (see the theory developed in Section 30), we know that

$$\begin{aligned} \int_T \rho \frac{d}{dt}\left(\frac{v_\beta v^\beta}{2} + \theta\right) d\tau &= \frac{d}{dt}\int_T \rho\left(\frac{v_\beta v^\beta}{2} + \theta\right) d\tau \\ &= \frac{d}{dt}(K + V). \end{aligned}$$

Further, by use of Gauss's theorem, we find that

$$\int_T \nabla_\alpha(\sigma^{\alpha\beta} v_\beta) \, d\tau = \int_S \sigma^{\alpha\beta} v_\beta n_\alpha \, d\sigma$$

[11] This is not an essential assumption.

where n_α is unit normal (drawn outward) to the surface S which bounds T. Thus, (56.12) furnishes the relation

$$\frac{d}{dt}(K + V) = \int_S \sigma^{\alpha\beta} v_\beta n_\alpha \, d\sigma - \int_T \sigma^{\alpha\beta} \dot{e}_{\alpha\beta} \, d\tau. \qquad (56.13)$$

The surface integral in the right-hand side of the above expresses the rate at which the stresses due to viscosity do work on the boundary S. This follows from the fact that, $\sigma^{\alpha\beta} n_\alpha$, represents the resultant force per unit are due to the viscous stresses. The significance of the last integral in the right-hand side of (56.13) can be obtained by use of the over-stress, rate of strain relationship of (56.4). We have already noted that, $g^{\alpha\beta}\dot{e}_{\alpha\beta} = \nabla_\alpha v^\alpha$ is the rate of dilation. By substituting (56.4) into this last integral of (56.13) we obtain

$$\int_T \sigma^{\alpha\beta} \dot{e}_{\alpha\beta} \, d\tau = \int_T \left[-p(\nabla_\alpha v^\alpha) - \frac{2}{3}\mu(\nabla_\alpha v^\alpha)^2 + 2\mu \dot{e}_{\alpha\beta}\dot{e}^{\alpha\beta} \right] d\tau. \qquad (56.14)$$

The integrals on the right-hand side of the above which involve $\nabla_\alpha v^\alpha$ represent the rate at which the pressure and viscosity contribute to the internal energy of the fluid by changing the density. If the fluid is incompressible ($\rho = c$), these terms vanish. On the other hand, the term of this last integral involving $\dot{e}^{\alpha\beta}\dot{e}_{\alpha\beta}$ must represent the rate at which viscosity dissipates energy. Such dissipation of energy must take the form of heat added to the fluid.

To summarize: The rate of change of kinetic plus potential energy is due to three sources; first, the rate at which the surface stresses do work; secondly, the rate of increase of internal energy (as measured by the change of density); thirdly, the rate of dissipation due to viscosity (which must increase the heat content of the fluid). The present theory is based upon the assumption that the pressure, p, is a function of only the density, ρ. Such a fluid has been called *isentropic*. The case where p is a function of both ρ and T, the temperature, will be discussed in Chapter XI.

Chapter XI

THE THEORY OF COMPRESSIBLE FLUIDS

57. A Survey of the Theory. In this chapter we shall attempt to show how tensor analysis enables one to better understand some of the essential ideas in the theory of three-dimensional non-steady flows of compressible fluids or gases. We shall consider three topics: (1) some thermodynamical relations; (2) the propagation of discontinuities (characteristics and shocks); (3) the theory of characteristic surfaces in steady three-dimensional flows.

58. Thermodynamic Relations. The theory of the flow of fluids or gases at high speeds involves thermodynamic considerations. As a matter of fact, we have already indicated in Sections 30(c) and 56(b) that the nature of the density, ρ, of the gas (or fluid) is very important. Hence, we shall give a brief review[1] of some well-known results in the theory of thermodynamics.

The elementary theory of thermodynamics depends upon two laws involving several thermodynamical variables: (1) the gas law; (2) the first law of thermodynamics. The simple thermodynamic variables are: p, the pressure; ρ, the density; T, the absolute temperature; S, the entropy; e, the internal energy; h, the enthalpy. Of these variables, *any two* may be considered as independent and then the remainder become dependent variables. Thus, *the thermodynamical configuration* (*or state*) of a gas (or fluid) may be described by points in a, ρ, T, plane, etc., or, more geometrically, by surfaces defined in a, T, ρ, p space, or in a T, ρ, S space, etc.

(a) ***The Gas Law.*** The *gas law* for ideal gases states that ρ, p, T and a constant R (which depends upon the gas) are related by

$$p = R\rho T$$

Liquids are not affected as much as gases by temperature changes. Hence, in general, the "gas" law for liquids is of the form, $p = p(\rho)$. Both of the

[1] R. Courant and K. O. Friedrichs, *Supersonic Flow and Shock Waves*, Interscience Publishers, New York, 1948.

above laws may be expressed by writing the equation

$$p = p(\rho, T). \tag{58.1}$$

(b) ***The First Law of Thermodynamics and the Entropy Concept.*** *The first law of thermodynamics* states that in a closed system[2] the increase in internal energy per unit mass, e, is equal to the heat added minus the work done by the gas or fluid. We shall write this law in the "differential" form

$$de = \delta Q - pd(\rho^{-1}) \tag{58.2}$$

where δQ is the heat added, and $pd(\rho^{-1})$, or $p\,dv$ (where v is the specific volume) is the work done by the gas. It will be noted that in the first law we have written δQ and not dQ. The reason for this is that in moving from one state of the gas to another state, the heat added to the gas and the work done by the gas depend upon the path. This is illustrated in Figure 62. On the other hand, the internal energy, e, depends entirely upon the

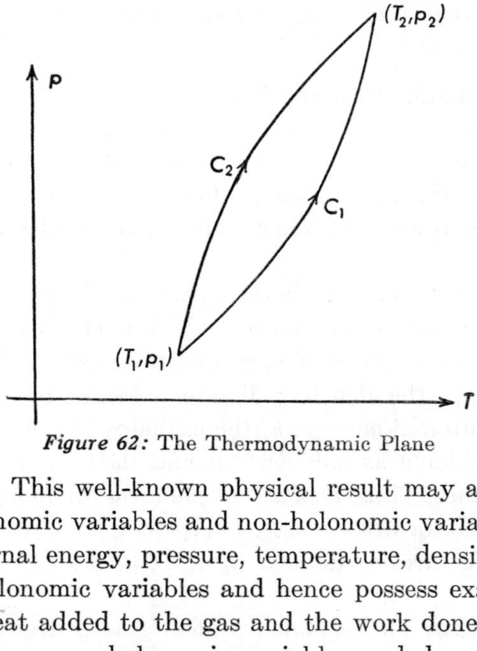

Figure 62: The Thermodynamic Plane

state of the gas. This well-known physical result may also be explained in terms of holonomic variables and non-holonomic variables [see Section 47(e)]. The internal energy, pressure, temperature, density, entropy, and enthalpy are holonomic variables and hence possess exact differentials. However, the heat added to the gas and the work done by the gas in a change of state are non-holonomic variables and do not possess exact differentials. Thus, we write the first law in the form (replacing δQ by dQ)

$$e(T_2, \rho_2) - e(T_1, \rho_1) = \int_C dQ - pd(\rho^{-1})$$

where C denotes the path of integration in the T, ρ plane.

[2] E. Fermi, *Thermodynamics*, Prentice-Hall, Inc., New York, 1937.

It is well known from the theory of differential equations that any two-dimensional form (or Pfaffian),

$$dQ = M(T, \rho)\, dT + N(T, \rho)\, d\rho$$

can always be multiplied by a function of T and ρ (an integrating factor) so that the resulting form is an exact differential. For reversible processes, it is shown by a study of the Carnot cycle that T^{-1} is an integrating factor and

$$dS = \frac{dQ}{T}$$

is an exact differential. The holonomic variable S, is called *the entropy;* the fact that, dS, is an exact differential is a consequence of the second law of thermodynamics.

Problem 58.1: For a polytropic gas, $e = kT$, show that the entropy, S, is determined by, $S = k \ln T + R \ln v + C$, where R is the gas constant and C is an arbitrary constant.

Problem 58.2: Consider a closed path in the p, v, thermodynamic plane (where $v = \rho^{-1}$). Show that the heat added to the system, Q, is the area enclosed by the path. *Hint:* Use Green's theorem on the line integral,

$$\oint \frac{\partial e}{\partial p}\, dp + \left(\frac{\partial e}{\partial v} + p\right) dv.$$

Problem 58.3: The Gibb's free energy function ψ, is defined by $\psi = e - TS$. By use of the first law, show that

$$d\psi = -S\, dT - p\, dv$$

and hence deduce the Maxwell relation, $(\partial S/\partial v)_T = (\partial p/\partial T)_v$.

(c) ***Other Forms of the Gas Law and Enthalpy.*** With the aid of the concept of entropy, the gas law may be expressed in other manners. For instance, for *polytropic gases* (where $e = kT$), one may write the gas law in the form

$$p = A(S)\rho^\gamma \tag{58.3}$$

where A is a function of the entropy, S, and γ is a constant (approximately 1.4 for air). The importance of the entropy concept for compressible fluids lies in the fact that when external forces and viscosity are neglected, the entropy remains constant along a stream line. The resulting flows[3] are called "adiabatic" and are characterized by

$$\frac{dS}{dt} = \frac{\partial S}{\partial t} + v^\lambda \frac{\partial S}{\partial x^\lambda} = 0, \qquad \lambda = 1, 2, 3 \tag{58.4}$$

[3] See R. Courant and K. O. Friedrichs, *loc. cit.*

where v^λ is the velocity vector and x^λ is a system of Cartesian coordinates. For generalized curvilinear coordinates in space, the "adiabatic" condition must be replaced by

$$\frac{\partial S}{\partial t} + v^\lambda \nabla_\lambda S = 0;$$

this relation follows from the energy relation. Before discussing the energy relation, we shall consider the term "enthalpy." We have introduced this term in Section 30. Here we remark that h is defined by

$$h = e + p\rho^{-1}.$$

By differentiation of the above and use of the first law (58.2) with δQ replaced by $T\,dS$, we find that

$$dh = \rho^{-1}\,dp + T\,dS. \tag{58.5}$$

For isentropic flows ($dS = 0$), the above relation reduces to the definition of h adopted in Section 30.

(d) ***The Energy and Bernoulli Relations for Compressible Flows.*** We have already derived an energy relation in Section 56 as an integral of the equations of motion. However, in the work of that section, we were not concerned with thermodynamical relations, but instead we discussed viscous effects. In the present work, we ignore the viscous effects. Thus, the viscosity vanishes; the stress tensor $\sigma^{\lambda\mu}$ of Section 56 reduces to, $-pg^{\lambda\mu}$; $2\dot{e}_{\lambda\mu}$ becomes $\nabla_\lambda v_\mu + \nabla_\mu v_\lambda$; and for the case of zero external force, the energy relation (56.12) reduces to (where $q^2 = v_\alpha v^\alpha$)

$$\frac{\rho}{2}\frac{d}{dt}q^2 + g^{\lambda\mu}\nabla_\lambda(pv_\mu) = pg^{\lambda\mu}\nabla_\lambda v_\mu. \tag{58.6}$$

The left-hand side of the above equation represents the rate of change of kinetic energy per unit mass plus the rate at which work is being done by the pressure (the only force acting). In tacit agreement with the energy principle, we stated in Section 56 that the right-hand side represents the rate of change of internal energy per unit mass. By use of the continuity relation (56.6), one may express this right-hand side of the above energy relation in the form

$$pg^{\lambda\mu}\nabla_\lambda v_\mu = -\frac{p}{\rho}\frac{d\rho}{dt}.$$

Further, the first law of thermodynamics may be expressed as

$$\frac{de}{dt} = T\frac{dS}{dt} - p\frac{d}{dt}\left(\frac{1}{\rho}\right).$$

From these last two relations we see that the right-hand side of the energy relation (58.6) will represent the rate of change of internal energy per unit mass *if and only if the entropy is constant along a stream line.* In fact, our derivation of the energy relation was based upon the assumption that ρ, p, v_λ could be determined when the three equations of motion, the equation of continuity, and the gas law were known. If the gas law consists of a relation between ρ, p, and a new scalar S, then we have a system of five equations in six unknowns (ρ, p, S, v_λ). Such a system is insufficient, in general, for the determination of the six unknowns. Thus, for gases, we must *postulate a new energy principle.* From the above discussion it appears desirable to *replace the previous energy relation by*

$$\frac{\rho}{2}\frac{d}{dt}q^2 + g^{\lambda\mu}\nabla_\lambda(pv_\mu) = -\rho\frac{de}{dt}, \qquad \text{or} \qquad \frac{dS}{dt} = 0 \tag{58.7}$$

and consider this relation *as an expression of the conservation of energy.* It is easily shown by a detailed but simple computation that the above relation may be written in the form

$$\frac{\partial}{\partial t}\left[\rho\left(\frac{q^2}{2} + e\right)\right] + \nabla_\lambda\left[\rho v^\lambda\left(\frac{q^2}{2} + h\right)\right] = 0.$$

In order to derive the various forms of the Bernoulli relation for compressible flows, we recall that the adiabatic condition (58.4) is a consequence of the above energy relation. If we require that the viscosity coefficient and the external force vanish, then the equations of motion (56.7) reduce to

$$\frac{\partial v^\mu}{\partial t} + v^\lambda\nabla_\lambda v^\mu = -\frac{g^{\lambda\mu}}{\rho}\nabla_\lambda p.$$

Further, we may write the enthalpy relation (58.5) in the form

$$\nabla_\lambda h = \frac{\nabla_\lambda p}{\rho} + T\nabla_\lambda S.$$

Using this last relation to eliminate the pressure in the equations of motion and forming the scalar product of the resulting equation with v^λ, we obtain in *the steady case*

$$\frac{d}{dt}\left(\frac{q^2}{2} + h\right) = Tv^\lambda\nabla_\lambda S.$$

The adiabatic condition of constant entropy along stream lines becomes in the case of steady flows, $v^\lambda\nabla_\lambda S = 0$. Hence, the previous relation may be expressed in the Bernoulli form

$$\frac{q^2}{2} + h = c \tag{58.8}$$

where the above constant varies from stream line to stream line. This Bernoulli relation coincides with the Bernoulli relation (30.11) which was deduced for the case of isentropic flows, $p = f(\rho)$. Similarly to the above, one may show that the other Bernoulli relations of Section 30 are valid for irrotational but non-isentropic fluid motions.

In concluding, we consider the case of *compressible viscous* fluids. One cannot use the previous energy relations. Since the essential contribution of viscosity to energy lies in the fact that kinetic energy of motion is converted into heat energy, it appears that one can no longer consider the flow as a *reversible* process. Hence, we must assume that, $\delta Q \neq T\, dS$. In this case, it appears reasonable to assume that the difference between δQ and $T\, dS$ is the viscous energy which is ultimately converted to heat energy. The most suitable method for obtaining the energy equation is to postulate conservation of the total energy of all types and write an "energy balance" equation.

59. The General Theory of Discontinuities. The theory of discontinuities in flows of compressible fluids has been treated by many authors beginning with B. Riemann and his contemporaries and culminating in the elegant theory of J. Hadamard[4] and the excellent texts by Courant-Hilbert[5] and Courant-Friedrichs.[6] Unfortunately, Hadamard's theory is based on the Lagrangian form of the equations of motion. In the following sections we shall show that by following a method developed by R. K. Luneberg[7] for electromagnetic theory, one may obtain a unified theory of discontinuities[8] in terms of the Eulerian equations of motion.

In this section we shall develop the general theory and then we shall apply this theory to discontinuities along characteristics and discontinuities along shocks.

(a) ***The General Theory of Discontinuities.*** We consider a four-dimensional Euclidean space-time manifold, E_4. The time variable will be denoted by t, and the space variables by x^λ, $\lambda = 1, 2, 3$. In particular, we assume that the space variables are Cartesian and define ∞^1 Euclidean three-spaces E_3 in E_4. The coordinate lines, $t =$ variable, will be assumed

[4] J. Hadamard, *Propagation des Ondes*, Chelsea Publishing Co., New York, 1949.

[5] R. Courant and D. Hilbert, *Methoden der Mathematischen Physik*, Interscience Publishers, New York, Vol. II.

[6] R. Courant and K. O. Friedrichs, *loc. cit.*

[7] R. K. Luneberg, "Asymptotic Development of Steady State Electromagnetic Fields," N.Y.U., Mathematics Research Group, *Research Report* No. *EM 14*, July, 1949.

[8] N. Coburn, "Discontinuities in Compressible Fluid Flow," *Mathematics Magazine*, May–June, 1954, Vol. 27, No. 5.

to be Euclidean (that is, lines in E_4). An analogous situation in ordinary Euclidean three-space is obtained by introducing rectangular Cartesian coordinates. The coordinate lines, $z =$ variable, would correspond to $t =$ variable and the variables x, y would correspond to the space variables, x^λ, $\lambda = 1, 2, 3$. It should be noted that in the above type of coordinate systems, the differentiation operators, $\partial/\partial t$, and $\partial/\partial x^\lambda = \nabla_\lambda$, are covariant derivatives.

The tensor formulation of the hydrodynamical equations in these preferred coordinate systems has the form

$$\frac{\partial}{\partial t}(\rho v_\lambda) + \nabla_\mu(\rho v^\mu v_\lambda + p\delta^\mu_\lambda) = 0 \tag{59.1}$$

$$\frac{\partial \rho}{\partial t} + \nabla_\mu(\rho v^\mu) = 0 \tag{59.2}$$

$$\frac{\partial}{\partial t}\left[\rho\left(\frac{q^2}{2} + e\right)\right] + \nabla_\mu\left[\rho v^\mu\left(\frac{q^2}{2} + h\right)\right] = 0. \tag{59.3}$$

The first set of equations (59.1) is equivalent to the Eulerian equations of motion for compressible non-viscous fluids when the body force vanishes; the second equation (59.2) is the equation of continuity; and equation (59.3) is the energy relation.

In order to initiate our study of discontinuities, we introduce the hypersurface (or lower dimensional manifold) in space-time along which the discontinuities occur. We denote this manifold by

$$\overset{j}{\phi}(t, x^\lambda) = \overset{j}{c}, \qquad j = 0, \text{ or } j = 0, 1, \text{ or } j = 0, 1, 2, \text{ or } j = 0, 1, 2, 3$$

where the $\overset{j}{c}$ are constants. If this system consists of only one equation ($j = 0$), then the discontinuity manifold defines a hypersurface. Similarly, if the system consists of two equations ($j = 0, 1$), then the equations define a surface; if this system contains three equations ($j = 0, 1, 2$), then the discontinuity lies along a curve; and if this system consists of four equations ($j = 0, 1, 2, 3$), then the discontinuity consists of a finite number of points. In any case, the vector fields for the various types of j, $\partial\overset{j}{\phi}/\partial t$, $\partial\overset{j}{\phi}/\partial x^\lambda$, determine vectors normal to the discontinuity manifold. Further, the unit normal vectors of this manifold are determined by

$$n_0 = \frac{\partial \phi}{\partial t} \Bigg/ \sqrt{\left(\frac{\partial \phi}{\partial t}\right)^2 + g^{\lambda\mu}\frac{\partial \phi}{\partial x^\lambda}\frac{\partial \phi}{\partial x^\mu}} \tag{59.4}$$

$$n_\lambda = \frac{\partial \phi}{\partial x^\lambda} \Bigg/ \sqrt{\left(\frac{\partial \phi}{\partial t}\right)^2 + g^{\lambda\mu}\frac{\partial \phi}{\partial x^\lambda}\frac{\partial \phi}{\partial x^\mu}}$$

where the superscript j has been omitted to gain simplicity in writing. It should be noted that our previous assumptions as to the types of permissible coordinate systems in E_4 imply that

$$g_{jj} = 1, \qquad g_{jk} = 0, \qquad j \neq k, \qquad j, k = 0, 1, 2, 3.$$

If we integrate (59.1) through (59.3) over some region of E_4 which is bounded by a closed hypersurface S_3, we obtain through use of the generalized Stokes's or Gauss's formula (see Section 51)

$$\int_{S_3} [n_0(\rho v_\lambda) + n_\mu(\rho v^\mu v_\lambda + p\delta^\mu_\lambda)]\, d\tau = 0 \tag{59.5}$$

$$\int_{S_3} [n_0\rho + n_\mu(\rho v^\mu)]\, d\tau = 0 \tag{59.6}$$

$$\int_{S_3} \left[n_0\rho \left(\frac{q^2}{2} + e\right) + n_\mu \rho v^\mu \left(\frac{q^2}{2} + h\right)\right] d\tau = 0. \tag{59.7}$$

The vector n_0, n_λ represents the unit normal vector to S_3. We shall show that *the above equations are the fundamental equations for the study of shock*[9] *discontinuities.*

In order to determine the fundamental equations for the study of characteristics, we proceed in a slightly different manner. First, we introduce the general covariant differentiation operator, ∇_j, $j = 0, 1, 2, 3$, where

$$\nabla_0 = \frac{\partial}{\partial t}, \qquad \nabla_\lambda = \frac{\partial}{\partial x^\lambda}, \qquad \lambda = 1, 2, 3.$$

By differentiation of (59.1) through (59.3) we obtain

$$\nabla_j \frac{\partial}{\partial t} (\rho v_\lambda) + \nabla_j \nabla_\mu (\rho v^\mu v_\lambda + p\delta^\mu_\lambda) = 0$$

$$\nabla_j \left(\frac{\partial \rho}{\partial t}\right) + \nabla_j \nabla_\mu (\rho v^\mu) = 0$$

$$\nabla_j \frac{\partial}{\partial t} \rho \left(\frac{q^2}{2} + e\right) + \nabla_j \nabla_\mu \left[\rho v^\mu \left(\frac{q^2}{2} + h\right)\right] = 0.$$

Since the space E_4 is Euclidean, we may interchange the order of covariant differentiation; here, actually ordinary differentiation, and write $\nabla_j \nabla_k v_\lambda = \nabla_k \nabla_j v_\lambda$. If the derivatives in the previous equations are treated in this manner and then the generalized Stokes's theorem is applied to the

[9] Shocks are irreversible thermodynamic processes. Hence, one must remember that an additional principle is needed: Entropy always increases across a shock.

resulting equations, we obtain

$$\int_{S_3} [n_0 \nabla_j(\rho v_\lambda) + n_\mu \nabla_j(\rho v^\mu v_\lambda + p\delta^\mu_\lambda)]\, d\tau = 0 \qquad (59.8)$$

$$\int_{S_3} [n_0(\nabla_j \rho) + n_\mu \nabla_j(\rho v^\mu)]\, d\tau = 0 \qquad (59.9)$$

$$\int_{S_3} \left\{ n_0 \nabla_j \left[\rho \left(\frac{q^2}{2} + e \right) \right] + n_\mu \nabla_j \left[\rho v^\mu \left(\frac{q^2}{2} + h \right) \right] \right\} d\tau = 0. \qquad (59.10)$$

The equations (59.8) through (59.10) are the fundamental equations for the study of discontinuities which propagate along characteristics.

Since the theorem of Stokes was used in deriving the above systems of equations, the region of E_4 bounded by the closed hypersurface S_3 cannot contain points at which ρ, p, v^λ, etc., and their derivatives are discontinuous. This is a very severe limitation on the formulas. In order to extend the above formulas to the case where E_4 contains points of discontinuity, three procedures are available: (1) one may attempt to apply the previous integral relations to the case where S_3 intersects a discontinuity manifold; (2) one may postulate that the above two systems of equations are the fundamental equations of fluid flow and apply whenever the integrals exist; (3) one may postulate that only equations (59.5) through (59.7) are the fundamental equations of fluid flow and apply whenever the integrals exist. The first procedure involves the use of complicated limit processes; the second procedure is logically sound and easy to apply but *appears to be redundant to the present author*. For these reasons we shall use the third procedure.

We postulate that the system of equations (59.5) through (59.7) are the fundamental equations of compressible fluid flow and apply whenever the integrals involved exist.[10] First, we note that if ρ, p, v^λ, etc., and their derivatives are continuous in a region of space-time and we apply the divergence theorem of Stokes, then the fundamental equations reduce to the equations of motion (59.1), the continuity relation (59.2), and the energy relation (59.3) respectively. Furthermore, the fundamental equations are applicable even when ρ, p, v^λ, etc., are discontinuous, provided that the integrals over the closed hypersurface S_3 exist. This means that our fundamental system of hydrodynamical equations can be applied to the case where the closed hypersurface S_3 intersects a manifold $\bar{S}_3$ along which ρ, p, v^λ, etc., have finite jumps. For, in this case, ρ, p, v^λ, etc., are not defined along the surface S_2 of intersection of S_3, $\bar{S}_3$. However, the inte-

[10] To apply the theory to lower dimensional discontinuity manifolds, we must be able to replace S_3 by S_2 or S_1.

grals (59.5) through (59.7) exist and are independent of which finite values are assigned to ρ, p, v^λ, etc., along S_2. This is due to the fact that the points of discontinuity along S_2 have zero three-dimensional measure.

We shall show that *the system* (*59.8*) *through* (*59.10*) can be deduced from our fundamental relations. To simplify the discussion we replace the fundamental equations by the single representative relation

$$\int_{S_3} [n_0 h_\lambda + n_\mu k^{\mu}_{\cdot\lambda}]\, d\tau = 0. \tag{59.11}$$

Thus, if (59.11) represents the equations of motion (59.5), then the tensors h_λ, $k^{\mu}_{\cdot\lambda}$ reduce to

$$h_\lambda = \rho v_\lambda, \qquad k^{\mu}_{\cdot\lambda} = \rho v^\mu v_\lambda + p\delta^{\mu}_{\lambda}.$$

To represent (59.6) and (59.7), we must replace h_λ by a scalar h, and $k^{\mu}_{\cdot\lambda}$ by a vector k_λ. However, we shall consider (59.11) as typical of all of our fundamental equations. First, we note that the arguments of h_λ, $k^{\mu}_{\cdot\lambda}$ are the coordinates of the Cartesian orthogonal system, x^λ, t. Now, we consider the one-parameter family of solutions of the representative equation

$$'h_\lambda = h_\lambda(x^1 + \xi, x^2, x^3, t), \qquad 'k^{\mu}_{\cdot\lambda} = k^{\mu}_{\cdot\lambda}(x^1 + \xi, x^2, x^3, t).$$

The existence of this one-parameter family of solutions follows directly from (59.11). That is, by use of the translation transformation of coordinates, $'x^1 = x^1 + \xi$, we see that

$$\int_{'S_3} ['n_0\, 'h_\lambda + 'n_\mu\, 'k^{\mu}_{\cdot\lambda}]\, d\tau = 0$$

where $'S_3$ is the translated hypersurface S_3 and $'n_0$, $'n_\lambda$ are the components of the unit normal of $'S_3$. However, S_3 is arbitrary. Hence, we may drop the primes from the surface quantities in the above equation and obtain

$$\int_{S_3} [n_0\, 'h_\lambda + n_\mu\, 'k^{\mu}_{\cdot\lambda}]\, d\tau = 0.$$

If $'h_\lambda$, $'k^{\mu}_{\cdot\lambda}$ are continuous functions of ξ (or h_λ, $k^{\mu}_{\cdot\lambda}$ are continuous functions of x^1) and if these functions possess unique derivatives with respect to ξ along S_3 then we may differentiate the above relation under the integral sign. Further, allowing ξ to approach zero, we obtain

$$\int_{S_3} \left[n_0 \frac{\partial h_\lambda}{\partial x^1} + n_\mu \frac{\partial k^{\mu}_{\cdot\lambda}}{\partial x^1} \right] d\tau = 0.$$

However, even if $'h_\lambda$, $'k^{\mu}_{\cdot\lambda}$ (or h_λ, $k^{\mu}_{\cdot\lambda}$) do not possess unique derivatives on a surface S_2 of S_3 but only one-sided derivatives, the above relation remains valid. Evidently, one may replace the derivatives with respect to x^1 by derivatives with respect to x^2, x^3, t. The tensor form of the resulting equations is

$$\int_{S_3} [n_0 \nabla_j h_\lambda + n_\mu \nabla_j k^{\mu}_{\cdot\lambda}] \, d\tau = 0.$$

Thus, we have shown that the system (59.8) through (59.10) may be deduced from the fundamental system. In the remainder of this section we consider equations (59.11) as typical of either system.

To obtain the desired discontinuity relations, we introduce the manifold $\bar{S}$ along which the discontinuity occurs. Let S_3 be a closed hypersurface

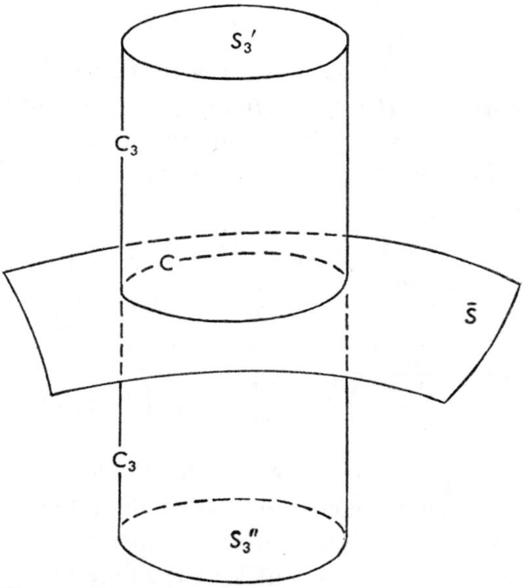

Figure 63: The Hypersurface, $S = S_3' + S_3'' + C_3$ and the Discontinuity Manifold, $\bar{S}$. The Hypersurfaces S, $\bar{S}$ Intersect in the Lower Dimensional Manifold C

which consists of three parts: (1) two hypersurfaces $'S_3$, $''S_3$ which do not intersect $\bar{S}$; and (2) a cylindrical hypersurface, C_3, which intersects $\bar{S}$ (see Figure 63). The typical equation (59.11) may be expanded into

$$\int_{'S_3} [n_0 h_\lambda + n_\mu k^{\mu}_{\cdot\lambda}] \, d\tau + \int_{''S_3} [n_0 h_\lambda + n_\mu k^{\mu}_{\cdot\lambda}] \, d\tau + \int_{C_3} [n_0 h_\lambda + n_\mu k^{\mu}_{\cdot\lambda}] \, d\tau = 0.$$

If we allow the generators of the cylinder C_3 to shrink to zero *on each side* of $\bar{S}$, then $'S_3$, $''S_3$ shrink to $\bar{S}$ and the above integral reduces to

$$\int_{\bar{S}+} [n_0 h_\lambda + n_\mu k^{\mu}_{\cdot\lambda}] \, d\tau + \int_{\bar{S}_-} [n_0 h_\lambda + n_\mu k^{\mu}_{\cdot\lambda}] \, d\tau = 0$$

where $\bar{S}-$, $\bar{S}+$ indicate that the integrands are to be evaluated on the positive and negative sides of $\bar{S}$. Recalling that the normal on $\bar{S}+$ has the same sense as that of $'S_3$ and that the normal of $\bar{S}-$ has the same sense as that of $''S_3$, we may reduce the above relation to

$$\int_{\bar{S}} [n_0 \bar{h}_\lambda + n_\mu \bar{k}^{\mu}_{\cdot\lambda}]\, d\tau = 0 \tag{59.12}$$

where $\bar{h}_\lambda$, $\bar{k}^{\mu}_{\cdot\lambda}$ are the "jumps" in h_λ, $k^{\mu}_{\cdot\lambda}$. Finally, since the above integral is taken over an arbitrary part of $\bar{S}$, we may replace the integral relation by the point condition

$$\frac{\partial \phi}{\partial t} \bar{h}_\lambda + \frac{\partial \phi}{\partial x^\mu} \bar{k}^{\mu}_{\cdot\lambda} = 0. \tag{59.13}$$

The relation (59.13) is valid at each point of the discontinuity manifold, $\bar{S}$.

(b) ***Discontinuities in the Derivatives of*** v^λ, p, ρ; ***the Characteristic Manifolds.*** In this case, we apply the formula (59.13) to the integrands of (59.8) through (59.10). We find the jumps in the derivatives satisfy the relations:

$$\frac{\partial \phi}{\partial t} \overline{\nabla_j(\rho v_\lambda)} + \frac{\partial \phi}{\partial x^\mu} \overline{\nabla_j(\rho v^\mu v_\lambda + p\delta^\mu_\lambda)} = 0 \tag{59.14}$$

$$\frac{\partial \phi}{\partial t} \overline{\nabla_j \rho} + \frac{\partial \phi}{\partial x^\mu} \overline{\nabla_j(\rho v^\mu)} = 0 \tag{59.15}$$

$$\frac{\partial \phi}{\partial t} \overline{\nabla_j \left[\rho\left(\frac{q^2}{2} + e\right)\right]} + \frac{\partial \phi}{\partial x^\mu} \overline{\nabla_j \left[\rho v^\mu \left(\frac{q^2}{2} + h\right)\right]} = 0. \tag{59.16}$$

along the discontinuity manifold, $\bar{S}$. In the above equations the vector $\partial\phi/\partial t$, $\partial\phi/\partial x^\lambda$, represents the components of *any vector normal to the discontinuity manifold.* In the future work of this section we assume that q, p, ρ, v^λ, e, h, S are continuous but that the derivatives of these quantities may be discontinuous. To simplify the discussion, we shall ignore the discontinuities of the derivatives of the quantities e, h, S and hence consider only the first two equations of the above system. Further, if we write the gas law as $p = p(S, \rho)$, where S is the entropy, then

$$\nabla_j p = c^2 \nabla_j \rho + \left.\frac{\partial p}{\partial S}\right)_\rho \nabla_j S, \qquad c^2 = \left.\frac{\partial p}{\partial \rho}\right)_S.$$

In view of our assumption, we may express the discontinuity in $\nabla_j p$ as

$$\overline{\nabla_j p} = c^2 \overline{\nabla_j \rho}.$$

First, we show that *no manifolds exist along which* $\nabla_j p$, $\nabla_j \rho$ *are discontinuous but* $\nabla_j v^\lambda$ *are continuous.* This result follows immediately from the equations of motion. However, we shall develop this result by considering the first two equations of the above system, (59.14) and (59.15). If we assume that $\nabla_j v^\lambda$ are continuous, then we may write

$$\overline{\nabla_j(\rho v_\lambda)} = v_\lambda \overline{\nabla_j \rho}, \qquad \overline{\nabla_j(\rho v^\mu v_\lambda)} = v^\mu v^\lambda \overline{\nabla_j \rho}$$
$$\overline{\nabla_j(\delta^\mu_\lambda p)} = \delta^\mu_\lambda \overline{\nabla_j p}.$$

Through use of these relations, the first two jump relations reduce to

$$\begin{aligned} \overline{\nabla_j \rho}\left[v_\lambda \left(\frac{\partial \phi}{\partial t} + v^\mu \frac{\partial \phi}{\partial x^\mu} \right) + c^2 \frac{\partial \phi}{\partial x^\lambda} \right] &= 0 \\ \overline{\nabla_j \rho}\left[\frac{\partial \phi}{\partial t} + v^\lambda \frac{\partial \phi}{\partial x^\lambda} \right] &= 0. \end{aligned} \tag{59.17}$$

These equations are satisfied if and only if $\phi(x^\lambda, t)$ is the solution of the system

$$\frac{\partial \phi}{\partial t} + v^\lambda \frac{\partial \phi}{\partial x^\lambda} = 0, \qquad \frac{\partial \phi}{\partial x^\lambda} = 0.$$

Since this system possesses the solutions

$$\overset{j}{\phi}(x^\lambda, t) = \overset{j}{c}, \qquad j = 0, 1, 2, 3$$

there exist only a finite number of points at which $\nabla_j v^\lambda$ are continuous but $\nabla_j \rho$, $\nabla_j p$ are discontinuous. From the second equation of (59.17), one can obtain one conclusion which is valid even when e, h, S have discontinuous derivatives. Since this equation remains valid, we see that the discontinuity manifolds for which v^λ, ρ, p, s, e, h, $\nabla_j v^\lambda$ are continuous but $\nabla_j \rho$, $\nabla_j S$ are discontinuous belong to the hypersurfaces

$$\frac{\partial \phi}{\partial t} + v^\mu \frac{\partial \phi}{\partial x^\mu} = 0.$$

These hypersurfaces consist of families of stream lines. This follows from the fact that the equation implies that $d\phi/dt = 0$, as we follow the gas or fluid.

Secondly, we shall state that *the discontinuity manifolds along which* $\nabla_j \rho$, $\nabla_j p$ *are continuous and* $\nabla_j v^\lambda$ *are discontinuous* consist of stream lines. The verification of this result is left to the problems (see Problem 59.3).

Finally, we consider the case where ρ, p, v^λ, etc., are continuous but possess discontinuous derivatives along $\bar{S}$. We shall show that *these discontinuities are propagated along the characteristic hypersurfaces which satisfy the partial differential equation*

$$\left(\frac{\partial \phi}{\partial t}\right)^2 + 2v^\mu \frac{\partial \phi}{\partial x^\mu}\frac{\partial \phi}{\partial t} + (v^\lambda v^\mu - c^2 g^{\lambda\mu}) \frac{\partial \phi}{\partial x^\lambda}\frac{\partial \phi}{\partial x^\mu} = 0. \tag{59.18}$$

In this case, the jumps in ρ, v^λ, p, satisfy the relations:

$$\begin{aligned}
\overline{\nabla_j(\rho v_\lambda)} &= \rho\overline{\nabla_j v_\lambda} + v_\lambda\overline{\nabla_j\rho} \\
\overline{\nabla_j(\rho v^\mu v_\lambda)} &= \rho v_\lambda\overline{\nabla_j v^\mu} + \rho v^\mu\overline{\nabla_j v_\lambda} + v^\mu v_\lambda\overline{\nabla_j\rho} \\
\overline{\nabla_j(\delta^\mu_\lambda p)} &= \delta^\mu_\lambda\overline{\nabla_j p}.
\end{aligned}$$

Substituting the above into the jump relations (59.14) and (59.15), we obtain:

$$\overline{\nabla_j\rho}\left(v_\lambda\frac{\partial\phi}{\partial t} + v_\lambda v^\mu\frac{\partial\phi}{\partial x^\mu} + \delta^\mu_\lambda c^2\frac{\partial\phi}{\partial x^\mu}\right) + \rho\overline{\nabla_j v_\lambda}\left(\frac{\partial\phi}{\partial t} + v^\mu\frac{\partial\phi}{\partial x^\mu}\right) + \overline{\nabla_j v^\mu}\left(\rho v_\lambda\frac{\partial\phi}{\partial x^\mu}\right) = 0,$$

$$\overline{\nabla_j\rho}\left(\frac{\partial\phi}{\partial t} + v^\mu\frac{\partial\phi}{\partial x^\mu}\right) + \rho\overline{\nabla_j v^\mu}\frac{\partial\phi}{\partial x^\mu} = 0. \qquad (59.19a)$$

If we solve the second equation for $\overline{\nabla_j v^\mu}(\partial\phi/\partial x^\mu)$ and substitute into the first, we obtain a simplified version of this first relation:

$$\overline{\nabla_j\rho}\, c^2\frac{\partial\phi}{\partial x^\lambda} + \rho\overline{\nabla_j v_\lambda}\left(\frac{\partial\phi}{\partial t} + v^\mu\frac{\partial\phi}{\partial x^\mu}\right) = 0. \qquad (59.19b)$$

By eliminating $\overline{\nabla_j v_\lambda}$ between (59.19), we obtain the characteristic equation (59.18), when $\overline{\nabla_j\rho} \neq 0$. It is easily shown that $\phi(x^\lambda, t)$ cannot consist of stream lines.

The two sets of equations (59.19) consist of sixteen linear homogeneous equations in sixteen unknowns $\overline{\nabla_j\rho}$, $\overline{\nabla_j v_\lambda}$. The characteristic condition (59.18) implies that the determinant[11] of this system vanishes and hence that the rank of the matrix of this linear system is less than or equal to fifteen. In addition, the original equations of motion furnish the four jump conditions.

$$\begin{aligned}
\overline{\frac{\partial v_\lambda}{\partial t}} + v^\mu\overline{\nabla_\mu v_\lambda} + \frac{c^2}{\rho}\overline{\nabla_\lambda\rho} &= 0 \\
\overline{\frac{\partial\rho}{\partial t}} + g^{\lambda\mu}\rho\overline{\nabla_\mu v_\lambda} + v^\mu\overline{\nabla_\mu\rho} &= 0.
\end{aligned}$$

Solving (59.19b) for $\overline{\nabla_j v_\lambda}$, we obtain

$$\overline{\nabla_j v_\lambda} = -\overline{\nabla_j\rho}\left(c^2\frac{\partial\phi}{\partial x^\lambda}\right)\Big/\rho\left(\frac{\partial\phi}{\partial t} + v^\mu\frac{\partial\phi}{\partial x^\mu}\right).$$

By substituting this relation into the above four jump conditions, we

[11] The determinant is C^4L^8 where $C = 0$ represents (59.18) and $L = 0$ represents the stream line condition ($\partial\phi/\partial t + v^\mu\partial\phi/\partial x^\mu = 0$).

obtain a system of four linear equations in the four unknowns, $\overline{\nabla_j \rho}$. Upon simplification, these equations become

$$\frac{\partial \phi}{\partial x^\lambda}\frac{\overline{\partial \rho}}{\partial t} + \left[v^\mu \frac{\partial \phi'}{\partial x^\lambda} - \delta^\mu_\lambda\left(\frac{\partial \phi}{\partial t} + v^\alpha \frac{\partial \phi}{\partial x^\alpha}\right)\right]\overline{\nabla_\mu \rho} = 0$$

$$\frac{\partial \phi}{\partial t}\frac{\overline{\partial \rho}}{\partial t} + \left[2v^\mu \frac{\partial \phi}{\partial t} + (v^\mu v^\alpha - c^2 g^{\mu\alpha})\frac{\partial \phi}{\partial x^\alpha}\right]\overline{\nabla_\mu \rho} = 0.$$

Evidently, the determinant[12] of this system of equations must vanish. We see that if

$$\overline{\nabla_j \rho} = \sigma \nabla_j \phi$$

where σ is a scalar, then the above jump conditions are *identically* satisfied. Further, the formula for $\overline{\nabla_j v_\lambda}$ becomes

$$\overline{\nabla_j v_\lambda} = -\sigma c^2 \frac{\partial \phi}{\partial x^\lambda}\nabla_j \phi \Big/ \rho\left(\frac{\partial \phi}{\partial t} + v^\mu \frac{\partial \phi}{\partial x^\mu}\right). \tag{59.20}$$

This last formula is well known for the irrotational case.[13]

Problem 59.1: Consider the heat equation, $\partial u/\partial t = k\,\partial^2 u/\partial x^2$. Show that if u is continuous but $\partial u/\partial x$ has a finite discontinuity then the permissible discontinuity manifolds are $t =$ constant. Hence, by a geometrical argument, show that these discontinuities occur at isolated points.

Problem 59.2: Consider the wave equation, $\partial^2 u/\partial x^2 - \partial^2 u/\partial t^2 = 0$. Show that the discontinuity manifolds of the first derivatives of u are the characteristic manifolds, $(\partial \phi/\partial x)^2 - (\partial \phi/\partial t)^2 = 0$ or $x \pm t = c$.

Problem 59.3: Show that if p, ρ, v^λ, are continuous, $\nabla_j \rho$, $\nabla_j p$ are continuous and $\nabla_j v_\lambda$ are discontinuous, then the only permissible discontinuity manifolds consist of stream lines.

Problem 59.4: Show that the vorticity tensor, $2\omega_{\lambda\mu} = \nabla_\lambda v_\mu - \nabla_\mu v_\lambda$, is continuous across the characteristic manifolds.

Problem 59.5: Show that (59.18) is the characteristic equation when the derivatives of S, the entropy (as well as of ρ and v_λ) are discontinuous across the characteristic manifolds.[14]

Problem 59.6: By definition, for a general wave, if $\overline{\nabla_\lambda v_\mu} = B_\mu(\partial g/\partial x^\lambda)$ then B_μ is the direction of the particle motion on the wave front and $(\partial g/\partial x^\lambda)$ is the direction of the normal to the wave front. Further, if,

[12] This determinant is CL^2.

[13] R. Courant and D. Hilbert, *loc. cit.*, Vol. II, p. 357.

[14] This result was obtained by Mr. J. McCulley in the author's course in compressible fluids.

$B^\lambda(\partial g/\partial x^\lambda) = 0$, the wave is transverse; if B_λ is parallel to $\partial g/\partial x^\lambda$, the wave is longitudinal. (1) Determine the direction of the characteristic waves; (2) consider the plane waves, $v_\mu = B_\mu\, g(t - h_\lambda x^\lambda)$, $\lambda = 1, 2$, and determine the conditions for transverse and longitudinal waves.

(c) ***Discontinuities of*** v_λ, p, ρ, S, e, h***; the Contact and Shock Manifolds.*** We assume that: (1) *on each side* of the discontinuity manifolds, the values of v_λ, p, ρ, S, e, h, and their space-time derivatives are continuous; (2) *in crossing* the discontinuity manifold the values of v_λ, p, ρ, S, e, h are discontinuous. If we apply the general formula (59.13) to the integrands of (59.5) through (59.7), we obtain the jump relations:

$$\frac{\partial \phi}{\partial t}\,\overline{\rho v_\lambda} + \frac{\partial \phi}{\partial x^\mu}\,(\overline{\rho v^\mu v_\lambda} + \delta^\mu_\lambda \bar{p}) = 0 \tag{59.21}$$

$$\frac{\partial \phi}{\partial t}\,\bar{\rho} + \frac{\partial \phi}{\partial x^\mu}\,\overline{\rho v^\mu} = 0 \tag{59.22}$$

$$\frac{\partial \phi}{\partial t}\left(\overline{\frac{\rho q^2}{2}} + \overline{\rho e}\right) + \frac{\partial \phi}{\partial x^\mu}\left(\overline{\frac{\rho q^2 v^\mu}{2}} + \overline{\rho h v^\mu}\right) = 0. \tag{59.23}$$

One may express the above system in terms of the values of ρ, v_λ, etc., *on one side of the discontinuity manifold,* $\bar{S}$, and the jumps, $\bar{\rho}$, $\bar{v}_\lambda$, etc. To do this, we note that if the subscripts 2 and 1 indicate values of functions on the sides of $\bar{S}$, then

$$\overline{\alpha\beta} = (\alpha\beta)_2 - (\alpha\beta)_1 = (\alpha_2 - \alpha_1)(\beta_2 - \beta_1) + \alpha_1\beta_2 + \alpha_2\beta_1 - 2\alpha_1\beta_1.$$

Upon simplifying the right-hand side of the above, we find that the jump may be expressed in the form

$$\overline{\alpha\beta} = \bar{\alpha}\bar{\beta} + \alpha_1\bar{\beta} + \beta_1\bar{\alpha}. \tag{59.24}$$

By use of a similar expansion we may write

$$\overline{\alpha\beta} = -\bar{\alpha}\bar{\beta} + \alpha_2\bar{\beta} + \beta_2\bar{\alpha}.$$

If we expand $\overline{\rho v_\lambda}$, $\overline{\rho v^\mu v_\lambda}$ in terms of $\bar{\rho}$, $\bar{v}_\lambda$, then the jump relations (59.21) and (59.22) become cubics and a quadratic in the jumps, $\bar{\rho}$, $\bar{v}_\lambda$, $\bar{p}$. Further, if (59.23) is expanded and the gas law is used, we obtain a fourth-degree equation in the jumps. This remark is essential in understanding the difference between characteristic manifolds and manifolds of contact and shock discontinuity. From the jump relations of Section 59(b), we see that *characteristic manifolds are determined by linear homogeneous equations in the unknown jumps,* $\overline{\nabla_j v_\lambda}$, etc. However, *shock and contact manifolds are determined by nonlinear homogeneous equations in the unknown jumps,* $\bar{\rho}$, $\bar{v}_\lambda$, etc. Due to the linear homogeneous property of the defining equations, one may easily determine the partial differential equation satisfied by the characteristic manifolds. This is obtained by requiring the determinant to vanish. Further, from the theory of linear homogeneous systems, we saw that if the characteristic manifold is a *hypersurface*, then the determinant of the equations in Section 59(b) is of rank fifteen, and all the jumps are known in terms of one jump. On the other hand, the theory of a nonlinear homogeneous algebraic system is diametrically opposed to that of the linear system.[15] In the nonlinear system, *no criterion (not involving the jumps) exists for determining the partial differential equation for the shock manifolds.* (*Except as we shall show that contact manifolds always consist of families of stream lines.*) However, if this shock manifold is known (also the values of ρ, p, v_λ on one side of it), then the jumps in v_λ, ρ, p may be determined.

We initiate our study of the discontinuity system for shock and contact manifolds, (59.21) through (59.23), by writing the first equation of this system in the expanded form

$$[\bar{\rho}\bar{v}_\lambda + \rho_1\bar{v}_\lambda + \bar{\rho}(v_\lambda)_1]\frac{\partial\phi}{\partial t} + [\overline{\rho v^\mu}\,\bar{v}_\lambda + \overline{\rho v^\mu}(v_\lambda)_1 + (\rho v^\mu)_1\bar{v}_\lambda]\frac{\partial\phi}{\partial x^\mu} + \bar{p}\frac{\partial\phi}{\partial x^\lambda} = 0.$$

Through use of the second jump relation (59.22), we may simplify the above equation and obtain

$$\rho_1\bar{v}_\lambda\left(\frac{\partial\phi}{\partial t} + v_1^\mu\frac{\partial\phi}{\partial x^\mu}\right) + \bar{p}\frac{\partial\phi}{\partial x^\lambda} = 0. \tag{59.25}$$

If we form the scalar product of this last equation and $e^{\alpha\beta\lambda}(\partial\phi/\partial x^\beta)$, we eliminate the unknown jump, $\bar{p}$, and obtain

$$\left(e^{\alpha\beta\lambda}\bar{v}_\lambda\frac{\partial\phi}{\partial x^\beta}\right)\left(\frac{\partial\phi}{\partial t} + v_1^\mu\frac{\partial\phi}{\partial x^\mu}\right) = 0.$$

The two possible solutions of the above are obtained by setting each factor equal to zero. The corresponding discontinuities will be denoted as contact and shock discontinuities. That is, along a *contact discontinuity*,

$$\frac{\partial\phi}{\partial t} + v_1^\mu\frac{\partial\phi}{\partial x^\mu} = 0 \tag{59.26}$$

and along a *shock discontinuity*,

$$e^{\alpha\beta\lambda}\bar{v}_\lambda\frac{\partial\phi}{\partial x^\beta} = 0. \tag{59.27}$$

[15] This is the author's point of view. Professor Erich Rothe has called the author's attention to the fact that in algebraic theory, criteria involving eliminants do exist for solving systems of nonlinear equations. The author knows of no such criteria for the system (59.21) through (59.23).

The contact discontinuity condition implies that *these discontinuity manifolds consist of families of stream lines.* By using the decomposition following (59.24), it is seen that instead of the contact condition (59.26) one may write

$$\frac{\partial \phi}{\partial t} + v_2^\mu \frac{\partial \phi}{\partial x^\mu} = 0.$$

On the other hand, *the shock discontinuity condition* implies that the *tangential component of velocity is continuous across a shock manifold.*

First, we consider the *contact discontinuities.* By expanding the second jump relation (59.22) and using the above contact condition, we find that along contact discontinuities

$$\bar{v}^\mu \frac{\partial \phi}{\partial x^\mu} = 0.$$

The above relation shows that *the normal component of velocity is continuous across a contact manifold.* Further, by use of the relations (59.25), and the above contact condition (59.26), we see that

$$\bar{p} = 0.$$

This means that the *pressure is continuous across a contact manifold.* From these results, we obtain the following conclusions as to the properties of contact manifolds:

(1) contact manifolds consist of families of stream lines;

(2) the normal component of velocity is continuous across a contact manifold; fluid mass is not transported across the discontinuity manifold;

(3) the tangential component of velocity is discontinuous across a contact manifold;

(4) the pressure is continuous across a contact manifold;

(5) the density is discontinuous (in general) across a contact manifold.

Since the contact manifolds consist of stream lines, it follows that the normal component of velocity at the contact manifold in the stationary case, $\frac{\partial \phi}{\partial t} = 0$, is zero. Hence, in this case, the velocity vector is tangent to the contact manifold. This type of discontinuity is equivalent to a vortex sheet.

Secondly, we consider the *shock manifolds*. Since the tangential component of velocity is continuous across the shock manifold, we may write

$$\bar{v}_\lambda = \left(\bar{v}^\mu \frac{\partial \phi}{\partial x^\mu}\frac{\partial \phi}{\partial x^\lambda}\right)\Big/\left(g^{\alpha\beta}\frac{\partial \phi}{\partial x^\alpha}\frac{\partial \phi}{\partial x^\beta}\right).$$

If we expand the second jump relation (59.22), multiply the resulting equation by

$$\frac{\partial \phi}{\partial x^\lambda}\Big/\left(g^{\alpha\beta}\frac{\partial \phi}{\partial x^\alpha}\frac{\partial \phi}{\partial x^\beta}\right),$$

and use the expression for $\bar{v}_\lambda$ derived in the preceding formula, we obtain the following relation between $\bar{v}_\lambda$ and ρ:

$$\bar{v}_\lambda = -\bar{p}\left(\frac{\partial \phi}{\partial t} + v_1^\mu \frac{\partial \phi}{\partial x^\mu}\right)\frac{\partial \phi}{\partial x^\lambda}\Big/(\rho_1 + \bar{\rho})g^{\alpha\beta}\frac{\partial \phi}{\partial x^\alpha}\frac{\partial \phi}{\partial x^\beta}.$$

Further, equation (59.25) shows that

$$\bar{v}_\lambda = -\bar{p}\frac{\partial \phi}{\partial x^\lambda}\Big/\rho_1\left(\frac{\partial \phi}{\partial t} + v_1^\mu \frac{\partial \phi}{\partial x^\mu}\right).$$

By equating the right-hand sides of the last two equations, we obtain the interesting relation

$$\bar{p}(\rho_1 + \bar{\rho})g^{\alpha\beta}\frac{\partial \phi}{\partial x^\alpha}\frac{\partial \phi}{\partial x^\beta} = \bar{p}\rho_1\left(\frac{\partial \phi}{\partial t} + v_1^\mu \frac{\partial \phi}{\partial x^\mu}\right)^2. \tag{59.28}$$

This formula may be used in showing that small disturbances propagate along characteristic manifolds [see Section 59(d)]. Further, this last relation is of some interest for the case of polytropic gases ($p = A\rho^\gamma$, A is a function of the entropy, $\gamma = 1.4$ for air at standard conditions). For such gases, it is easily shown that

$$\gamma p = \rho c^2.$$

Now consider a shock manifold which separates a region of "quiet" ($v_1^\lambda = 0$, $\rho_1 =$ constant, $p_1 =$ constant, $c_1^2 \neq 0$) from a moving fluid. By use of the above gas law and the above conditions in the region of "quiet," we find that (59.28) reduces to

$$\overline{\rho c^2}(\rho_1 + \bar{\rho})\, g^{\alpha\beta}\frac{\partial \phi}{\partial x^\alpha}\frac{\partial \phi}{\partial x^\beta} = \gamma\bar{\rho}\rho_1\left(\frac{\partial \phi}{\partial t}\right)^2.$$

Thus, if c^2, ρ are known, then one may determine the shock manifold.

Due to the nonlinear character of the jump equations (59.21) through (59.23), very little *general* theory exists for the shock manifolds. However, the one-dimensional shocks have been thoroughly studied. We refer the reader to the literature[16] for further details of this subject.

Problem 59.7: By use of the relation (59.28), verify that small disturbances propagate along the characteristic manifolds of Section 59(b).

Problem 59.8: For stationary shocks ($\partial\phi/\partial t = 0$), show that the shock conditions imply that Bernoulli's law (58.8) is valid across the shock.

(d) ***The Propagation of Small Disturbances; Wave Fronts.*** If we expand the jump relations (59.21), (59.22) by means of (59.24) and neglect the quadratic and cubic jumps, we obtain the relations

$$\rho_1\left(\frac{\partial\phi}{\partial t} + v_1^\mu\frac{\partial\phi}{\partial x^\mu}\right)\bar{v}_\lambda + \rho_1(v_\lambda)_1\frac{\partial\phi}{\partial x^\mu}\bar{v}^\mu + (v_\lambda)_1\left(\frac{\partial\phi}{\partial t} + v_1^\mu\frac{\partial\phi}{\partial x^\mu}\right)\bar{\rho} + \frac{\partial\phi}{\partial x^\lambda}\bar{p} = 0, \tag{59.29a}$$

$$\rho_1\frac{\partial\phi}{\partial x^\mu}\bar{v}^\mu + \left(v_1^\mu\frac{\partial\phi}{\partial x^\mu} + \frac{\partial\phi}{\partial t}\right)\bar{\rho} = 0. \tag{59.29b}$$

By use of the second relation (59.29b) we may replace the first equation of the system by the relation

$$\rho_1\left(\frac{\partial\phi}{\partial t} + v_1^\mu\frac{\partial\phi}{\partial x^\mu}\right)\bar{v}_\lambda + \frac{\partial\phi}{\partial x^\lambda}\bar{p} = 0. \tag{59.30}$$

The system (59.29b) and (59.30) consists of four linear equations in the five unknown jumps, $\bar{v}_\lambda$, $\bar{p}$, $\bar{\rho}$. Evidently, we must adjoin the jump relation (59.23) to this system. In order to avoid extensive computation, we shall assume that the entropy changes are negligible and

$$\bar{p} = c^2\bar{\rho}.$$

By solving (59.30) for $\bar{v}_\lambda$ and using this result to eliminate $\bar{v}_\lambda$ in (59.29b) we obtain the characteristic equation (59.18). This result is often stated in the following form: *Weak shocks are propagated along characteristic manifolds.*

At any given time, t_0, the characteristic discontinuity manifold S_2

$$\phi(x^\lambda, t_0) = \text{constant} = \bar{c},$$
$$t = t_0$$

[16] R. Courant and K. O. Friedrichs, *loc. cit.*

is a surface in space-time. *Such a surface is called a wave front.* By varying t_0, $\bar{c}$, we obtain ∞^2 wave fronts. If we fix $\bar{c}$ and vary t_0, we determine those wave fronts which are the space-like cross sections of a given characteristic manifold at various times. Finally, if we fix t_0 and vary $\bar{c}$, we obtain the Mach surfaces. For the case of steady flows, the Mach surfaces coincide with the characteristic surfaces.

We shall prove that $c = \sqrt{dp/d\rho}$ *is the velocity of the wave fronts on the characteristic manifolds determined by (59.18).* Let us consider a fluid particle whose Lagrangian coordinates are, a^λ. By expressing the characteristic manifolds in the Lagrangian form

$$\phi[x^\lambda(a^\mu, t), t] = \bar{c}$$

we see that to each value of t there corresponds a value of $\bar{c}$ and hence a wave front. Evidently

$$\frac{d\phi}{dt} = \frac{d\bar{c}}{dt}$$

is a measure of the rate at which these wave fronts propagate. If we follow the fluid particle with coordinates a^λ on the wave fronts, we find that

$$\frac{d\phi}{dt} = \frac{\partial \phi}{\partial t} + v^\lambda \frac{\partial \phi}{\partial x^\lambda}.$$

Squaring both sides of this equation and using the relation (59.18), we may express the above equation as

$$\left(\frac{d\phi}{dt}\right)^2 = c^2 \left[g^{\lambda\mu} \frac{\partial \phi}{\partial x^\lambda} \frac{\partial \phi}{\partial x^\mu} \right].$$

The expression in the brackets in this last equation represents the magnitude of the *x^λ-space gradient of ϕ.* That is, if the arc length element along the x^λ-space orthogonal trajectories of the wave fronts, with $\bar{c}$ variable, is denoted by ds, then

$$g^{\lambda\mu} \frac{\partial \phi}{\partial x^\lambda} \frac{\partial \phi}{\partial x^\mu} = \left(\frac{d\phi}{ds}\right)^2.$$

From these last two equations, we find that

$$\frac{ds}{dt} = c.$$

Thus, the scalar, c, is the ratio of the distance, perpendicular to the wave front, moved by a particle on the front, to the time. This ratio seems to be a reasonable measure of the local velocity of a wave front.

In the two-dimensional and time illustration, Figure 64, a geometric picture of the above result is shown. The fluid particle is located at P on the wave front $\phi = \bar{c}$ at time $t = t_0$. At time, $t = t_0 + \Delta t$ this fluid particle moves to $'P$ on the wave front, $\phi = \bar{c} + \Delta\bar{c}$. The element PQ is an orthogonal trajectory of the wave fronts

$$\begin{cases} \phi = \bar{c} \\ t = t_0 \end{cases} \qquad \begin{cases} \phi = \bar{c} + \Delta\bar{c} \\ t = t_0 \end{cases}$$

and Δs is the arc length along this orthogonal trajectory. One often says that "c is the local sound speed."

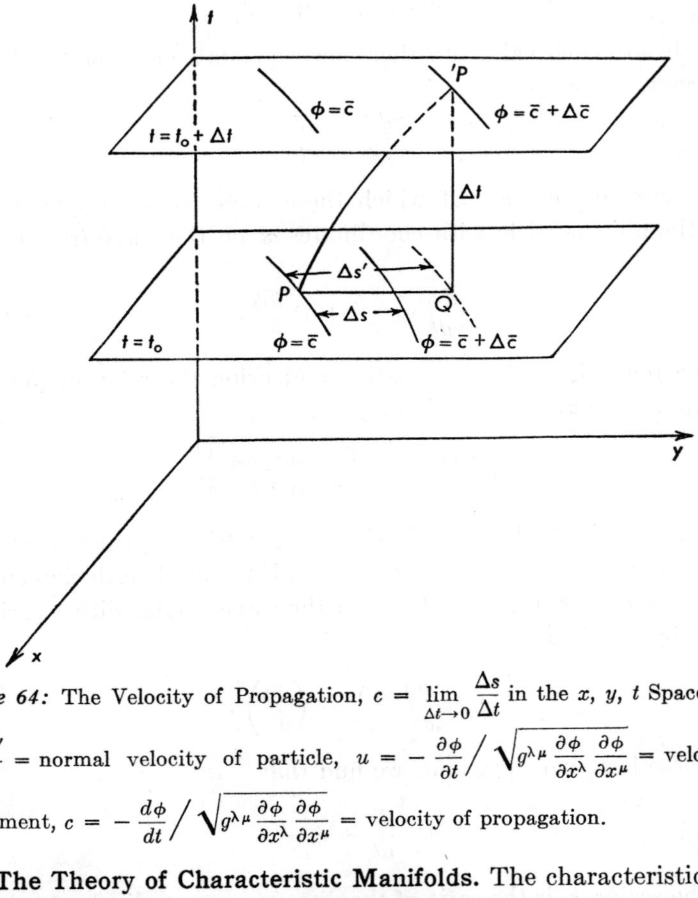

Figure 64: The Velocity of Propagation, $c = \lim\limits_{\Delta t \to 0} \dfrac{\Delta s}{\Delta t}$ in the x, y, t Space. Note, $q_n = \dfrac{ds'}{dt}$ = normal velocity of particle, $u = -\dfrac{\partial\phi}{\partial t}\Big/\sqrt{g^{\lambda\mu}\dfrac{\partial\phi}{\partial x^\lambda}\dfrac{\partial\phi}{\partial x^\mu}}$ = velocity of displacement, $c = -\dfrac{d\phi}{dt}\Big/\sqrt{g^{\lambda\mu}\dfrac{\partial\phi}{\partial x^\lambda}\dfrac{\partial\phi}{\partial x^\mu}}$ = velocity of propagation.

60. The Theory of Characteristic Manifolds. The characteristic manifolds were introduced in Section 59(b). Here, we shall show that these manifolds play an important role in simplifying the equations of motion (59.1). In order to do this, we shall introduce the bicharacteristic curves and then discuss the formulation of the equations of motion in terms of the characteristic variables.

(a) ***The Bicharacteristic Curves.*** In Section 48(c), we introduced the terms, characteristic directions and curves. To avoid confusion with the characteristic manifolds, defined by (59.18), we shall call these curves "bicharacteristic curves" in the future. With this terminology, we may say that in Section 48 we discussed the bicharacteristic directions and curves associated with a linear first-order partial differential equation. As we saw, these curves play an essential role in determining the solutions of the partial differential equation. In the case of a nonlinear first-order partial differential equation, such as (59.18), one may generalize the previous theory of the linear first-order partial differential equation and introduce bicharacteristic cones of directions and families of curves. The theory is classical. Hence, we shall offer a brief geometric interpretation and refer the reader to the literature[17] for more details.

Let us assume that some solution of the equations of motion is given and hence v^λ, c^2, are known as functions of t, x^λ. Then at each point of space-time (t, x^λ), the characteristic equation (59.18) defines ∞^2 possible normal vectors $(\partial\phi/\partial t, \partial\phi/\partial x^\lambda)$ to the characteristic manifolds. We say that (59.18) defines a *cone of normals* to the characteristic manifolds. In the linear case, at each point, equation (48.9) with $k = 1$ defines a plane of normal vectors. In the nonlinear case, if we move from the point $P\ (t, x^\lambda)$ to the arbitrary point $'P\ (t + dt, x^\lambda + dx^\lambda)$ in space-time, then at $'P$, one determines another *cone of normals*. Let us move from $'P$ back toward P in the direction determined by

$$dx^1 : dx^2 : dx^3 : dt.$$

For a proper displacement, the normal cone at $'P$ will in the limit intersect the cone at P in a *specific normal element* of this latter cone. Let us denote this normal element by the unit vector

$$n_j = \frac{\partial\phi}{\partial x^j} \Big/ \sqrt{\left(\frac{\partial\phi}{\partial t}\right)^2 + g^{\lambda\mu}\frac{\partial\phi}{\partial x^\lambda}\frac{\partial\phi}{\partial x^\mu}}$$

where $x^0 = t$. Further, let us denote the above displacement by the unit vector

$$t^j = \frac{dx^j}{ds} \tag{60.1}$$

[17] R. Courant and D. Hilbert, *Methoden der Mathematischen Physik,* Interscience Publishers, New York, Vol. II.

where ds is the space-time arc length element of a curve in the direction of the displacement. *The vector, t^i, of (60.1) is called the bicharacteristic direction associated with the normal element, n_j.* Corresponding to the ∞^2 normals of the cone (59.18), one may determine ∞^2 bicharacteristic associated directions. At each point P these bicharacteristic directions form a cone which is called the cone of bicharacteristics. In Figure 65, t^i and n^i, and $\bar{t}^i$ and $\bar{n}^i$ are two pairs of associated directions; the first direction in each pair belongs to the bicharacteristic cone at P and the second direction in each pair belongs to the normal (or characteristic) cone at P.

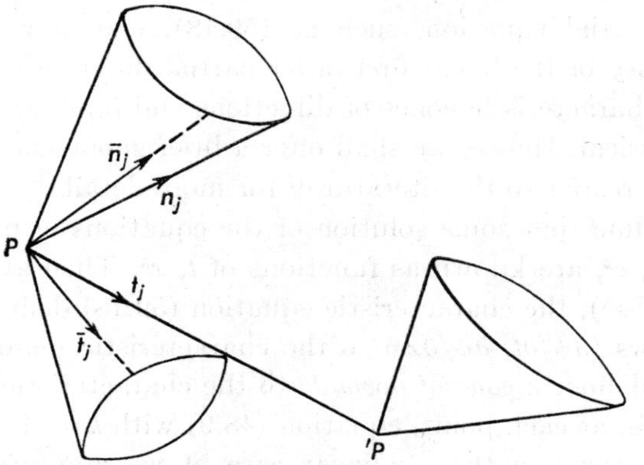

Figure 65: The Normal Cones at P, $'P$ and the Bicharacteristic Cone at P

The above construction shows how one may determine the bicharacteristic directions at any point P. By picking one bicharacteristic direction at P, and choosing *any other bicharacteristic direction* at a neighboring point $'P$ (lying on the initial bicharacteristic line element), etc., one may generate infinitely many curves. These curves are called the *focal curves.* It is shown in the classical theory that if σ is a proper parameter along any one of these curves, then these curves are determined in space-time [for the case of (59.18)] by the differential equations

$$\begin{aligned} \frac{dx^\lambda}{d\sigma} &= v^\lambda \frac{\partial \phi}{\partial t} + (v^\lambda v^\mu - c^2 g^{\lambda\mu}) \frac{\partial \phi}{\partial x^\mu} \\ \frac{dt}{d\sigma} &= \frac{\partial \phi}{\partial t} + v^\mu \frac{\partial \phi}{\partial x^\mu}. \end{aligned} \tag{60.2}$$

Instead of choosing the bicharacteristic direction at the neighboring point $'P$ in an arbitrary manner, we shall impose a definite manner of choice. Let us require that the normal vectors n^j at P and $'n^j$ at $'P$ are normal to a piece of hypersurface. In this way we can determine one (or more) definite directions at $'P$ for extending the original bicharacteristic direction. The condition that n^j and $'n^j$ are normal to a hypersurface involves an integrability condition which is called the *strip condition* in the literature. For the characteristic surfaces of (59.18) this strip condition is [where, t^μ, x^λ, $\partial\phi/\partial t$, $\partial\phi/\partial x^\lambda$ are considered to be independent variables in forming the derivatives in the right-hand side of (60.3)]:

$$\begin{aligned}\frac{d}{d\sigma}\left(\frac{\partial\phi}{\partial x^\lambda}\right) &= -\frac{1}{2}\frac{\partial}{\partial x^\lambda}\left[\left(\frac{\partial\phi}{\partial t}\right)^2 + 2v^\mu\frac{\partial\phi}{\partial x^\mu}\frac{\partial\phi}{\partial t} + (v^\alpha v^\mu - c^2 g^{\alpha\mu})\frac{\partial\phi}{\partial x^\alpha}\frac{\partial\phi}{\partial x^\mu}\right] \\ \frac{d}{d\sigma}\left(\frac{\partial\phi}{\partial t}\right) &= -\frac{1}{2}\frac{\partial}{\partial t}\left[\left(\frac{\partial\phi}{\partial t}\right)^2 + 2v^\mu\frac{\partial\phi}{\partial x^\mu}\frac{\partial\phi}{\partial t} + (v^\alpha v^\mu - c^2 g^{\alpha\mu})\frac{\partial\phi}{\partial x^\alpha}\frac{\partial\phi}{\partial x^\mu}\right].\end{aligned} \tag{60.3}$$

Essentially, this condition tells one how to choose successive normals. When n^j are chosen so as to satisfy the strip condition (60.3), the associated bicharacteristic directions determine the *bicharacteristic curves.* The system (60.2) and (60.3) of ordinary differential equations in x^λ, t, $\partial\phi/\partial x^\lambda$, $\partial\phi/\partial t$ is called the *characteristic system.* It is easily shown that through each point of space-time there passes one solution curve (a bicharacteristic) of the characteristic system determined by an initial set of values of n_j or $(\partial\phi/\partial t, \partial\phi/\partial x^\lambda)$. Any family of ∞^2 bicharacteristic curves determines a characteristic hypersurface, $\phi(x^\lambda, t) =$ constant. Thus, in space-time the bicharacteristic directions determined by (60.2) are normal to the corresponding normal vector, n^j or $(\partial\phi/\partial t, \partial\phi/\partial x^\lambda)$. This is easily verified by use of (60.2).

In order to gain some insight into the nature of the bicharacteristic directions, let us consider (60.2) in some detail. It is easily shown that the characteristic equation (59.18) may be written in the form

$$\frac{\partial\phi}{\partial t} + v^\mu\frac{\partial\phi}{\partial x^\mu} = \pm c\sqrt{g^{\lambda\mu}\frac{\partial\phi}{\partial x^\lambda}\frac{\partial\phi}{\partial x^\mu}}. \tag{60.4}$$

With the aid of the above we may write the second relation of (60.2) in the form

$$\frac{dt}{d\sigma} = \pm c\sqrt{g^{\lambda\mu}\frac{\partial\phi}{\partial x^\mu}\frac{\partial\phi}{\partial x^\lambda}}. \tag{60.5}$$

Let us introduce the *space-normalized* components, $\bar{n}_j$, of the normal vector n_j by means of the relations

$$\bar{n}_\lambda = \frac{\partial\phi}{\partial x^\lambda}\Big/\sqrt{g^{\alpha\beta}\frac{\partial\phi}{\partial x^\alpha}\frac{\partial\phi}{\partial x^\beta}}, \qquad \bar{n}_0 = \frac{\partial\phi}{\partial t}\Big/\sqrt{g^{\alpha\beta}\frac{\partial\phi}{\partial x^\alpha}\frac{\partial\phi}{\partial x^\beta}}.$$

Forming the quotient of the first relation in (60.2) and (60.5), we obtain

$$\frac{dx^\lambda}{dt} = \pm \left[v^\lambda \frac{\partial \phi}{\partial t} + (v^\lambda v^\mu - c^2 g^{\lambda\mu}) \frac{\partial \phi}{\partial x^\mu} \right] \Big/ c \sqrt{g^{\alpha\beta} \frac{\partial \phi}{\partial x^\alpha} \frac{\partial \phi}{\partial x^\beta}}.$$

If we eliminate $\partial\phi/\partial t$ from this last equation by use of (60.4), we find that

$$\frac{dx^\lambda}{dt} = v^\lambda \pm \left[\left(c g^{\lambda\mu} \frac{\partial \phi}{\partial x^\mu} \right) \Big/ \sqrt{g^{\alpha\beta} \frac{\partial \phi}{\partial x^\alpha} \frac{\partial \phi}{\partial x^\beta}} \right].$$

By introducing the space-normalized vector $\bar{n}_j$ into this last relation, we obtain the result

$$\frac{dx^\lambda}{dt} = v^\lambda \pm c\bar{n}^\lambda. \tag{60.6}$$

The equation (60.6) shows why one-dimensional non-steady flows are easily treated but two- or three-dimensional non-steady flows are difficult to study. In the one-dimensional, non-steady case, x^λ has the components $(x, 0, 0)$; v^λ has the components $(u, 0, 0)$; and $\bar{n}^\lambda$ has the components $(1, 0, 0)$. Thus (60.6) reduces to the well-known equation of Riemann for the bicharacteristics

$$\frac{\partial x}{\partial \alpha} = (u \pm c) \frac{\partial t}{\partial \alpha}$$

where α is a parameter along the family of bicharacteristics. On the other hand, if the flow is non-steady and more than one-dimensional, the $\bar{n}^\lambda$ vector enters in a rather complicated geometric manner.

In the case of *supersonic steady* flows, $q^2 > c^2$, the bicharacteristic equations (60.2) are rather easy to characterize geometrically. Since the characteristic surfaces are independent of time, the characteristic equation (59.18) reduces to

$$a^{\lambda\mu} \frac{\partial \phi}{\partial x^\lambda} \frac{\partial \phi}{\partial x^\mu} = 0 \tag{60.7}$$

where the tensor $a^{\lambda\mu}$ is defined by the relation

$$a^{\lambda\mu} = v^\lambda v^\mu - c^2 g^{\lambda\mu}.$$

Further, the bicharacteristic equations (60.2) may be written as

$$\frac{dx^\lambda}{d\sigma} = a^{\lambda\mu} \frac{\partial \phi}{\partial x^\mu}. \tag{60.8}$$

If we introduce the unit normal vector of the characteristic surfaces

$$n_u = \frac{\partial \phi}{\partial x^\mu} \Big/ \sqrt{g^{\alpha\beta} \frac{\partial \phi}{\partial x^\alpha} \frac{\partial \phi}{\partial x^\beta}}$$

into the characteristic equation (60.7), and the bicharacteristic relation, (60.8), we obtain the results

$$v^\lambda n_\lambda = \pm c$$

$$\frac{dx^\lambda}{d\sigma} = c\sqrt{g^{\alpha\beta}\frac{\partial\phi}{\partial x^\alpha}\frac{\partial\phi}{\partial x^\beta}}\,(v^\lambda - cn^\lambda).$$

These relations have immediate geometric interpretations. The first equation states that the *velocity vector is the axis of the normal cone* in steady flow, and *the projection of* v^λ *onto* n^λ *has the value* c [the local sound speed—Section 59(d)]. The signs ($\pm$) have no essential significance in the case of three-dimensional flows. We may express this result by introducing a unit vector t^λ lying along the intersection of a plane through n^λ and v^λ with the characteristic surface and writing

$$v^\lambda = cn^\lambda + \sqrt{q^2 - c^2}\,t^\lambda. \tag{60.9}$$

By substituting this formula into the second of the above relations, we see that t^λ *lies along the bicharacteristic direction*. Further, (60.9) shows that

$$v^\lambda t_\lambda = \sqrt{q^2 - c^2}$$

and hence that the velocity vector lies along the axis of the bicharacteristic cone. We illustrate these results in Figure 66. The relation (60.9) is

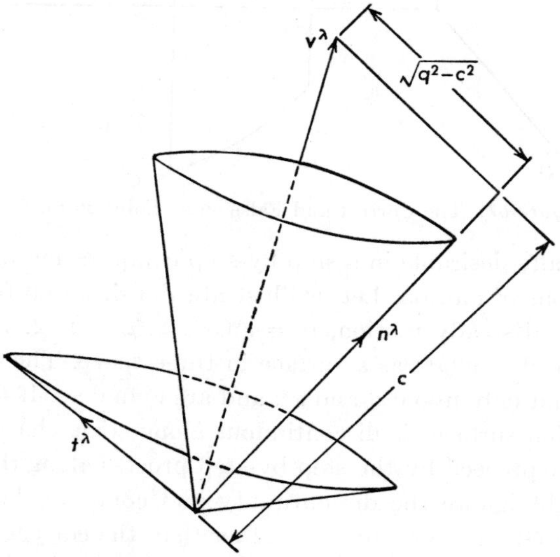

Figure 66: The Normal Cone, n^λ, and the Bicharacteristic Cone, t^λ, in Steady Supersonic Flow

usually referred to as the *first characteristic condition*. Essentially, this equation defines the directions t^λ, n^λ.

If $q^2 < c^2$, the bicharacteristic curves and the characteristic surfaces become imaginary. The flow is said to be *subsonic*. In the case of non-steady flows, the characteristic surfaces and the bicharacteristic curves are always real.

(b) ***The Equations of Motion in Terms of Characteristic Variables.*** We limit our discussion to the *steady supersonic* flow case. Our problem is to simplify the equations of motion. In particular, we would like to reduce the number of independent variables which enter into the equations of motion. Further, we would like to express the equations of motion in terms of independent variables related to the characteristic surfaces.

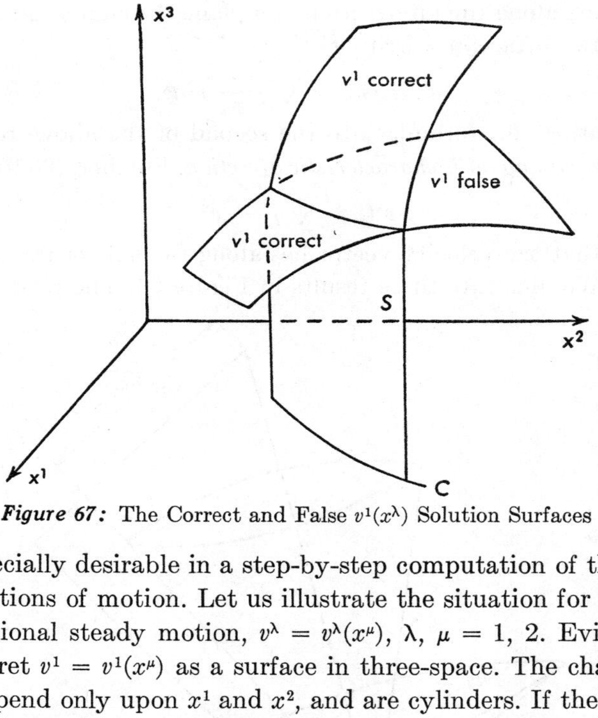

Figure 67: The Correct and False $v^1(x^\lambda)$ Solution Surfaces

This is especially desirable in a step-by-step computation of the solution of the equations of motion. Let us illustrate the situation for the case of two-dimensional steady motion, $v^\lambda = v^\lambda(x^\mu)$, λ, $\mu = 1, 2$. Evidently, we may interpret $v^1 = v^1(x^\mu)$ as a surface in three-space. The characteristic surfaces depend only upon x^1 and x^2, and are cylinders. If the derivative of v^1 (a solution surface) is discontinuous along some characteristic surface, S, and we proceed by the step-by-step process along the x^1,x^2-plane, then one might ignore the discontinuity and compute the extension of the v^1 surface (the false v^1 surface) rather than the correct v^1 (see Figure 67). This difficulty may be avoided by proceeding along the curves C of the characteristic surfaces S during the step-by-step computation.

To introduce the characteristic variables, we study a natural coordinate system in Euclidean three-space. Our procedure is similar to that used by

E. W. Titt,[18] whose method is an extension of the method of H. Lewy.[19] Consider an arbitrary surface (the initial surface) along which the velocity vector is given. Let us introduce a family of ∞^1 curves with unit tangent vector, l^λ, on this given surface. We make one restriction on this family of curves; we require that the plane perpendicular to l^λ at any point P shall cut the normal cone at P in two distinct generators. Thus, at each point of the given initial surface, two distinct normals to characteristic surfaces are defined. By considering the characteristic equation (60.7) as a partial differential equation for a characteristic surface and knowing two normals along each curve l^λ of the initial surface, two

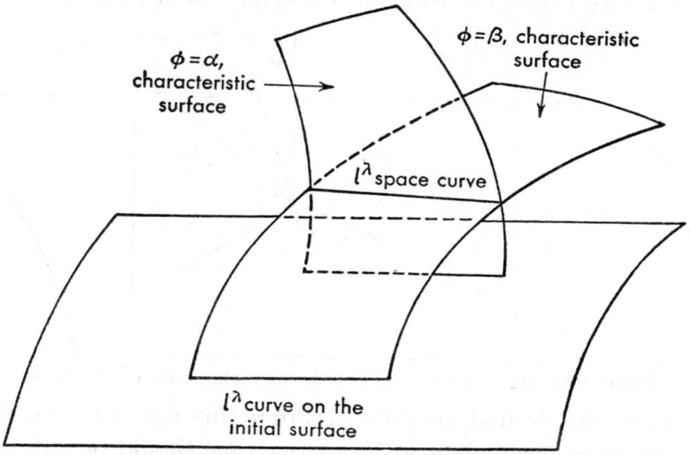

Figure 68: The Initial Surface and Two Members of the Families of Characteristic Surfaces

families of characteristic surfaces are defined throughout the flow space. Evidently the two families of characteristic surfaces intersect the initial surface in the curves l^λ. We define l^λ in space as the unit vector of a space family of curves which are the intersections of the two families of characteristic surfaces, $\phi = \alpha$ (a constant) and $\phi = \beta$ (a constant). This situation is indicated in Figure 68. If through each point of a space region there passes one and only one curve of a family of curves, we say that the family determines a *congruence* of curves. This means that three important congruences of curves exist in the flow space: (1) the congruence, l^λ; (2) the congruence of bicharacteristics with unit tangent vector, t^λ, which lie on the characteristic surfaces, $\phi = \alpha$; (3) the congruence of bichar-

[18] E. W. Titt, "The Three-Dimensional Hyperbolic Equation," *Annals of Math.*, 2nd Series, Vol. 40, 1939.

[19] R. Courant and D. Hilbert, Vol. II, *loc. cit.*, p. 327.

acteristics with unit tangent vector, $'t^\lambda$, which lie on the characteristic surfaces, $\phi = \beta$.

It is important to note that on the initial given surface, one may determine the l^λ curves so that: (1) *l^λ is orthogonal to both of the congruences t^λ, $'t^\lambda$*; (2) *l^λ is orthogonal to v^λ*. This may be accomplished in the following manner. At any point P of the initial surface S pass a plane, M, through the given v^λ and the normal, i^λ, to the initial surface. This plane will intersect the normal cone in two initial vectors, n^λ, $'n^\lambda$ which are normal to characteristic surfaces (to be constructed). Further, the corresponding bicharacteristics, t^λ, $'t^\lambda$ will lie in this plane [see (60.9)]. If we construct the vector l^λ (see Figure 69) which is orthogonal to M at the point P then

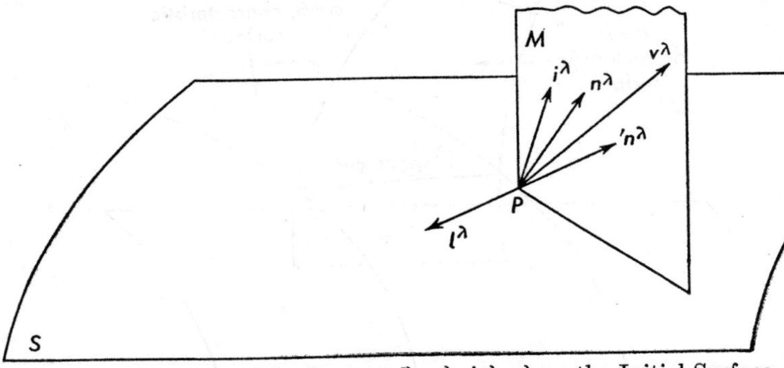

Figure 69: The Vectors, l^λ, n^λ, $'n^\lambda$, v^λ on the Initial Surface, S

l^λ will satisfy the desired conditions. From this construction, it would appear that when l^λ is extended into space, one should be able to prove that l^λ is always orthogonal to v^λ. This result is valid in the two following cases: (1) *plane flows;* (2) *flows with axial symmetry.*

For plane flows (Figure 70), the initial surface, S, is a cylindrical surface with generators parallel to the z-axis; the velocity vector, v^λ, is parallel to the xOy-plane and is such that

$$v^\lambda(x, y, z) = v^\lambda(x, y, 0).$$

By passing a plane, M (the x,y-plane), through v^λ and the vector i^λ, normal to S, and determining the intersections of M with the normal cone at P (say, n^λ, $'n^\lambda$), we see that the desired vector l^λ lies along the generators of S. The two families of characteristic surfaces are cylindrical surfaces with generators parallel to the z-axis. It is evident that the intersection curves of these surfaces define a space congruence l^λ which possesses the desired two properties: (1) l^λ is orthogonal to the congruences t^λ, $'t^\lambda$; (2) l^λ is orthogonal to v^λ. In the two-dimensional analysis of plane flows, one considers the initial curve, C, rather than the cylindrical surface, S.

For flows with axial symmetry (Figure 71), the initial surface, S, is a surface of revolution about Oz which is determined by a meridian curve, C, lying in a meridian plane, M. The initial velocity vectors lie in the meridian planes. Further, the normals, i^λ, to S lie in the meridian planes. Hence, these planes are the planes M of our previous theory. The congruence l^λ coincides with the small circles of S. Due to the symmetry, it is evident that the characteristic surfaces are surfaces of revolution

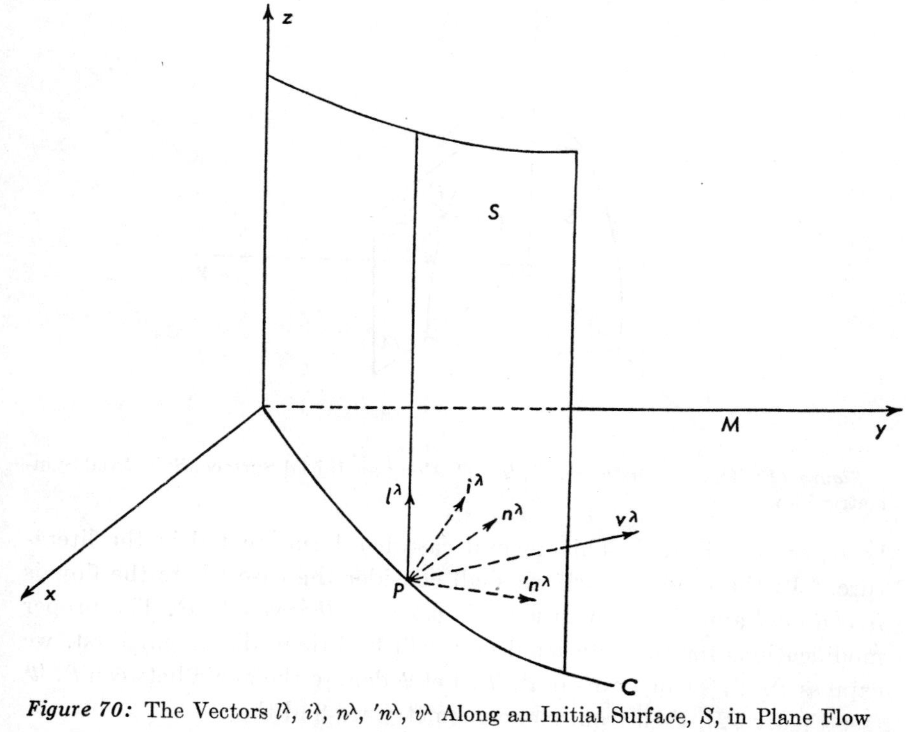

Figure 70: The Vectors l^λ, i^λ, n^λ, $'n^\lambda$, v^λ Along an Initial Surface, S, in Plane Flow

about Oz. The space congruence consists of circles which lie in planes perpendicular to Oz and possess the two desired properties.

In spite of the existence of the above examples, the following statement is still a conjecture: *If l^λ is orthogonal to v^λ on the initial surface, then l^λ is orthogonal to v^λ in space.* A proof of this result would simplify the "characteristic system" which we shall discuss shortly. From the above examples, one sees one further result. *The congruences t^λ, $'t^\lambda$ determine a family of surfaces in the flow space.* In his paper, Titt has shown by special methods that this result is valid in the case of the general hyperbolic nonlinear equation in three dimensions. It would appear desirable to connect the theory of integrability conditions for a linear system (see Section 48) with those of the present nonlinear equation (59.18) or (60.7) and furnish a general proof of this result.

With the aid of the above preliminary work, we are in a position to obtain a *formulation of the equations of motion in terms of the characteristic variables*. If we assume that l^λ is *not orthogonal* to v^λ, t^λ, $'t^\lambda$, then the theory

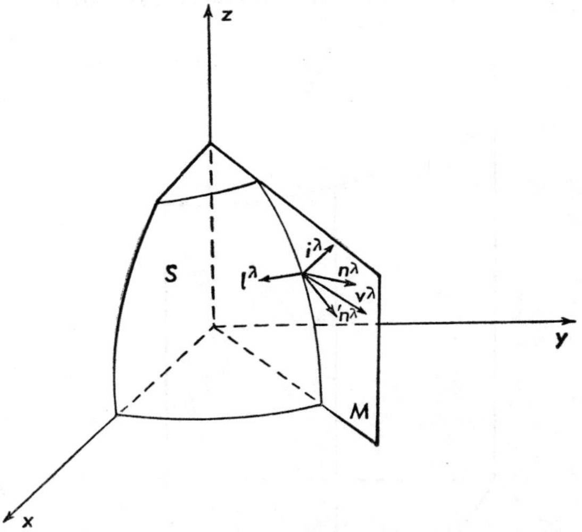

Figure 71: The Vectors l^λ, i^λ, n^λ, $'n^\lambda$, v^λ Along an Initial Surface, S, in Axial Symmetric Flows

becomes complicated. This general case has been treated in the literature.[20] In the present work we shall consider the case where the flow is *irrotational* and the l^λ congruence is *always orthogonal* to v^λ. The proper modifications for the rotational case will be briefly discussed. First, we express v^λ, n^λ, $'n^\lambda$ in terms of t^λ, $'t^\lambda$. Let ψ denote the angle between t^λ, $'t^\lambda$ (see Figure 72), then from plane geometry we find that

$$\cos\frac{\psi}{2} = \frac{\sqrt{q^2 - c^2}}{q}, \qquad s = \frac{q}{2}\sec\frac{\psi}{2} = \frac{q^2}{2\sqrt{q^2 - c^2}}.$$

By use of the above relations and Figure 72, we obtain the formula

$$v^\lambda = \frac{q^2}{2\sqrt{q^2 - c^2}}(t^\lambda + 't^\lambda). \tag{60.10}$$

[20] C. L. Dolph and N. Coburn, "The Method of Characteristics in Three-Dimensional, Steady, Irrotational Supersonic Flows," Symposium in Applied Math., Vol. I. American Mathematical Society, New York, 1949.

This equation is essentially another formulation of the first characteristic condition (60.9). By substituting (60.9) into (60.10), the following expression is obtained

$$n^\lambda = \frac{2c^2 - q^2}{2c\sqrt{q^2 - c^2}} t^\lambda + \frac{q^2}{2c\sqrt{q^2 - c^2}} {'t^\lambda}. \qquad (60.11)$$

Use of a similar substitution enables one to write

$$'n^\lambda = \frac{2c^2 - q^2}{2c\sqrt{q^2 - c^2}} {'t^\lambda} + \frac{q^2}{2c\sqrt{q^2 - c^2}} t^\lambda.$$

Now, we decompose the tensor, $\nabla_\mu v_\lambda$, with respect to the orthogonal

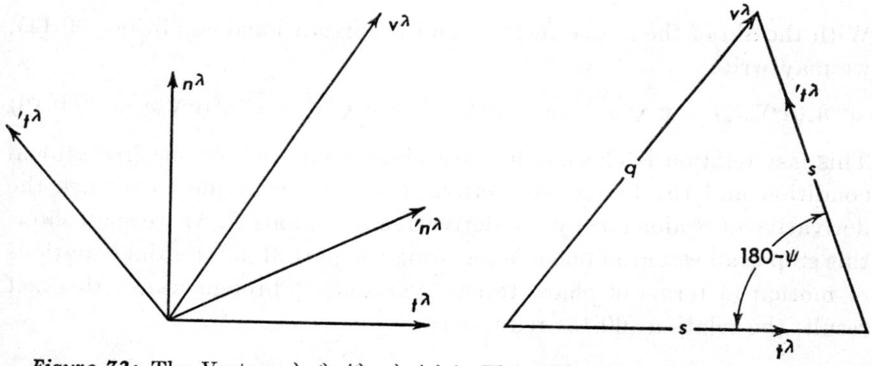

Figure 72: The Vectors v^λ, t^λ, $'t^\lambda$, n^λ, $'n^\lambda$ in Three-Dimensional Steady Supersonic Flow

triads (see Section 47) $(n^\lambda, t^\lambda, l^\lambda)$, $('n^\lambda, 't^\lambda, l^\lambda)$. This is accomplished by writing

$$\nabla_\mu v_\lambda = n_\mu a_\lambda + t_\mu b_\lambda + l_\mu c_\lambda = {'n_\mu}\, {'a_\lambda} + {'t_\mu}\, {'b_\lambda} + l_\mu\, {'c_\lambda}$$

where a_λ, b_λ, c_λ, $'a_\lambda$, $'b_\lambda$, $'c_\lambda$ are unknown vectors. By use of the scalar product, we obtain

$$a_\lambda = n^\mu \nabla_\mu v_\lambda, \qquad b_\lambda = t^\mu \nabla_\mu v_\lambda, \qquad c_\lambda = l^\mu \nabla_\mu v_\lambda \qquad (60.12)$$

and similar relations for $'a_\lambda$, $'b_\lambda$, $'c_\lambda$ in terms of $'n_\lambda$, $'t_\lambda$, l_λ. We shall use the above decomposition of $\nabla_\mu v_\lambda$ very shortly.

For steady, isentropic, irrotational flows, the equations of motion (59.1) and the continuity relation (59.2) may be expressed in a simplified form. By solving for $\nabla_\mu \rho$ in the equations of motion and substituting into the equation of continuity, we obtain the relation

$$a^{\lambda\mu} \nabla_\lambda v_\mu = 0, \qquad a^{\lambda\mu} = v^\lambda v^\mu - c^2 g^{\lambda\mu}. \qquad (60.13)$$

The irrotationality condition may be expressed by

$$\nabla_\mu v_\lambda = \nabla_\lambda v_\mu, \qquad \text{or} \qquad v_\lambda = \nabla_\lambda \Omega \tag{60.14}$$

where Ω is the velocity potential.

Our problem is to express the system of equations (60.10), (60.13), and (60.14) in terms of derivatives along the t^λ, $'t^\lambda$, l^λ congruences. If we substitute the orthogonal decomposition of $\nabla_\mu v_\lambda$ into the relation (60.13), we obtain

$$a^{\lambda\mu}n_\lambda(n^\alpha\nabla_\alpha v_\mu) + a^{\lambda\mu}t_\lambda(t^\alpha\nabla_\alpha v_\mu) + a^{\lambda\mu}l_\lambda(l^\alpha\nabla_\alpha v_\mu) = 0. \tag{60.15}$$

A relation similar to the above is valid for the primed variables, $'t^\lambda$, $'n^\lambda$, and l^λ. Through use of (60.9) and the definition of $a^{\lambda\mu}$, we find that

$$a^{\lambda\mu}n_\lambda = (v^\lambda v^\mu - c^2 q^{\lambda\mu})n_\lambda = c(v^\mu - cn^\mu) = c\sqrt{q^2 - c^2}\, t^\mu.$$

With the aid of the above relation and the irrotational condition (60.14), we may write

$$a^{\lambda\mu}n_\lambda(n^\alpha\nabla_\alpha v_\mu) = c\sqrt{q^2 - c^2}\, t^\mu(n^\alpha\nabla_\alpha v_\mu) = c\sqrt{q^2 - c^2}\, n^\mu(t^\alpha\nabla_\alpha v_\mu). \tag{60.16}$$

This last relation is of some interest since it shows how the irrotational condition and the first characteristic condition combine to replace the derivative of v^λ along n^λ by the derivative of v^λ along t^λ. As we shall show, this step is an essential one in expressing the partial differential equations of motion in terms of characteristic variables. Through use of this last result, the relation (60.15) reduces to

$$(a^{\lambda\mu}t_\lambda + c\sqrt{q^2 - c^2}\, n^\mu)t^\alpha\nabla_\alpha v_\mu + (a^{\lambda\mu}l_\lambda)l^\alpha\nabla_\alpha v_\mu = 0.$$

By evaluating the vectors in the parenthesis of the above equation, we obtain

$$a^{\lambda\mu}t_\lambda + c\sqrt{q^2 - c^2}\, n^\mu = 2\sqrt{q^2 - c^2}\, v^\mu - q^2 t^\mu$$
$$a^{\lambda\mu}l_\lambda = -c^2 l^\mu.$$

Hence, (60.15) may be reduced to the form

$$(2\sqrt{q^2 - c^2}\, v^\mu - q^2 t^\mu)(t^\alpha\nabla_\alpha v_\mu) - c^2 l^\mu(l^\alpha\nabla_\alpha v_\mu) = 0. \tag{60.17}$$

The corresponding equation in the prime variables is

$$(2\sqrt{q^2 - c^2}\, v^\mu - q^2\, 't^\mu)('t^\alpha\nabla_\alpha v_\mu) - c^2 l^\mu(l^\alpha\nabla_\alpha v_\mu) = 0.$$

These last two equations are usually referred to as *the second characteristic conditions;* these relations express the equations of motion in terms of derivatives along the t^λ, $'t^\lambda$, l^λ directions.

Further, one may express the irrotational condition (60.14) in terms of differentiations along the directions t^λ, $'t^\lambda$, l^λ. To do this, we form the scalar products of that equation with the pairs, $t^\lambda\ 't^\mu$, $t^\lambda l^\mu$, $'t^\lambda l^\mu$ and obtain

$$\begin{aligned} t^\lambda('t^\mu\nabla_\mu v_\lambda) &= 't^\lambda(t^\mu\nabla_\mu v_\lambda) \\ t^\lambda(l^\mu\nabla_\mu v_\lambda) &= l^\lambda(t^\mu\nabla_\mu v_\lambda) \\ 't^\lambda(l^\mu\nabla_\mu v_\lambda) &= l^\lambda('t^\mu\nabla_\mu v_\lambda). \end{aligned} \tag{60.18}$$

The above procedure must be altered to treat the cases of isentropic, rotational flows or non-isentropic, rotational flows. The treatment of both cases is similar. However, the first case involves fewer technical difficulties and will be briefly discussed.[21] If the vorticity is assumed to be nonzero, then one may easily modify the previous second characteristic conditions and irrotational conditions. That is, instead of the equation (60.14), we must write

$$\nabla_\mu v_\lambda = \nabla_\lambda v_\mu + 2\omega_{\mu\lambda} \tag{60.19}$$

where $\omega_{\mu\lambda}$ is the *vorticity tensor*. Note the *vorticity vector*, ω^α, is related to the vorticity tensor $\omega_{\mu\lambda}$ by the relations

$$\omega^\alpha = \frac{e^{\alpha\lambda\mu}}{\sqrt{g}}\,\omega_{\lambda\mu}, \qquad 2\omega_{\beta\rho} = \sqrt{g}\,e_{\alpha\beta\rho}\omega^\alpha.$$

Hence (60.16) must be replaced by

$$\begin{aligned} a^{\lambda\mu}n_\lambda(n^\alpha\nabla_\alpha v_\mu) &= c\sqrt{q^2 - c^2}\,t^\mu n^\alpha(\nabla_\mu v_\alpha + 2\omega_{\alpha\mu}) \\ &= c\sqrt{q^2 - c^2}\,n^\alpha[t^\mu\nabla_\mu v_\alpha + 2t^\mu\omega_{\alpha\mu}]. \end{aligned}$$

By use of the first characteristic condition (60.9) we may eliminate n^α from the above relation. Then, proceeding as in the irrotational case, we may show that the second characteristic relation corresponding to (60.17) is

$$(2\sqrt{q^2 - c^2}\,v^\mu - q^2t^\mu)(t^\alpha\nabla_\alpha v_\mu) - c^2l^\mu(l^\alpha\nabla_\alpha v_\mu) + 2\sqrt{q^2 - c^2}\,t^\mu v^\alpha\omega_{\alpha\mu} = 0.$$

Similarly, if the term, $2\sqrt{q^2 - c^2}\,'t^\mu v^\alpha\omega_{\alpha\mu}$, is added to the left-hand side of the equation following (60.17) we obtain the new second characteristic relation involving the prime variables, $'t^\mu$. Further, by forming the scalar products of the vorticity relations (60.19) with $t^\lambda\ 't^\mu$, $t^\lambda l^\mu$, $'t^\lambda l^\mu$, the formulas *corresponding* to (60.18) are obtained. Finally, by the procedure of Section 48(e), it may be shown that the integrability condition for the equation (60.19) is (see Problems 48.3 and 48.4)

$$\nabla_{[\alpha}\omega_{\lambda\mu]} = 0$$

[21] R. Sauer, *Theoretische Einfuhrung in die Gasdynamik*, Berlin, 1943. A. Vazsonyi, "A New Derivation of a Method. . . . ," *Quarterly of Applied Math.*, Vol. V, No. 4, January, 1948.

where the brackets indicate that the alternating sum is to be found. This condition leads to only one equation. In order to express this equation in terms of derivatives in the l^λ, t^λ, $'t^\lambda$ directions, we form the scalar product with $l^\alpha t^\lambda\, 't^\mu$ and obtain

$$l^\alpha t^\lambda\, 't^\mu \nabla_{[\alpha}\omega_{\lambda\mu]} = 0.$$

(c) ***The Equations of Motion Expressed in Terms of the Characteristic Parameters*** (***Irrotational Case***). If we assume that the vector field l^λ is orthogonal to a family of surfaces (the surfaces determined by t^λ, $'t^\lambda$), then we may parameterize the coordinate lines whose unit tangent vectors are l^λ, t^λ, $'t^\lambda$. That is, we may write in the Cartesian orthogonal coordinate system x^λ:

$$t^\lambda = A^{-1}\frac{\partial x^\lambda}{\partial \alpha}, \qquad 't^\lambda = B^{-1}\frac{\partial x^\lambda}{\partial \beta}, \qquad l^\lambda = C^{-1}\frac{\partial x^\lambda}{\partial \gamma}$$

where A, B, C are the metric coefficients and $g_{\lambda\mu} = 1$, $\lambda = \mu$, $g_{\lambda\mu} = 0$, $\lambda \neq \mu$,

$$A^2 = g_{\lambda\mu}\frac{\partial x^\lambda}{\partial \alpha}\frac{\partial x^\mu}{\partial \alpha}, \qquad B^2 = g_{\lambda\mu}\frac{\partial x^\lambda}{\partial \beta}\frac{\partial x^\mu}{\partial \beta}, \qquad C^2 = g_{\lambda\mu}\frac{\partial x^\lambda}{\partial \gamma}\frac{\partial x^\mu}{\partial \gamma},$$

and where $\alpha =$ constant, $\beta =$ constant are two families of characteristic surfaces and $\gamma =$ constant are a family of surfaces orthogonal to these surfaces. Further, by use of the chain rule for differentiation, we see that

$$t^\alpha \nabla_\alpha v^\lambda = A^{-1}\frac{\partial v^\lambda}{\partial \alpha}, \qquad 't^\alpha \nabla_\alpha v^\lambda = B^{-1}\frac{\partial v^\lambda}{\partial \beta}, \qquad l^\alpha \nabla_\alpha v^\lambda = C^{-1}\frac{\partial v^\lambda}{\partial \gamma}.$$

By use of the above relations, we may translate the characteristic conditions into differential equations involving the characteristic parameters α, β, γ. We shall treat only the case of steady, irrotational, isentropic flows. A simple computation shows that the first and second characteristic relations of Section 60(b) become

$$v^\lambda = \frac{q^2}{2\sqrt{q^2 - c^2}}\left(A^{-1}\frac{\partial x^\lambda}{\partial \alpha} + B^{-1}\frac{\partial x^\lambda}{\partial \beta}\right)$$

$$A^{-1}\left[\frac{q^2}{2}\left(B^{-1}\frac{\partial x^\lambda}{\partial \beta} - A^{-1}\frac{\partial x^\lambda}{\partial \alpha}\right) + \sqrt{q^2 - c^2}\, v^\lambda\right]\frac{\partial v_\lambda}{\partial \alpha} = C^{-2}c^2\frac{\partial x^\lambda}{\partial \gamma}\frac{\partial v_\lambda}{\partial \gamma} \tag{60.20}$$

$$B^{-1}\left[\frac{q^2}{2}\left(A^{-1}\frac{\partial x^\lambda}{\partial \alpha} - B^{-1}\frac{\partial x^\lambda}{\partial \beta}\right) + \sqrt{q^2 - c^2}\, v^\lambda\right]\frac{\partial v_\lambda}{\partial \beta} = C^{-2}c^2\frac{\partial x^\lambda}{\partial \gamma}\frac{\partial v_\lambda}{\partial \gamma}.$$

Further, the irrotational relations (60.18) reduce to

$$\frac{\partial x^\lambda}{\partial \alpha}\frac{\partial v_\lambda}{\partial \beta} = \frac{\partial x^\lambda}{\partial \beta}\frac{\partial v_\lambda}{\partial \alpha}$$

and the two other equations obtained by replacing (α, β) by (β, γ), and (α, γ). The importance of this system of equations is due to the following theorem.[22] *This system of eight equations for the six dependent variables, x^λ, v^λ as functions of α, β, γ is consistent and furnishes sufficient conditions to determine a solution of the equations of motion for proper boundary data.*

In computational procedures, this differential system is usually replaced by a system of difference equations. The fact that A, B, C are sums of squares causes considerable difficulty. By introducing proper angle variables, some of this difficulty may be removed. For example, we may write

$$\frac{\partial x^1}{\partial \alpha} = A \cos \theta \sin \phi, \qquad \frac{\partial x^2}{\partial \alpha} = A \sin \theta \sin \phi, \qquad \frac{\partial x^3}{\partial \alpha} = A \cos \phi,$$

$$\frac{\partial x^1}{\partial \beta} = B \cos \bar{\theta} \sin \bar{\phi}, \text{ etc.}$$

The integrability conditions of the above equations are of the type

$$\frac{\partial}{\partial \beta}\left(\frac{\partial x^\lambda}{\partial \alpha}\right) = \frac{\partial}{\partial \alpha}\left(\frac{\partial x^\lambda}{\partial \beta}\right).$$

These relations furnish a system of first-order partial differential equations involving the derivatives of A, B, θ, ϕ, $\bar{\theta}$, $\bar{\phi}$, etc., in a *linear manner.* By adjoining this system of linear equations to the above system (60.20) where A, B, C, θ, ϕ, etc., are now dependent variables, one may reduce the problem to one of solving a system of *linear difference* equations. Numerical methods for treating such systems are well known.

In the case of two-dimensional steady flows, the characteristic system simplifies considerably. It should be noted that a sense of orientation exists in the plane and hence if the pairs of vectors (t^λ, n^λ), $('t^\lambda, 'n^\lambda)$ are to be oriented then the proper nappes of the characteristic and bicharacteristic "cones" must be used. One may show that this means that the previous relations are valid except that t^λ must be replaced by $(-t^\lambda)$ *or* $'t^\lambda$ must be replaced by $(-'t^\lambda)$.

Problem 60.1: For two-dimensional plane flows of a compressible gas (steady and irrotational) show that:

(1) the first characteristic relation may be written as

$$\sigma_+ = \frac{\partial y}{\partial \beta} \Big/ \frac{\partial x}{\partial \beta}, \qquad \sigma_- = \frac{\partial y}{\partial \alpha} \Big/ \frac{\partial x}{\partial \alpha}$$

where

$$\sigma_\pm = \frac{-uv \pm c\sqrt{q^2 - c^2}}{c^2 - u^2} = \frac{c^2 - v^2}{-uv \mp c\sqrt{q^2 - c^2}};$$

[22] E. W. Titt, "The Three-Dimensional Hyperbolic Equation," *loc. cit.*

(2) the second characteristic relation may be written as

$$\frac{c^2 - u^2}{c^2 - v^2}\sigma_+ = -\frac{\partial v}{\partial \beta}\bigg/\frac{\partial u}{\partial \beta}, \qquad \frac{c^2 - u^2}{c^2 - v^2}\sigma_- = -\frac{\partial v}{\partial \alpha}\bigg/\frac{\partial u}{\partial \alpha};$$

(3) the irrotationality conditions imply that the maps of the characteristic curves in the physical x,y-plane and the hodograph u,v-plane are orthogonal.

Problem 60.2: For the case of steady, rotational, two-dimensional plane flows of a compressible gas, determine the formulas corresponding to Problem 60.1 for the first and second characteristic relations.

Chapter XII

THE THEORY OF HOMOGENEOUS STATISTICAL TURBULENCE

61. General Remarks. In the modern theory of homogeneous statistical turbulence, one finds many useful applications of tensor analysis. O. Reynolds introduced the first mathematical theory of turbulence in 1883. He observed that when a fluid flows in a pipe, two types of phenomena may arise, depending upon the constants of the flow: (1) laminar motion; (2) turbulent motion. The dimensionless scalar which determines which of the above two motions occurs is known as Reynolds' number, R, and is defined as $R = aV/\nu$, where, a is a typical length associated with the flow (such as the diameter of the pipe), V is a typical velocity (such as the mean velocity of the flow), ν is the kinematic viscosity ($\nu = \mu/\rho$). For sufficiently small values of R, the flow is very regular and is called *laminar*. This type of flow can be studied by use of the theory of viscous fluids. When R becomes sufficiently large, the flow becomes very irregular and consists of a wildly eddying motion. The resulting state of flow is called *turbulent*. Reynolds investigated turbulent flows in Cartesian orthogonal coordinates x^λ by decomposing the instantaneous velocity vector V^λ, at any point into two components: (1) U^λ, the mean velocity of the flow; (2) v^λ, the velocity of the fluctuations:

$$V^\lambda = U^\lambda + v^\lambda.$$

Further, he assumed that: (1) ρ, the density, is constant; (2) the average of v^λ, denoted by $\bar{v}^\lambda$, is zero. There appears to be considerable ambiguity in deciding exactly how to define U^λ, v^λ. Again, the type of average to which $\bar{v}^\lambda$ refers is not discussed. In spite of these difficulties, Reynolds showed by use of the Navier-Stokes equations that the determination of the solutions for U^λ, the mean velocity of flow, depended upon the evaluation of the averaged terms

$$R^{\lambda\mu} = \overline{v^\lambda\, 'v^\mu}$$

where $'v^\lambda$ is the velocity of fluctuation at a point $'P('x^\lambda)$. In fact, Reynolds showed that the terms, $-\rho\overline{v^\lambda\, 'v^\mu}$, act as stresses. At present, we usually denote these terms by the name, "Reynolds stresses."

The modern theory of *homogeneous statistical* turbulence is due to G. I. Taylor[1] who studied the *isotropic* case. However, the theory has been extended by various authors to the *axial symmetric* and *other cases.* The essence of Taylor's idea is: (1) a *statistical theory of turbulence* must be concerned with only the statistical fluctuations, v^λ, and not both U^λ, v^λ; (2) the turbulence is assumed to be *homogeneous.* This last statement means that the averages, $R^{\lambda\mu} = \overline{v^\lambda\, 'v^\mu}$, depend upon the difference vector in the Cartesian orthogonal coordinates, x^λ, $'x^\lambda$,

$$\xi^\lambda = 'x^\lambda - x^\lambda$$

and not upon the points $'x^\lambda$, x^λ, separately. Thus we may write

$$R^{\lambda\mu}('x^\alpha, x^\alpha, t) = R^{\lambda\mu}(\xi^\alpha, t). \tag{61.1}$$

From the geometric point of view, the assumption of homogeneity means that we can study averages by considering points in a new Euclidean space, with Cartesian coordinates ξ^λ (*the correlation space*), rather than by considering *two points* $'x^\lambda$, x^λ *of the Euclidean physical space.* Physically, Taylor's assumption implies that the averages, $R^{\lambda\mu}$, are independent of the group of translations in the physical space.

In concluding this introductory section, we will make a few remarks as to the significance and properties of the term "average." At present, there is no general agreement as to the exact significance of this term. However, most authors agree that a logical and useful definition can be obtained. An interesting approach is due to L. Agostini and J. Bass.[2] These authors view statistical turbulence as a stochastic process and introduce scalar probability density functions such as $f(v^\lambda, x^\lambda, t)$ where

$$f(v^\lambda, x^\lambda, t)\, dv^1\, dv^2\, dv^3$$

represents the conditional probability that if a fluid particle at the time t is at the point $P(x^\lambda)$, the velocity components will lie between v^1 and $v^1 + dv^1$, v^2 and $v^2 + dv^2$, and v^3 and $v^3 + dv^3$. Then, the average $R^{\lambda\mu}$ may be defined as

$$R^{\lambda\mu} = \overline{v^\lambda\, 'v^\mu} = \int v^\lambda\, 'v^\mu f(v^\alpha, x^\alpha, t) f('v^\alpha, 'x^\alpha, t)\, d\tau \tag{61.2}$$

[1] G. I. Taylor, "Statistical Theory of Turbulence, I–V," *Proc. of Royal Soc. of London,* 1935.

[2] L. Agostini and J. Bass, *Les Theories de la Turbulence,* Publications Scientifiques et Techniques, Paris, 1950.

where $d\tau$ is volume element $dv^1\, dv^2\, dv^3\, d\,'v^1\, d\,'v^2\, d\,'v^3$ and the integration is performed over all possible values of v^λ, $'v^\mu$. For our future purpose, it is important to note that with the aid of a definition of this type, one may determine stochastic derivatives by differentiating under the averaging sign. We *postulate* that one may write

$$\frac{\partial}{\partial x^\gamma}\overline{v^\lambda(x^\alpha, t)'v^\mu('x^\alpha, t)} = \overline{\frac{\partial v^\lambda}{\partial x^\gamma}\,'v^\mu}. \tag{61.3}$$

Further, with the aid of the chain rule for differentiation, the relation $\xi^\lambda = 'x^\lambda - x^\lambda$ (note, both x^λ, $'x^\lambda$ are independent variables), and use of the homogeneity property (61.1), we find that

$$\overline{\frac{\partial v^\lambda}{\partial x^\gamma}\,'v^\mu} = -\frac{\partial R^{\lambda\mu}}{\partial \xi^\gamma} = -\overline{v^\lambda\frac{\partial\,'v^\mu}{\partial\,'x^\gamma}}. \tag{61.4}$$

The formulas of the type (61.4) are very useful in the theory of turbulence.

62. The Correlation Tensors in Homogeneous Turbulence. We shall consider the following topics: (1) the correlation coefficients and the correlation tensors; (2) the structure and properties of the correlation tensors; (3) the expressions for the energy of turbulence, E and the energy dissipated by viscosity, ϵ, in terms of the correlation tensors.

(a) ***The Correlation Coefficients,*** $R(\xi^\lambda, a^\lambda, 'a^\lambda)$. Taylor's original work was concerned primarily with quantities of the type

$$\begin{aligned} R(\xi^\lambda, a^\lambda, 'a^\lambda) &= \overline{v^\lambda a_\lambda\, 'v^\mu\, 'a_\mu} = \overline{v^\lambda\, 'v^\mu} a_\lambda\, 'a_\mu \\ &= R^{\lambda\mu} a_\lambda\, 'a_\mu \end{aligned} \tag{62.1}$$

where a_λ, $'a_\lambda$ are unit vectors in arbitrary directions at the points $P(x^\lambda)$, $'P('x^\lambda)$ of the physical space or at the origin of the Euclidean correlation space, ξ^λ. This is illustrated in Figure 73. The notation $R(\xi^\lambda, a^\lambda, 'a^\lambda)$ is due to H. P. Robertson,[3] who first pointed out the invariant theory significance of these scalars, and introduced the axial symmetric case. The scalar quantities, $R(\xi^\lambda, a^\lambda, 'a^\lambda)$ are called *correlation coefficients* or *scalars.*

In a very fundamental paper,[4] von Kármán showed that the *correlation tensors* play the fundamental role in the statistical theory of turbulence. Actually, von Kármán discussed the isotropic case. Further, we have already introduced the *second-order correlation tensor,* $R^{\lambda\mu}$, under the term, "average." If p, v^λ denote the pressure and velocity vectors at $P(x^\lambda)$, and

[3] H. P. Robertson, "An Invariant Theory of Isotropic Turbulence," *Proc. of the Cambridge Philosophical Soc.*, 36, 1940.

[4] T. von Kármán and L. Howarth, "On the Statistical Theory of Isotropic Turbulence," *Proc. of London Royal Soc.*, Series A, 164, 1938.

if $'p$, $'v^\lambda$ denote the pressure and velocity vectors at $'P('x^\lambda)$, then the following *correlation tensors* of von Kármán play an important role in the theory of *homogeneous statistical turbulence:*

$$R^\lambda(\xi^\alpha) = \overline{p\ 'v^\lambda}, \text{ the first pressure correlation tensor,} \quad (62.2)$$
$$R^{\lambda\mu}(\xi^\alpha) = \overline{v^\lambda\ 'v^\mu}, \text{ the second-order velocity correlation tensor,} \quad (62.3)$$
$$R^{\lambda\mu\gamma}(\xi^\alpha) = \overline{v^\lambda v^\mu\ 'v^\gamma}, \text{ the first third-order velocity correlation tensor,} \quad (62.4)$$
$$*R^\lambda(\xi^\alpha) = \overline{'pv^\lambda}, \text{ the second pressure correlation tensor,} \quad (62.5)$$
$$*R^{\lambda\mu\gamma}(\xi^\alpha) = \overline{'v^\lambda\ 'v^\mu v^\gamma}, \text{ the second third-order velocity correlation tensor.} \quad (62.6)$$

Evidently, $R^{\lambda\mu\gamma}$, $*R^{\lambda\mu\gamma}$ are symmetric in the first two indices. By use of definitions of the type (61.2), one sees that the quantities R^λ, $R^{\lambda\mu}$, etc.,

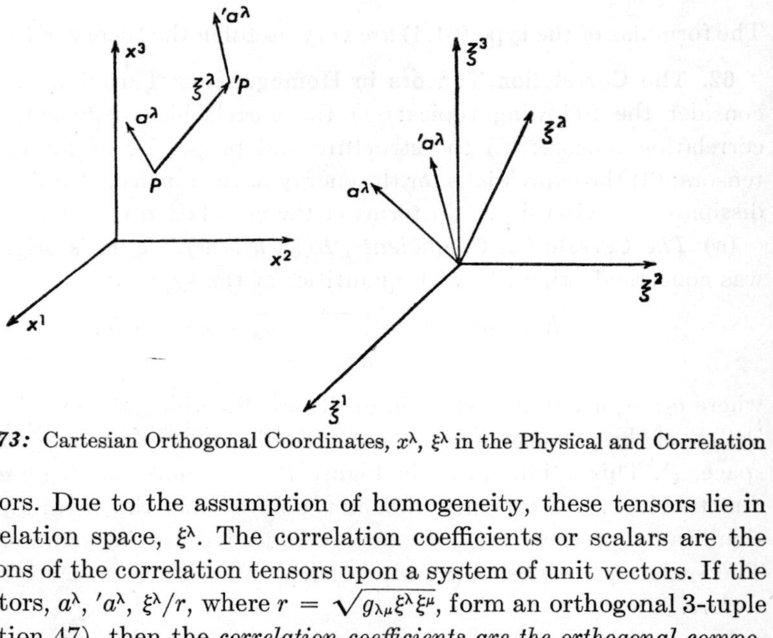

Figure 73: Cartesian Orthogonal Coordinates, x^λ, ξ^λ in the Physical and Correlation Spaces

are tensors. Due to the assumption of homogeneity, these tensors lie in the correlation space, ξ^λ. The correlation coefficients or scalars are the projections of the correlation tensors upon a system of unit vectors. If the unit vectors, a^λ, $'a^\lambda$, ξ^λ/r, where $r = \sqrt{g_{\lambda\mu}\xi^\lambda\xi^\mu}$, form an orthogonal 3-tuple (see Section 47), then the *correlation coefficients are the orthogonal components in correlation space of the correlation tensors.*

The homogeneity of turbulence implies that the tensors R^λ, $*R^\lambda$ and $R^{\lambda\mu\gamma}$, $*R^{\lambda\mu\gamma}$ *are algebraically related.* To determine these relations, we express the correlation tensors $R^\lambda(\xi^\alpha)$, $R^{\lambda\mu\gamma}(\xi^\alpha)$, in terms of the physical space variables, x^λ, $x^\lambda + \xi^\lambda$. We find that

$$R^\lambda(\xi^\alpha) = \overline{p(x^\alpha)v^\lambda(x^\alpha + \xi^\alpha)}$$
$$R^{\lambda\mu\gamma}(\xi^\alpha) = \overline{v^\lambda(x^\alpha)v^\mu(x^\alpha)v^\gamma(x^\alpha + \xi^\alpha)}.$$

From these last relations we see that

$$R^{\lambda}(-\xi^{\alpha}) = \overline{p(x^{\alpha})v^{\lambda}(x^{\alpha} - \xi^{\alpha})}$$
$$R^{\lambda\mu\gamma}(-\xi^{\alpha}) = \overline{v^{\lambda}(x^{\alpha})v^{\mu}(x^{\alpha})v^{\gamma}(x^{\alpha} - \xi^{\alpha})}.$$

If we replace x^{α} by $'x^{\alpha} + \xi^{\alpha}$ in the last formulas and then drop the primes (implying use of the homogeneity condition), we obtain the relations

$$R^{\lambda}(-\xi^{\alpha}) = \overline{v^{\lambda}(x^{\alpha})p(x^{\alpha} + \xi^{\alpha})} = {}^{*}R^{\lambda}(\xi^{\alpha}) \tag{62.7}$$
$$R^{\lambda\mu\gamma}(-\xi^{\alpha}) = \overline{v^{\gamma}(x^{\alpha})v^{\lambda}(x^{\alpha} + \xi^{\alpha})v^{\mu}(x^{\alpha} + \xi^{\alpha})} = {}^{*}R^{\lambda\mu\gamma}(\xi^{\alpha}). \tag{62.8}$$

Further, it should be noted that the tensor $R^{\lambda\mu}$ has the following property:

$$R^{\lambda\mu}(-\xi^{\alpha}) = R^{\mu\lambda}(\xi^{\alpha}). \tag{62.9}$$

This last result follows from the definition of $R^{\lambda\mu}$ and the homogeneity condition. It is the analogue of the previous equations for the second-order correlation tensor. It should be stressed that the correlation tensors are functions of ξ^{α} *and* t. We have omitted the variable, t, in order to clearly exhibit the arguments, ξ^{α}.

(b) ***The Structure of the Correlation Tensors.*** In order to assign structures to the correlation tensors, it is necessary to introduce further assumptions. G. I. Taylor introduced the assumption of *isotropy* and in this manner characterized the structure of the *correlation coefficients.* T. von Kármán showed how this assumption determines the structure of the correlation tensors. We shall follow a slightly different procedure[5] which shows how one may characterize *isotropic turbulence, axial symmetric turbulence, conical turbulence,* and other types of turbulence.

For this purpose, we introduce two unit orthogonal vectors, i^{λ} and k^{λ}, at the origin of the correlation space. In the *isotropic case,* we assume that i^{λ} and k^{λ} are orthogonal to ξ^{λ}; in the *axial symmetric case,* we assume that i^{λ} and k^{λ} are orthogonal to the unit vector j^{λ} in the preferential direction; in particular, i^{λ} is considered to be orthogonal to both ξ^{λ}, j^{λ}; in the *conical symmetric case,* i^{λ}, k^{λ} are chosen orthogonal to j^{λ} as in axial symmetric case, except that i^{λ} is no longer orthogonal to both j^{λ}, ξ^{λ}. This situation is illustrated in Figure 74. In terms of the above triads of unit vectors, we may characterize the cases of isotropic, axial symmetric, conical symmetric turbulence by the following assumptions, respectively:

(1) *isotropic case;* the correlation tensors are invariant under the orthogonal group operating on the vectors i^{λ}, k^{λ}; the correlation scalars are functions of r;

[5] N. Coburn, "A Method for Constructing Correlation Tensors in Homogeneous Turbulence," *U. of Illinois Symposium of Fluid Dynamics,* 1950, Edwards Bros., Ann Arbor, 1951, pp. 129–141.

(2) *the axial symmetry case;* the correlation tensors are invariant under the orthogonal group operating on the vector i^λ; the correlation scalars are functions of r, ϕ;

(3) *the conical symmetric case;* the correlation tensors are invariant under the orthogonal group operating on the vectors i^λ, k^λ; the correlation scalars are functions of r, ϕ.

In order to show how the above assumptions determine the structure of the correlation tensors, we consider the tensors R^λ, $R^{\lambda\mu}$ of (62.2) and

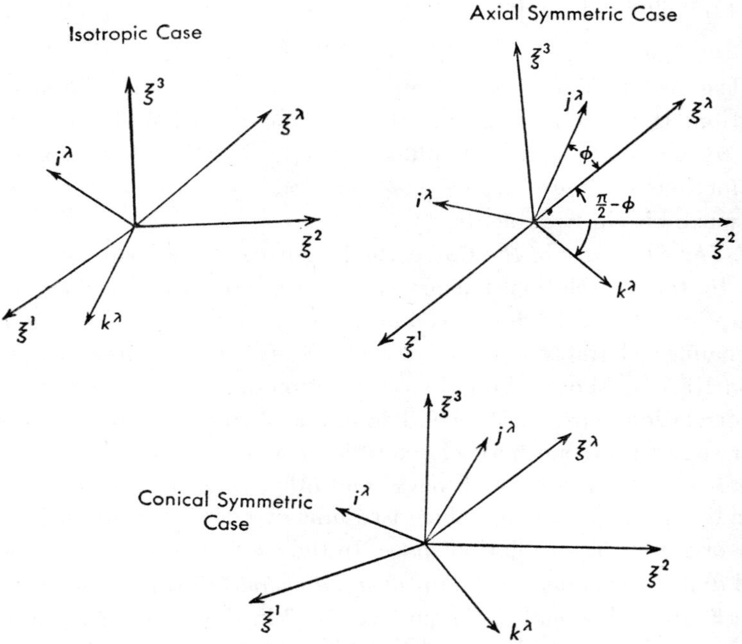

Figure 74: The Vector Fields, i^λ, k^λ, j^λ, ξ^λ in Homogeneous Turbulence

(62.3). The tensor $R^{\lambda\mu\gamma}$ of (62.4) may be treated in the same manner except that the computations are rather involved.

In this paragraph, we consider the case of *isotropic turbulence.* Let v_0, v_1, v_2 denote the components of the velocity vector, v^λ, along the orthogonal triad of unit vectors, ξ^λ/r, i^λ, k^λ, respectively:

$$v^\lambda = v_0 \frac{\xi^\lambda}{r} + v_1 i^\lambda + v_2 k^\lambda.$$

Similarly, we may decompose $'v^\lambda$ into

$$'v^\lambda = 'v_0 \frac{\xi^\lambda}{r} + 'v_1 i^\lambda + 'v_2 k^\lambda.$$

By use of the definitions of R^λ, $R^{\lambda\mu}$, and the above decompositions, we find that

$$R^\lambda = \overline{p\ 'v_0}\,\frac{\xi^\lambda}{r} + \overline{p\ 'v_1}\, i^\lambda + \overline{p\ 'v_2}\, k^\lambda \tag{62.10}$$

$$\begin{aligned} R^{\lambda\mu} = {} & \overline{v_0\ 'v_0}\,\frac{\xi^\lambda \xi^\mu}{r^2} + \overline{v_1\ 'v_0}\, i^\lambda \frac{\xi^\mu}{r} + \overline{v_2\ 'v_0}\, k^\lambda \frac{\xi^\mu}{r} \\ & + \overline{v_0\ 'v_1}\,\frac{\xi^\lambda}{r} i^\mu + \overline{v_1\ 'v_1}\, i^\lambda i^\mu + \overline{v_2\ 'v_1}\, k^\lambda i^\mu \\ & + \overline{v_0\ 'v_2}\,\frac{\xi^\lambda}{r} k^\mu + \overline{v_1\ 'v_2}\, i^\lambda k^\mu + \overline{v_2\ 'v_2}\, k^\lambda k^\mu. \end{aligned} \tag{62.11}$$

The scalars $\overline{v_0\ 'v_0}$, $\overline{v_1\ 'v_0}$, etc., are correlation coefficients or correlation scalars. That is, by forming the scalar products of the last relation with, say $i^\lambda i^\mu$, we find that

$$R(\xi^\lambda, i^\lambda, i^\lambda) = R^{\lambda\mu} i_\lambda i_\mu = \overline{v_1\ 'v_1}.$$

From this last equation, we verify the fact that the scalars, $\overline{v_0\ 'v_0}$, etc., are the orthogonal components [see (47.5)] of the tensor $R^{\lambda\mu}$. Our fundamental assumption for the isotropic case is that the tensors R^λ, $R^{\lambda\mu}$, $R^{\lambda\mu\gamma}$ are invariant under the group of transformations

$$\bar{i}^\lambda = a i^\lambda + b k^\lambda, \qquad \bar{k}^\lambda = c i^\lambda + d k^\lambda, \qquad \bar{\xi}^\lambda = \xi^\lambda \tag{62.12}$$

where

$$a^2 + b^2 = c^2 + d^2 = 1, \qquad ac + bd = 0.$$

The group (62.12) consists of rotations and reflections of the orthogonal pair of vectors i^λ, k^λ in the planes perpendicular to ξ^λ. Since R^λ, $R^{\lambda\mu}$ are invariant under this group, we may write the previous relations for R^λ, $R^{\lambda\mu}$ with $(-i^\lambda)$ replacing i^λ and $(-k^\lambda)$ replacing k^λ. This corresponds to using (62.12) with $d = a = -1$, $b = c = 0$, and represents a rotation of 180° about ξ^λ. Thus, we may write

$$R^\lambda = \bar{R}^\lambda = \overline{p\ 'v_0}\,\frac{\xi^\lambda}{r} - \overline{p\ 'v_1}\, i^\lambda - \overline{p\ 'v_2}\, k^\lambda$$

and a similar equation for $R^{\lambda\mu}$. Subtracting the above equation for R^λ from the previous equation for R^λ, (62.10), we obtain the result

$$\overline{p\ 'v_1}\, i^\lambda + \overline{p\ 'v_2}\, k^\lambda = 0.$$

Since the vectors i^λ, k^λ are orthogonal, the above relation implies that

$$\overline{p\ 'v_1} = \overline{p\ 'v_2} = 0.$$

By treating the tensor $R^{\lambda\mu}$ in the same manner, we find that

$$\overline{v_0\ 'v_1} = \overline{v_1\ 'v_0} = \overline{v_0\ 'v_2} = \overline{v_2\ 'v_0} = 0.$$

Similarly, if we replace k^λ by i^λ and i^λ by $(-k^\lambda)$ in (62.11), and require that $R^{\lambda\mu}$ be invariant under this 90° rotation, we obtain

$$\overline{v_2\,'v_1} = \overline{v_1\,'v_2}, \qquad \overline{v_1\,'v_1} = \overline{v_2\,'v_2}.$$

Finally, if we require that (62.11) be invariant under the reflection

$$\bar{\imath}^\lambda = i^\lambda, \qquad \bar{k}^\lambda = -k^\lambda, \qquad \bar{\xi}^\lambda = \xi^\lambda$$

we find that

$$\overline{v_2\,'v_1} = \overline{v_1\,'v_2} = 0.$$

Substituting the above results into the expressions for R^λ, $R^{\lambda\mu}$, (62.10) and (62.11), we obtain the formulas

$$R^\lambda = \overline{p\,'v_0}\,\frac{\xi^\lambda}{r}$$

$$R^{\lambda\mu} = \overline{v_0\,'v_0}\,\frac{\xi^\lambda\xi^\mu}{r^2} + \overline{v_1\,'v_1}(i^\lambda i^\mu + k^\lambda k^\mu). \tag{62.13}$$

We have seen that the metric tensor, $g_{\lambda\mu}$, may be expressed in terms of the 3-tuple i^λ, k^λ, ξ^λ/r (the vector fields i^λ, k^λ, ξ^λ/r may be considered as defined by parallelism) by means of the relation (47.4)

$$g^{\lambda\mu} = i^\lambda i^\mu + k^\lambda k^\mu + \frac{\xi^\lambda\xi^\mu}{r^2}.$$

Thus, the above relation for $R^{\lambda\mu}$ may be reduced to

$$R^{\lambda\mu} = \frac{\overline{v_0\,'v_0} - \overline{v_1\,'v_1}}{r^2}\,\xi^\lambda\xi^\mu + \overline{v_1\,'v_1}\,g^{\lambda\mu}. \tag{62.14}$$

By use of a similar procedure it may be shown that the tensor $R^{\lambda\mu\gamma}$ may be expressed by

$$R^{\lambda\mu\gamma} = \frac{\overline{v_0v_0\,'v_0} - \overline{v_1v_1\,'v_0} - 2\overline{v_0v_1\,'v_1}}{r^3}\,\xi^\lambda\xi^\mu\xi^\gamma + \frac{\overline{v_1v_1\,'v_0}}{r}\,\xi^\gamma g^{\lambda\mu}$$
$$+ \frac{\overline{v_0v_1\,'v_1}}{r}\,(\xi^\lambda g^{\mu\gamma} + \xi^\mu g^{\lambda\gamma}). \tag{62.15}$$

As an additional example, we consider the case of *axial symmetric turbulence*. Here, the permissible group of transformations is

$$\bar{\imath}^\lambda = a i^\lambda, \qquad \bar{\jmath}^\lambda = j^\lambda, \qquad \bar{k}^\lambda = k^\lambda$$

where $a^2 = 1$. Instead of the decomposition for the isotropic case, we write

$$v^\lambda = v_1 i^\lambda + v_2 j^\lambda + v_3\,k^\lambda. \tag{62.16}$$

By use of the previous procedure, one may show that

$$R^\lambda = \overline{p\ 'v_2}\, j^\lambda + \overline{p\ 'v_3}\, k^\lambda \tag{62.17}$$

$$\begin{aligned} R^{\lambda\mu} = {} & (\overline{v_2\ 'v_2} - \overline{v_1\ 'v_1}) j^\lambda j^\mu + (\overline{v_3\ 'v_3} - \overline{v_1\ 'v_1}) k^\lambda k^\mu \\ & + \overline{v_1\ 'v_1}\, g^{\lambda\mu} + \overline{v_2\ 'v_3}\, j^\lambda k^\mu + \overline{v_3\ 'v_2}\, k^\lambda j^\mu. \end{aligned} \tag{62.18}$$

The third-order correlation tensor $R^{\lambda\mu\gamma}$ is rather complicated and contains ten scalars, $\overline{v_1 v_1\ 'v_1}$, etc. One may eliminate the vector, k^λ, by noting that (see Figure 74)

$$\frac{\xi^\lambda}{r} = j^\lambda \cos\phi + k^\lambda \sin\phi.$$

The above equations for R^λ, $R^{\lambda\mu}$ are then expressed in terms of the known j^λ, ξ^λ vectors and the metric tensor, $g^{\lambda\mu}$. It should be noted that the correlation coefficients $\overline{p\ 'v_2}$, etc., are functions of r, ϕ.

Finally, we consider the case of *conical symmetric turbulence*. We define this case by requiring that the correlation tensors be invariant under the group of transformations

$$\bar{i}^\lambda = a i^\lambda + b k^\lambda, \qquad \bar{k}^\lambda = c i^\lambda + d k^\lambda, \qquad \bar{j}^\lambda = j^\lambda$$

where a, b, c, d satisfy the orthogonality relations. If we express the vector ξ^λ in terms of i^λ, j^λ, k^λ by

$$r^{-1}\xi^\lambda = \alpha j^\lambda + \beta i^\lambda + \gamma k^\lambda$$

where α, β, γ are scalars, then under the above group, the vector, ξ^λ, goes into

$$r^{-1}\bar{\xi}^\lambda = r^{-1}\xi^\lambda + d^\lambda$$

where d^λ is orthogonal to j^λ. That is, the correlation tensors are invariant under rotations of ξ^λ about j^λ. By use of the decomposition (62.16), we can easily show that the correlation tensors have the following structures:

$$\begin{aligned} R^\lambda &= \overline{p\ 'v_2}\, j^\lambda \\ R^{\lambda\mu} &= (\overline{v_2\ 'v_2 - v_1\ 'v_1}) j^\lambda j^\mu + \overline{v_1\ 'v_1}\, g^{\lambda\mu} \\ R^{\lambda\mu\gamma} &= (\overline{v_2 v_2\ 'v_2} - \overline{v_1 v_1\ 'v_2} - 2\overline{v_1 v_2\ 'v_2}) j^\lambda j^\mu j^\gamma \\ &\quad + \overline{v_1 v_2\ 'v_1}(j^\lambda g^{\mu\gamma} + j^\mu g^{\lambda\gamma}) + \overline{v_1 v_1\ 'v_2}\, j^\gamma g^{\lambda\mu}. \end{aligned} \tag{62.19}$$

In the present case, the only effect of the correlation vector, ξ^λ, is contained in the correlation coefficients $\overline{p\ 'v_2}$, etc. These scalars are functions of r, ϕ.

It is important to note one further property of the correlation tensors. By multiplying the equation of continuity (56.6) at $'P('x^\lambda)$ by p, v^λ, $v^\lambda v^\mu$

and averaging, we find that

$$\overline{p\frac{\partial\ 'v^\gamma}{\partial\ 'x^\gamma}} = \overline{v^\lambda\frac{\partial\ 'v^\gamma}{\partial\ 'x^\gamma}} = \overline{v^\lambda v^\mu\frac{\partial\ 'v^\gamma}{\partial\ 'x^\gamma}} = 0.$$

Introducing the correlation tensors into this relation and using the differentiation formulas of the type (61.4), we see that

$$\frac{\partial R^\gamma}{\partial \xi^\gamma} = \frac{\partial R^{\lambda\gamma}}{\partial \xi^\gamma} = \frac{\partial R^{\lambda\mu\gamma}}{\partial \xi^\gamma} = 0. \tag{62.20}$$

The tensors R^λ, $R^{\lambda\mu}$, $R^{\lambda\mu\gamma}$ are solenoidal or possess zero divergence. Note that the correlation variables, ξ^λ, are considered as Cartesian orthogonal variables in a Euclidean correlation space. Hence, the ordinary derivative coincides with the covariant derivative. Professor S. Chandrasekhar has raised the following problem: To determine the tensors R^λ, $R^{\lambda\mu}$, $R^{\lambda\mu\gamma}$ in terms of such correlation scalars so that the solenoidal conditions (62.20) are identically satisfied. Such scalars are called "independent scalars" by Chandrasekhar. In his paper, Chandrasekhar[6] has determined these scalars for the case of axial symmetric turbulence by use of vector identities. The following general scheme will determine the correlation tensors in terms of independent scalars.[7] Construct the tensors $\bar{R}^\lambda$, $\bar{R}^{\lambda\mu}$, $\bar{R}^{\lambda\mu\gamma}$ by means of the relations

$$\bar{S}_\gamma = e_{\gamma\lambda\beta}R^\lambda\xi^\beta, \qquad \bar{R}^\alpha = e^{\alpha\gamma\rho}\frac{\partial\bar{S}_\gamma}{\partial\xi^\rho}$$

$$\bar{S}_\gamma^{\cdot\mu} = e_{\gamma\lambda\beta}R^{\lambda\mu}\xi^\beta, \qquad \bar{R}^{\mu\alpha} = e^{\alpha\gamma\rho}\frac{\partial\bar{S}_\gamma^{\cdot\mu}}{\partial\xi^\rho}$$

$$\bar{S}_\gamma^{\cdot\lambda\mu} = e_{\gamma\alpha\beta}R^{\lambda\mu\alpha}\xi^\beta, \qquad \bar{R}^{\lambda\mu\nu} = e^{\nu\gamma\rho}\frac{\partial\bar{S}_\gamma^{\cdot\lambda\mu}}{\partial\xi^\rho}.$$

then these tensors ($\bar{R}^\lambda$, $\bar{R}^{\lambda\mu}$, $\bar{R}^{\lambda\mu\gamma}$) will be expressed in terms of independent scalars. Actually, additional correlation tensors depending upon j^λ, etc., may be constructed. But, we shall not discuss this topic further.

(c) ***The Expressions for E, the Energy of Turbulence, and ϵ, the Energy Dissipated by Viscosity, in Terms of the Correlation Tensor, $R^{\lambda\mu}$.*** The *energy of turbulence* per unit mass, E, is defined as

$$2E = [\overline{(v_1)^2} + \overline{(v_2)^2} + \overline{(v_3)^2}]$$

[6] S. Chandrasekhar, "The Theory of Axisymmetric Turbulence," *Phil. Trans. of the Royal Soc. of London,* Series A, Sept., 1950.

[7] N. Coburn, "The 'Independent Scalars' in Homogeneous Turbulence," *American Journal of Mathematics,* Vol. LXXIV, No. 2, April, 1952. For the theory on compressible media, see M. Z. v. Krzywoblocki, "The 'Independent Scalars' in Homogeneous Turbulence in Compressible Media," *Journal of Phys. Soc. of Japan,* Vol. 8, No. 6, Nov.–Dec., 1953.

where $\overline{(v_1)^2}$, $\overline{(v_2)^2}$, $\overline{(v_3)^2}$, are the averages of the squares of the components of the velocity. In terms of the correlation tensor $R^{\lambda\mu}$ (62.3), we may express E by the formula

$$2E = g_{\lambda\mu}R^{\lambda\mu}(0, t). \tag{62.21}$$

If we introduce the scalar, R, associated with $R^{\lambda\mu}$, $R = g_{\lambda\mu}R^{\lambda\mu}$, then the above formula reduces to

$$2E = R(0, t).$$

Next, we consider the *vorticity correlation tensor*,

$$\omega^{\lambda\mu} = \overline{\omega^{\lambda\,\prime}\omega^{\mu}}$$

where the vorticity vector ω^λ is defined by

$$\omega^\lambda = e^{\lambda\alpha\beta}\frac{\partial v_\alpha}{\partial x^\beta}.$$

Substituting this last relation into the expression for the vorticity correlation tensor, we obtain the formula

$$\omega^{\lambda\mu} = e^{\lambda\alpha\beta}e^{\mu\delta\rho}\,\overline{\frac{\partial v_\alpha}{\partial x^\beta}\frac{\partial\,'v_\delta}{\partial\,'x^\rho}}.$$

By differentiation of the formula (61.4), we find that

$$-\frac{\partial^2 R_{\alpha\delta}}{\partial\xi^\beta\,\partial\xi^\rho} = \overline{\frac{\partial v_\alpha}{\partial x^\beta}\frac{\partial\,'v_\delta}{\partial\,'x^\rho}}.$$

Hence, the relation for $\omega^{\lambda\mu}$ reduces to

$$\omega^{\lambda\mu} = -e^{\lambda\alpha\beta}e^{\mu\delta\rho}\frac{\partial^2 R_{\alpha\delta}}{\partial\xi^\beta\,\partial\xi^\rho}. \tag{62.22}$$

The scalar, ω, of the vorticity correlation tensor is defined by $\omega = g_{\lambda\mu}\omega^{\lambda\mu}$. With the aid of the above relation for $\omega^{\lambda\mu}$ (62.22), we may express ω as[8]

$$\omega = -g^{\delta\theta}g^{\rho\mu}\delta^{\alpha\beta}_{\theta\mu}\frac{\partial^2 R_{\alpha\delta}}{\partial\xi^\rho\,\partial\xi^\beta}$$

where $\delta^{\alpha\beta}_{\theta\mu}$ is the generalized Kronecker tensor of Section 32. Simplifying the above expression for ω, we find by use of the solenoidal condition (62.20) that

$$\omega = -\nabla^2 R \tag{62.23}$$

where ∇^2 is the Laplacian operator in the ξ^λ coordinates, and $R = g_{\lambda\mu}R^{\lambda\mu}$. Since the scalar $\omega(0, t)$ is the mean square vorticity, the above formula

[8] In Cartesian orthogonal coordinates, $e^{\mu\delta\rho} = g^{\mu\sigma}g^{\delta\theta}g^{\rho\nu}e_{\sigma\theta\nu}$.

shows that this correlation is determined by the Laplacian of R according to the relation

$$\omega(0, t) = \overline{(\omega_1)^2} + \overline{(\omega_2)^2} + \overline{(\omega_3)^2} = -(\nabla^2 R)_{0,t}. \qquad (62.24)$$

The energy dissipated by viscosity was obtained in Section 56 [see (56.14) and the discussion following this equation]. There, we showed that this energy per unit mass is

$$\frac{\nu}{2}\left[g^{\lambda\alpha}g^{\mu\beta}\left(\frac{\partial v_\lambda}{\partial x^\mu} + \frac{\partial v_\mu}{\partial x^\lambda}\right)\left(\frac{\partial v_\alpha}{\partial x^\beta} + \frac{\partial v_\beta}{\partial x^\alpha}\right)\right]$$

where ν is the kinematic viscosity, $\nu = \mu/\rho$. Hence, we define the turbulent energy per unit mass dissipated by viscosity, ϵ, by

$$\epsilon = \frac{\nu}{2}\left[g^{\lambda\alpha}g^{\mu\beta}\overline{\left(\frac{\partial v_\lambda}{\partial x^\mu} + \frac{\partial v_\mu}{\partial x^\lambda}\right)\left(\frac{\partial v_\alpha}{\partial x^\beta} + \frac{\partial v_\beta}{\partial x^\alpha}\right)}\right].$$

Expanding the above expression, we obtain

$$\epsilon = \frac{\nu}{2}\left[g^{\lambda\alpha}g^{\mu\beta}\left(\overline{\frac{\partial v_\lambda}{\partial x^\mu}\frac{\partial v_\alpha}{\partial x^\beta}} + \overline{\frac{\partial v_\lambda}{\partial x^\mu}\frac{\partial v_\beta}{\partial x^\alpha}} + \overline{\frac{\partial v_\mu}{\partial x^\lambda}\frac{\partial v_\alpha}{\partial x^\beta}} + \overline{\frac{\partial v_\mu}{\partial x^\lambda}\frac{\partial v_\beta}{\partial x^\alpha}}\right)\right].$$

From the differentiation formula (61.4), we see that

$$-\left(\frac{\partial^2 R_{\lambda\mu}}{\partial \xi^\beta\,\partial \xi^\alpha}\right)_{\xi^\alpha=0} = \overline{\frac{\partial v_\lambda}{\partial x^\alpha}\frac{\partial v_\mu}{\partial x^\beta}}.$$

With the aid of this last formula and the scalar $R = g_{\lambda\mu}R^{\lambda\mu}$, we may express the various terms of the energy, ϵ, by the formulas of the type

$$g^{\lambda\alpha}g^{\mu\beta}\overline{\frac{\partial v_\lambda}{\partial x^\mu}\frac{\partial v_\alpha}{\partial x^\beta}} = -g^{\lambda\alpha}g^{\mu\beta}\left(\frac{\partial^2 R_{\lambda\alpha}}{\partial \xi^\mu\,\partial \xi^\beta}\right)_{\xi^\alpha=0} = -g^{\mu\beta}\left(\frac{\partial^2 R}{\partial \xi^\mu\,\partial \xi^\beta}\right)_{\xi^\alpha=0} = -\nabla^2 R)_{\xi^\alpha=0}$$

$$g^{\lambda\alpha}g^{\mu\beta}\overline{\frac{\partial v_\lambda}{\partial x^\mu}\frac{\partial v_\beta}{\partial x^\alpha}} = -g^{\lambda\alpha}g^{\mu\beta}\left(\frac{\partial^2 R_{\lambda\beta}}{\partial \xi^\mu\,\partial \xi^\alpha}\right)_{\xi^\alpha=0} = -\left(\frac{\partial^2 R^{\alpha\mu}}{\partial \xi^\alpha\,\partial \xi^\mu}\right)_{\xi^\alpha=0} = 0.$$

Note that the solenoidal condition (62.20) was used in evaluating the last of the above expressions. Thus, the energy, ϵ, may be expressed in the form

$$\epsilon = -\nu(\nabla^2 R)_{\xi^\alpha=0}. \qquad (62.25)$$

By comparing (62.24) and (62.25) we see that *the energy dissipated by viscosity is proportional to the mean square vorticity.* It should be noted that both E and ϵ depend upon the scalar, R.

Problem 62.1: For isotropic turbulence, show that the boundedness of the correlation coefficient $\overline{p'v_0}$ implies that this coefficient must vanish and hence $R^\lambda = {}^*R^\lambda = 0$. *Hint:* Use the solenoidal condition (62.20).

Problem 62.2: For isotropic turbulence, Kármán writes the second-order correlation tensor, $R^{\lambda\mu}$, as

$$R^{\lambda\mu} = \overline{u^2}\left[\frac{f-g}{r^2}\,\xi^\lambda\xi^\mu + g g^{\lambda\mu}\right]$$

where $\overline{u^2} = \overline{v^1v^1} = \overline{v^2v^2} = \overline{v^3v^3}$. Show: (1) the relation of the scalars, $f(r, t)$, $g(r, t)$ to the independent scalars $\overline{v_0\,'v_0}$, $\overline{v_1\,'v_1}$; (2) that the solenoidal relation (62.20) reduces to $g = f + (r/2)\partial f/\partial r$; (3) that the scalar R is equal to $\overline{u^2}(r(\partial f/\partial r) + 3f)$.

Problem 62.3: Kármán writes the third-order correlation tensor, $R^{\lambda\mu\gamma}$, in isotropic turbulence as

$$R^{\lambda\mu\gamma} = (\overline{u^2})^{3/2}\left[\frac{l-h-2q}{r^3}\,\xi^\lambda\xi^\mu\xi^\gamma + \frac{h}{r}\,\xi^\gamma g^{\lambda\mu} + \frac{q}{r}\,(\xi^\lambda g^{\mu\gamma} + \xi^\mu g^{\lambda\gamma})\right].$$

Determine the significance of the scalars $l(r, t)$, $h(r, t)$, $q(r, t)$ and derive the relations between these scalars due to the solenoidal condition.

Problem 62.4: Calculate the mean square vorticity in isotropic turbulence in terms of the scalars f, g and their derivatives.

63. The Wave Tensors in Homogeneous Turbulence. By expanding the correlation tensors in powers of ξ^α and using the solenoidal condition and the algebraic conditions (62.7) through (62.9), one may obtain properties of these tensors in the neighborhood of the origin of correlation space, $\xi^\alpha = 0$. Further information may be obtained by the use of the equations of motion (to be considered in the next section). However, these properties are valid for small ξ^α, or as one often says, "for small eddies." We should like to obtain some information as to the nature of large eddies. The natural tool for this purpose is the Fourier transform. In this section, we shall discuss the following topics: (1) wave space and the wave tensors, W^λ, etc.; (2) the structure of wave tensors and the properties of the wave tensors which correspond to the algebraic properties (62.7) through (62.9) and the solenoidal conditions (62.20); (3) the expression for the energy of turbulence, E, and the energy dissipated by viscosity, ϵ, in terms of the spectral tensor, $F^{\lambda\mu}$.

(a) ***Wave Space and the Wave Tensors.*** We have introduced two spaces in our earlier work, the physical space, with Cartesian orthogonal coordinates x^λ, and the correlation space, with Cartesian orthogonal coordinates, ξ^λ. Now, we introduce a third space, the wave space with Cartesian orthogonal coordinates, η^λ. These spaces are indicated in Figure 75. The physical and correlation spaces are related by the transformations, $\xi^\lambda = {}'x^\lambda - x^\lambda$. However, the wave space is related to the correlation space through the fact that the wave tensors are the Fourier transforms of the correlation tensors. In the remainder of this section we follow the work of G. K. Batchelor[9] who first introduced and studied these tensors in a systematic manner.

We define the wave tensors, $W^\lambda(\eta^\alpha, t)$, $W^{\lambda\mu}(\eta^\alpha, t)$, $W^{\lambda\mu\gamma}(\eta^\alpha, t)$, $*W^\lambda(\eta^\alpha, t)$, $*W^{\lambda\mu\gamma}(\eta^\alpha, t)$ as the Fourier transforms of the tensors, $R^\lambda(\xi^\alpha, t)$, $R^{\lambda\mu}(\xi^\alpha, t)$, $R^{\lambda\mu\gamma}(\xi^\alpha, t)$, $*R^\lambda(\xi^\alpha, t)$, $*R^{\lambda\mu\gamma}(\xi^\alpha, t)$, respectively. We illustrate the relation

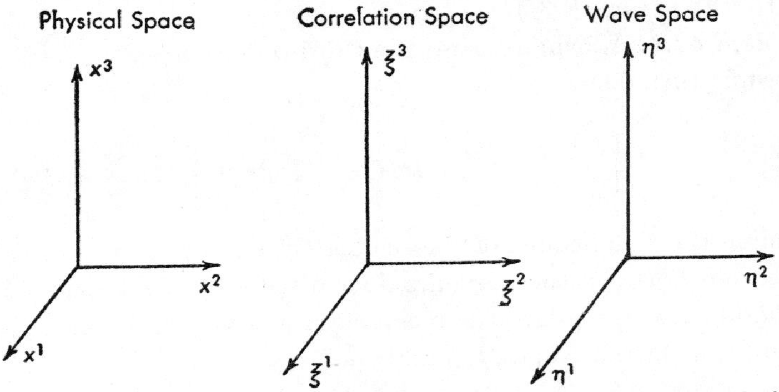

Figure 75: Cartesian Orthogonal Coordinates in the Physical, Correlation, and Wave Spaces

between these pairs of tensors by considering the second order tensors, $R^{\lambda\mu}$, $W^{\lambda\mu}$. By definition,

$$8\pi^3 W^{\lambda\mu}(\eta^\alpha, t) = \int_V R^{\lambda\mu}(\xi^\alpha, t) e^{i\eta^\alpha \xi_\alpha}\, dv \tag{63.1}$$

where $i^2 = -1$, dv is the element of volume in correlation space, and the integral is evaluated over the whole of correlation space, V. The expression, $\eta^\alpha \xi_\alpha$, represents the scalar product of the vectors η^α, ξ^α. For the above integrals to exist, it is sufficient that

$$\int_V |R^{\lambda\mu}(\xi^\alpha, t)|\, dv$$

shall be bounded. We assume that this condition is satisfied. The inverse transform of (63.1) is

$$R^{\lambda\mu}(\xi^\alpha, t) = \int_T W^{\lambda\mu}(\eta^\alpha, t) e^{-i\eta^\alpha \xi_\alpha}\, d\tau$$

where $d\tau$ is the element of volume in wave space, and the integral is evaluated over the whole of wave space, T.

[9] G. K. Batchelor, "The Role of Big Eddies in Homogeneous Turbulence," *Proc. of the Royal Soc.*, 1949. See also, G. K. Batchelor, *The Theory of Homogeneous Turbulence*, Cambridge U. Press., 1953.

(b) ***Properties and Structure of the Wave Tensors.*** The algebraic properties (62.7) through (62.9) of the correlation tensors can be translated immediately into properties of the corresponding wave tensors. For instance, the property (62.7) may be expressed by

$$\begin{aligned} 8\pi^3 W^\lambda(\eta^\alpha, t) &= \int_V R^\lambda(\xi^\alpha, t) e^{i\eta^\alpha \xi_\alpha}\, dv \\ &= \int_V R^\lambda(-\xi^\alpha, t) e^{-i\eta^\alpha \xi_\alpha}\, dv \\ &= \int_V {}^*R^\lambda(\xi^\alpha, t) e^{i(-\eta^\alpha)\xi_\alpha}\, dv = 8\pi^3\, {}^*W^\lambda(-\eta^\alpha, t). \end{aligned}$$

Thus, the relations (62.7) and (62.8) furnish the results

$$\begin{aligned} W^\lambda(\eta^\alpha, t) &= {}^*W^\lambda(-\eta^\alpha, t) \\ W^{\lambda\mu\gamma}(\eta^\alpha, t) &= {}^*W^{\lambda\mu\gamma}(-\eta^\alpha, t). \end{aligned} \tag{63.2}$$

By use of a similar procedure, we find that (62.9) leads to the relation

$$W^{\lambda\mu}(\eta^\alpha, t) = W^{\mu\lambda}(-\eta^\alpha, t). \tag{63.3}$$

The wave tensors are complex tensors. That is, these tensors are functions of complex arguments, $i\eta^\alpha$, as is evident by examining the relation (63.1). Let us denote the complex conjugate of a wave tensor by writing a bar over the tensor. This means that in the expressions for the components of the wave tensor, i is replaced by $-i$. From the defining relations for the wave tensors and the above formulas (63.2), it follows that

$$\begin{aligned} \bar{W}^\lambda(\eta^\alpha, t) &= W^\lambda(-\eta^\alpha, t) = {}^*W^\lambda(\eta^\alpha, t) \\ \bar{W}^{\lambda\mu\gamma}(\eta^\alpha, t) &= W^{\lambda\mu\gamma}(-\eta^\alpha, t) = {}^*W^{\lambda\mu\gamma}(\eta^\alpha, t). \end{aligned} \tag{63.4}$$

Thus, *the Fourier transforms of* ${}^*R^\lambda$, ${}^*R^{\lambda\mu\gamma}$ *are the complex conjugates of the Fourier transforms of* R^λ, $R^{\lambda\mu\gamma}$. The relation corresponding to the above for $W^{\lambda\mu}$ is

$$\bar{W}^{\lambda\mu}(\eta^\alpha, t) = W^{\lambda\mu}(-\eta^\alpha, t). \tag{63.5}$$

By combining (63.3) and (63.5), *we see that* $W^{\lambda\mu}$ *is hermitian symmetric,*

$$\bar{W}^{\lambda\mu}(\eta^\alpha, t) = W^{\mu\lambda}(\eta^\alpha, t). \tag{63.6}$$

The relation (63.6) for $W^{\lambda\mu}$ is a "strong form" of the relation (63.4) for W^λ, $W^{\lambda\mu\gamma}$.

Further, *the relations (63.5) show that the real part of the tensor,* $W^{\lambda\mu}$, *is an even function of* η^α *and the imaginary part of the tensor,* $W^{\lambda\mu}$, *is an odd function of* η^α. To verify this result, we denote the real and imaginary part of $W^{\lambda\mu}$ by $R[W^{\lambda\mu}]$, $I[W^{\lambda\mu}]$, respectively. Then,

$$\begin{aligned} 2R[W^{\lambda\mu}(\eta^\alpha, t)] &= W^{\lambda\mu}(\eta^\alpha, t) + \bar{W}^{\lambda\mu}(\eta^\alpha, t) \\ 2I[W^{\lambda\mu}(\eta^\alpha, t)] &= W^{\lambda\mu}(\eta^\alpha, t) - \bar{W}^{\lambda\mu}(\eta^\alpha, t). \end{aligned}$$

Through use of the above relations and (63.5) the desired conclusion is obtained.

The solenoidal relations (62.20) may be expressed in wave space by use of the inverse transform of (63.1). By differentiation of this formula, we find that

$$\frac{\partial R^{\lambda\mu}}{\partial \xi^{\mu}} = -\int i\eta_{\mu} W^{\lambda\mu}(\eta^{\alpha}, t) e^{-i\eta^{\alpha}\xi_{\alpha}}\, d\tau = 0.$$

From the theory of the Fourier transform, it is well known that only the null function has a zero transform. Thus, the above result leads to the relation

$$W^{\lambda\mu}\eta_{\mu} = 0. \tag{63.7}$$

By use of (63.6) and the above relation, we see that $W^{\lambda\mu}\eta_{\lambda} = 0$. This last result corresponds to the fact that the theory of Section 62 implies that $\partial R^{\lambda\mu}/\partial \xi^{\lambda} = 0$. Further, the above relations for $W^{\lambda\mu}$ *show that the tensor* $W^{\lambda\mu}$ *lies in the two-dimensional subspace orthogonal to* η^{α}. By similar computations, the remaining solenoidal conditions may be written as

$$W^{\lambda}\eta_{\lambda} = W^{\lambda\mu\gamma}\eta_{\gamma} = 0. \tag{63.8}$$

The first of these two relations shows that *the wave vector,* W^{λ}, *lies in the two-dimensional subspace orthogonal to* η^{α}.

Finally, we consider the following question, "*What is the structure of the wave tensors which correspond to the correlation tensors in the cases of isotropic, axial symmetric, conical, etc., turbulence?*" Here we shall consider only the case of the second-order tensor, $W^{\lambda\mu}$, in the isotropic case. We shall show that *the structure of* $W^{\lambda\mu}$ *in terms of the* η^{α}*'s is exactly the same as that of* $R^{\lambda\mu}$ *in terms of the* ξ^{α}*'s*. The method of proof indicates that the corresponding theorem is valid for any correlation tensor in any type of homogeneous turbulence. Let us express the formula for $R^{\lambda\mu}$, (62.14), as

$$R^{\lambda\mu} = Ag^{\lambda\mu} + B\xi^{\lambda}\xi^{\mu}$$

where A and B are functions of r and t. We introduce the wave space scalars

$$8\pi^3\tilde{A} = \int_V A(r, t)e^{i\eta^{\alpha}\xi_{\alpha}}\, dv, \qquad 8\pi^3\tilde{B} = \int_V B(r, t)e^{i\eta^{\alpha}\xi_{\alpha}}\, dv \tag{63.9}$$

and wish to show that $\tilde{A}$, $\tilde{B}$ are functions of k (where

$$k = \sqrt{(\eta^1)^2 + (\eta^2)^2 + (\eta^3)^2}$$

is the distance of the point η^{α} from the origin of wave space) and the time, t. To do this, we introduce a new system of Cartesian orthogonal coordinates, $'\xi^\alpha$, in the correlation space such that the vector η^α lies along the $o'\xi^3$ axis. Further, we introduce spherical coordinates (r, ϕ, θ) in the new

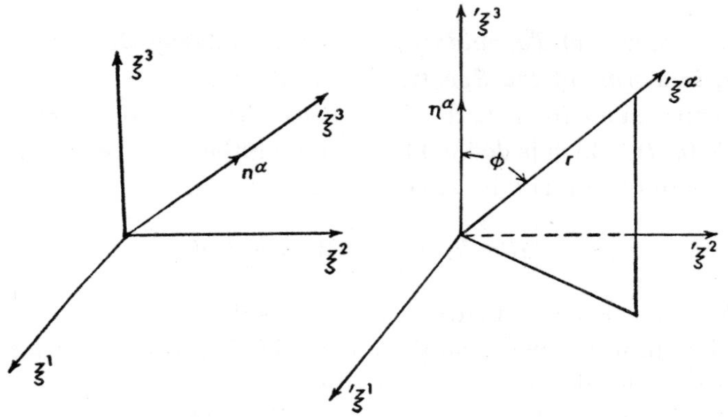

Figure 76: The Wave Vector η^α, in the Correlation Spaces, $'\xi^\alpha$, ξ^α

coordinate system. Evidently, $A(r, t)$, $B(r, t)$ *are invariant under this coordinate transformation.* From Figure 76, we find

$$\xi^\alpha\eta_\alpha = {}'\xi^\alpha\eta_\alpha = rk \cos \phi$$
$$dv = r^2 \sin \phi \, d\theta \, d\phi \, dr.$$

Thus, the formulas for $\tilde{A}$, $\tilde{B}$ (63.9) may be expressed as

$$8\pi^3\tilde{A} = \int_V A(r, t)e^{ikr\cos\phi}r^2 \sin \phi \, d\phi \, d\theta \, dr$$
$$8\pi^3\tilde{B} = \int_V B(r, t)e^{ikr\cos\phi}r^2 \sin \phi \, d\phi \, d\theta \, dr.$$

From these last formulas, *it follows that* $\tilde{A}$, $\tilde{B}$ *are functions of* k, t. By differentiation of (63.9) under the integral sign (assuming that this operation is permissible), we obtain

$$8\pi^3 \frac{\partial^2\tilde{A}}{\partial\eta^\alpha\,\partial\eta^\beta} = -\int_V A(r, t)\xi_\alpha\xi_\beta e^{i\eta^\alpha\xi_\alpha}\,dv.$$

Hence, the Fourier transform of the expression for $R^{\lambda\mu} = A\xi^\lambda\xi^\mu + Bg^{\lambda\mu}$ becomes

$$W_{\alpha\beta} = -\frac{\partial^2\tilde{A}}{\partial\eta^\alpha\,\partial\eta^\beta} + \tilde{B}g_{\alpha\beta}.$$

Recalling that $\tilde{A}$ is a function of k, t and using the chain rule for differentiation, we obtain

$$\frac{\partial^2\tilde{A}}{\partial\eta^\alpha\,\partial\eta^\beta} = \frac{\partial^2\tilde{A}}{\partial k^2}\frac{\eta_\alpha\eta_\beta}{k^2} + \frac{\partial\tilde{A}}{\partial k}\left(\frac{g_{\alpha\beta}}{k} - \frac{\eta_\alpha\eta_\beta}{k^2}\right).$$

The above equations show that *in isotropic turbulence, the wave tensor,* $W^{\lambda\mu}$, *has the same structure in terms of* η^α *as the correlation tensor,* $R^{\lambda\mu}$, *has in terms of* ξ^α.

(c) ***The Energy of Turbulence, E, and the Energy Dissipated by Viscosity, ϵ, in Terms of the Spectral Tensors, $F_{\lambda\mu}$.*** In order to obtain convenient expressions for E and ϵ, it is customary to introduce the *spectral tensor,* $F_{\lambda\mu}(k, t)$, which is defined by averaging the wave tensor, $W_{\lambda\mu}(\eta^\alpha, t)$, over a sphere of radius k in wave space:

$$4\pi F^{\lambda\mu}(k, t) = \int_\sigma W^{\lambda\mu}(\eta^\alpha, t)\, d\sigma \tag{63.10}$$

where $d\sigma$ is the element of surface area of a sphere of radius k and center at the origin of wave space and the integration is taken over the surface of this sphere, σ. Evidently, we may write

$$W^{\lambda\mu}(\eta^\alpha, t) = \frac{W^{\lambda\mu} + \bar{W}^{\lambda\mu}}{2} + \frac{W^{\lambda\mu} - \bar{W}^{\lambda\mu}}{2}.$$

Since the imaginary part of $W^{\lambda\mu}$ is an odd function of η^α, the integral of $(W^{\lambda\mu} - \bar{W}^{\lambda\mu})/2$, over the surface of the sphere vanishes. Thus, *the spectral tensor,* $F^{\lambda\mu}(k, t)$, *is always real.*

In addition, the spectral tensor, $F^{\lambda\mu}(k, t)$ is an *even function of* k. To verify this result, we use the formula (63.1), which defines $W^{\lambda\mu}$, and the definition of $F^{\lambda\mu}$, (63.10), and find

$$32\pi^4 F^{\lambda\mu}(k, t) = \int_\sigma d\sigma \int_V R^{\lambda\mu}(\xi^\alpha, t) e^{i\eta^\alpha \xi_\alpha}\, dv.$$

Now, we may replace the triple integral in the right-hand side of the last equation by

$$\int_V R^{\lambda\mu}(\xi^\alpha, t) e^{i\eta^\alpha \xi_\alpha}\, dv = \int_0^\infty dr \int\!\!\int_S R^{\lambda\mu}(\xi^\alpha, t) e^{i\eta^\alpha \xi_\alpha}\, dS$$

where S is a sphere of radius r. With the aid of the above formula and an interchange of the order of integration, the formula for $F^{\lambda\mu}(k, t)$ reduces to

$$32\pi^4 F^{\lambda\mu}(k, t) = \int_0^\infty dr \left\{ \int_S R^{\lambda\mu}(\xi^\alpha, t) \left[\int_\sigma e^{i\eta^\alpha \xi_\alpha}\, d\sigma \right] dS \right\}.$$

To evaluate the integral in the brackets on the right-hand side of the above equation, we introduce a coordinate system *in the wave space* which is the analogue of Figure 76. We find that

$$\int_\sigma e^{i\eta^\alpha \xi_\alpha}\, d\sigma = k^2 \int_\sigma e^{ikr\cos\phi} \sin\phi\, d\theta\, d\phi = \frac{4\pi k}{r} \sin kr.$$

The above expression is constant over the surface of the sphere, S. Hence, if we denote the following integral by $S^{\lambda\mu}(r, t)$

$$4\pi S^{\lambda\mu}(r, t) = \int_S R^{\lambda\mu}(\xi^\alpha, t)\, dS$$

then the expression for $F^{\lambda\mu}(k, t)$ reduces to

$$2\pi^2 F^{\lambda\mu}(k, t) = \int_0^\infty \left(\frac{k}{r} \sin kr\right) S^{\lambda\mu}(r, t)\, dr.$$

Since the expression within the parenthesis of the last integral is an even function of k, it follows that $F^{\lambda\mu}(k, t)$ is an even function of k. Finally, we introduce the scalar, F, of the tensor, $F^{\lambda\mu}$, by writing

$$F = 2\pi g_{\lambda\mu} F^{\lambda\mu}.$$

When written in this form, F coincides with W. Heisenberg's spectral function. Evidently, *F is an even function of k and is real.*

In order to deduce formulas for E and ϵ, we return to the basic formulas of Section 62(c). From the Fourier transform formula for $R^{\lambda\mu}$, we find that

$$R^{\lambda\mu}(0, t) = \int_0^\infty dk \int_\sigma W^{\lambda\mu}(\eta^\alpha, t)\, d\sigma$$

$$(\nabla^2 R^{\lambda\mu})_{0,t} = -\int_0^\infty k^2\, dk \int_\sigma W^{\lambda\mu}(\eta^\alpha, t)\, d\sigma.$$

Forming the scalar products of the above with the metric tensor, $g_{\lambda\mu}$, whose components are constants, and using the definitions of $F^{\lambda\mu}$, F, given in this section, we obtain

$$R(0, t) = 2 \int_0^\infty F(k, t)\, dk$$

$$(\nabla^2 R)_{0,t} = -2 \int_0^\infty k^2 F(k, t)\, dk.$$

By use of the expressions for E, ϵ (62.21 and 62.25), the above formulas become

$$E = \int_0^\infty F(k, t)\, dk \qquad (63.11)$$

$$\epsilon = 2\nu \int_0^\infty k^2 F(k, t)\, dk. \qquad (63.12)$$

These last two formulas show how the energy of turbulence, E, and the energy dissipated by viscosity, ϵ, are related to the spectral function, $F(k, t)$. These formulas have a decided advantage over the formulas for E and ϵ in terms of the correlation tensor. This advantage lies in the fact that integration is a "smoothing" process, whereas differentiation has exactly the opposite effect. Because of the structure of equation (63.11), one often says that

$$F(k, t)\, dk$$

represents the energy of turbulence between the wave numbers or frequencies k and k + dk.

In the isotropic case, the scalars $R(r, t)$ and $F(k, t)$ are related by the Fourier sine-transform. That is, one may easily verify by use of our previous methods that

$$R(r, t) = 2\int_0^\infty \frac{\sin kr}{kr} F(k, t)\, dk$$

$$F(k, t) = \frac{1}{\pi}\int_0^\infty kr \sin kr R(r, t)\, dr.$$

Problem 63.1: For isotropic turbulence, show that:

$$\overline{u^2}f = 2\int_0^\infty F(k)\left[\frac{\sin kr}{k^3r^3} - \frac{\cos kr}{k^2r^2}\right] dk$$

$$\overline{u^2}g = \int_0^\infty F(k)\left[\frac{\sin kr}{kr} + \frac{\cos kr}{k^2r^2} - \frac{\sin kr}{k^3r^3}\right] dk.$$

Hence, show that f, g are even functions of r. *Hint:* See Problem 62.2.

Problem 63.2: Show that the averaged tensor, $S_{\lambda\mu}(r, t) = (r^2R/3)g_{\lambda\mu}$, in the isotropic case. Further, show that for general homogeneous turbulence

$$S_{\lambda\mu}(r, t) = 4\pi\int_0^\infty \frac{r \sin kr}{k} F_{\lambda\mu}(k, t)\, dk.$$

Problem 63.3: Show that for isotropic turbulence:

$$R(r, t) = g_{\lambda\mu}R^{\lambda\mu} = 2\int_0^\infty \frac{\sin kr}{kr} F(k, t)\, dk.$$

Hint: Prove that $F^{\lambda\mu} = (1/6\pi)Fg^{\lambda\mu}$ and use the results of Problem 63.2.

Problem 63.4: For isotropic turbulence, show that the third-order wave tensor, $W^{\lambda\mu\gamma}$, may be written as

$$W^{\lambda\mu\gamma}(\eta^\alpha, t) = G(k, t)\left[\frac{\eta^\lambda\eta^\mu\eta^\gamma}{k^3} - \frac{1}{2k}(\eta^\lambda g^{\mu\gamma} + \eta^\mu g^{\lambda\gamma})\right].$$

Further, since we may write

$$g_{\gamma\mu}\eta_\lambda W^{\lambda\mu\gamma} = -kG(k, t)$$

show that

$$G(k, t) = -i\frac{(\overline{u^2})^{3/2}}{2\pi^2k^2}\int_0^\infty (l + 2q)(kr \cos kr - \sin kr)\, dr$$

where l, q are two of the three third-order correlation scalars.

64. The Dynamical Equations. In this section we shall draw some conclusions from the Navier-Stokes equation. Further, we shall point out the principal unsolved problem of the theory of homogeneous statistical turbulence.

(a) ***The Dynamical Equations in Terms of the Correlation Tensors.*** The Navier-Stokes equations were developed in Section 56 [see (56.7)]. If the body force vanishes and the fluid is incompressible, then at $P(x^\lambda)$ these equations are

$$\frac{\partial v^\lambda}{\partial t} + v^\alpha \frac{\partial v^\lambda}{\partial x^\alpha} = -\frac{g^{\lambda\alpha}}{\rho}\frac{\partial p}{\partial x^\alpha} + \nu g^{\mu\alpha}\frac{\partial^2 v^\lambda}{\partial x^\mu\,\partial x^\alpha}. \tag{64.1}$$

Further, similar equations are valid at the point $'P('x^\lambda)$ in terms of the variables $'p$, $'v^\lambda$. In virtue of the equation of continuity

$$\frac{\partial v^\lambda}{\partial x^\lambda} = \frac{\partial\,'v^\lambda}{\partial\,'x^\lambda} = 0$$

and the differentiation formulas of the type (61.4), we may write

$$\overline{v^\alpha \frac{\partial v^\lambda}{\partial x^\alpha}\,'v^\mu} = -\frac{\partial R^{\alpha\lambda\mu}}{\partial \xi^\alpha}, \qquad \overline{'v^\alpha \frac{\partial\,'v^\mu}{\partial\,'x^\alpha}\,v^\lambda} = \frac{\partial\,{}^*R^{\alpha\mu\lambda}}{\partial \xi^\alpha}.$$

Multiplying (64.1) by $'v^\mu$ and forming averages, we find that the Navier-Stokes equations lead to

$$\overline{\frac{\partial v^\lambda}{\partial t}\,'v^\mu} - \frac{\partial R^{\alpha\lambda\mu}}{\partial \xi^\alpha} = \frac{1}{\rho} g^{\lambda\alpha}\frac{\partial R^\mu}{\partial \xi^\alpha} + \nu\nabla^2 R^{\lambda\mu}$$

where $\nabla^2 = [\partial^2/(\partial\xi^1)^2 + \partial^2/(\partial\xi^2)^2 + \partial^2/(\partial\xi^3)^2]$. By using similar procedures for the Navier-Stokes equations at $'P('x^\lambda)$, we find that

$$\overline{v^\lambda \frac{\partial\,'v^\mu}{\partial t}} + \frac{\partial\,{}^*R^{\alpha\mu\lambda}}{\partial \xi^\alpha} = -\frac{1}{\rho} g^{\mu\alpha}\frac{\partial\,{}^*R^\lambda}{\partial \xi^\alpha} + \nu\nabla^2 R^{\lambda\mu}.$$

If we add the above two relations, we obtain the desired expression for the Navier-Stokes equations in terms of the correlation tensors. This fundamental relation for the correlation tensors is

$$\frac{\partial R^{\lambda\mu}}{\partial t} + \frac{\partial}{\partial \xi^\alpha}({}^*R^{\alpha\mu\lambda} - R^{\alpha\lambda\mu}) = \frac{1}{\rho}\left(g^{\lambda\alpha}\frac{\partial R^\mu}{\partial \xi^\alpha} - g^{\mu\alpha}\frac{\partial\,{}^*R^\lambda}{\partial \xi^\alpha}\right) + 2\nu\nabla^2 R^{\lambda\mu}. \tag{64.2}$$

Through use of the algebraic relations (62.7) and (62.8), one may replace the tensors ${}^*R^{\lambda\mu\gamma}$, ${}^*R^\lambda$ by $R^{\lambda\mu\gamma}$, R^λ but then one must insert the arguments of the tensors $R^{\lambda\mu\gamma}$, R^λ.

First, we obtain the equation of energy from the fundamental equation (64.2). In order to do this, we note that in virtue of the definitions of the third-order correlation tensors and the equation of continuity

$$\left[\frac{\partial}{\partial \xi^\alpha}\,({}^*R^{\alpha\mu\lambda} - R^{\alpha\lambda\mu})\right]_{\xi^\alpha=0} = -\left[\overline{{}'v^\alpha\,{}'v^\mu\,\frac{\partial v^\lambda}{\partial x^\alpha}} + \overline{v^\alpha v^\lambda\,\frac{\partial\,{}'v^\mu}{\partial\,{}'x^\alpha}}\right]_{\xi^\alpha=0}$$

$$= -\left[\overline{v^\alpha v^\mu\,\frac{\partial v^\lambda}{\partial x^\alpha}} + \overline{v^\alpha v^\lambda\,\frac{\partial v^\mu}{\partial x^\alpha}}\right]$$

$$= -\frac{\partial}{\partial x^\alpha}\,\overline{v^\alpha v^\mu v^\lambda} = \frac{\partial}{\partial \xi^\alpha}\,[R^{\alpha\mu\lambda}(0, t)].$$

In virtue of the assumption of homogeneity, this last term vanishes. That is, we obtain the relation

$$\left[\frac{\partial}{\partial \xi^\alpha}\,({}^*R^{\alpha\mu\lambda} - R^{\alpha\lambda\mu})\right]_{\xi^\alpha=0} = 0. \tag{64.3}$$

Further, in virtue of the solenoidal condition satisfied by the correlation tensors, R^λ, ${}^*R^\lambda$, we find that

$$\frac{g_{\lambda\mu}}{\rho}\left(g^{\lambda\alpha}\,\frac{\partial R^\mu}{\partial \xi^\alpha} - g^{\mu\alpha}\,\frac{\partial\,{}^*R^\lambda}{\partial \xi^\alpha}\right) = \frac{1}{\rho}\left(\frac{\partial R^\mu}{\partial \xi^\mu} - \frac{\partial\,{}^*R^\lambda}{\partial \xi^\lambda}\right) = 0. \tag{64.4}$$

Let us multiply the Navier-Stokes equations (64.2) by $g_{\lambda\mu}$ and evaluate at $\xi^\alpha = 0$. With the aid of the above expressions for the first- and third-order correlation tensors, we see that the following relation is obtained:

$$\left.\frac{\partial R}{\partial t}\right)_{0,t} = 2\nu(\nabla^2 R)_{0,t}.$$

Introducing the energy of turbulence, E, and the energy dissipated by viscosity [see Section 62(c)], the above relation becomes the *energy relation*

$$\frac{dE}{dt} = -\epsilon. \tag{64.5}$$

The Navier-Stokes equations (64.2) furnish information as to the rate of growth of vorticity. By multiplying these equations by $g_{\lambda\mu}\nabla^2$, and by use of the vorticity relation (62.23) we obtain the following equation for the vorticity correlation scalar, $\omega(r, t)$:

$$\frac{\partial \omega}{\partial t} - g_{\lambda\mu}\nabla^2\left[\frac{\partial}{\partial \xi^\alpha}\,({}^*R^{\alpha\mu\lambda} - R^{\alpha\lambda\mu})\right] = \nu\nabla^2\omega. \tag{64.6}$$

This last equation is the *analogue of equation (56.10) for viscous fluids.* From this equation we see that: (1) *viscosity diffuses the vorticity correlation;* (2) *the inertia terms* (since these terms originate in $v^\alpha\partial v^\lambda/\partial x^\alpha$)

$$g_{\lambda\mu}\,\frac{\partial}{\partial \xi^\alpha}\,(\nabla^2\,{}^*R^{\alpha\mu\lambda} - \nabla^2 R^{\alpha\lambda\mu})$$

act to increase the vorticity correlation by convolving the vortex tubes. If we evaluate (64.6) for $\xi^\alpha = 0$, we see that the mean square vorticity, $\omega(0, t)$, satisfies a similar relation. Note, in spite of (64.3), the inertia term in the vorticity correlation equation does not vanish at $\xi^\alpha = 0$.

(b) ***The Dynamical Equations in Terms of the Wave Tensors.*** Forming the Fourier transforms of the Navier-Stokes equations (64.2), we obtain the relation

$$\frac{\partial W^{\lambda\mu}}{\partial t} + 2\nu k^2 W^{\lambda\mu} + i\left[\eta_\alpha(\overline{W}^{\alpha\mu\lambda} - W^{\alpha\lambda\mu}) + \frac{1}{\rho}(\eta^\mu \overline{W}^\lambda - \eta^\lambda W^\mu)\right] = 0.$$

By integrating both sides of this relation over the surface of a sphere of radius k, with center at the origin of wave space, we obtain the following equation for the spectral tensor, $F^{\lambda\mu}(k, t)$:

$$\frac{\partial F^{\lambda\mu}}{\partial t} + 2\nu k^2 F^{\lambda\mu} + \frac{i}{4\pi}\int_\sigma \eta_\alpha(\overline{W}^{\alpha\mu\lambda} - W^{\alpha\lambda\mu})\, d\sigma + \frac{i}{4\pi\rho}\int_\sigma (\eta^\mu \overline{W}^\lambda - \eta^\lambda W^\mu)\, d\sigma = 0. \quad (64.7)$$

Since the expression

$$F(k, t)\, dk = 2\pi g_{\lambda\mu} F^{\lambda\mu}(k, t)\, dk$$

measures the energy of turbulence which lies between the wave numbers (or frequencies) k and $k + dk$, and since $F^{\lambda\mu}(k, t)$ is the average in wave space of the Fourier transform of $R^{\lambda\mu} = \overline{v^\lambda\, 'v^\mu}$, it appears that $F^{\lambda\mu}(k, t)\, dk$ may be interpreted as the energy of turbulence transformed from the velocity component v^λ to the component $v^\mu (\lambda \neq \mu)$ in the range of wave numbers k to $k + dk$. Hence, the total energy transformed from one velocity component to another is

$$\int_0^\infty F^{\lambda\mu}(k, t)\, dk.$$

By integrating (64.7) from 0 to ∞ over the variable, k, and noting that the inertia terms become the Fourier transform of (64.3), we obtain the relation

$$\frac{\partial}{\partial t}\int_0^\infty F^{\lambda\mu}(k, t)\, dk + 2\nu \int_0^\infty k^2 F^{\lambda\mu}(k, t)\, dk = -\frac{i}{4\pi\rho}\int_T (\eta^\mu \overline{W}^\lambda - \eta^\lambda W^\mu)\, d\tau.$$

Thus, *the inertia terms (the terms due to the third-order correlation tensor) do not contribute toward transforming energy from one velocity component to another but the pressure terms (the terms due to the first-order correlation tensor) do act in this manner.* This result is due to G. K. Batchelor.

On the other hand, if we form the scalar product of (64.7) with $g_{\lambda\mu}$, and use (64.4), we obtain the formula

$$\frac{\partial F}{\partial t} + 2\nu k^2 F + \frac{i}{2} \int_\sigma g_{\lambda\mu} \eta_\alpha (\bar{W}^{\alpha\mu\lambda} - W^{\alpha\lambda\mu})\, d\sigma = 0. \tag{64.8}$$

This formula shows that *the pressure terms do not contribute to the energy density function* $F(k, t)$ *but the inertia terms do contribute to this density function*. This result is also due to G. K. Batchelor. From these results and the fact that *neither the pressure nor the inertia terms contribute to the total energy of turbulence*, E, [see (64.5)], we see that: (1) *the pressure acts to shift a given amount of energy from one velocity component to another at a given frequency*, k; (2) *the inertia acts in redistributing a given amount of energy among the various wave numbers or frequencies*, k. For this reason, the inertia term is often called the "transfer term."

(c) ***The Principal Problem of Turbulence.*** One of the very important problems in the theory of turbulence is to determine the spectral function, $F(k, t)$, and hence E and ϵ. The simplest equation involving F is (64.8). However, this equation contains unknown inertia terms. Up to the present, various assumptions have been made as to the relation of these inertia terms and the F function. The most successful theories are due to: (1) W. Heisenberg and C. F. von Weizsäcker; (2) A. N. Kolmogoroff. Other very recent theories are due to T. von Kármán and C. C. Lin, S. Goldstein, L. Kovasznay and others. Since these theories do not furnish immediate applications of tensor analysis, we leave the theory of homogeneous turbulence.

Problem 64.1: Show that the dynamical equations of Navier-Stokes reduce for isotropic turbulence to

$$\frac{\partial}{\partial t}(f\overline{u^2}) + 2(\overline{u^2})^{3/2}\left(\frac{\partial h}{\partial r} + \frac{4}{r}h\right) = 2\nu\overline{u^2}\left(\frac{\partial^2 f}{\partial r^2} + \frac{4}{r}\frac{\partial f}{\partial r}\right).$$

Hint: Use the solenoidal relations of Section 62 and note f and h are functions of r and t but $\overline{u^2}$ is a function of only t.

Problem 64.2: From the dynamical equation of the above problem and by use of the relations, $\lim\limits_{r\to\infty} (r^4 h) = \lim\limits_{r\to\infty}\left(r^4 \frac{\partial f}{\partial r}\right) = 0$, show that

$$\Lambda = \overline{u^2} \int_0^\infty r^4 f(r, t)\, dr$$

is a constant; Λ is known as Loitsiansky's invariant. *Hint:* Multiply the dynamical equation of Problem 64.1 by r^4.

APPENDIX I

In this section, we prove that: (1) if three vectors $\mathbf{a}^j, j = 1, 2, 3$ in three-space are independent then the determinant, a, does not vanish and conversely; (2) if the reduced cofactors, A^i_k, of the elements, a^k_j, satisfy, $A^i_j a^k_i = \delta^k_j$, then they also satisfy the relations, $A^k_i a^i_j = \delta^k_j$. In view of the fact that A^k_j determine vectors

$$\mathbf{A}_1 = A^1_1\mathbf{i} + A^2_1\mathbf{j} + A^3_1\mathbf{k}, \text{ etc.},$$

which are reciprocal to $\mathbf{a}^i$, it is evident that $\mathbf{A}_j$ (and hence A^k_j) are unique. The above theory is valid in n-space.

(a) ***Linear Dependence of Vectors and Determinants.*** Consider three vectors with the following components in rectangular Cartesian coordinates:

$$\mathbf{a}^1 = a^1_1\mathbf{i} + a^1_2\mathbf{j} + a^1_3\mathbf{k}, \text{ etc.}$$

First, we wish to prove: *if the vectors* $\mathbf{a}^j, j = 1, 2, 3$ *are independent, then the determinant*

$$a = \begin{vmatrix} a^1_1 & a^1_2 & a^1_3 \\ a^2_1 & a^2_2 & a^2_3 \\ a^3_1 & a^3_2 & a^3_3 \end{vmatrix}$$

cannot vanish and conversely. This result follows the fact that the above determinant represents the triple scalar product of $\mathbf{a}^1, \mathbf{a}^2, \mathbf{a}^3$ (see Section 8). But, the triple scalar product vanishes if and only if the vectors $\mathbf{a}^i$ are linearly dependent. It should be noted that the upper index in a^k_j orders the row and the lower index orders the column position of a^k_j.

(b) ***The Reduced Cofactors*** A^j_i ***of*** a^i_j. Our second result is concerned with the solutions of the system

$$A^i_j a^k_i = \delta^k_j, \qquad k, j, i = 1, 2, 3. \tag{1}$$

We shall show *that* (1) *implies that*

$$A^k_i a^i_j = \delta^k_j. \tag{2}$$

To verify this result with a minimum of algebraic theory, we multiply (1) by a^j_l and obtain

$$(a^j_l A^i_j) a^k_i = a^k_l.$$

Let us assume that

$$a_l^i A_j^i = \delta_l^i + \alpha_l^i \tag{3}$$

where α_l^i are nine unknown quantities. We shall show that α_l^i must vanish. Eliminating $a_l^j A_j^i$ between the last two equations, we obtain

$$(\delta_l^i + \alpha_l^i)a_i^k = a_l^k.$$

Since $\delta_l^i a_i^k = a_l^k$, the last equation reduces to $\alpha_l^i a_i^k = 0$, which can only possess the solution, $\alpha_l^i = 0$. This follows from the fact that the determinant, a, was assumed to be nonzero; or, geometrically, from the fact that only zero vectors are orthogonal to three linearly independent vectors $\mathbf{a}^k$. Thus, $\alpha_l^i = 0$ and hence (3) reduces to (2). It is evident from our method of proof *that if* (2) *is valid, then* (1) *is also valid.*

APPENDIX II

Here, we shall define the terms, matrix and rank of a matrix. We shall discuss the relation of the terms, matrix, and, second-order tensor. Finally, we shall show if the rank of a matrix is $(n - 1)$ then a unique relation exists between the vectors, $\mathbf{a}^j$, which determine the matrix. We shall work directly with n-space.

(a) ***Matrix and the Rank of a Matrix.*** First, we define the terms *matrix* and *rank of a matrix*. By the term, matrix, we mean any array of quantities that can be ordered into row and column positions. Thus, if the set of numbers, a^i_j, has been ordered into rows by the upper index and columns by the lower index, and constitute a matrix, we may write

$$[a^i_j] = \begin{bmatrix} a^1_1 & \cdots & a^1_n \\ \cdot & & \cdot \\ \cdot & & \cdot \\ \cdot & & \cdot \\ a^m_1 & \cdots & a^m_n \end{bmatrix} \qquad i = 1 \cdots m, \qquad j = 1 \cdots n, \qquad n \geq m,$$

to indicate this n by m matrix. In matrix theory, the emphasis is on the position of a quantity. Hence, one often speaks of the matrix of a coordinate transformation, etc., but seldom of the matrix of the components of a second order tensor. This is due to the fact that in tensor analysis the emphasis is on the transformation properties of the components of tensors and not on their ordering.[1] Thus, a matrix is a more general conception than the tensor of the second order. One may also speak of p-way matrices.

The term "rank of a matrix" is defined as follows. Evaluate all of the possible m by m, $m - 1$ by $m - 1$, etc., determinants of the above matrix. If at least one r by r determinant does not vanish, but all of the $(r + 1)$ by $(r + 1)$ determinants do vanish, then we say the *rank of the matrix* is r. It can be shown that this process determines a unique r.

Consider a system of n equations for the vectors $\mathbf{a}^j$ in terms of the n independent unit base vectors, $\mathbf{u}^j$, of a Cartesian orthogonal coordinate system in n-space:

$$\mathbf{a}^j = a^j_k \mathbf{u}^k, \qquad j = 1 \cdots m, \qquad k = 1 \cdots n. \tag{1}$$

[1] L. Brillouin, *Les Tenseurs*, Dover Publications, New York, 1946, p. 15. J. A. Schouten, *Tensor Analysis for Physicists*, Oxford U. Press, London, 1950, p. 40.

The above system is the extension to n-space of the system studied in Appendix I. With the aid of the representation (1), we may characterize the rank of the matrix $[a^i_j]$ in vector terms. *In fact, if the system of vectors* $\mathbf{a}^j$ *contains r independent vectors, then* $[a^i_j]$ *is of rank r.* In the following paragraphs, we shall demonstrate this theorem for $r = n, n - 1$.

We shall prove: *If the rank of* $[a^i_j]$ *is n* $(m = n)$ *(or if the determinant of the* a^i_j *does not vanish), then no linear relation can exist among the vectors* $\mathbf{a}^j$. Let us assume that a linear relation does exist among the $\mathbf{a}^j$. We shall show that this assumption of linear dependence of the $\mathbf{a}^j$ leads to a contradiction. Let us denote this relation by

$$c_j\mathbf{a}^j = 0$$

where not all the c_j may vanish. From this relation and (1), we obtain

$$c_ja^j_k = 0, \qquad k = 1, \cdot \cdot \cdot n.$$

If c_1 does not vanish, we may interpret the above formula as showing that the first row of the determinant of the a^j_k's is a linear combination of the other rows. By use of the third property of determinants of Section 42(a), we find that the determinant, a, must vanish. Since this result contradicts our original assumption, it follows that no linear relation can exist among the $\mathbf{a}^j$.

We shall now prove the result: *If the rank of the* $[a^i_j]$ *matrix is* $n - 1$*, and hence the determinant, a, does vanish, then a unique linear relation exists between the* $\mathbf{a}^j$. Since $a = 0$, it follows from the fifth result stated in Section 42(a) that

$$a^k_l\bar{A}^j_k = 0, \qquad l, j, k = 1, \cdot \cdot \cdot n.$$

Multiplying (1) by the cofactors $\bar{A}^l_j$ and using the above equation, we find

$$\bar{A}^l_j\mathbf{a}^j = 0.$$

The form of this last result appears to indicate that n relations exist among the $\mathbf{a}^j$, rather than a unique relation. To show the uniqueness of the relation we assume that two independent relations exist. By eliminating $\mathbf{a}^n$ between these relations, we find that a linear relation involving only $\mathbf{a}^1 \cdot \cdot \cdot \mathbf{a}^{n-1}$ exists. Thus the first $(n - 1)$ rows of the matrix $[a^j_k]$ are linearly related and every $(n - 1)$-th order determinant formed from these rows vanishes. Similarly by eliminating any other vector, $\mathbf{a}^k$, we can show that every other $(n - 1)$-th order determinant vanishes. This means that the rank of the matrix of $[a^j_k]$ is at most $(n - 2)$. Since this result contradicts our assumption, it follows that a unique linear relation exists between the vectors $\mathbf{a}^j$.

REFERENCE BOOKS

Vector and Tensor Analysis

Brand, L., *Vector and Tensor Analysis*, John Wiley & Sons, Inc., New York, 1947.

Brillouin, L., *Les Tenseurs en Mécanique et en Élasticité*, Dover Publications, New York, 1946.

Coffin, J. G., *Vector Analysis*, John Wiley & Sons, Inc., New York, 1911.

Craig, H. V., *Vector and Tensor Analysis*, McGraw-Hill, New York, 1943.

Duschek, A. und Hochrainer, A., *Grundzüge der Tensorrechnung in Analytischer Darstellung*, Teile I, II; Springer, Berlin, 1950.

Gans, R., *Vector Analysis*, Blackie and Son, London, 1931.

Gibbs, J. W., and Wilson, E. B., *Vector Analysis*, C. Scribner's Sons, New York, 1901.

Hay, G. E., *Vector and Tensor Analysis*, Dover Publications, New York, 1953.

Jeffrey, H., *Cartesian Tensors*, Cambridge U. Press, London, 1931.

Lass, H., *Vector and Tensor Analysis*, McGraw-Hill, New York, 1950.

Levi-Civita, T., *The Absolute Differential Calculus*, Blackie and Son, London, 1927.

McConnell, A. J., *Applications of the Absolute Differential Calculus*, Blackie and Son, London, 1931.

Michal, A. D., *Vector and Tensor Analysis*, John Wiley & Sons, Inc., New York, 1947.

Ollendorff, F., *Die Welt der Vektoren*, Springer, Vienna, 1950.

Phillips, H. B., *Vector Analysis*, John Wiley & Sons, Inc., New York, 1933.

Schouten, J. A., *Tensor Analysis for Physicists*, Clarendon Press, Oxford, 1951.

Sokolnikoff, I. S., *Tensor Analysis*, John Wiley & Sons, New York, 1951.

Spain, B., *Tensor Calculus*, Interscience Publishers, Inc., New York, 1953.

Synge, J. L. and Schild, A., *Tensor Calculus*, U. of Toronto Press, Toronto, 1949.

Taylor, J. H., *Vector Analysis*, Prentice-Hall, New York, 1939.

Thomas, T. Y., *The Elementary Theory of Tensors*, McGraw-Hill, New York, 1931.

Weatherburn, C. E., *Elementary Vector Analysis*, G. Bell and Sons, London, 1921.

Weatherburn, C. E., *Advanced Vector Analysis*, G. Bell and Sons, London, 1944.

Wills, H. P., *Vector Analysis*, Prentice-Hall, New York, 1931.

Algebra

Bromwich, T. J. P. A., *Quadratic Forms and Their Classification*, Cambridge Tracts, No. 3, Cambridge U. Press, London, 1906.

Riemannian Geometry

Eisenhart, L. P., *Riemannian Geometry,* Princeton U. Press, Princeton, 1926.

Schouten, J. A. and Struik, D. J., *Einfuhrung in die Neueren Methoden der Differentialgeometrie,* P. Noordhoff, Gronigen, Batavia, Vol. I, 1935; Vol. II, 1938.

Schouten, J. A., *Der Ricci-Kalkül,* J. Springer, Berlin, 1924.

Thomas, T. Y., *Differential Invariants of Generalized Spaces,* Cambridge U. Press, London, 1934.

Veblen, O., *Invariants of Quadratic Differential Forms,* Cambridge U. Press, London, 1927.

Differential Geometry

Eisenhart, L. P., *An Introduction to Differential Geometry,* Princeton U. Press, Princeton, 1947.

Hlavaty, V., *Differentialgeometrie der Kurven und Flächen und Tensorrechnung,* Übersetzung von M. Pinl, Noordhoff, Groningen, 1939.

Struik, D. J., *Lectures on Classical Differential Geometry,* Addison-Wesley, Boston, 1950.

Analysis

Courant, R., *Differential and Integral Calculus,* Vols. I and II (translated by E. J. McShane), Nordeman Publishing Co., New York, 1937.

de la Vallee Poussin, Ch-J., *Cours d'Analyse Infinitesimale,* Gauthier-Villars, Paris, 1914.

Mechanics

Coe, C. J., *Theoretical Mechanics,* The Macmillan Co., New York, 1938.

Milne, E. A., *Vectorial Mechanics,* Interscience Publishers, Inc., New York, 1948.

Synge, J. L. and Griffith, B. A., *Principles of Mechanics,* McGraw-Hill, New York, 1949.

Mathematical Physics

Courant, R. and Hilbert, D., *Methoden der Mathematischen Physik,* J. Springer, Berlin, 1931.

Fermi, E., *Thermodynamics,* Prentice-Hall, New York, 1937.

Kellogg, O. D., *Foundations of Potential Theory,* J. Springer, Berlin, 1920.

Page, L., *Introduction to Theoretical Physics,* D. van Nostrand Co., New York, 1935.

Webster, A. G., *Partial Differential Equations of Mathematical Physics,* Hafner Publishing Co., New York, 1947.

Elasticity

Love, A. E. H., *Elasticity,* Dover Publications, New York, 1944.

Murnaghan, F. D., *Finite Deformations of an Elastic Solid,* John Wiley & Sons, Inc., New York, 1951.

Sokolnikoff, I. S., *Mathematical Theory of Elasticity* (with collaboration of R. D. Specht), McGraw-Hill, New York, 1946.

Hydrodynamics

Agostini, L. and Bass, J., *Les Theories de la Turbulence,* Publications Scientifiques et Techniques, Paris, 1950.

Batchelor, G. K., *The Theory of Homogeneous Turbulence,* Cambridge U. Press, New York, 1953.

Courant, R. and Friedrichs, K. O., *Supersonic Flow and Shock Waves,* Interscience Publishers, Inc., New York, 1948.

Hadamard, J., *Lecons sur la Propagation des Ordes,* Chelsea Publishing Co., New York, 1949.

Lamb, H., *Hydrodynamics,* Dover Publications, New York, 1945.

Milne-Thompson, L. M., *Theoretical Hydrodynamics,* Macmillan and Co., London, 1938.

Sauer, R., *Theoretische Einfuhrung in die Gasdynamik,* Edwards Bros., Ann Arbor, 1945.

Historical

Bell, E. T., *Men of Mathematics,* Simon and Schuster, New York, 1937.

Struik, D. J., *A Concise History of Mathematics,* Dover Publications, New York, Vols. I and II, 1948.

INDEX

YORK [illegible] COLLEGE LIBRARY
YORK, PENNA.

QA261 .C58 010101 000
Coburn, Nathaniel.
Vector and tensor analysis.
0 2002 0044509 2
YORK COLLEGE OF PENNSYLVANIA 17403

YORK JUNIOR COLLEGE LIBRARY
YORK, PENNA.